Test Bank
for

UNIVERSE

Seventh Edition

Thomas Krause

W. H. Freeman and Company
New York

ISBN: 0-7167-8772-5
EAN: 9780716787723

Printed in the United States of America

Second printing

W. H. Freeman and Company
41 Madison Avenue
New York, NY 10010
Houndmills, Basingstoke RG21 6XS England

www.whfreeman.com

Contents

Chapter 1: Astronomy and the Universe

1. Which unique quality distinguishes human beings from other living things?
    A) the continuing need to test the ability and strength of their leaders
    B) curiosity, the need to explore and understand our surroundings
    C) social behavior, the desire to protect the young, the old and the weak
    D) the will to fight to resolve conflicts
    Ans: B   Section: Opening Paragraph

2. Which scientific discipline can be considered to be truly universal?
    A) astronomy   B) social studies   C) geology   D) biological science
    Ans: A   Section: Opening Paragraph

3. Astronomy
    A) has not yet influenced our lives significantly, although future developments like mining on the Moon may become important.
    B) studies only far-away places and has no application to our lives here on Earth.
    C) allows us to predict our individual destinies from the movements of the planets, but has never had any other useful application.
    D) has had important practical applications including the development of Newtonian mechanics, on which much of modern technology is based.
    Ans: D   Section: 1-1

4. The intellectual foundation of science is
    A) rejection of all observations that disagree with theory.
    B) observation, faith, and acceptance.
    C) logical derivation entirely from fundamental principles.
    D) observation, logic, and skepticism.
    Ans: D   Section: 1-1

5. In science, if new observations disagree with a well established theory then
    A) this should be accepted as part of the overall incomprehensibility of the universe, and both the observations and the theory should be retained.
    B) the theory must be discarded immediately.
    C) the theory must be modified.
    D) the observations must be discarded.
    Ans: C   Section: 1-1

6. A scientist observes a new phenomenon that disagrees with the scientist's own explanation or hypothesis. Following the scientific method, the correct procedure is to
   A)   accept the disagreement as part of the fundamental incomprehensibility of the universe.
   B)   modify the hypothesis.
   C)   wait until someone develops an adequate explanation before announcing the new observation.
   D)   discard the observation as erroneous.
   Ans: B   Section: 1-1

7. The scientific method is a major force in science and has been developed to ensure that
   A)   theories about physical phenomena are so good and our faith in them is so strong that we never need to test them against observations.
   B)   theories about physical phenomena agree with the wisdom of the ancients.
   C)   results from experiments can be adjusted to agree with our carefully developed theories about physical phenomena.
   D)   theories about physical phenomena agree with what we find in experiments and observations.
   Ans: D   Section: 1-1

8. According to the scientific method, a hypothesis that is proposed to explain a particular physical phenomenon is considered to be wrong if
   A)   leading scientists in the world believe that it is wrong.
   B)   it is in conflict with the results of just one reliable and repeatable observation.
   C)   it appears to defy logic and logical reasoning.
   D)   it disagrees with the accepted theory at the time of the proposal.
   Ans: B   Section: 1-1

9. In applying the scientific method to the study of our natural surroundings, scientists are
   A)   developing a theoretical view of the universe that incorporates all previous ideas and myths as part of an overall philosophy.
   B)   formulating hypotheses or models that describe the present observations of nature and that predict possible further tests for these models.
   C)   discovering by observation the absolute truth about limited areas of science and are therefore slowly building up the correct view of the universe.
   D)   slowly amassing a vast bank of observations of nature, which, some time in the future, will be assembled into the correct description of the universe.
   Ans: B   Section: 1-1

10. In following the principles of the scientific method, a theory proposed to explain a given phenomenon must
    A) explain all previous and reliable observations in a consistent manner but need not suggest new tests for the theory since a theory should be complete in itself.
    B) explain all known and reliable observations and predict new experiments and observations.
    C) agree with and build on previous theories but need not explain all observations since some of these may be erroneous.
    D) predict new and different experiments that will extend the scope of the theoretical understanding but need not explain all the previous observations since no theory is expected to explain everything completely.
    Ans: B   Section: 1-1

11. The rules that govern the behavior of matter and have inspired major advances in engineering are known as
    A) Murphy's laws.   C) the laws of social behavior.
    B) the laws of physics.   D) the laws of chance.
    Ans: B   Section: 1-1

12. Modern science is founded
    A) in part on the myths and legends of antiquity.
    B) in part on the philosophical approach of the ancient Greeks.
    C) only upon developments since Isaac Newton and his contemporaries.
    D) only upon developments during the past hundred years.
    Ans: B   Section: 1-1

13. The laws of physics developed in laboratories on Earth are generally assumed to be valid
    A) only on Earth.   C) only in our galaxy.
    B) only in our solar system.   D) everywhere in the universe.
    Ans: D   Section: 1-1

14. The most important reason for exploring other planets is that
    A) the study of the solar system is our greatest source of information on the formation of the universe.
    B) it allows us to understand our own planet more thoroughly.
    C) it extends human's thoughts onto a plane that is totally removed from our limited existence here on Earth.
    D) it has become vital for us to develop these planets as sources of raw materials.
    Ans: B   Section: 1-2

15. Which of the following space exploits has not yet been accomplished by humans?
    A)   walking on the surface of the Moon
    B)   landing a spacecraft on Saturn's surface
    C)   studying the surface of Venus under its thick, permanent cloud cover
    D)   discovering active volcanoes on other worlds
    Ans: B   Section: 1-2

16. In our exploration of the planets, we have sent spacecraft to
    A)   only the closer planets, Venus, Mars, Jupiter, and Saturn.
    B)   all the planets except Pluto.
    C)   only the nearest planets to Earth, Venus, and Mars.
    D)   all planets from Mercury to Pluto.
    Ans: B   Section: 1-2

17. So far, our study of the other bodies in our solar system is based upon
    A)   Earth-based telescopic observations only.
    B)   telescopic observations from the Earth and from spacecraft only.
    C)   telescopic observations from Earth and spacecraft plus geologic samples brought back from the Moon.
    D)   telescopic observations from Earth and spacecraft plus information from manned landing on about half the planets.
    Ans: C   Section: 1-2

18. The idea of thermonuclear fusion, the release of energy following the conversion of hydrogen nuclei into a helium nucleus, was first suggested as the source of energy in
    A)   the interior of Earth.   C)   a weapon of mass destruction.
    B)   the central core of the Sun.   D)   a controllable nuclear power station.
    Ans: B   Section: 1-3

19. The lifetime of a typical star appears to be
    A)   a few thousands of years.
    B)   a few millions of years.
    C)   a few billions of years.
    D)   essentially infinite because we know of no mechanism that can terminate the nuclear processes in a star's interior.
    Ans: C   Section: 1-3

20. Heavy elements, such as those throughout the Earth and within our bodies, appear to have been formed
    A)   only during the initial Big Bang formation of the universe.
    B)   by radioactive decay here on Earth.
    C)   inside the Sun.
    D)   deep inside some now-vanished star.
    Ans: D   Section: 1-3

21. The study of galaxies gives astronomers important clues about the
    A)   origin of intellect.
    B)   existence of life in the universe beyond Earth.
    C)   formation of planets.
    D)   creation of the universe.
    Ans: D   Section: 1-4

22. Astronomers sometimes announce that they have discovered a new solar system beyond
    our own, or a new galaxy beyond our own. Which choice correctly describes the terms
    "solar system" and "galaxy"?
    A)   A solar system is a large assemblage of stars similar to the Sun, whereas a galaxy
          is much larger and consists of all different types of stars.
    B)   A solar system consists of an immense number of stars (i.e., suns), and a galaxy is
          a cluster of many such systems.
    C)   A galaxy consists of planets and other objects orbiting around a single star,
          whereas a solar system is a system consisting of an immense number of stars (i.e.,
          suns).
    D)   A solar system consists of planets and other objects orbiting around a star,
          whereas a galaxy is a system consisting of an immense number of stars.
    Ans: D   Section: 1-4

23. If we could view each of the following objects from the same distance, which would be
    the brightest?
    A) a star   B) a quasar   C) a normal galaxy   D) a solar system
    Ans: B   Section: 1-4

24. The number of degrees in a full circle is
    A) 57.3.   B) 60.   C) 3600.   D) 360.
    Ans: D   Section: 1-5

25. In angular measurements used in astronomy, how many right angles are there in a full
    circle?
    A) two   B) six   C) one   D) four
    Ans: D   Section: 1-5

26. The angle of 60 degrees between the line from the Sun to Jupiter and the line from the
    Sun to the Trojan group of asteroids (see Fig. 17-8, Freedman and Kaufmann, *Universe*,
    7th ed.) is what fraction of a full circle?
    A) 1/2   B) 1/3   C) 1/5   D) 1/6
    Ans: D   Section: 1-5

27. An arcsecond is a measure of
    A)   length along a circle.
    B)   time interval between oscillations of a standard clock.
    C)   time interval between successive orbital positions.
    D)   angle.
    Ans: D   Section: 1-5

28. One arcsecond is equal to
    A)   1/3600 degree.   C)   1/60 of a full circle.
    B)   1/60 degree   D)   1/3600 of a full circle.
    Ans: A   Section: 1-5

29. One arcminute is equal to
    A) 1/60 of a full circle.   B) 60 degrees.   C) 1/60 degree.   D) 1/60 arcsecond.
    Ans: C   Section: 1-5

30. The Moon's angular diameter in our sky is measured to be half a degree. From this, we
    can find the
    A)   bulk density of the Moon (the average number of kilograms per cubic meter of
         Moon material).
    B)   distance to the Moon even if we have no other information about the Moon.
    C)   diameter of the Moon in kilometers even if we have no other information about
         the Moon.
    D)   diameter of the Moon in kilometers if we know the Moon's distance.
    Ans: D   Section: 1-5

31. Which one of the following statements about angle is correct?
    A)   50 arcseconds is half of a degree.   C)   30 arcminutes is half of a degree.
    B)   50 arcminutes is half of a degree.   D)   30 arcseconds is half of a degree.
    Ans: C   Section: 1-5

32. On a particular night, Jupiter subtends an angle of 42 arcseconds as seen from Earth.
    This angle is
    A)   roughly three-quarters of an arcminute.
    B)   less than half an arcminute.
    C)   more than an arcminute, although less than a degree.
    D)   more than a degree.
    Ans: A   Section: 1-5

33. If Venus has an angular diameter of 30 arcseconds when viewed from Earth at a
    particular time, how does this compare with the typical angular diameter of the Moon?
    A) 1/3600 as large   B) 1/30 as large   C) 60 times larger   D) 1/60 as large
    Ans: D   Section: 1-5

34. The angle subtended at an observer by a city transit bus (length 9 m) at a distance of 1000 m is close to
    A) 1000/9 arcsecond.
    C) 9/1000 arcsecond.
    B) 9000 arcminutes.
    D) 1/2 degree.
    Ans: D   Section: 1-5 and Box 1-1

35. The angle subtended by the Moon (diameter 3500 km) to an observer on Earth (Moon-Earth distance is about 400,000 km) is approximately
    A) 1/2 degree.   B) 1700 degrees.   C) 1/1700 degree.   D) 1/2 arcminute.
    Ans: A   Section: 1-5 and Box 1-1

36. If the Moon subtends about 30 arcminutes in the sky and is at about 400,000 km from Earth at the time, what is its approximate diameter?
    A) 350 km   B) 60 km   C) 3500 km   D) 35,000 km
    Ans: C   Section: 1-5 and Box 1-1

37. Astronauts on the Moon look back at Earth, a distance of about 400,000 km away. If the cities of Washington, D.C., and New York are separated by about 300 km, what will be the angle between them when viewed from the Moon?
    A) 2.5 arcminutes   B) 3/4 degree   C) 1300 degrees   D) 2.5 degrees
    Ans: A   Section: 1-5 and Box 1-1

38. Astronauts on the Moon look back at the Earth, whose diameter is about 12,800 km. Since the Earth-Moon distance is about 400,000 km, how much bigger will the Earth appear in their sky than the Moon does in our sky?
    A) 0.27 times   B) 3.7 times   C) 220 times   D) the same, obviously
    Ans: B   Section: 1-5 and Box 1-1

39. Two very bright fireworks are exploded at the same time during the July 4 celebrations, one in New York, the other in Los Angeles (4000 km apart). How far apart in angle will these flashes appear to astronauts on the Moon, who are 400,000 km from the Earth?
    A) 1/100 degree   B) 34.4 arcminutes   C) 5.7 degrees   D) 206.3 arcseconds
    Ans: B   Section: 1-5 and Box 1-1

40. A nearby star 10 light-years from Earth is suspected by astronomers to have a companion planet with an orbit of radius 6 AU. (1 AU is the mean distance from the Earth to the Sun, and 1 light-year is about 6×10^4 AU). The maximum angular separation of this planet from the star as seen from the Earth is expected to be
    A) 1.6 degrees.   B) 2 arcminutes.   C) 2 arcseconds.   D) 0.6 degree.
    Ans: C   Section: 1-5 and Box 1-1

41. The *Saturn 5* rocket, used to send astronauts to the Moon, stood about 110 meters high. At what distance would you have to stand in order to have the rocket subtend an angle of about 2.5 degrees? (This angle is the field of view of a 600-mm focal length telephoto lens on a 35-mm camera.)
    A) 275 km   B) 0.25 km   C) 2700 km   D) 2.5 km
    Ans: D   Section: 1-5 and Box 1-1

42. At what distance would a friend have to hold a dime (about 1 cm diameter) for it to subtend an angle of 2 arcseconds?
    A) at the distance of the Moon   B) 1 km   C) 10 cm   D) 10^5 km
    Ans: B   Section: 1-5 and Box 1-1

43. Using a technique known as very long baseline interferometry (VLBI), in which the signals received by two radio telescopes located on different continents are combined as if they were a single radio telescope, astronomers can resolve two objects separated by only 0.00001 second of arc. What is the smallest detail we can see in a quasar 15 billion light-years away using this kind of interferometer?
    A) 0.7 ly   B) 44 ly   C) 2400 ly   D) 150,000 ly
    Ans: A   Section: 1-5 and Box 1-1

44. The Crab Nebula shown in Fig. 1-6, Freedman and Kaufmann, *Universe,* 7th ed., has a diameter of about 10 light-years and is at a distance of 6500 light-years. What angle will this supernova remnant subtend in our sky?
    A)   630 arcseconds   C)   5.3 arcminutes
    B)   31.7 arcseconds   D) 1.5×10^{-3} arcseconds
    Ans: C   Section: 1-5 and Box 1-1

45. A globular cluster of stars is measured to have an angular diameter of 20.6 arcseconds, and its distance from the Earth is measured to be 200,000 light-years. What is its approximate physical diameter in light-years?
    A) 200,000 ly   B) 1/20 ly   C) 20 ly   D) 2 ly
    Ans: C   Section: 1-5 and Box 1-1

46. What is the approximate angular diameter of the Sun in arcseconds?
    A) 186   B) 930   C) 1.86   D) 1860
    Ans: D   Section: 1-5 and Box 1-1

47. On January 1, 2004, the planet Saturn had an angular diameter of 20.6 arcseconds as viewed from Earth. Which of the following is a correct statement about this angular diameter?
    A) This value is constant. Saturn always has that angular diameter when viewed from Earth.
    B) This value changes. The angular diameter gets larger as the distance to Saturn becomes larger, and smaller as the distance to Saturn becomes smaller.
    C) This value changes. The angular diameter gets larger as the distance to Saturn becomes smaller, and smaller as the distance to Saturn becomes larger.
    D) This value changes. It is always larger during that part of Saturn's orbit when Saturn is closer to the Sun, and it is smaller when Saturn is farther from the Sun.
    Ans: C   Section: 1-5

Use the following to answer questions 48-49:

You are sitting in the center of a circle of radius 10 meters. You are looking at a straight stick that has both ends on the circumference of the circle (10 meters away) and that subtends an angle of 30 degrees or $30 \times 3600 = 108,000$ arcseconds.

48. What does the formula derived in Box 1-1 give you as the length of this stick?
    A) 1.26 meters   B) 5.24 meters   C) 6.40 meters   D) 11.8 meters
    Ans: B   Section: 1-5

49. A circle of radius 10 meters has a circumference $C = 2\pi R = 62.83$ meters. A 30 degree angle would intercept an arc that is 30/360 or 1/12 of this, namely 5.24 meters. What does this result suggest about the validity of the formula derived in Box 1-1?
    A) The formula is valid even for angles as large as 30 degrees.
    B) The formula actually calculates the length of subtended by a given angle at a given distance. Thus the formula computes a length that is longer than length D in Box 1-1.
    C) The formula actually calculates the length of subtended by a given angle at a given distance. Thus the formula computes a length that is shorter than length D in Box 1-1.
    D) The formula is valid for angles larger than 30 degrees but not for angles smaller than 30 degrees.
    Ans: B   Section: 1-5

50. The average distance from the Earth to the Sun, 149,600,000 km can be written in shorthand notation as
    A) 1.496×10^9 km.   C) 1.496×10^8 km.
    B) 1.496×10^6 km.   D) 1.496×10^7 km.
    Ans: C   Section: 1-6

51. The diameter of the hydrogen atom, 0.000,000,000,11 meters can be written in shorthand notation as
    A) 1.1×10^{-8} m.   B) 1.1×10^{-11} m.   C) 1.1×10^{-9} m.   D) 1.1×10^{-10} m.
    Ans: D   Section: 1-6

52. The mean distance of Jupiter from the Sun, 778,300,000 km can be written in shorthand notation as
    A) 7.783×10^{8} km.   C) 7.783×10^{7} km.
    B) 7.783×10^{9} km.   D) 7.783×10^{6} km.
    Ans: A   Section: 1-6

53. There are 1000 mm in one meter. This means that a distance of 5 mm is
    A) 5×10^{3} meter.   C) 2×10^{-4} meter.
    B) 5×10^{-3} meter.   D) 5×10^{-2} meter.
    Ans: B   Section: 1-6

54. 0.0064 meter is
    A) 0.64 mm.   B) 640 mm.   C) 6.4 mm.   D) 64 mm.
    Ans: C   Section: 1-6

55. 10×10^{5} =
    A) 1 billion   B) 10 million   C) 1 million   D) 10 thousand
    Ans: C   Section: 1-6

56. 10^{0} (10 to the power 0) is
    A) 10.   B) undetermined, not a real number.   C) 0.   D) 1.
    Ans: D   Section: 1-6

57. 2^{5} =
    A) 100,000   B) 32   C) 25   D) 200,000
    Ans: B   Section: 1-6

58. $(1/2)^{3}$ =
    A) 8   B) 1.25×10^{-1} C) 0.5   D) 0.167
    Ans: B   Section: 1-6

59. $(0.5)^{2}$ =
    A) 2.5×10^{-2} B) 0.25   C) 2.5   D) 1.0
    Ans: B   Section: 1-6

60. The number five hundred thousand is written in powers-of-ten notation as
    A) $(5 \times 10^{2}) \times 10^{-3} = 5 \times 10^{-1}$.   B) 5×10^{5}.   C) 5×10^{4}.   D) 5×10^{-5}.
    Ans: B   Section: 1-6 and Box 1-2

61. $10^{-2} \times 10^2 =$
    A) 0   B) 1/100   C) 1   D) 10,000
    Ans: C   Section: 1-6 and Box 1-2

62. $(3 \times 10^4)^4 =$
    A) 8.1×10^{16} B) 2.7×10^{16} C) 9×10^{16} D) 8.1×10^{17}
    Ans: D   Section: 1-6 and Box 1-2

63. $(2 \times 10^2)^3 =$
    A) 6×10^6 B) 8×10^6 C) 8×10^5 D) 6×10^5
    Ans: B   Section: 1-6 and Box 1-2

64. $10^5 \times 10^8 =$
    A) 10^{40} B) 10^3 C) 10^{13} D) 10^{20}
    Ans: C   Section: 1-6 and Box 1-2

65. $10^6/10^9 =$
    A) 10^{54} B) 10^{15} C) 10^{-3} D) 10^3
    Ans: C   Section: 1-6 and Box 1-2

66. $10^6/10^6 =$
    A) 1   B) 10   C) 0   D) 10^{12}
    Ans: A   Section: 1-6 and Box 1-2

67. $(9.0 \times 10^5)/(1.5 \times 10^3) =$
    A) 13.5×10^{15} B) 3×10^{-2} C) 600   D) 7.5×10^{-2}
    Ans: C   Section: 1-6 and Box 1-2

68. $2.5 \times 10^4 \times 2.5 \times 10^{-4} =$
    A) 5.0×10^{-8} B) 5.0   C) 6.25   D) 1.0×10^6
    Ans: C   Section: 1-6 and Box 1-2

69. One billionth divided by one millionth is equal to
    A) 10^{-15}.   B) 10^{15}.   C) 10^{-3}.   D) 10^3.
    Ans: C   Section: 1-6 and Box 1-2

70. By what approximate factor in powers-of-ten notation is a human being (height about 2 m) larger than the nucleus of a hydrogen atom, or proton (diameter about 10^{-15} m)?
    A) 2×10^{30} B) 2×10^{15} C) 2×10^{13} D) 2×10^{-15}
    Ans: B   Section: 1-6 and Box 1-2

71. How many powers of ten is the diameter of the Sun (1.4×10^5 km) greater than the length of a beetle (14 mm)?
    A) 5   B) 11   C) 8   D) 10
    Ans: D   Section: 1-6 and Box 1-2

72. In this age of space exploration, humans have now traveled to the Moon. By how many orders of magnitude (powers of ten) did humans travel in this journey than did Columbus when he traveled from the Old World to the Americas?
    A)   two orders of magnitude, or 10^2 C)   six orders of magnitude, or 10^6
    B)   three orders of magnitude, or 10^3 D)   one order of magnitude, or 10^1
    Ans: A   Section: 1-6 and Box 1-2

73. By how many orders of magnitude is one million larger than one millionth?
    A) 10^{12} B) 10^6 C) 6   D) 12
    Ans: D   Section: 1-6

74. A particular molecule has a diameter of 12 billionths of a meter. This distance is equal to
    A)   1.2 nanometers, or 1.2 nm.   C)   12 nanometers, or 12 nm.
    B)   1.2 micrometers, or 1.2 μm.   D)   12 micrometers, or 12 μm.
    Ans: C   Section: 1-7

75. An astronomer is measuring the brightness of a star using infrared light of wavelength 7.8 μm. This corresponds to a wavelength of
    A)   7.8 millionths of a meter.
    B)   7.8 billionths of a meter.
    C)   7.8 trillionths of a meter (where 1 trillion = 1 million million)
    D)   780 millionths of a meter.
    Ans: A   Section: 1-7

76. One astronomical unit, or one AU is defined as the
    A)   distance traveled by light in one year.
    B)   mean distance between the Sun and the Earth.
    C)   distance from which Earth-Sun distance will subtend an angle of one arcsecond.
    D)   distance traveled by light in one second.
    Ans: B   Section: 1-7

77. An astronomical unit or 1 AU is a unit of
    A)   time, equal to 1 billion years.
    B)   length, the average distance between the Sun and Earth.
    C)   length defined as one wavelength of light from krypton gas.
    D)   mass, equal to one solar mass.
    Ans: B   Section: 1-7

78. A light-year is a measure of
    A)   arc length along an orbit.   C)   time.
    B)   expansion rate of the universe. D)   distance.
    Ans: D   Section: 1-7

79. One light-year is the
    A)   distance that light travels in one year.
    B)   time taken for the Earth to orbit the Sun once.
    C)   distance between Earth and Sun.
    D)   time taken for light to travel from the Sun to the Earth.
    Ans: A   Section: 1-7

80. If you were able to travel out into space until the angular distance between the Earth and the Sun was 1 second of arc, how far would you be from the Sun? (Assume that the Earth-Sun line is at right angles to your line of sight.)
    A) 1 ly   B) 1 Mpc   C) 1 AU   D) 1 pc
    Ans: D   Section: 1-7

81. The distance from Earth to the star Betelgeuse (in the constellation Orion) has been measured as 520 light-years. Expressed in parsecs, this is approximately
    A) 160 pc.   B) 350 pc.   C) 520 Mpc (megaparsecs).   D) 1700 pc.
    Ans: A   Section: 1-7

82. The distance to the star τ Scorpii has been measured as 230 pc. Expressed in light-years, this is approximately
    A) 230 Mly (million light-years).   B) 340 ly.   C) 750 ly.   D) 70 ly.
    Ans: C   Section: 1-7

83. The star γ Aquilii is 340 ly from Earth. Expressed in parsecs, this is approximately
    A) 1100 pc.   B) 105 pc.   C) 750 pc.   D) 0.340 kpc (kiloparsecs).
    Ans: B   Section: 1-7

84. The star ζ Puppis is about 750 pc from Earth. Expressed in light-years, this is approximately
    A) 230 ly.   B) 1500 ly.   C) 2445 ly.   D) 7.5×10^5 ly.
    Ans: C   Section: 1-7

85. An astronomer finds an object at a distance of 6.8 AU from Earth. Based on the distance, which of the following is this object most likely to be?
    A)   a star in our galaxy   C)   a distant galaxy
    B)   an artificial satellite orbiting the   D)   a comet in our solar system
          Earth
    Ans: D   Section: 1-7

86. An astronomer finds an object at a distance of 5.6 pc from Earth. Based on the distance, which of the following is this object most likely to be?
    A)   an asteroid in our solar system   C)   an artificial satellite orbiting the
                                                    Earth
    B)   a star in our galaxy   D)   a distant galaxy
    Ans: B   Section: 1-7

87. An astronomer discovers an object at a distance of 28 Mpc from Earth. Based on the distance, which of the following is this object most likely to be?
    A)   an artificial satellite orbiting the   C)   a star in our galaxy
         Earth
    B)   a comet in our solar system   D)   a distant galaxy
    Ans: D   Section: 1-7

88. What is the distance between Earth and the nearest star? (THINK carefully about your answer!) (Check the list of stars in the Appendix 4 of Freedman and Kaufmann, *Universe,* 7th ed.)   -
    A) 5.2 AU   B) 4.3 parsecs   C) 1 AU   D) 4.3 light-years
    Ans: C   Section: 1-7

89. The Orion Nebula is shown in Figure 1-5 of Freedman and Kaufmann, *Universe,* 7th ed. How long has the light been traveling from this object before it arrives on Earth?
    A) 750 years   B) 4890 years   C) 460 years   D) 1500 years
    Ans: D   Section: 1-7

90. If a radio message were sent toward the nearest star to the Sun and a reply were sent back immediately on receipt of the message by intelligent beings from a planet near that star, how long after transmission would we have to wait for a reply?
    A) 8.6 years   B) a few minutes   C) about 6 months   D) 20,000 years
    Ans: A   Section: 1-7

91. The time taken for light to travel from Jupiter to Earth when they are closest to each other is (you need to think carefully about this, and draw a diagram)
    A) 12 years.   B) 34 minutes.   C) 8 minutes.   D) a few seconds.
    Ans: B   Section: 1-7

92. The Crab Nebula (Fig. 1-6, Freedman and Kaufmann, *Universe,* 7th ed.) is the result of a supernova explosion of a star that occurred at a distance of about 1.99 kpc from Earth. If people on Earth saw the explosion in the year 1054 A.D., when did the explosion actually occur?
    A) 936 A.D.   B) about 1048 A.D.   C) about 5446 B.C.   D) 936 B.C.
    Ans: C   Section: 1-7

93. If a supernova was first seen in the year of Christ's birth (the Star of Bethlehem?) and its distance from Earth is measured to be 2 kpc, approximately when did the supernova actually explode?
    A) 2 B.C.   B) 6520 B.C.   C) 2000 B.C.   D) 6520 A.D.
    Ans: B   Section: 1-7

94. If one of the three wisemen lit a candle at the moment of Christ's birth in Nazareth, approximately how far out in space has some of that light now reached? (Note to instructors: This question must be modified yearly.)
    A) $2004 \times (3 \times 10^8)$ m $= 6 \times 10^{11}$ m
    C) 2004 light-years
    B) 2004 AU
    D) 2004 parsecs
    Ans: C   Section: 1-7

95. Light from a campfire lit by the shepherds at the time of Christ's birth travels out into space at the speed of light. Which is the farthest of the 20 brightest stars (See Appendix 4, Freedman and Kaufmann, *Universe,* 7th ed.) beyond which this light will now have traveled?
    A) Sirius   B) Rigel   C) Betelgeuse   D) Deneb
    Ans: D   Section: 1-7

96. Suppose that at the same time on the same night we see one supernova (a star exploding) in the Andromeda galaxy, 2 million light-years away from us, and another in the galaxy M82, 6 million light-years away from us. Which of the following statements is correct?
    A) Both stars exploded at the same time, because we saw the explosions at the same time.
    B) We cannot tell which star actually exploded first, because they are so far away.
    C) The supernova in the Andromeda galaxy actually occurred after the one in M82.
    D) The supernova in the Andromeda galaxy actually occurred before the one in M82.
    Ans: C   Section: 1-7

97. In 2004, an inhabitant of a planet orbiting a distant star observes the flash of the first nuclear explosion on Earth, which occurred in July 1945. Approximately how far away is his solar system from Earth?
    A) 56 pc   B) 1.71 pc   C) 171.8 pc   D) 17.1 pc
    Ans: D   Section: 1-7

98. If an extraterrestrial being were to send a signal to Earth immediately to confirm the sighting in 2004 of a nuclear explosion on Earth in July, 1945, and we were ready to receive such a message, when would we expect it? (Note to instructors: This question is linked to the previous question.)
    A) 2018 A.D.   B) 2113 A.D.   C) 2002 A.D.   D) 2057 A.D.
    Ans: D   Section: 1-7

99. The time taken for light to travel to the Earth from a galaxy that is 10 Mpc away is
    A) 32.6 years.   B) 3.07×10^6 years.   C) 10^7 years.   D) 3.26×10^7 years.
    Ans: D   Section: 1-7

100. One yard is the same distance as
    A) 0.9144 meters.   B) 1.0936 meters.   C) 100 cm   D) 10^{-3} kilometers.
    Ans: A   Section: 1-7 and Box 1-3

101. The speed of light is approximately 3×10^8 meters/sec. This is the same as
   A) 1.34×10^8 mi/hr   C) 4.41×10^8 mi/hr
   B) 3.35×10^8 mi/hr   D) 6.71×10^8 mi/hr
   Ans: D   Section: 1-7 and Box 1-3

102. An object on the surface of the Earth has a mass of 40 kg. This is the same as
   A) 4×10^4 grams.   B) 3.92×10^5 grams.   C) 40 pounds.   D) 392 pounds.
   Ans: A   Section: 1-7 and Box 1-3

103. If the 40-kg object in the previous problem were taken to the surface of the Moon its mass would be
   A) 4×10^4 grams.   B) 6.53×10^4 grams.   C) 40 pounds.   D) 65.3 pounds.
   Ans: A   Section: 1-7 and Box 1-3

104. One foot is the same distance as
   A) 3.048×10^{-7} μm.   C)   0.621 km.
   B) 3.048×10^8 nm.   D) 5.28×10^{-3} mile.
   Ans: B   Section: 1-7 and Box 1-3

105. Which of the following statements best represents the overall rationale for scientific investigation?
   A)   Reality is comprehensible, and a limited number of fundamental principles govern the nature and behavior of the universe.
   B)   There are certain patterns in nature from which future events can be predicted, but there are no underlying basic principles or laws.
   C)   The universe is a hodgepodge of unrelated things behaving in unpredictable ways, but we must continue to observe it in case this behavior threatens Earth.
   D)   The behavior of the whole universe is governed by our observation of it in such a way as to hide the fundamental truth.
   Ans: A   Section: 1-8

106. An underlying theme of astronomy is that the
   A)   fundamental physical laws differ randomly from galaxy to galaxy, but they can be learned for a given galaxy by detailed observation.
   B)   fundamental physical laws governing the universe change in a predictable way with increasing distance from the Earth.
   C)   universe is a hodgepodge of unrelated things behaving in arbitrary and unexplainable ways.
   D)   entire universe is governed by a single set of fundamental physical laws.
   Ans: D   Section: 1-8

Chapter 2: Knowing the Heavens

1. Which of the following was not obtained by people of ancient civilizations from observations of the night sky?
   A) the relative distances of Sun, Moon, and stars from Earth
   B) timing information, both daily and yearly
   C) patterns of stars in the sky about which stories and myths were devised
   D) directions for navigation
   Ans: A   Section: 2-1

2. Two opposite sides of the Egyptian pyramids are aligned with which direction(s) on the horizon?
   A) northeast to southwest   C) north-south
   B) midsummer sunrise   D) rising of the star Sirius
   Ans: C   Section: 2-1

3. Meaningful observations of the sky by ancient peoples
   A) were, of necessity, restricted to the Western Hemisphere.
   B) were, of necessity, restricted to the regions north of the equator.
   C) were, of necessity, restricted to the regions south of the equator.
   D) were made in regions throughout the world.
   Ans: D   Section: 2-1

4. In modern astronomy, the constellations are
   A) clusters of stars that are held together by the mutual gravitational attractions of the individual stars in the cluster.
   B) nearby galaxies to which astronomers have given specific names.
   C) 12 regions of sky through which the Sun, Moon, and planets move as seen from the Earth.
   D) 88 regions of sky, covering the entire sky.
   Ans: D   Section: 2-2

5. Describing a star as being in the constellation Cygnus (the Swan) tells a modern astronomer that the star is
   A) in a distant galaxy located in a particular direction from the Earth.
   B) inside our solar system.
   C) somewhere in a particular region of sky having definite boundaries.
   D) one of a set of bright stars that make up a particular "picture" in the sky.
   Ans: C   Section: 2-2

6. If a star is described as being in the constellation Leo, a modern astronomer knows that it is
   A) somewhere in a particular region of sky having definite boundaries.
   B) in a distant galaxy located in a particular direction from Earth.
   C) inside a region of the sky bounded by two lines of right ascension in the sky.
   D) one of a few individual bright stars that make a picture (of a lion) in the sky.
   Ans: A   Section: 2-2

7. Which of the following statements correctly describes the relationship between stars and constellations?
   A) Only those stars that were visible to the ancient Greeks are located in constellations.
   B) Only the brighter stars are in constellations.
   C) Only stars within the zodiac close to the ecliptic, the Earth's orbital plane, are located in constellations.
   D) Every star is located in a constellation.
   Ans: D   Section: 2-2

8. If the unaided human eye is sensitive enough to see about 6000 of the stars in the entire sky, about how many stars would be seen at one time on a given night from a single location from which the horizon is completely visible around the observer?
   A) 3000
   B) only 1000 out of 6000 because the rest are hidden by Earth
   C) depends on the observer's latitude; observers at the poles will see 6000, while equatorial observers will see only ½ of this number, or 3000
   D) 6000
   Ans: A   Section: 2-2

9. Which one of the following statements about constellations is correct?
   A) If you point randomly to some direction in the sky, you are pointing at *some* constellation.
   B) Only if you point in the vicinity of one of the brighter stars are you pointing at a constellation.
   C) Astronomers are seeking to discover new constellations.
   D) Astronomers are constantly inventing new constellations.
   Ans: A   Section: 2-2

10. Compared with its appearance to a person in mid-latitude northern latitudes, how will the constellation Orion appear to an observer in Australia?
    A) exactly the same since the stars of Orion are very far away from Earth
    B) upside-down but with the same orientation of stars
    C) upside-down and inverted left-to-right, a mirror image of that seen in the northern hemisphere
    D) same way up but inverted left-to-right
    Ans: B   Section: 2-2

11. The constellation whose stars are used as pointers to the north celestial pole in the northern hemisphere is
    A)   Leo, the lion, containing the bright star Regulus.
    B)   Ursa Major, the Big Dipper.
    C)   Ursa Minor, the Little Bear, containing the bright star Polaris.
    D)   Bootes, the shepherd, containing the bright star Arcturus.
    Ans: B   Section: 2-3

12. Diurnal motion of objects in the sky is caused by the
    A)   precession of the Earth's axis.   C)   motion of the Moon across the sky.
    B)   revolution of Earth around the Sun.   D)   rotation of the Earth on its axis.
    Ans: D   Section: 2-3

13. The nightly motion of objects across our the sky is caused by the
    A)   revolution of Earth around the Sun.
    B)   rotation of the whole celestial sphere of stars around the fixed Earth.
    C)   rotation of the Earth on its axis.
    D)   motion of the solar system around the galaxy.
    Ans: C   Section: 2-3

14. The most readily observed east-to-west motion of objects in the night sky is caused by the
    A)   motion of the Moon and planets across the sky.
    B)   rotation of the Earth on its axis.
    C)   relative motions of stars with respect to each other in the sky.
    D)   revolution of the Earth around the Sun.
    Ans: B   Section: 2-3

15. The pattern of stars that is visible from one position on the Earth gradually shifts from east to west across the sky over one night. This is caused by the
    A)   atmospheric motions and winds.
    B)   rotation of the Earth about its own north-south axis.
    C)   motion of the Moon and planets across the sky.
    D)   motion of the Earth around the Sun.
    Ans: B   Section: 2-3

16. The most easily observed motion in the night sky is produced by the
    A)   revolution of the Earth around the Sun.
    B)   motion of stars with respect to each other in the sky.
    C)   motion of the planets along their orbits around the Sun.
    D)   rotation of the Earth on its axis.
    Ans: D   Section: 2-3

17. The phrase "diurnal motion" refers to the
    A) slow change in position of the constellations from east to west from night to night, resulting in different constellations being visible at 11 p.m. in May than at 11 p.m. in December.
    B) apparent motion of the Sun along the ecliptic over the course of a year.
    C) change in position of the Moon in the sky as it runs through its phases over the course of a month.
    D) gradual motion of the constellations from east to west across the sky each night, resulting in different constellations being visible at 4 a.m. than at 10 p.m. on any given night.
    Ans: D   Section: 2-3

18. Over the course of one night, an observer at any given location on the Earth sees the constellations gradually move from east to west across the sky. This is caused primarily by the
    A) inherent rotation of the universe.
    B) wind.
    C) motion of the Earth around the Sun.
    D) rotation of the Earth around its own axis.
    Ans: D   Section: 2-3

19. What basic pattern do stars seem to trace out in our sky if you watch (or photograph) stars near the north celestial pole for a period of several hours?
    A) circles, with the north celestial pole at the center
    B) spirals, as the stars move while the Earth rotates
    C) almost straight lines, rising from the horizon towards the zenith
    D) ellipses, with the north pole at one focus
    Ans: A   Section: 2-3

20. When we watch the nighttime sky, we find that
    A) the stars and constellations remain fixed in our sky, not rising or setting in a time as short as one night because they are so far away.
    B) most stars and constellations slowly rise in the west, pass overhead, and set in the east.
    C) all stars and constellations reach their highest point in the sky at midnight.
    D) most stars and constellations slowly rise in the east, pass overhead, and set in the west.
    Ans: D   Section: 2-3

21. Which way are you moving with respect to the stars during the rotation of the Earth?
    A) eastward   B) southward   C) westward   D) northward
    Ans: A   Section: 2-3

22. With respect to the stars, the rotation of the Earth carries you toward the
    A) south. B) east. C) west. D) north.
    Ans: B   Section: 2-3

23. If the stars Polaris and Arcturus (as shown in Fig. 2-6, Freedman and Kaufmann, *Universe,* 7th ed.), are known to be 71° apart, how far away from Polaris is the closest star in Ursa Major?
    A) 25° B) 2.5° C) 250° D) 7.1°
    Ans: A   Section: 2-3

24. If the stars Polaris and Spica are 101° apart (as shown in Fig. 2-6 of Freedman and Kaufmann, *Universe,* 7th ed.), how far away from Polaris is the closest star in Ursa Major, from our view?
    A) 2.5° B) 260° C) 77° D) 25°
    Ans: D   Section: 2-3

25. Which of the following directions DO(ES) NOT always remain fixed in place relative to an observer's horizon?
    A)   summer solstice
    B)   north celestial pole
    C)   points where the celestial equator contacts the horizon
    D)   zenith
    Ans: A   Section: 2-3

26. Which of the following points remains fixed in the sky relative to an observer's horizon?
    A)   north celestial pole
    B)   direction to a distant star (e.g., Betelgeuse, in Orion)
    C)   vernal equinox
    D)   winter solstice
    Ans: A   Section: 2-3

27. Which of the following directions remains fixed in the sky relative to an observer's horizon?
    A)   zenith
    B)   direction to the Moon at noon, over one month
    C)   direction to the Sun at noon, over one year
    D)   autumnal equinox
    Ans: A   Section: 2-3

28. During a given night, some stars will be observed to pass through the
    A) vernal equinox. B) zodiac. C) celestial equator. D) zenith.
    Ans: D   Section: 2-3

29. If you were standing on the equator, which of the following positions in the sky would pass through your zenith at some time in one 24-hour period?
    A) position of the Sun at summer solstice
    B) north celestial pole, or perpendicular to the celestial equator
    C) ecliptic pole, or perpendicular to the ecliptic plane
    D) vernal equinox, or 0 hours right ascension, 0° declination
    Ans: D   Section: 2-3

30. In late September, Andromeda appears high in the sky at midnight. Six months later Virgo appears high in the sky at midnight. Where is Andromeda at this time?
    A) It is still high in the sky at midnight.
    B) It has moved to the western horizon.
    C) It has moved to the eastern horizon.
    D) It is high in the sky at *noon* and is thus not visible.
    Ans: D   Section: 2-3

31. Perseus appears high in the sky at midnight in November. Andromeda appears high in the sky at midnight in September. (See Fig. 2-5, Freedman and Kaufmann, *Universe*, 7th ed.) Where is Andromeda at midnight in November?
    A) It remains high in the center of the sky.
    B) It will be near the eastern horizon.
    C) It will be near the western horizon.
    D) It will be high in the sky at noon and thus will not be visible.
    Ans: C   Section: 2-3

32. Cygnus appears high in the sky at midnight in July. Andromeda appears high in the sky at midnight in September. (See Fig. 2-5, Freedman and Kaufmann, *Universe*, 7th ed.) Where is Andromeda at midnight in July?
    A) It is still high in the sky at midnight.
    B) It has moved to the western horizon.
    C) It has moved to the eastern horizon.
    D) It is high in the sky at *noon* and is thus not visible.
    Ans: B   Section: 2-3

33. Sirius is the brightest star in the night sky. You watch it set behind the western horizon about 2 AM in the middle of February. About what time will it set in the middle of March?
    A) 10 PM   B) midnight   C) 2 AM   D) 4 AM
    Ans: B   Section: 2-3

34. How much of the overall sky is north of the celestial equator, that is, in the northern hemisphere?
    A)   all of it, by definition
    B)   exactly one half
    C)   less than one half, because of the tilt of the equator to the ecliptic plane
    D)   more than one half, because of the precession of the poles
    Ans: B   Section: 2-4

35. The celestial equator is defined as the
    A)   line in the sky that is perpendicular to the Earth's spin axis.
    B)   line traced in our sky by the Moon each month against the background stars.
    C)   line traced in our sky by the Sun over one year against the background stars.
    D)   band of constellations through which the Sun and Moon move in our sky.
    Ans: A   Section: 2-4

36. Which of the following lines or points is always directly over your head, no matter where on the Earth you go?
    A) zenith   B) celestial equator   C) ecliptic   D) 90° north declination
    Ans: A   Section: 2-4

37. If you point toward the zenith today and point there again 45 days later, you will have pointed twice in the same direction relative to the
    A) Moon.   B) Sun.   C) fixed stars.   D) horizon.
    Ans: D   Section: 2-4

38. The zenith defines a direction
    A)   vertically above a point on the equator.
    B)   vertically above an observer.
    C)   toward the Sun at noon.
    D)   vertically above the North Pole.
    Ans: B   Section: 2-4

39. If you are standing on the Earth's equator, your zenith (the vertical direction above your head) over a period of one year will maintain which of the following alignments?
    A)   a fixed angle of 23.5° to the spin axis of the Earth
    B)   an angle to the Earth's spin axis that will vary between 0° and 23.5° over a period of 6 months
    C)   parallel to the Earth's spin axis
    D)   perpendicular to the Earth's spin axis
    Ans: D   Section: 2-4

40. As the Earth rotates, the zenith of a person standing on the equator sweeps out
    A) a path between north and south poles, along the observer's celestial meridian.
    B) the celestial equator.
    C) a variable path across the sky within the zodiac but not always on the celestial equator.
    D) the ecliptic plane.
    Ans: B   Section: 2-4

41. A given star in the sky will reach its highest point to a particular observer in the northern hemisphere when it passes through the
    A) celestial equator.   C) ecliptic plane.
    B) zodiac.   D) region of the sky due south.
    Ans: D   Section: 2-4

42. Polaris, the "pole star," is at present
    A) within 1° of the north celestial pole.
    B) exactly perpendicular to the ecliptic plane (ecliptic pole).
    C) above the the Earth's magnetic pole.
    D) precisely at the north celestial pole.
    Ans: A   Section: 2-4

43. As the Earth rotates, the apparent motion of the pole star, Polaris, in a period of a day is
    A) a slow drift across the sky.
    B) a wobble back and forth in a straight line.
    C) a small circle with a radius of less than 1° in about 24 hours.
    D) zero; there is no motion of the pole star by definition.
    Ans: C   Section: 2-4

44. For an observer at a fixed location on the Earth, the angle between the north celestial pole and an observer's horizon depends on the
    A) time of year.
    B) time of day.
    C) observer's latitude (north or south of the equator).
    D) observer's longitude (east or west of Greenwich).
    Ans: C   Section: 2-4 and Figure 2-10

45. To navigators in the northern hemisphere, their latitude in degrees is equal to
    A) 15 times the number of hours since the sun set.
    B) the angle between their meridian and the north celestial pole.
    C) the angle between the north celestial pole and their zenith.
    D) the angle between the north celestial pole and their northern horizon.
    Ans: D   Section: 2-4

46. The angle between an observer's horizon and the north celestial pole is governed by
    A) latitude.   B) local time.   C) sidereal time.   D) longitude.
    Ans: A   Section: 2-4 and Figure 2-10

47. The elevation angle between the northern horizon of a fixed observer and the north celestial pole is equal to
    A)   the observer's longitude.
    B)   the observer's latitude.
    C)   the right ascension of the vernal equinox.
    D)   a variable value, depending on the time of year.
    Ans: B   Section: 2-4 and Figure 2-10

48. Over what range of declination will stars be circumpolar (i.e., be visible at any time of the night on any night of the year) for an observer at 30° north latitude?
    A)   60° to 90° N and 60° to 90° S   C)   30° to 90° N
    B)   60° to 90° N   D)   0° to 30° N
    Ans: B   Section: 2-4

49. Over what range of declination will stars be circumpolar (i.e., be visible at any time of the night on any night of the year) for an observer at the South Pole?
    A)   0° to 90°N   C)   90°S to 90°N (the whole sky!)
    B)   only stars at the south celestial pole   D)   0° to 90° S
    Ans: D   Section: 2-4

50. The two angles used by astronomers to define the position of a star in the sky and define a coordinate system applicable anywhere on Earth are
    A)   azimuth and elevation.   C)   horizontal and vertical angles.
    B)   latitude and longitude.   D)   right ascension and declination.
    Ans: D   Section: 2-4

51. The celestial coordinates that together describe a star's position precisely and unambiguously are
    A)   right ascension and declination.   C)   sidereal time and latitude.
    B)   right ascension and sidereal time.   D)   longitude and latitude.
    Ans: A   Section: 2-4 and Box 2-1

52. The declination angle between the north celestial pole and the celestial equator is
    A)   360°.
    B)   89° because of the displacement of the Pole Star.
    C)   180°.
    D)   90°.
    Ans: D   Section: 2-4 and Box 2-1

53. The declination of a star is a measure of its
    A) position measured above the observer's horizon along a great circle passing through the observer's zenith.
    B) time of rising above the horizon.
    C) position measured along the celestial equator.
    D) position north or south of the celestial equator along a great circle passing through the north and south celestial poles.
    Ans: D   Section: 2-4 and Box 2-1

54. The declination of a star in our sky is defined as the angle between the
    A) Sun and the star, measured along the ecliptic.
    B) celestial equator and the star, measured along a great circle passing through both celestial poles.
    C) center of the galaxy and the star, measured along the galactic equator.
    D) vernal equinox and the star, measured along the celestial equator.
    Ans: B   Section: 2-4 and Box 2-1

55. The right ascension of a star is one coordinate of its position, measured along the
    A) observer's meridian.   C) observer's horizon.
    B) celestial equator.   D) ecliptic.
    Ans: B   Section: 2-4 and Box 2-1

56. In the right ascension coordinate direction, 1 hour corresponds to what equivalent angle?
    A) 15°   B) 360°   C) 1°   D) variable depending on the time of year
    Ans: A   Section: 2-4 and Box 2-1

57. A comet moving northward from the equator across our sky can be described as having its
    A) declination increase with time.   C) declination decrease with time.
    B) right ascension decrease with time.   D) right ascension increase with time.
    Ans: A   Section: 2-4 and Box 2-1

58. What is the angle, measured in degrees between two stars of RA = 4^h, declination = 0°, and RA = 8^h, declination = 0°?
    A) 4°   B) 0°, since declinations are equal   C) 120°   D) 60°
    Ans: D   Section: 2-4 and Box 2-1

59. The summer solstice position coordinates are RA = $6^h 0^m 0^s$, declination = +23° 27′. What are the coordinates of the winter solstice?
    A)   RA = $18^h 0^m 0^s$, declination = +23° 27′
    B)   RA = $0^h 0^m 0^s$, declination = 0° 0°, by definition
    C)   RA = $12^h 0^m 0^s$, declination = −23° 27′
    D)   RA = $18^h 0^m 0^s$, declination = −23° 27′
    Ans: D   Section: 2-4 and Box 2-1

60. A star with RA = 4^h is in your meridian at a certain time. Which of the following stars will be on your meridian 2.5 hours from now?
    A)   RA = $6^h 30^m$
    B)   RA = $4^h 2^m 30^s$
    C)   RA = $1^h 30^m$
    D)   RA = 4^h, since RA of a star does not change with time
    Ans: A   Section: 2-4 and Box 2-1

61. At what approximate value of declination was the Sun on March 21 this year?
    A) 0°   B) 23.5°   C) 180°   D) no unique value
    Ans: A   Section: 2-4 and Box 2-1

62. At what approximate value of declination was the Sun on June 21 this year?
    A) −23.5°   B) 90°   C) 0°   D) 23.5°
    Ans: D   Section: 2-4 and Box 2-1

63. At what approximate value of declination was the Sun on September 22 this year?
    A) 23.5°   B) 90°   C) 180°   D) 0°
    Ans: D   Section: 2-4 and Box 2-1

64. At what approximate value of declination was the Sun on December 21 this year?
    A) 23.5°   B) 90°   C) 0°   D) −23.5°
    Ans: D   Section: 2-4 and Box 2-1

65. At what approximate value of right ascension was the Sun this year on March 21?
    A) 1 hour   B) no particular value   C) 12 hours   D) 0 hours
    Ans: D   Section: 2-4 and Box 2-1

66. At what approximate value of right ascension was the Sun this year on June 21?
    A) 18 hours   B) 0 hours   C) 12 hours   D) 6 hours
    Ans: D   Section: 2-4 and Box 2-1

67. At what approximate value of right ascension was the Sun this year on September 22?
    A) 18 hours   B) 0 hours   C) 6 hours   D) 12 hours
    Ans: D   Section: 2-4 and Box 2-1

68. At what approximate value of right ascension was the Sun this year on December 21?
    A) 0 hours   B) 12 hours   C) 18 hours   D) 6 hours
    Ans: C   Section: 2-4 and Box 2-1

69. The change in the right ascension of the Sun between June 21 and September 22 is approximately
    A) 0 hours.   B) 18 hours.   C) 6 hours.   D) 12 hours.
    Ans: C   Section: 2-4 and Box 2-1

70. The change in the right ascension of the Sun between June 21 and December 21 is approximately
    A) 0 hours 0 minutes.   B) 12 hours.   C) 18 hours.   D) 6 hours.
    Ans: B   Section: 2-4 and Box 2-1

71. The change in the declination of the Sun between December 21 and June 21 is approximately
    A) 90°.   B) 180°.   C) 47°.   D) 23.5°.
    Ans: C   Section: 2-4 and Box 2-1

72. The change in the declination of the Sun between March 21 and June 21 is approximately
    A) 23.5°.   B) 90°.   C) 180°.   D) 47°.
    Ans: A   Section: 2-4 and Box 2-1

73. The difference in declination angles between the north and south celestial poles is
    A) variable, depending on the season.   B) 23.5°.   C) 180°.   D) 90°.
    Ans: C   Section: 2-4 and Box 2-1

74. The celestial coordinates of the star ß Tauri are right ascension $5^h 25^m$, declination +28°, and those of the star ß Geminorum are right ascension $7^h 44^m$, declination +28°. Measured along the shortest angle in the sky between the two stars, ß Tauri is
    A)   west of ß Geminorum.   C)   north of ß Geminorum.
    B)   south of ß Geminorum.   D)   east of ß Geminorum.
    Ans: A   Section: 2-4 and Box 2-1

75. The celestial coordinates of the star γ Geminorum are right ascension $6^h 37^m$, declination +16°, and those of the star α (alpha) Tauri are right ascension $4^h 35^m$, declination +16°. Measured along the shortest angle in the sky between the two stars, γ Geminorum is
    A)   north of α Tauri.   C)   south of α Tauri.
    B)   east of α Tauri.   D)   west of α Tauri.
    Ans: B   Section: 2-4 and Box 2-1

76. The celestial coordinates of the star γ (gamma) Persei are right ascension $3^h 03^m$, declination +53°, and those of the star ρ (rho) Persei are right ascension $3^h 03^m$, declination +39°. Measured along the shortest angle in the sky between the two stars, γ Persei is
    A)   west of ρ Persei.   C)   south of ρ Persei.
    B)   north of ρ Persei.   D)   east of ρ Persei.
    Ans: B   Section: 2-4 and Box 2-1

77. The celestial coordinates of the star ζ (zeta) Leonis are right ascension $10^h 16^m$, declination $+24°$, and those of the star λ (lambda) Ursae Majoris are right ascension $10^h 16^m$, declination $+43°$. Measured along the shortest angle in the sky between the two stars, ζ Leonis is
    A)   west of λ Ursae Majoris.
    B)   north of λ Ursae Majoris.
    C)   east of λ Ursae Majoris.
    D)   south of λ Ursae Majoris.
    Ans: D   Section: 2-4 and Box 2-1

78. The two bright stars in the constellation Gemini, the Twins, are Castor (right ascension $7^h 33^m$, declination $+31° 56!$) and Pollux (right ascension $7^h 44^m$, declination $+28° 5!$). From these coordinates you can see that
    A)   Pollux is slightly southeast of Castor.
    B)   Pollux is slightly northwest of Castor.
    C)   Pollux is slightly northeast of Castor.
    D)   Pollux is slightly southwest of Castor.
    Ans: A   Section: 2-4 and Box 2-1

79. You are looking at the star Aldebaran (right ascension $4^h 34^m$, declination $+16° 28!$) from a location in the northern hemisphere. Where is the star Betelgeuse (right ascension $5^h 54^m$, declination $+7° 24!$)?
    A)   below Aldebaran and to the left
    B)   above Aldebaran and to the left
    C)   below Aldebaran and to the right
    D)   above Aldebaran and to the right
    Ans: A   Section: 2-4 and Box 2-1

80. The declination of Polaris, the north pole star, when viewed from a location 35 degrees north of the equator, is
    A) 0 degrees.   B) 35 degrees.   C) 55 degrees.   D) 90 degrees.
    Ans: D   Section: 2-4 and Box 2-1

81. The apparent path of the Sun across our sky, day by day, throughout the year, is known as the
    A) celestial meridian.   B) zenith.   C) ecliptic.   D) celestial equator.
    Ans: C   Section: 2-5

82. The ecliptic is defined as the
    A)   band of constellations through which the Sun and Moon move in our sky.
    B)   line in the sky that is perpendicular to the Earth's spin axis.
    C)   line traced in our sky by the Moon each month against the background stars.
    D)   line traced in our sky by the Sun over one year against the background stars.
    Ans: D   Section: 2-5

83. The ecliptic crosses the celestial equator at
    A)   two points, known as solstices.
    B)   one point only, known as the vernal equinox.
    C)   the meridian.
    D)   two points, known as equinoxes.
    Ans: D   Section: 2-5

84. If we could observe background stars in daylight, how would the Sun appear to move against this background because of our motion on an orbiting Earth?
    A)   1° per day, from west to east   C)   1° per day, from east to west
    B)   15° per hour, from east to west   D)   15° per hour, from west to east
    Ans: A   Section: 2-5

85. If the daytime sky were not bright, in which direction would we see the Sun move along the ecliptic over the course of a year, relative to the background stars?
    A)   toward the east   C)   toward the west
    B)   toward the southwest   D)   toward the northwest
    Ans: A   Section: 2-5

86. Which way are you moving with respect to the background stars because of the revolution of the Earth *in its orbit around the Sun?*
    A) westward   B) northeastward   C) northwestward   D) eastward
    Ans: D   Section: 2-5

87. At what average speed does the Sun appear to move across our sky with respect to the stars in order to move through one full circle in one year?
    A)   15° per hour
    B)   about 1° per day
    C)   The Sun never appears to move with respect to the stars in the sky.
    D)   about 13° per day
    Ans: B   Section: 2-5

88. If the Earth's spin axis were perpendicular to the Earth's orbital plane (the ecliptic plane), then the seasons and seasonal variation would be
    A)   very little different from the present seasons.
    B)   much faster (shorter seasons), but less severe.
    C)   much more severe.
    D)   nonexistent.
    Ans: D   Section: 2-5

89. The tilt of the Earth's spin axis to the direction perpendicular to the ecliptic plane
    (known as the ecliptic pole) is
    A)   variable between 0° and 23.5° over each three-month season.
    B)   0°.
    C)   23.5°.
    D)   90°.
    Ans: C   Section: 2-5

90. The Earth would not have seasons if
    A)   its axis of rotation were perpendicular to its equatorial plane.
    B)   its equatorial plane were perpendicular to its orbital plane.
    C)   its axis of rotation were perpendicular to its orbital plane.
    D)   the observer's zenith were perpendicular to the Earth's orbital plane.
    Ans: C   Section: 2-5

91. Over a period of six months, the tilt of Earth's spin axis with respect to the background
    stars changes by an angle of
    A) 47°.   B) 23.5°.   C) 180°.   D) 0°.
    Ans: D   Section: 2-5

92. In the northern hemisphere, summertime occurs when
    A)   the Earth is closest to the Sun in its elliptical orbit.
    B)   sunlight falls more directly on this hemisphere, heating it more than at other times
          of the year.
    C)   the Earth's equator is parallel to the plane of its orbit.
    D)   sunlight falls less directly on this hemisphere, spreading the heat out over a
          greater area.
    Ans: B   Section: 2-5

93. Summertime in the northern hemisphere is when
    A)   the Sun is closest to the Earth.
    B)   the Sun is closest to the ecliptic.
    C)   the Moon is closest to the Earth.
    D)   more direct sunlight shines on this hemisphere.
    Ans: D   Section: 2-5

94. Winter in the northern hemisphere occurs when
    A)   the Earth is farthest from the Sun in the elliptical orbit.
    B)   sunlight falls most obliquely on this region of Earth.
    C)   the Earth's axis is at its largest angle with respect to the ecliptic plane because of
          precession.
    D)   the Earth is farthest from the ecliptic plane.
    Ans: B   Section: 2-5

95. The lowest amount of solar energy per square meter is incident on the surface of Earth in the northern hemisphere on or about
    A) March 21, the end of winter.
    B) February 5, midwinter.
    C) September 21, the beginning of autumn.
    D) December 21, the beginning of winter.
    Ans: D   Section: 2-5

96. At what time of the year will the shadow of a vertical pole (a sundial) at any site in the northern hemisphere be the shortest?
    A) noon, August 5, midsummer
    B) noon, December 21, at the beginning of winter
    C) dawn, June 21, at the beginning of summer
    D) noon, June 21, at the beginning of summer
    Ans: D   Section: 2-5

97. At which time of the year will your shadow in sunlight at midday be shortest?
    A) midwinter, or early January
    B) midsummer, or about August 5
    C) the first day of summer, or about June 21
    D) the first day of spring, or about March 21
    Ans: C   Section: 2-5

98. It is warmer in summer than winter because
    A) the Sun is higher in the sky and the days are shorter.
    B) the Sun is lower in the sky and sunlight passes through more atmosphere, thereby warming it more during summer.
    C) Earth is closer to the Sun in summer.
    D) the Sun is higher in the sky and the days are longer.
    Ans: D   Section: 2-5

99. Seasonal variations on a planet's surface occur because
    A) the planet's distance from the Sun varies periodically over the orbital path.
    B) clouds alternately form and decay away in a periodic way.
    C) the planet's axis of spin is tilted with respect to the perpendicular to the orbital plane.
    D) volcanoes periodically cloud out the atmospheres of planets because of tidal interactions and distortions.
    Ans: C   Section: 2-5

100. One required condition for seasons to occur is that a planet's
    A) spin axis be tilted with respect to the perpendicular to its orbital plane.
    B) axis be perpendicular to its orbital plane.
    C) atmosphere be thick.
    D) distance from the Sun vary.
    Ans: A   Section: 2-5

101. The vernal equinox is one time of the year when the Sun
    A) crosses the Moon's orbital path in the sky.
    B) crosses the celestial equator.
    C) crosses the ecliptic plane.
    D) is at its lowest point in the sky at midday.
    Ans: B   Section: 2-5

102. The vernal equinox is that time of the year when the
    A) Sun crosses the equatorial plane, or celestial equator, moving north.
    B) Sun crosses the equatorial plane or celestial equator, moving south.
    C) Sun crosses the ecliptic plane.
    D) Earth is at the closest point to the Sun in its elliptical orbit.
    Ans: A   Section: 2-5

103. The equinoxes are located at the intersections of the
    A) ecliptic and the horizon.   C) ecliptic and the Moon's orbit.
    B) ecliptic and the celestial equator. D) horizon and the celestial equator.
    Ans: B   Section: 2-5

104. When the Sun is at one of the equinoxes,
    A) day and night are of equal length only for people on the equator.
    B) the day is longer than the night in one hemisphere of Earth and shorter in the other hemisphere.
    C) people on the equator have perpetual daylight.
    D) day and night are of equal length everywhere on Earth.
    Ans: D   Section: 2-5

105. The Sun rises due east in the sky when viewed from any site
    A) on Earth only on the first day of spring and the first day of fall.
    B) on the equator on every day of the year.
    C) along the Earth's equator at midsummer and midwinter.
    D) on Earth on the first day of summer and the first day of winter.
    Ans: A   Section: 2-5

106. Twice per year, when day and night are equal in length, the Sun is at one of two positions in the sky known as equinoxes. These points are the intersections of which two planes in the sky?
    A)   ecliptic and celestial meridian
    B)   ecliptic and arctic circle
    C)   celestial meridian and celestial equator
    D)   celestial equator and ecliptic
    Ans: D   Section: 2-5

107. The autumnal equinox is that time of the year when the
    A)   Sun crosses the ecliptic plane, moving north.
    B)   Earth is at the closest point to the Sun in its elliptical orbit.
    C)   Sun crosses the equatorial plane, moving south.
    D)   Sun passes through the galactic plane.
    Ans: C   Section: 2-5

108. On the day of the vernal equinox (approximately March 21 each year), which of the following conditions holds?
    A)   The Sun rises at its most northerly point on the horizon on this day.
    B)   Both day and night are almost exactly 12 hours long at all locations on the Earth.
    C)   Daylight is longest on this day.
    D)   The Sun passes through an observer's zenith only on this day each year.
    Ans: B   Section: 2-5

109. The approximate date March 21 represents the beginning of which season to people living in New Zealand?
    A) winter   B) summer   C) autumn   D) spring
    Ans: C   Section: 2-5

110. The time of autumnal equinox, about September 22, is what season for Australians in the southern hemisphere?
    A)   beginning of spring   C)   middle of summer
    B)   middle of winter   D)   beginning of autumn or fall
    Ans: A   Section: 2-5

111. At the summer solstice in the northern hemisphere, the Sun
    A)   is nearest to the Earth.
    B)   reaches its highest angle above the southern horizon for the whole year.
    C)   is on the celestial equator.
    D)   is at its lowest angle above the southern horizon at midday for the whole year.
    Ans: B   Section: 2-5

112. As a result of the tilt of the spin axis of Earth to the plane of the Earth's orbit (the ecliptic plane), sunrise in the winter months in the mid-latitude northern hemisphere occurs in which direction in the observer's sky?
A) The Sun always rises due west.   B) southwest   C) northeast   D) southeast
Ans: D   Section: 2-5

113. If the horizon is considered to be split into northern and southern parts by the east-west line, can the Sun ever rise in the southern part of the sky when viewed from a mid-latitude site in the northern hemisphere?
A)   yes, for exactly half a year
B)   no, since the site is in the northern hemisphere
C)   yes, but only for a few days around midsummer
D)   yes, for most of the year, since the observing site is in the northern hemisphere
Ans: A   Section: 2-5

114. If the horizon is considered to be split into northern and southern parts by the east-west line, can the Sun ever rise in the northern part of the sky when viewed from a mid-latitude site in the southern hemisphere?
A)   yes, for exactly half a year
B)   no, since the site is in the southern hemisphere
C)   yes, but only for a few days around midsummer
D)   yes, for most of the year, since the observing site is in the southern hemisphere
Ans: A   Section: 2-5

115. In winter in the southern hemisphere, the Sun will rise on the
A)   northwestern horizon.   C)   southwestern horizon.
B)   northeastern horizon.   D)   southeastern horizon.
Ans: B   Section: 2-5

116. The lowest latitude above which, for at least one day per year, one can see the Sun for a full 24 hours is approximately
A) 23.5°.   B) 52°.   C) 66.5°.   D) 90°.
Ans: C   Section: 2-5

117. Astronomers living north of the Arctic Circle around the time of summer solstice will enjoy which of the following?
A)   24 hours of sunlight
B)   continuous observation of the full Moon for several weeks
C)   a period of several weeks during which the Moon does not appear, allowing uninterrupted views of faint objects in the background sky
D)   24 hours of continuous darkness
Ans: A   Section: 2-5

118. Where would you have to be in the northern or southern hemispheres for the Sun to remain below the horizon for a 24-hour period for at least a part of the year?
    A)   above about 23.5° latitude
    B)   nowhere, since the Sun is always visible at some time of the day anywhere on Earth
    C)   only at 90°, or at the poles
    D)   above about 66.5° latitude
    Ans: D   Section: 2-5

119. Approximately how long will the Sun remain above the horizon once it first appears at the beginning of spring at the North Pole?
    A) 18 hours   B) 6 months   C) about 1 hour   D) 12 hours
    Ans: B   Section: 2-5

120. The Arctic Circle is at a latitude of
    A) 66.5° N.   B) 66.5° S.   C) 23.5° N.   D) a variable average of 66.5°.
    Ans: A   Section: 2-5

121. The Arctic Circle is defined as a line on the Earth where the Sun
    A)   is always 23.5° or more above or below the horizon.
    B)   never shines at any time of the year.
    C)   always shines, winter and summer.
    D)   can be seen for 24 hours on at least one day of the year.
    Ans: D   Section: 2-5

122. The "Land of the Midnight Sun" is so named because
    A)   the Sun is above the horizon for a full 24 hours at a certain time of the year.
    B)   the Sun passes overhead in this region at least once during the year.
    C)   twilight is bright and lasts all night through the summer months since the Sun never gets far below the horizon from these locations.
    D)   the full Moon is always up whenever the Sun sets, maintaining light skies throughout the summer months.
    Ans: A   Section: 2-5

123. If you were standing on the equator, which of the following positions in the sky would pass directly over your head (i.e., through your zenith) at some time in one 24-hour period? (See Fig. 2-14, Freedman and Kaufmann, *Universe*, 7th ed.)
    A)   the position of the Sun at summer solstice
    B)   the ecliptic pole, or perpendicular to the direction of the ecliptic plane
    C)   the vernal equinox, or the zero point of the right ascension on the celestial equator
    D)   the north celestial pole, or perpendicular to the direction of the celestial equator
    Ans: C   Section: 2-5

124. In what region of Earth would you have to be to have the Sun pass through your zenith at some time during the year?
    A)   within the Arctic Circle
    B)   at any latitude
    C)   within +/− 23.5° of the equator—the tropics
    D)   only on the equator, nowhere else
    Ans: C   Section: 2-5

125. If the Sun passes through your zenith sometime during the year, then you must be
    A)   anywhere within 23.5° of the equator.
    B)   anywhere within 66.5° of the equator.
    C)   exactly on the equator.
    D)   anywhere on the Earth (no limitation).
    Ans: A   Section: 2-5

126. If you stand at latitude 10° N, how many times during the year will the Sun pass precisely through your zenith?
    A) twice   B) once   C) never   D) every day for a half a year
    Ans: A   Section: 2-5

127. Where would you have to be to see the south celestial pole on your horizon?
    A)   at the North Pole
    B)   about 1° away from the South Pole, to allow for precession
    C)   at the South Pole
    D)   on the equator
    Ans: D   Section: 2-5

128. During one complete year, an observer on the equator would be able to see what fraction of the overall sky?
    A)   50%
    B)   a variable amount, depending on the person's longitude
    C)   a variable amount, depending on which year
    D)   100%
    Ans: D   Section: 2-5

129. During one complete year, an observer at the South Pole would be able to see what fraction of the overall sky?
    A)   50%
    B)   a variable amount, depending on which year
    C)   100%
    D)   a variable amount, depending on the person's longitude
    Ans: A   Section: 2-5

130. From the North Pole,
    A)   only stars within 66.5° of the north celestial pole can be seen.
    B)   only half the celestial sphere can be seen on every clear night.
    C)   only stars 23.5° above the celestial equator can be seen.
    D)   the whole celestial sphere is visible at some time during the year.
    Ans: B   Section: 2-5

131. Where would you have to be in order to see the north celestial pole in your zenith?
    A)   about 1° away from the South Pole, to account for precession
    B)   North Pole
    C)   South Pole
    D)   equator
    Ans: B   Section: 2-5

132. If you were standing on the South Pole with the south celestial pole in your zenith at the time of the vernal equinox, where would you see the Sun all day?
    A)   on your horizon   C)   well below your horizon
    B)   23.5° above the horizon   D)   at your zenith
    Ans: A   Section: 2-5

133. If you were at the South Pole for a full year, what would be the highest angle the Sun would reach above your horizon (at midday, of course)?
    A)   90°
    B)   0°; it would reach only the horizon
    C)   It would never reach above the horizon, since the South Pole is always in darkness.
    D)   23.5°
    Ans: D   Section: 2-5

134. If you were standing on the South Pole at the time of the autumnal equinox, where would you expect the Sun to be at midday?
    A)   on your horizon   C)   at your zenith
    B)   well below your horizon   D)   23.5° above your horizon
    Ans: A   Section: 2-5

135. Where would you expect to see the Sun in your sky if you were at the North Pole at the beginning of fall (about Sept 24)?
    A)   at your zenith
    B)   about 23.5° above your horizon all day
    C)   on the horizon
    D)   below your horizon all day
    Ans: C   Section: 2-5

136. What would be the position and motion of the Sun on December 21 from the South Pole on Antarctica?
    A)   It would rise in the east at 6 A.M. and set in the west at 6 P.M., reaching 47° above the horizon at midday.
    B)   It would pass across the sky from the horizon at midnight to reach an angle of 23.5° above the horizon at midday and then return to the horizon.
    C)   It would remain below the horizon for the whole 24 hours.
    D)   It would move completely around the sky in 24 hours while maintaining an angle of 23.5° above the horizon.
    Ans: D   Section: 2-5

137. In its motion across our sky against the background stars in the course of a month, the Moon appears to move about
    A)   0.5° per day, its own diameter, from west to east.
    B)   1.0° per day, twice its diameter, from west to east.
    C)   0.5° per hour, its own diameter, from east to west.
    D)   0.5° per hour, its own diameter, from west to east.
    Ans: D   Section: 2-6

138. The zodiac is a
    A)   band of sky extending 8° on each side of the celestial equator.
    B)   constellation representing a boat in the sky.
    C)   band of sky extending 8° on either side of the ecliptic.
    D)   band of sky 8° wide centered on the ecliptic.
    Ans: C   Section: 2-6

139. The total width of the zodiac surrounding the ecliptic plane in the sky is approximately
    A) 8°.   B) 16°.   C) 23.5°.   D) 1°.
    Ans: B   Section: 2-6

140. Precession is
    A)   the motion of the Earth along its orbital path.
    B)   a very slow conical motion of the Earth's axis of rotation.
    C)   the occasional reversal of the direction of spin of the Earth.
    D)   the daily spinning motion of the Earth.
    Ans: B   Section: 2-6

141. Precession is
    A)   the slow coning motion of the spin axis of the Earth, similar to that of a spinning top.
    B)   the daily spinning motion of the Earth, producing the apparent motion of the Sun and the stars.
    C)   another name for a parade.
    D)   the motion of the Earth along its orbital path during a year.
    Ans: A   Section: 2-6

142. Precession of the Earth's spin axis results in a
    A)   cyclic variation over a period of a year of the constellations visible at night from
          Earth.
    B)   daily shift in the position of the observer's zenith relative to the celestial equator
          (for an observer at a fixed location on Earth).
    C)   gradual shift in the angle between the ecliptic and the celestial equator.
    D)   gradual shift of the vernal equinox along the ecliptic.
    Ans: D   Section: 2-6

143. A science fiction writer, writing a story about inhabitants on Earth in 14,000 A.D. who
     have survived a disaster that included the loss of modern navigational aids, describes
     them traveling due north across barren wastes by walking toward Polaris, the Pole Star.
     What is wrong with this situation?
    A)   Polaris will have moved away from due north since it is moving rapidly with
          respect to surrounding stars.
    B)   Polaris will no longer be due north, because of Earth's precession.
    C)   By that time, Polaris will be due south, not due north, because of the reversal of
          the Earth's spin axis.
    D)   Polaris will no longer be visible since its lifetime is only a few thousand years.
    Ans: B   Section: 2-6

144. Polaris is our "pole star" at the present time. At approximately what time in history or in
     the future would the star Thuban be our "pole star"? (See Fig. 2-18, Freedman and
     Kaufmann, *Universe*, 7th ed.)
    A)   never, since Polaris will always be our "pole star" when viewed from Earth
    B)   1 A.D.
    C)   3000 A.D.
    D)   3000 B.C.
    Ans: D   Section: 2-6

145. Precession of the Earth's axis of rotation is caused by
    A)   changes in the rate of rotation (length of the day) of the Earth caused primarily by
          the gravitational pull of the Moon.
    B)   changes in the shape of the Earth's orbit due to the gravitational pull of the Moon.
    C)   the gravitational pull of the Moon and the Sun on the equatorial bulge of the
          Earth.
    D)   changes in the shape of the Earth's orbit due to the gravitational pull of the Sun.
    Ans: C   Section: 2-6

146. The reason for the slow movement of the vernal equinox through our sky against the background stars over long periods of time is the
    A)   precession of the spin axis of the Earth.
    B)   overall movement of local stars in our sky.
    C)   movement of the Sun in the Milky Way Galaxy.
    D)   motion of the Earth in its orbit.
    Ans: A   Section: 2-6

147. The phenomenon of precession of the Earth's spin axis is caused by the
    A)   varying intensity of sunlight on Earth throughout the year.
    B)   tidal ebb and flow of ocean waters on Earth.
    C)   variation of the spin rate of Earth.
    D)   gravitational pull of Moon and Sun on the Earth's equatorial bulge.
    Ans: D   Section: 2-6

148. If the polar axis of Earth precesses through a full circle (See Fig. 2-18, Freedman and Kaufmann, *Universe,* 7th ed.) in 26,000 years, how long will it take for the line between the axis and the center of the circle to move through 1°?
    A) 720 years   B) 0.014 years   C) 7.2 years   D) 72 years
    Ans: D   Section: 2-6

149. To what constellation will the north celestial pole be closest in the year 14,000 A.D.?
    A)   Draco
    B)   Lyra
    C)   Cepheus
    D)   Ursa Major, since the north celestial pole never moves.
    Ans: B   Section: 2-6

150. The precessional motion of the north celestial pole of Earth over a period of 26,000 years is a circle of 47° diameter in the northern sky. The equivalent motion of the south celestial pole is
    A)   a circle of 47° diameter, covered in 26,000 years.
    B)   a much smaller circle, covered in 26,000 years.
    C)   a circle of 47° diameter, covered in a much shorter time, about 1000 years.
    D)   the south celestial pole does not move at all during this precession.
    Ans: A   Section: 2-6

151. The time that will elapse before the spin axis of the Earth points toward the present pole star again as a result of precession is
    A) 9 years.   B) at least 1 million years.   C) 13,000 years.   D) 26,000 years.
    Ans: D   Section: 2-6

152. The slow coning pattern of the spin axis of the Earth's precession will move the end of this axis in a complete circle in a period of
    A) 26 million years.   B) 26,000 years.   C) 2600 years.   D) 1 year.
    Ans: B   Section: 2-6

153. The position of the vernal equinox in the sky is at present in the constellation
    A) Ursa Major.   B) Pisces.   C) Aquarius.   D) Aries.
    Ans: B   Section: 2-6

154. Why do the astronomical coordinates of right ascension and declination of a star change systematically night by night?
    A)   They do not change, since they are positions on a fixed star chart.
    B)   motion of the Earth in its orbit around the Sun
    C)   bending of light by the Earth's atmosphere
    D)   precession of the Earth's spin axis
    Ans: D   Section: 2-6

155. Earlier in this chapter we discussed some ancient buildings that were constructed so that they were aligned to the rising of the Sun at vernal equinox or some other important astronomical date. How does the precession of the equinoxes affect these alignments in a building, say, 2000 years old?
    A)   The alignments of such a building should still be perfect.
    B)   The alignments will vary slightly, but after a mere 2000 years the discrepancy in alignment will be almost too small to measure.
    C)   The alignments will vary significantly after 2000 years, but only for buildings within 23.5 degrees of the equator.
    D)   The alignments will vary significantly after 2000 years for buildings anywhere on Earth.
    Ans: D   Section: 2-6

156. The Moon's equatorial plane is nearly the same as the
    A)   Earth's equatorial plane.
    B)   ecliptic.
    C)   plane passing through both poles and the zenith (for an observer on Earth).
    D)   plane passing through both poles and the vernal equinox (for an observer on Earth).
    Ans: B   Section: 2-6

157. In one year the apparent path of the Sun through the background of the stars passes through
    A) only the 12 Zodiac constellations defined by the ancients.
    B) the 12 Zodiac constellations plus the constellation Ophiuchus.
    C) only 11 of the original 12 Zodiac constellations: the path no longer passes through Ares.
    D) only the north circumpolar constellations.
    Ans: B   Section: 2-6

158. Which direction in an observer's sky is not always on his/her meridian?
    A)   the zenith   C)   due south on the horizon
    B)   the north celestial pole   D)   the vernal equinox
    Ans: D   Section: 2-7

159. An observer's meridian passes through
    A)   his zenith and the north and south celestial poles.
    B)   his zenith and the east and west positions on his horizon.
    C)   the north and south celestial poles and the vernal equinox position.
    D)   his zenith and the vernal and autumnal equinoxes.
    Ans: A   Section: 2-7

160. A given star in the sky will reach its highest point for a particular observer when it passes through the
    A) zodiac.   B) ecliptic plane.   C) meridian.   D) celestial equator.
    Ans: C   Section: 2-7

161. An observer's celestial meridian is the
    A)   arc joining the north and south celestial poles through the observer's zenith.
    B)   extension of the horizon onto the sky.
    C)   plane of the Earth's orbit extended onto the sky.
    D)   extension of the Earth's equator onto the sky.
    Ans: A   Section: 2-7

162. The line on the sky joining the north and south celestial poles through a person's zenith is known as the
    A) meridian.   B) celestial equator.   C) zodiac.   D) horizon.
    Ans: A   Section: 2-7

163. The star grouping Leo (the lion) extends for about 30° along and close to the celestial equator. At low to mid-latitudes, roughly how long does it take Leo to rise above the horizon?
    A) 5 hours   B) 30 seconds   C) 30 minutes   D) 2 hours
    Ans: D   Section: 2-7 and Box 2-2

164. By observing the sky closely night by night, you would note that a particular star rises
   A)   at a varying time every night, sometimes earlier, sometimes later than a specified time.
   B)   about 4 minutes later every night.
   C)   about 4 minutes earlier every night.
   D)   at the same time every night.
   Ans: C   Section: 2-7 and Box 2-2

165. Any star (except the Sun), when viewed from low and mid-latitudes, rises in the east
   A)   about an hour later each evening.   C)   about 4 minutes earlier each evening.
   B)   about 4 minutes later each evening.   D)   at the same time each evening.
   Ans: C   Section: 2-7 and Box 2-2

166. The Big Dipper, or Ursa Major, will return to the same position in an observer's sky in what time period in solar time?
   A)   24 hours 4 minutes   C)   23 hours 56 minutes
   B)   365.25 days   D)   24 hours exactly
   Ans: C   Section: 2-7 and Box 2-2

167. The Sun appears to be about 0.5° in diameter. On the equator, approximately how long does it take for the Sun to set, from first contact with the horizon to the Sun completely below that horizon?
   A) 2 seconds   B) 4 minutes   C) 2 minutes   D) about 1 hour
   Ans: C   Section: 2-7 and Box 2-2

168. When viewed from Earth, Venus subtends an angle of about 1 arcminute ($1/60°$) when it is at the closest point to Earth in its orbit. If you were watching Venus set in the west over a clear horizon (e.g., ocean), how long would it take from Venus first reaching the horizon to Venus completely setting below the horizon?
   A)   0.25 sec
   B)   about 4 seconds
   C)   about 4 minutes
   D)   almost instantaneous (much less than 1 second)
   Ans: B   Section: 2-7 and Box 2-2

169. If a person on the equator sees a particular star cross the horizon at 10 P.M. (2200 hours) on a particular night, what time would the same person (at the same location) see that star cross the horizon on the next night?
   A)   10:04 P.M.
   B)   This star will not rise the next night and will be seen again only after one year.
   C)   10:00 P.M.
   D)   9:56 P.M.
   Ans: D   Section: 2-7 and Box 2-2

170. On December 1 at 10 P.M., the bright star Procyon will just be rising on the eastern horizon. At approximately what time would you see this star rising on Christmas Day (24 days later)?
A) 9:36 P.M.   B) 11:36 P.M.   C) 10 P.M.   D) 8:24 P.M.
Ans: D   Section: 2-7 and Box 2-2

171. At 10 P.M. on December 1, the bright star Procyon is seen to rise on the eastern horizon. At approximately what time will this star rise 7 days later, on December 8?
A) 10:28 P.M.   B) 9:53 P.M.   C) 9:32 P.M.   D) 10:00 P.M.
Ans: C   Section: 2-7 and Box 2-2

172. A sundial is not considered to be a good timekeeper because the
A)   sky is often cloudy.
B)   Earth's rotation rate changes throughout the year.
C)   Sun's large angular diameter produces a fuzzy shadow.
D)   Earth's orbital speed around the ecliptic is variable.
Ans: D   Section: 2-7

173. Compared to clocks in California in winter, those in New York (maintaining civil time, or mean solar time) will be
A)   the same.   C)   three hours behind.
B)   two hours ahead.   D)   three hours ahead.
Ans: D   Section: 2-7

174. Time, as indicated by an uncorrected sundial, can differ from true time by as much as 15 minutes at certain times of the year. This is because the
A)   Earth moves nonuniformly along an orbit inclined to the celestial equator.
B)   Sun moves with respect to the background stars because of our motion on an orbiting Earth.
C)   time zones are poorly defined on the Earth's surface, leading to time errors that vary through the year.
D)   Earth's rotation rate varies throughout the year.
Ans: A   Section: 2-7

175. Sidereal time is the more fundamental time, since it is a measure of the true rotation rate of Earth. Why then do we govern our lives by solar time rather than sidereal time?
A)   We cannot divide the day into 24 equal hours of sidereal time.
B)   In sidereal time, the Sun would reach the meridian early or late, sometimes by as much as 17 minutes at certain times of the year.
C)   Different clocks tick at different rates depending on latitude in sidereal time.
D)   We wish to remain in time with the Sun's illumination on Earth, with high Sun angle at about midday every day.
Ans: D   Section: 2-7

176. The difference between 1 second of sidereal time and 1 second of solar time is
    A)   very small but variable because of the variable motion of the Earth in its orbit.
    B)   0, since they are defined to be equal.
    C)   a very small but finite and fixed interval of time.
    D)   very large, because 1 sidereal second measures a fraction of a year while 1 solar second measures the same fraction of a solar day.
    Ans: C   Section: 2-7 and Box 2-2

177. At a particular time, the vernal equinox passes through the celestial meridian of an observer. What is the sidereal time at that site?
    A)   12 hours exactly
    B)   0 hours exactly
    C)   variable, depending on the observer's latitude
    D)   variable, depending on the time of year
    Ans: B   Section: 2-7 and Box 2-2

178. The beginning of a sidereal day (at midnight, sidereal time) at any location on Earth is defined by the passage of the
    A)   pole star through the lower meridian at that site
    B)   Sun through the position of the vernal equinox
    C)   vernal equinox through the upper meridian at that site
    D)   pole star through the upper meridian at that site
    Ans: C   Section: 2-7

179. I record the time in New York and know that it is the *same* time in California. This scenario can be true if the time I am measuring is
    A) solar time only.   B) sidereal time only.   C) UTC only.   D) any of these.
    Ans: C   Section: 2-7

180. Which of the following years were leap years according to the calendar then in use: 1000, 1492, 1600, 1776?
    A) just 1600   B) just 1492 and 1776   C) all except 1600   D) all of them
    Ans: D   Section: 2-8

181. The tropical year is about 20 minutes shorter than the sidereal year. What does this tell you about precession?
    A)   The vernal equinox moves eastward along the ecliptic.
    B)   The vernal equinox moves westward along the ecliptic.
    C)   The vernal equinox remains fixed on the ecliptic, but the Sun progressively changes its apparent position against the background stars from one sidereal year to the next.
    D)   This time difference has nothing to do with the precession of the equinoxes.
    Ans: B   Section: 2-8

Chapter 3: Eclipses and the Motion of the Moon

1. Which of the following is the correct sequence of appearances of Moon phases in the sky?
    A)   new moon, full moon, waxing crescent, waning crescent
    B)   waxing crescent, first quarter, waxing gibbous, full moon
    C)   full moon, waxing gibbous, third quarter, waning crescent
    D)   new moon, waning crescent, first quarter, full moon
    Ans: B   Section: 3-1

2. Why do we see different phases of the Moon?
    A)   The motion of the Moon in its orbit around the Earth causes us to see different amounts of the Earth's shadow falling on the Moon.
    B)   The motion of the Moon in its orbit around the Earth causes us to see different amounts of the sunlit side of the Moon.
    C)   The distance of the Moon from the Earth changes because of the elliptical orbit of the Moon, causing the sunlit side of the Moon to move relative to the Earth.
    D)   The rotation of the Moon around its own axis causes us to see different amounts of the sunlit side of the Moon.
    Ans: B   Section: 3-1

3. The Earth's shadow falling on the Moon is the reason we see
    A)   solar eclipses.
    B)   The Earth's shadow cannot fall on the Moon.
    C)   lunar eclipses.
    D)   the phases of the Moon.
    Ans: C   Section: 3-1

4. What is the one major difference between the Sun and the Moon in our sky?
    A)   Their apparent motion across the sky with respect to the horizon in one day is very different.
    B)   Their diameters subtend very different angles.
    C)   The spectrum of their light is very different.
    D)   The Sun emits light while the Moon merely reflects it.
    Ans: D   Section: 3-1

5. Where in the northern hemisphere can you see the true astronomical new moon?
    A)   always in the south
    B)   in a direction opposite to that of the Sun
    C)   the Moon is not visible at new moon
    D)   in a direction at right angles to that of the Sun
    Ans: C   Section: 3-1

6. When the Moon is between the Sun and the Earth and the Sun and Moon are almost in line, we call its phase
   A) new moon.
   B) full moon.
   C) The Moon can never get between the Sun and the Earth.
   D) gibbous.
   Ans: A   Section: 3-1

7. At what approximate time will the new moon rise?
   A) midday   B) sunset   C) sunrise   D) midnight
   Ans: C   Section: 3-1

8. When the Sun and Moon have the same right ascension, the phase of the Moon is a
   A) gibbous.   B) new moon.   C) full moon.   D) first quarter.
   Ans: B   Section: 3-1

9. If the Moon is located at the vernal equinox on the first day of spring, what then is the phase of the Moon?
   A) third quarter   B) first quarter   C) full   D) new
   Ans: D   Section: 3-1

10. Which way will the "horns," or sharp ends of the crescent, of the Moon point in the sky when the Moon is above the western horizon at sunset, at a phase 3 days after new moon? (Hint: Think about what causes the crescent phase of the Moon; Fig. 3-2 of Freedman and Kaufmann, *Universe*, 7th ed., may help.)
    A) toward the Sun, westward
    B) The Moon is not crescent-shaped at this phase.
    C) at right angles to the Sun direction, northward
    D) away from the Sun, eastward
    Ans: D   Section: 3-1

11. Suppose that on a given evening you notice that the sunlit portion of the Moon has a crescent shape. This simple observation tells you
    A) that at that particular time the Moon is closer to the Sun than you are.
    B) that at that particular time the Moon is farther from the Sun than you are.
    C) that the line from you to the Moon is exactly at right angles to the line from you to the Sun.
    D) nothing at all about where the Moon is in space compared to you and the Sun.
    Ans: A   Section: 3-1

12. Which of the following phases of the Moon is most easily seen during the daytime (mid-morning or mid-afternoon, not near sunrise or sunset)?
    A) The Moon is never visible in daylight.   B) new   C) full   D) quarter
    Ans: D   Section: 3-1

13. When will the first quarter moon rise, approximately? (You may want to examine Figure 3-2 of Freedman and Kaufmann, *Universe*, 7th ed., and think about where you would need to stand on the Earth to see the first quarter moon rising.)
    A) 6 A.M.   B) noon   C) 3 A.M.   D) 6 P.M.
    Ans: B   Section: 3-1

14. The phase of the Moon when the Sun and Moon are separated by 6 hours of right ascension is always
    A) full moon.   B) new moon.   C) crescent.   D) either first or third quarter.
    Ans: D   Section: 3-1

15. If on a particular day the Sun is at one of the solstices and the Moon is at one of the equinoxes, then the lunar phase on that day is
    A)   not predictable from this information alone.
    B)   full.
    C)   new.
    D)   either first or last quarter.
    Ans: D   Section: 3-1

16. How much of the total surface of the Moon is illuminated by the Sun when it is at quarter phase?
    A) one quarter   B) very little   C) all of it   D) one half
    Ans: D   Section: 3-1

17. When the Moon is in its gibbous phase, the positions of Moon, the Earth, and Sun are such that the
    A)   relative distances of the Earth and Moon from the Sun at successive gibbous phases change as the Earth orbits around the Sun.
    B)   Sun and Moon are 90° apart as seen from the Earth.
    C)   Moon is closer to the Sun than is the Earth.
    D)   Moon is farther from the Sun than is the Earth.
    Ans: D   Section: 3-1

18. When the Moon is in its gibbous phase, the right ascensions of the Sun and the Moon differ by
    A) more than 6 hours.   B) 6 hours.   C) 0 hours.   D) less than 6 hours.
    Ans: A   Section: 3-1

19. The gibbous phase of the Moon occurs when the Moon passes
    A)   from third quarter to new moon.
    B)   between the two positions when the moon and the Sun are at right angles to each other during which new moon occurs.
    C)   from new moon to first quarter.
    D)   from first quarter to full moon.
    Ans: D   Section: 3-1

20. At what approximate time does a full moon rise?
    A) midnight   B) sunrise   C) noon   D) sunset
    Ans: D   Section: 3-1

21. A full moon always occurs
    A)   on the first of every month.
    B)   when the Moon is at right angles to the direction of the Sun.
    C)   when the Moon is closer to Sun than is the Earth.
    D)   when the Moon is farther from the Sun than is the Earth.
    Ans: D   Section: 3-1

22. A full moon is always at its highest in our sky at
    A) midnight.   B) sunset.   C) midday.   D) sunrise.
    Ans: A   Section: 3-1

23. A full moon will be on the horizon at
    A)   any time, day or night, with no restriction.
    B)   sunrise or sunset.
    C)   midnight.
    D)   midday.
    Ans: B   Section: 3-1

24. When the Sun and Moon are separated by 12 hours of right ascension, the phase of the
    Moon is always
    A)   full moon.   C)   third quarter.
    B)   first quarter.   D)   either first or third quarter.
    Ans: A   Section: 3-1

25. If the Moon is located at the vernal equinox on September 20, what is the phase of the
    Moon?
    A) new   B) third quarter   C) first quarter   D) full
    Ans: D   Section: 3-1

26. On a particular day, the Sun is at the vernal equinox and the Moon is at the autumnal
    equinox. The lunar phase on this particular day is
    A) quarter.   B) new.   C) not predictable from this information alone.   D) full.
    Ans: D   Section: 3-1

27. When does the third quarter moon rise? (You may want to examine Figure 3-2 of
    Freedman and Kaufmann, *Universe*, 7th ed., and think about where you would need to
    stand on the Earth to see the third quarter moon rising.)
    A) about 6 A.M.   B) close to noon   C) about 6 P.M.   D) close to midnight
    Ans: D   Section: 3-1

28. Which of the following planets will be seen from Earth as crescent shaped at certain times in its orbit?
    A) Jupiter   B) Uranus   C) Mars   D) Venus
    Ans: D   Section: 3-1

29. Which of the following will never be seen from Earth as a crescent?
    A) Mercury   B) Venus   C) Mars   D) Moon
    Ans: C   Section: 3-1

30. If you were on Mars, which of the following would never be seen as a crescent?
    A) Venus   B) Moon   C) Earth   D) Jupiter
    Ans: D   Section: 3-1

31. If you were on the Moon, which of the following could occasionally appear as crescent shaped?
    A) the asteroid Ceres   B) Mars   C) Earth   D) Jupiter
    Ans: C   Section: 3-1

32. The Moon is visible in the sky in the daytime from most places on Earth
    A)   almost never; only during solar eclipses when the sky is dark.
    B)   some time every day, but it is difficult to see because of the blue sky.
    C)   only at full Moon phases, when it is very bright.
    D)   about half the time, or for two weeks in every month.
    Ans: D   Section: 3-1

33. Is the Moon ever visible during the daytime (on a clear day)?
    A)   only during solar eclipses, when the sky is dark
    B)   no, the Moon is never visible during the daytime
    C)   yes, but only if the Sun is very close to the horizon (just after sunrise or just before sunset)
    D)   yes, whenever the Moon is above the horizon and it is not close to new moon
    Ans: D   Section: 3-1

34. The Moon would *not* go through phases if
    A)   it were tilted on its axis, like the Earth.
    B)   it did not rotate.
    C)   it took one year to go around the Earth.
    D)   (in addition to the Moon going around the Earth) the Sun went around the Earth instead of the Earth around the Sun.
    Ans: C   Section: 3-1

35. If an observer on Earth sees the Moon to be full, than at the same time an observer on the Moon would see the Earth to be at what phase?
    A) full
    B) new
    C) third quarter
    D) The Earth does not appear to go through phases when observed from the Moon.
    Ans: B   Section: 3-1

36. If an observer on Earth sees the Moon to be at first quarter, then at the same time, an observer on the Moon would observe the Earth to be at what phase?
    A) first quarter
    B) third quarter
    C) full
    D) The Earth does not appear to go through phases when observed from the Moon.
    Ans: B   Section: 3-1

37. How does the Moon rotate to keep one face pointed toward the Earth at all times, as can be seen in Fig. 3-4, Freedman and Kaufmann, *Universe,* 7th ed.?
    A) It rotates once per month.   C) It rotates once per day.
    B) It rotates once per year.   D) It does not rotate at all.
    Ans: A   Section: 3-2

38. The Moon is seen to keep one face toward Earth at all times. If viewed from a point directly above the plane of the planetary system, how does it have to rotate to maintain this alignment?
    A) It must rotate once per year as Earth and Moon orbit the Sun together.
    B) It must rotate once per day.
    C) It must not rotate at all, since we always see the same face from Earth.
    D) It must rotate once per month, or once per orbit around Earth.
    Ans: D   Section: 3-2

39. The Moon rotates around its own axis in the same length of time that it takes to orbit once around the Earth. This equality of rotation period and orbital period, which results in the same side of the Moon facing the Earth at all times, is called
    A) coincidental rotation.   C) synchronous rotation.
    B) precession.   D) relative motion.
    Ans: C   Section: 3-2

40. In its orbit around the Earth, the Moon
    A) always keeps the same side toward the Sun.
    B) always keeps the same side toward the Earth.
    C) always keeps the sunlit side toward the Earth.
    D) rotates once every 24 hours to keep in step with the Earth.
    Ans: B   Section: 3-2

41. To observers on Earth, the Moon shows
    A)   its whole surface once per year as Earth moves around the Sun.
    B)   its whole surface once per month as it rotates.
    C)   only one side to Earth at all times.
    D)   only the sunlit side at all times.
    Ans: C   Section: 3-2

42. If you were standing on the Moon in darkness on the opposite side from the Earth at a particular time, which of the following conditions would be true?
    A)   You would never see the Sun from that position.
    B)   You would see the Earth in about 7 days.
    C)   It would take about ¼ year (3 months) before you would see the Earth from that position.
    D)   You would never see the Earth from that position.
    Ans: D   Section: 3-2

43. The time for the Moon to rotate around its own axis, relative to the stars, is about
    A) 1 year.   B) 1 month.   C) 1 day.   D) infinite, since the Moon never rotates.
    Ans: B   Section: 3-2

44. Which of the following statements about the Moon's position and motion is NOT correct?
    A)   The Moon does not rotate at all, since it keeps one face toward the Earth at all times.
    B)   The Moon's rotation period is equal to its orbital period.
    C)   The time from full moon to full moon is longer than the Moon's orbital period.
    D)   The time from full moon to full moon is longer than the Moon's rotation period on its axis.
    Ans: A   Section: 3-2

45. When viewed from a point directly above the plane of the planetary system, the Moon would appear to rotate on its axis
    A)   once per day to maintain its direction toward Earth.
    B)   once per year as Earth and Moon orbit the Sun together.
    C)   once per month, or once per revolution about Earth.
    D)   not at all, since on Earth we always see the same face.
    Ans: C   Section: 3-2

46. As seen by a distant observer who is fixed with respect to the stars, approximately how long does it take for the Moon to rotate once around its own axis?
    A)   1 month
    B)   forever; since one side of the Moon always faces toward the Earth, the Moon does not rotate
    C)   1 day
    D)   1 year
    Ans: A   Section: 3-2

47. The approximate rotation period of the Moon is
    A)   1 day.
    B)   1 week.
    C)   1 month.
    D)   infinite, since the Moon does not rotate, but keeps one face toward the Earth at all times.
    Ans: C   Section: 3-2

48. You are standing at the equator of the Moon and a particular star is overhead at that time. How long will it be before that star is approximately overhead again?
    A)   The star will always remain overhead since the Moon does not rotate on its axis.
    B)   29½ days
    C)   365¼ days
    D)   27 days
    Ans: D   Section: 3-2

49. Approximately how long will it take for the dark-light dividing line on the Moon, the terminator, to move through 90° of lunar longitude?
    A)   91 days or ¼ year
    B)   6 hours or ¼ day
    C)   The dark-light line never moves around the Moon since the Moon does not rotate on its axis.
    D)   7 days
    Ans: D   Section: 3-2

50. One day from sunrise to sunrise for a space explorer at her lunar base will be how many Earth days long? (A diagram might help!)
    A) 365¼ days   B) 29½ days   C) 1 day   D) 27 days
    Ans: B   Section: 3-2

51. The term "synodic month" refers to the
    A)   time from one lunar eclipse to the next.
    B)   time from new moon to new moon.
    C)   month containing Easter, as defined by the ecclesiastical calendar.
    D)   time over which the Moon completes one orbit around Earth, relative to the stars.
    Ans: B   Section: 3-2

52. The term "sidereal month" refers to the
   A)   time from new moon to new moon.
   B)   time over which the Moon completes one orbit around Earth, relative to the stars.
   C)   time from one lunar eclipse to the next.
   D)   month containing Easter, as defined by the ecclesiastical calendar.
   Ans: B   Section: 3-2

53. One synodic month is longer than one sidereal month by about
   A) 1 week.   B) 1 hour.   C) 4 minutes.   D) 2.2 days.
   Ans: D   Section: 3-2

54. Why is the period between two successive full moons not equal to the Moon's orbital period, or sidereal month?
   A)   The Moon's orbit is elliptical, and the Moon therefore moves irregularly around the Earth.
   B)   The Moon's orbit is inclined at about 5° to the Earth's orbital plane.
   C)   Two time intervals are not related, since full-moon time depends on the Moon's rotation period about its own axis.
   D)   The Earth-Moon system is also orbiting the Sun.
   Ans: D   Section: 3-2

55. The fact that the Earth-Moon system orbits the Sun (covering 30° per month) while the Moon orbits the Earth means that the time between successive full moons, the synodic month, compared to one lunar orbital (sidereal) period is
   A)   about twice as long.   C)   about 2 days shorter.
   B)   about 2 days longer.   D)   about 2 weeks longer.
   Ans: B   Section: 3-2

56. The length of time for the Moon to move from new moon to new moon is known as one synodic month. Compared to one full orbital period with respect to the star background, or one sidereal month, this synodic month is
   A)   exactly the same length.   C)   about 2 days shorter.
   B)   about twice as long.   D)   about 2 days longer.
   Ans: D   Section: 3-2

57. If you were on the Moon at the dividing line between dark and light (the terminator) at a particular time, say sunrise, how long would it be before this dividing line returned to your position?
   A) 27 days   B) 365¼ days   C) 23 hours 56 minutes   D) 29½ days
   Ans: D   Section: 3-2

58. The Moon rises later each day because each day it has moved farther along its orbit around Earth (except for observers at polar latitudes, for whom the Moon can remain above or below the horizon for 24 hours each day). On average, how much later does it rise each day (you might attempt to verify this by observation)? (Hint: What fraction of a month does a day take up?)
    A) 4 minutes   B) 20 minutes   C) 2 hours   D) 1 hour
    Ans: D   Section: 3-2

59. How fast does the Moon move across our sky against the background of stars? (Hint: Through what angle does the Moon move around the sky in one month?)
    A)   15° per hour   C)   Its own diameter per day
    B)   1° per day   D)   13° per day
    Ans: D   Section: 3-2

60. In 1 hour, the motion of the Moon across our sky as seen against the background of stars is (Hint: Through what angle around the sky does the Moon move in one month?)
    A) its own diameter or ½°   B) 4°   C) 1/10 degree   D) 13°
    Ans: A   Section: 3-2

61. The Earth and the Moon both move eastward in their orbits. Suppose the Moon moved westward instead, at the same rate as its actual eastward movement. What consequence would this have?
    A)   A synodic month would be the same length it is now.
    B)   A sidereal month would be the same length it is now.
    C)   Both synodic and sidereal months would be shorter than they are now.
    D)   Both synodic and sidereal months would be longer than they are.
    Ans: B   Section: 3-2

62. The Moon moves eastward in its orbit. It always keeps the same face toward the Earth. This means that it
    A)   does not rotate.
    B)   rotates toward the east.
    C)   rotates toward the west.
    D)   rotates toward the east half the time and toward the west the other half of the time.
    Ans: B   Section: 3-2

63. The Earth rotates eastward on its axis. The Moon moves to the east in its orbit around the Earth. The Moon also rises about an hour later each night. Suppose the Moon moved westward instead. What consequence would this have?
    A)   The Moon would still rise about an hour later each night.
    B)   The Moon would rise about an hour earlier each night.
    C)   The Moon would rise earlier each night, but only be about half an hour.
    D)   The Moon would rise later each night, but only be about half an hour.
    Ans: B   Section: 3-2

64. During a lunar eclipse the
    A)   Sun goes below the horizon.
    B)   Earth comes between the Sun and the Moon.
    C)   Sun comes between Earth and the Moon.
    D)   Moon comes between Earth and the Sun.
    Ans: B   Section: 3-3

65. A lunar eclipse is caused by the
    A)   Sun passing behind the Moon.
    B)   Moon passing into the shadow of the Earth.
    C)   Moon passing behind the Sun.
    D)   Earth moving into the Moon's shadow.
    Ans: B   Section: 3-3

66. What is the phase of the Moon during a total lunar eclipse?
    A) new   B) gibbous   C) full   D) first quarter
    Ans: C   Section: 3-3

67. Eclipses of the Moon can occur only
    A)   at new Moon.
    B)   in June and December, when the Sun is near the solstices.
    C)   in the spring and fall, when the Sun is on the ecliptic plane.
    D)   at full Moon.
    Ans: D   Section: 3-3

68. At the time of lunar eclipse, the phase of the Moon is
    A) full.   B) first quarter.   C) The Moon can be at any phase.   D) new.
    Ans: A   Section: 3-3

69. Which of the following statements is correct for eclipses in the Sun-Earth-Moon system?
    A)   An eclipse of the Moon occurs only at new Moon.
    B)   An eclipse of the Sun occurs only at first-quarter Moon.
    C)   An eclipse of the Sun occurs only at full Moon.
    D)   An eclipse of the Sun occurs only at new Moon.
    Ans: D   Section: 3-3

70. Which of the following statements is NOT correct for eclipses in the Sun-Earth-Moon system?
    A)   Eclipses of Moon and Sun do not occur at quarter Moon phases.
    B)   An eclipse of the Sun occurs only at new Moon.
    C)   An eclipse of the Moon occurs only at full Moon.
    D)   An eclipse of the Sun occurs only at full Moon.
    Ans: D   Section: 3-3

71. During a solar eclipse, the
    A) Sun comes between the Earth and the Moon.
    B) Moon comes between the Earth and the Sun.
    C) Sun goes below the horizon.
    D) Earth comes between the Sun and the Moon.
    Ans: B   Section: 3-3

72. A solar eclipse occurs on Earth when the
    A) Sun passes in front of the Moon.   C) Moon casts a shadow on the Earth.
    B) Moon passes behind the Sun.   D) Earth casts a shadow on the Moon.
    Ans: C   Section: 3-3

73. Which of the following conditions holds for relative distances during a solar eclipse?
    A) The Moon is closer to the Sun than is the Earth.
    B) The Earth is closer to the Sun than is the Moon.
    C) The Moon and the Earth have to be at the same distance from the Sun.
    D) Since the condition for a solar eclipse is independent of relative distances of the Earth and Moon from the Sun, either the Moon or the Earth can be closest to the Sun.
    Ans: A   Section: 3-3

74. What is the phase of the Moon during a total solar eclipse?
    A) full   B) new   C) crescent   D) first quarter
    Ans: B   Section: 3-3

75. The phase of the Moon at the time of solar eclipse is
    A) third quarter.   B) any phase; new, quarter, or full.   C) full.   D) new.
    Ans: D   Section: 3-3

76. In a period of 1 month, the Moon moves across the sky
    A) parallel to the horizon.
    B) precisely along the ecliptic plane.
    C) precisely along the celestial equator.
    D) along a plane that is neither the ecliptic plane nor the celestial equator, nor is it parallel to the horizon.
    Ans: D   Section: 3-3

77. There is about a 5° angle between the orbit of the Moon and the
    A) plane of the Sun's equator.
    B) plane of the ecliptic, or the Earth's orbit.
    C) spin axis of the Earth.
    D) plane of the Earth's equator.
    Ans: B   Section: 3-3

78. What is the approximate inclination of the Moon's orbit to the ecliptic plane?
    A) 5°   B) 23.5°   C) 17°   D) 0°
    Ans: A   Section: 3-3

79. The Moon's location in our sky
    A)   is confined to regions north of the celestial equator.
    B)   is always on the ecliptic plane, by definition.
    C)   is confined to a band of sky around the ecliptic, the zodiac.
    D)   can be anywhere in our sky.
    Ans: C   Section: 3-3

80. Which of the following is a necessary condition for lunar or solar eclipses?
    A)   The Earth must be on the celestial equator.
    B)   The Sun must be on the celestial equator.
    C)   The Sun must be close to or crossing the ecliptic plane.
    D)   The Moon must be close to or crossing the ecliptic plane.
    Ans: D   Section: 3-3

81. A lunar eclipse does not occur at every full moon because
    A)   a lunar eclipse cannot occur after sunset.
    B)   the orbit of the Moon is not a perfect circle.
    C)   the plane of the Moon's orbit is at an angle to the plane of the Earth's orbit.
    D)   the path of the Sun is inclined at an angle of 5° to the ecliptic plane.
    Ans: C   Section: 3-3

82. If the plane of the Moon's orbit were to be the same as the ecliptic plane, there would be a lunar eclipse
    A) twice per month.   B) once a month.   C) twice per year.   D) once a day.
    Ans: B   Section: 3-3

83. If the Moon in its orbit around the Earth moves between Earth and Sun and then two weeks later it moves to the other side of Earth as seen from the Sun, why then do we not see both a solar and a lunar eclipse every month?
    A)   The Moon's orbital plane is at right angles to the ecliptic.
    B)   The Earth's orbital plane is slightly inclined to the ecliptic.
    C)   The Moon's orbital plane is slightly inclined to the ecliptic.
    D)   The Moon's orbital plane is inclined slightly to the celestial equator.
    Ans: C   Section: 3-3

84. The line of nodes of the Moon's orbit is the line of intersection between the orbit with the
    A) celestial equator.
    B) observer's celestial meridian.
    C) ecliptic plane.
    D) celestial meridian through Greenwich, England.
    Ans: C   Section: 3-3

85. The line of nodes of the Moon's orbit is the
    A) line joining the points of the Moon's nearest (perigee) and farthest (apogee) distances from the Earth.
    B) line of intersection between the Moon's orbit and the Earth's orbit (the ecliptic plane).
    C) minor axis (shortest diameter) of the Moon's elliptical orbit.
    D) line between the Earth and Moon when the Moon is farthest from the ecliptic plane.
    Ans: B   Section: 3-3

86. Eclipses of the Moon can occur
    A) twice per month.
    B) only once per year.
    C) once every month.
    D) only during two specific periods in any year.
    Ans: D   Section: 3-3

87. You travel to an exotic place to observe a total solar eclipse in December and someone on this trip tells you that the next eclipse to occur on Earth will be a lunar eclipse in March. Is this likely to be true?
    A) It could be true, since such an eclipse can occur when the Sun's position with respect to the celestial equator is changing rapidly.
    B) Yes, but only once about every thousand years.
    C) No.
    D) Yes.
    Ans: C   Section: 3-3

88. The maximum number of eclipses (both solar and lunar) that can occur in one calendar year is
    A) one.   B) two.   C) five.   D) seven.
    Ans: D   Section: 3-3

89. To witness an eclipse we must wait until which one of the following conditions is met?
    A)   the Earth must be on the ecliptic plain
    B)   the Sun must be on the ecliptic plain
    C)   the Moon must be on the ecliptic plain
    D)   the Moon must be on the ecliptic plain and the line of nodes must point in the general direction of the Sun
    Ans: D   Section: 3-3

90. In a penumbral lunar eclipse
    A)   all parts of the Moon are partly (not totally) shaded from the Sun.
    B)   no points on the Moon are shaded from the Sun, either totally or partially.
    C)   some points on the Moon are totally shaded from the Sun, while others are only partly shaded.
    D)   all of the Moon is shaded from the Sun.
    Ans: A   Section: 3-4

91. A total lunar eclipse is visible in principle (assuming clear skies everywhere)
    A)   only to people in a long narrow and very specific path, much smaller than a hemisphere.
    B)   only to people in a circular area on the Earth having a diameter equal to that of the Moon.
    C)   to everyone on the Earth.
    D)   to everyone in one hemisphere of the Earth.
    Ans: D   Section: 3-4

92. For someone on the Earth who is watching a total lunar eclipse, the
    A)   Sun is hidden below the horizon.
    B)   Sun is relatively high in the sky, since the Earth-Moon line is at right angles to Earth-Sun line.
    C)   Sun is hidden behind the Moon.
    D)   Moon is hidden behind the Sun.
    Ans: A   Section: 3-4

93. The Earth's shadow at the distance of the Moon's orbit from the Earth is
    A)   considerably wider than the Moon.
    B)   slightly less wide than the size of the Moon.
    C)   almost exactly as wide as the Moon.
    D)   extremely small, leaving only a narrow shadow band on the Moon during eclipse.
    Ans: A   Section: 3-4 and Figure 3-8

94. What is the maximum length of totality for a lunar eclipse?
    A) 7 minutes   B) 2 minutes   C) several hours   D) 1 hour 40 minutes
    Ans: D   Section: 3-4

95. When in total lunar eclipse, the Moon shows a reddish color because
    A) light from the northern and southern lights (the aurora) on Earth, which is predominantly red, illuminates the Moon.
    B) this is the color of the residual thermal glow from a still-warm Moon, after the abrupt removal of the heat of the Sun.
    C) the Moon is illuminated only by the residual glow from the dark side of the Earth, which is predominantly red.
    D) only the red part of the solar spectrum is deflected onto it by the Earth's atmosphere.
    Ans: D   Section: 3-4

96. The difference between an umbral eclipse and a penumbral eclipse is
    A) entirely dependent upon your viewing position on the Earth.
    B) whether the Moon is farther from the Sun than the Earth is or whether it is closer to the Sun than the Earth is.
    C) the distance of the Moon above or below the ecliptic.
    D) whether the Earth's rotation axis is tilted toward or away from the Moon during the eclipse.
    Ans: C   Section: 3-4

97. Which of the following factors makes it far more likely that a person will have seen a total lunar eclipse than a total solar eclipse?
    A) The Moon appears brighter during a total lunar eclipse than does the Sun during a total solar eclipse.
    B) A total lunar eclipse occurs at full Moon when the Moon is bright and high in the sky, while a total solar eclipse occurs at new Moon when the Moon is dark and low in the sky.
    C) A total lunar eclipse can be seen by people on most of the nighttime side of Earth, while a specific total solar eclipse can be seen only by people within a narrow strip of the Earth's surface.
    D) Total solar eclipses occur much less frequently than total lunar eclipses.
    Ans: C   Section: 3-5

98. A person standing in the Moon's penumbra will see a
    A) partial solar eclipse.   C)   total solar eclipse.
    B) partial lunar eclipse.   D)   total lunar eclipse.
    Ans: A   Section: 3-5

99. We can occasionally see a total eclipse of the Sun on Earth because
    A) the Moon is cooler than the Sun.
    B) the angular sizes of Sun and Moon, when viewed from Earth, are almost the same.
    C) the physical sizes of Sun and Moon are almost the same.
    D) both the Moon and Sun move precisely along the ecliptic plane.
    Ans: B   Section: 3-5

100. What is the maximum time of totality for any total solar eclipse observed from the Earth's surface?
   A) about 7.5 minutes
   B) a full 12-hour period
   C) about 2 hours
   D) only a few seconds
   Ans: A   Section: 3-5

101. The total phase of a particular solar eclipse can be seen
   A) only within a specific narrow strip across the Earth's surface.
   B) only over a region of the Earth within +/−23.5° of the Earth's equator, that is, in the tropics.
   C) anywhere on the surface of the Earth.
   D) from anywhere on the sunlit hemisphere of the Earth.
   Ans: A   Section: 3-5

102. Where on Earth would you have to be to observe a particular total solar eclipse?
   A) within 250 km of the Earth's equator
   B) within a narrow and specific strip of the Earth's surface less than 250 km wide
   C) on the dark side of the Earth
   D) always within 23.5° of the equator (i.e., in the tropics)
   Ans: B   Section: 3-5

103. Assuming clear skies everywhere, a total solar eclipse is visible
   A) to people anywhere in the sunlit hemisphere of Earth.
   B) to everyone on Earth.
   C) only to people in a circular area on Earth having a diameter equal to that of the Moon.
   D) only to people in a long narrow path much smaller than a hemisphere.
   Ans: D   Section: 3-5

104. Which of the following parameters will dictate whether a particular solar eclipse appears as a total or an annular eclipse to an observer on the centerline of the Moon's shadow?
   A) the distance of the Earth from the Sun at the time of eclipse
   B) the distance of the Moon from the Earth at the time of eclipse
   C) the phase of the Moon (whether it is new, quarter, or full)
   D) the time of day or night
   Ans: B   Section: 3-5

105. During the particular solar eclipse, when the Moon and Sun are precisely in line, the eclipse can be either total (Sun completely covered) or annular (Sun not quite covered) when viewed from the eclipse centerline because
    A) the Moon's orbit is inclined at several degrees to that of the Earth.
    B) the Moon has deep valleys on its surface.
    C) of the time of day at the viewing site; since annular eclipses only occur in early morning and early evening.
    D) the Moon's distance from Earth varies from eclipse to eclipse.
    Ans: D   Section: 3-5

106. The accurate prediction of the time and position of a total solar eclipse is
    A) difficult because of the varying distances of the Earth from the Sun and the Moon from the Earth in their elliptical orbits.
    B) not easy because of inaccurate knowledge of the rotation of the Earth on its axis and of the revolution of the Earth in its orbit.
    C) difficult because the Moon's motion is unpredictable, since it is affected in a major way by the tidal ebb and flow of water on the Earth.
    D) relatively easy since the motions of Earth and Moon in space are predictable and accurately known.
    Ans: D   Section: 3-5

107. An observer can see a total solar eclipse from within a narrow band along the Earth's surface. This band
    A) is always along the equator.
    B) is always parallel to the equator.
    C) always crosses the equator at a right angle.
    D) can begin almost anywhere on the Earth's surface.
    Ans: D   Section: 3-5

108. What is the cause of an annular eclipse?
    A) The Earth's position in its orbit is near aphelion, its farthest point from the Sun.
    B) The Earth's position in its orbit is near perihelion, its nearest point to the Sun.
    C) The Moon's position in its orbit is near apogee, its farthest point from the Earth.
    D) The Moon's position in its orbit is near perigee, its nearest point to the Earth.
    Ans: C   Section: 3-5

109. One eclipse year is the time needed for
    A) three saros intervals.
    B) the line of nodes of the Moon's orbit to go from alignment with respect to the Sun-Earth line to the next identical alignment.
    C) 365 successive eclipses.
    D) two consecutive identical alignments of the Sun, the Moon, and the line of nodes.
    Ans: B   Section: Box 3-2

110. The saros is the period of time between
    A)   successive solar eclipses in a series of similar eclipses at about the same latitude on Earth.
    B)   two successive total lunar eclipses, seen from the same point of the Earth.
    C)   two successive passages of the Sun through the vernal equinox.
    D)   two successive eclipse seasons, about six months.
    Ans: A   Section: Box 3-2

111. Total solar eclipses seen at approximately the same latitude occur in a sequence with a time interval, the saros, of 223 lunar sidereal months. How many eclipse years is this?
    A) 19   B) 16.7   C) 18   D) 17.6
    Ans: A   Section: Box 3-2

112. The time interval between one total solar eclipse and the next total solar eclipse, visible from the same location on Earth, must be all of the following except one. Which is the exception?
    A)   a whole number of lunar months   C)   a whole number of eclipse years
    B)   a whole number of sidereal months   D)   a whole number of saros intervals
    Ans: B   Section: Box 3-2

113. Which significant observation led the Greeks to accept the idea that the Earth was a sphere?
    A)   The shape of the darkening across the Sun's disk during a solar eclipse always appeared circular.
    B)   The shape of the Earth's shadow on the Moon during a lunar eclipse was always circular.
    C)   The Sun disappears below one horizon each day and reappears above the opposite horizon.
    D)   The shape of the eclipse shadow on Earth during a solar eclipse was always circular.
    Ans: B   Section: 3-6

114. The Greek astronomer who first measured the radius of the Earth reasonably accurately was
    A) Archimedes.   B) Eratosthenes.   C) Aristotle.   D) Ptolemy.
    Ans: B   Section: 3-6

115. Eratosthenes, an ancient Greek astronomer, is famous for
    A)   measuring the diameter of the Earth by comparing the direction to the Sun at noon at two different points on the Earth.
    B)   measuring the diameter of the Earth by timing how long it took the Moon to traverse the Earth's shadow during a lunar eclipse.
    C)   measuring the relative distances to the Sun and the Moon by timing the exact moments when the Moon was at first and third quarter.
    D)   measuring the distance to each of the known planets by timing how long it took the planet to orbit the Sun.
    Ans: A   Section: 3-6

116. Eratosthenes measured the radius of the Earth by
    A)   timing the disappearance of the Sun at sunset for two different positions on Earth on the same day of the year.
    B)   estimating the size of the shadow of the Earth on the Moon during a lunar eclipse.
    C)   measuring the angular position of the pole star from several positions on Earth.
    D)   noting the different angles of the Sun at midday on the same day of the year at different positions on Earth.
    Ans: D   Section: 3-6

117. Eratosthenes, an astronomer in ancient Greece, measured the radius of the Earth by making observations of
    A)   the Sun's direction at midday at two positions on Earth, on the same day of the year.
    B)   the tidal ebb and flow of ocean waters.
    C)   the deviation of magnetic north, as seen from a compass, from true north.
    D)   relative times of arrival of the Sun due south of an observer at two positions on Earth.
    Ans: A   Section: 3-6

118. The ancient Greek astronomer Aristarchus is famous for devising a method for measuring the
    A)   length of an eclipse cycle.
    B)   diameter of the Earth.
    C)   relative distances of the Sun and the Moon.
    D)   precise distance between Alexandria and Syene in ancient Egypt.
    Ans: C   Section: 3-6

119. Aristarchus, in about 280 B.C., devised a method of estimating the relative distance of the Sun and the Moon from the Earth by
    A)   measuring the angle between the Sun and Moon when the Moon is at first or third quarter.
    B)   calculating their orbital radii from their orbital periods around the Earth, using Kepler's law.
    C)   noting the size of the Earth's shadow on the Moon during a lunar eclipse.
    D)   estimating the positions of the Moon and Sun in the sky from different positions on the Earth as they passed through the due south direction on the same day.
    Ans: A   Section: 3-6

120. Which of the following investigations did the Ancient Greeks NOT carry out?
    A)   determination that the Earth's orbit around the Sun is an ellipse
    B)   determination that the Earth is approximately spherical.
    C)   measurement of the relative distances of the Moon and the Sun from the Earth
    D)   measurement of the Earth's radius
    Ans: A   Section: 3-6

121. How did the ancient Greek astronomer Aristarchus of Samos determine that the Moon's diameter was about 1/3 that of the Earth?
    A)   by measuring the time it takes the Moon to cross the face of the Sun during a solar eclipse
    B)   by measuring the relative durations of lunar and solar eclipses
    C)   by measuring the time it takes the Moon to pass in front of a background star
    D)   by measuring the time it takes the Moon to move through the Earth's shadow during a lunar eclipse
    Ans: D   Section: 3-6

122. What is the diameter of the Moon compared to that of the Earth, as measured by the ancient Greek astronomer Aristarchus of Samos?
    A)   1/3 the diameter of the Earth   C)   20 times the diameter of the Earth
    B)   1/20 the diameter of the Earth   D)   3 times the diameter of the Earth
    Ans: A   Section: 3-6

123. One of the most significant achievements of the ancient Greeks was the
    A)   logical thinking and mathematical reasoning that they applied to natural phenomena.
    B)   precision with which they measured the distances of Sun and Moon from the Earth.
    C)   acceptance that the Sun and not the Earth was at the center of the universe.
    D)   strengthening of the belief in Gods who controlled the behavior of the natural world.
    Ans: A   Section: 3-6

124. The attempt by Aristarchus to measure the relative distances to the Sun and to the Moon from the Earth produced a result now known to be incorrect. The source of this error was that
    A)   Aristarchus did not know the distance to the Moon to any great precision.
    B)   Aristarchus' hypothesis was fundamentally incorrect.
    C)   Aristarchus was unable to measure accurately the angle between the Moon and Sun at first or third quarter.
    D)   the Moon-Sun-Earth angle is not really a right angle at first and third quarters.
    Ans: C   Section: 3-6

125. At the ancient Egyptian city of Syene the Sun was directly overhead only at summer solstice. Thus Syene must have been very close to
    A)   the equator.   C)   the Tropic of Capricorn.
    B)   the Tropic of Cancer.   D)   the prime meridian.
    Ans: B   Section: 3-6

126. Aristarchus measured the Sun-Earth-Moon angle at quarter Moon to be 87 degrees and calculated that the Sun is 20 times as far away as the Moon. Actually, the Sun is almost 400 times as far away as the Moon. Thus the actual Sun-Earth-Moon angle at quarter Moon must be
    A) less than 45 degrees.   B) 45 degrees.   C) 86.5 degrees.   D) 89.5 degrees.
    Ans: D   Section: 3-6

Chapter 4: Gravitation & the Waltz of the Planets

1. Why do you think the planets were chosen as key indicators of a person's destiny by early astrologers?
   A)   They stayed in the same places with respect to the stars but were very bright.
   B)   They moved in complicated (but predictable) patterns with respect to the stars.
   C)   They twinkled and their colors varied randomly.
   D)   They moved very uniformly across the sky, night by night.
   Ans: B   Section: 4-1

2. The ancient Greek thinker Pythagoras held the view that
   A)   natural phenomena were wonderful to watch but could not be described by mathematics.
   B)   the Sun was at the center of the planetary system.
   C)   natural phenomena could be described mathematically.
   D)   triangles did not exist.
   Ans: C   Section: 4-1

3. A major theme of Ancient Greek philosophy was that stars and planets in the sky
   A)   followed patterns that could be described logically.
   B)   could be controlled by the thoughts and actions of humans.
   C)   were at the mercy of gods and spirits, and the behavior of these objects was dependent on their whims.
   D)   behaved chaotically, and their future behavior was totally unpredictable.
   Ans: A   Section: 4-1

4. The correct order of "appearance" of the following "actors" on the "stage" of scientific discovery is
   A)   Ptolemy, Copernicus, Newton, Kepler, Einstein.
   B)   Ptolemy, Kepler, Copernicus, Newton, Einstein.
   C)   Copernicus, Newton, Kepler, Einstein, Ptolemy.
   D)   Ptolemy, Copernicus, Kepler, Newton, Einstein.
   Ans: D   Section: 4-1

5. The word planet is derived from a Greek term meaning
   A)   astrological sign.   C)   bright nighttime object.
   B)   non-twinkling star.   D)   wanderer.
   Ans: D   Section: 4-1

6. Before the invention of the telescope, the known planets were
   A)   Mercury, Venus, Mars, Jupiter, and Saturn.
   B)   Mercury, Venus, Mars, Jupiter, and Uranus.
   C)   Jupiter, Venus, Pluto, Mars, and Saturn.
   D)   Mars, Neptune, Jupiter, Mercury, and Venus.
   Ans: A   Section: 4-1

7. In the Greek era, it was almost universally believed that the
   A) pole star represented the center of the universe, around which Earth and all other objects revolved.
   B) Earth was at the center of the universe.
   C) Sun was at the center of the universe.
   D) Milky Way represented the observable universe, with its center as the center of the universe.
   Ans: B   Section: 4-1

8. The center, or fixed point, of the Greek model of the universe was
   A) the center of the galaxy.
   B) close to Earth's center.
   C) a point midway between Earth and Sun.
   D) the Sun's center.
   Ans: B   Section: 4-1

9. Planets move past the background stars as seen by someone on Earth. What is the normal direction of this motion?
   A) east to west because of the motion of the planet along its orbit
   B) east to west because of the rotation of Earth
   C) west to east because of the motion of the planet along its orbit
   D) west to east because of the motion of Earth along its orbit
   Ans: C   Section: 4-1

10. When observing planetary motions from Earth, the phrase "direct motion" refers to
    A) the motion of the planet directly toward or away from Earth at certain parts of the planet's orbit.
    B) a slow eastward motion of the planet from night to night against the background stars.
    C) a slow westward motion of the planet from night to night against the background stars.
    D) the apparent westward motion of the planet (along with the Sun, Moon, and stars) across the sky due to the rotation of Earth.
    Ans: B   Section: 4-1

11. When observing planetary motions from Earth, the phrase "retrograde motion" refers to
    A) motion of the planet away from Earth during part of its orbit.
    B) a slow eastward motion of the planet from night to night against the background stars.
    C) the apparent westward motion of the planet (along with the Sun, Moon, and stars) across the sky due to the rotation of Earth.
    D) a slow westward motion of the planet from night to night against the background stars.
    Ans: D   Section: 4-1

12. An apparent eastward motion of a planet from night to night compared to the background stars (as viewed from Earth) is referred to as
    A)   rising (if in the east) or setting (if in the west).
    B)   direct motion.
    C)   precession.
    D)   retrograde motion.
    Ans: B   Section: 4-1

13. An apparent westward motion of a planet from night to night compared to the background stars (as viewed from Earth) is referred to as
    A)   precession.
    B)   retrograde motion.
    C)   rising (if in the east) or setting (if in the west).
    D)   direct motion.
    Ans: B   Section: 4-1

14. The motions of the planets against the background stars in our sky can best be described as
    A)   regular and uniform eastward motion.
    B)   general eastward motion interrupted by occasional stationary periods when planets do not appear to move with respect to the stars.
    C)   regular patterns, with general eastward motion interrupted by periods of westward motion.
    D)   regular patterns, with general westward motion interrupted by periods of eastward motion.
    Ans: C   Section: 4-1

15. Retrograde motion of a planet is
    A)   motion away from Earth.
    B)   westward motion against the star background.
    C)   westward motion with respect to the foreground on Earth.
    D)   eastward motion against the star background.
    Ans: B   Section: 4-1

16. Retrograde motion of a planet against the background stars is always
    A)   movement northward away from the ecliptic plane.
    B)   movement from west to east.
    C)   movement from east to west.
    D)   the apparent motion of the planet away from Earth.
    Ans: C   Section: 4-1

17. The direction of retrograde motion for a planet as seen by an observer on Earth is
    A)   west to east relative to the background stars.
    B)   east to west relative to objects on the person's horizon.
    C)   west to east relative to objects on the person's horizon.
    D)   east to west relative to the background stars.
    Ans: D   Section: 4-1

18. Retrograde motion of a planet refers to which motion, when viewed from Earth?
    A)   the setting of the planet in the west to any observer, caused by Earth rotation
    B)   southward motion as it moves away from the northern sky
    C)   apparent westward motion with respect to the stars
    D)   apparent eastward motion with respect to the stars
    Ans: C   Section: 4-1

19. When the planet Mars is moving in a retrograde direction, its motion against the background stars is seen to be
    A)   stationary, with no motion against the stars.
    B)   eastward.
    C)   exactly perpendicular to the equator.
    D)   westward.
    Ans: D   Section: 4-1

20. The Greek scientist who developed an early and viable geocentric model of the universe was
    A) Brahe.   B) Eratosthenes.   C) Aristotle.   D) Ptolemy.
    Ans: D   Section: 4-1

21. Ptolemy's nationality was
    A) Italian.   B) Egyptian.   C) Greek.   D) Polish.
    Ans: C   Section: 4-1

22. Ptolemy's model for the solar system was
    A)   Sun-centered, with planets moving in circles around it.
    B)   Earth-centered, with Sun, Moon, and planets moving in ellipses in the sky.
    C)   Sun-centered, with elliptical planetary orbits.
    D)   Earth-centered, with epicyclic planetary orbits.
    Ans: D   Section: 4-1

23. Ptolemy developed
    A)   a heliocentric model for the solar system.
    B)   the design for Stonehenge.
    C)   a geocentric model of the solar system.
    D)   a method for the measurement of Earth's radius.
    Ans: C   Section: 4-1

24. In the geocentric model of the solar system developed by Ptolemy, planets move
    A) in circular epicycles around the Sun while the Sun moves in a circular orbit around Earth.
    B) at constant speeds in circular orbits around Earth.
    C) with varying speeds in elliptical orbits around Earth.
    D) in circular epicycles while the centers of the epicycles move in circular orbits around the Earth.
    Ans: D   Section: 4-1

25. One major contribution of Ptolemy to the development of astronomy was to
    A) develop and expand on a mathematical model for the solar system, in which planets move in epicycles around centers that move in circles around Earth.
    B) derive a mathematical model for the solar system, in which planets move around the Sun in circular orbits.
    C) originate the idea of a geocentric (Earth-centered) cosmology in which planets move in circles around Earth, which was later developed mathematically by Aristarchus.
    D) derive a mathematical model for the solar system, in which planets move around Earth in elliptical orbits, moving fastest when closest to Earth.
    Ans: A   Section: 4-1

26. During retrograde motion according to the Ptolemaic model of the Solar system (Fig. 4-3, Freedman and Kaufmann, *Universe,* 7th ed.), a planet is
    A) at varying distances from Earth, sometimes closer and sometimes farther away than the average distance.
    B) closer to Earth than average.
    C) farther away from Earth than average.
    D) always at the same distance from Earth, since the planet orbits Earth in a circle in this model.
    Ans: B   Section: 4-1

27. The purpose of describing planetary orbits in terms of epicycles and deferents was to account for the
    A) generally eastward motion of a planet compared to background stars while the whole sky appeared to move westward.
    B) variation of brightness of a planet with time.
    C) difference between the sidereal period and the synodic period of a planet.
    D) pattern of direct and retrograde motion of a planet as it moved slowly against the background of stars.
    Ans: D   Section: 4-1

28. The epicycle in the Greek planetary model is
    A)   the circle centered on Earth about which the center of the smaller circular motion moves.
    B)   a small circle through which the planet moves as the center of this circle orbits Earth.
    C)   the focus of the ellipse that is the orbit of the planet around Earth.
    D)   the off-center point in the planetary system occupied by Earth.
    Ans: B   Section: 4-1

29. In the geocentric model for the solar system developed by Ptolemy, to what does the word "epicycle" refer?
    A)   one complete cycle of planetary motions, after which the motions repeat themselves (almost) exactly
    B)   a small circle around which a planet moves while the center of this circle moves around Earth
    C)   the large circle (orbit) centered on Earth about which the center of a smaller circle moves while the planet itself is moving along the smaller circle
    D)   the length of time taken by a planet to go between two successive times when it is farthest from Earth
    Ans: B   Section: 4-1

30. In Ptolemy's geocentric theory of the solar system, what name is given to the small circle around which the planet moves while the center of this circle orbits Earth?
    A) celestial equator   B) ecliptic   C) deferent   D) epicycle
    Ans: D   Section: 4-1

31. In Ptolemy's description of the solar system, the deferent is
    A)   a circular path (around the Sun) along which the center of a planet's epicycle moves.
    B)   a circular path (around Earth) along which the center of a planet's epicycle moves.
    C)   an elliptical path along which a planet moves around the Sun.
    D)   a circular path along which a planet moves while the center of this circular path itself moves in a circle around Earth.
    Ans: B   Section: 4-1

32. In the geocentric model for the solar system developed by Ptolemy, to what does the word "deferent" refer?
    A)   the large circle around Earth through which the center of a smaller circle moves while the planet moves around the smaller circle
    B)   the distance of the center of the epicycle from the center of Earth
    C)   the offset distance between the center of Earth and the center of a planet's circular orbit
    D)   a small circle about which a planet moves while the center of this circle moves around Earth
    Ans: A   Section: 4-1

33. The deferent in the Greek planetary model is the
    A) circle through which each planet's epicycle center moves.
    B) off-center point in the planetary system occupied by Earth.
    C) part of the planet's orbit when it appears to move "backward" (i.e., westward) in the sky.
    D) small circle through which the planet moves as the center of the circle orbits Earth.
    Ans: A   Section: 4-1

34. In Ptolemy's geocentric theory of the solar system, what name is given to the large circle centered on Earth through which the center of a smaller circle moves as the planet moves around the smaller circle?
    A) ecliptic   B) deferent   C) celestial equator   D) epicycle
    Ans: B   Section: 4-1

35. In the geocentric universe, when is a planet closest to Earth?
    A) during its direct eastward motion
    B) during its retrograde westward motion
    C) There is no specific time in the orbit when the planet is closest to Earth.
    D) when the planet is crossing the deferent
    Ans: B   Section: 4-1

36. In the geocentric Ptolemiac model that described the apparent motions of planets against the background sky as viewed from a stationary Earth, at what distance with respect to its deferent is a particular planet on its epicycle when it appears to stop moving for a short period in its motion against the background?
    A) at a distance greater than the radius of the deferent
    B) anywhere around the epicycle
    C) at a distance well inside the deferent
    D) close to the deferent
    Ans: D   Section: 4-1

37. The *Almagest* is
    A) a collection of ancient data and predictions of positions of the Sun, Moon, and planets, compiled by Ptolemy.
    B) a detailed multivolume account of a heliocentric cosmology produced by ancient Greek astronomers.
    C) a Renaissance book describing in detail the development of a heliocentric Universe, with elliptical orbits, the law of equal areas, and the harmonic law.
    D) an ancient book describing the construction of Stonehenge.
    Ans: A   Section: 4-1

38. The *Almagest*, a collection of early astronomical data and description of planetary position calculations, was written by
A) Ptolemy.   B) Copernicus.   C) Kepler.   D) Erathosthenes.
Ans: A   Section: 4-1

39. One unsatisfactory feature of the Ptolemiac description of the planetary system, particularly from a philosophical point of view was
A)   that it needed continuous updating of the parameters of epicycle and deferent sizes and speeds to match planetary motions over time periods of more than one or two decades.
B)   the fact that, although it described planetary motions in general, it could not be used for prediction of future planetary positions.
C)   the requirement of many unrelated parameters, such as epicycle and deferent sizes and speeds, with no unifying rules.
D)   the fact that it placed Earth at the center of the system, whereas Greek philosophers were convinced that the Sun was at the center.
Ans: C   Section: 4-1

40. Which of the following most closely expresses the principle of Occam's Razor as it applies to theoretical explanations of physical phenomena?
A)   The theory that has the longest history is the most likely explanation.
B)   The theory requiring the most assumptions is the most likely explanation.
C)   The newest theory is most likely to be the correct one.
D)   The theory requiring the fewest assumptions is the most likely explanation.
Ans: D   Section: 4-1

41. The concept called Occam's Razor tells us that
A)   the theory that is applicable to the greatest range of phenomena is more likely to be correct.
B)   when two theories describe the same phenomena equally accurately, choose the simpler theory.
C)   the theory that describes phenomena more accurately is more likely to be correct.
D)   when two theories describe the same phenomena equally accurately, choose the theory with the greater complexity.
Ans: B   Section: 4-1

42. Retrograde motion of a planet when viewed from Earth is caused by
A)   the relative motions of Sun and planet.
B)   its elliptical orbital path.
C)   the relative motions of Earth and planet.
D)   the inclination of its orbit to the ecliptic plane.
Ans: C   Section: 4-1

43. Retrograde motion of a planet when viewed from Earth is caused by the fact that the
    A)   Sun is moving.
    B)   planet's orbit is inclined at an angle to Earth's orbit.
    C)   Earth is moving.
    D)   planet's orbit is elliptical.
    Ans: C   Section: 4-1

44. The occasional retrograde motion of Mars against the background stars is the result of the
    A)   observation of a moving Mars from Earth, whose orbital motion is faster than that of Mars.
    B)   observation of a rapidly moving Mars from a more slowly moving Earth.
    C)   variable speed of Mars because its orbit is elliptical.
    D)   observation of Mars from the rapidly rotating Earth.
    Ans: A   Section: 4-1

45. When viewed from Earth, the celestial sphere (the background of stars) moves east to west on a daily basis. This motion is caused by
    A)   the rotation of the Earth on its axis.
    B)   the revolution of the Earth around the Sun.
    C)   the motion of the Sun through the galaxy.
    D)   the motion of the stars around the galactic center.
    Ans: A   Section: 4-1

46. From the Earth, we observe occasional retrograde motion in the motion of
    A)   only the inner planets: Mercury and Venus
    B)   only the outer planets: Mars and beyond.
    C)   all the planets.
    D)   all the planets and the Moon.
    Ans: C   Section: 4-1

47. If you were observing Earth's motion from another planet, would you observe occasional retrograde motion?
    A)   No.
    B)   Yes, but only from the inner planets: Mercury and Venus.
    C)   Yes, but only from the outer planets: Mars and beyond.
    D)   Yes, from any of the planets.
    Ans: D   Section: 4-1

48. In the path of Mars against the background stars shown in Figure 4-2, Freedman and Kaufmann, *Universe,* 7th ed., the planet appears from Earth to move in a loop, moving westward for a period of time. What is the angle between Earth-Sun line and Earth-Mars line when the planet is halfway through the westward, or retrograde, motion on about February 1?
    A) 180°   B) It can be any angle.   C) 0°   D) 90°
    Ans: A   Section: 4-2

49. One reason that the geocentric model for the solar system became unsatisfactory to astronomers compared with the heliocentric model early in the sixteenth century A.D. was that
    A)   Isaac Newton was able to derive all planetary motion from one universal law of gravity.
    B)   the heliocentric model was conceptually simpler.
    C)   the invention of the telescope provided observations that were in better agreement with a heliocentric model.
    D)   observations by spacecraft proved that all planets orbited the Sun.
    Ans: B   Section: 4-2

50. Copernicus lived
    A)   after Kepler but before Ptolemy.   C)   after Newton but before Kepler.
    B)   after Kepler but before Newton.   D)   after Ptolemy but before Kepler.
    Ans: D   Section: 4-2

51. The early Copernican system for planetary motions is
    A)   Earth-centered, with planets, the Sun, and the stars moving in perfect circles.
    B)   Earth-centered, with planets moving in epicycle patterns around Earth.
    C)   Sun-centered, with planets moving in perfect circles around the Sun.
    D)   Sun-centered, with planets moving in elliptical orbits, the Sun being at one focus of the ellipse.
    Ans: C   Section: 4-2

52. Copernicus' model for the planetary system
    A)   retained Earth at the center of the solar system but eliminated epicycles.
    B)   placed the Sun at the center of the solar system and eliminated epicycles completely.
    C)   placed the Sun at the center of the solar system but retained the idea of epicycles.
    D)   had Earth at the center of the solar system and the planets moving in epicycles.
    Ans: C   Section: 4-2

53. Nicolaus Copernicus was the first person to
    A)   develop a mathematical model for a Sun-centered solar system.
    B)   use a telescope to observe the sky at night.
    C)   use ellipses to describe the orbits of the planets.
    D)   describe planetary orbits using the force of gravity.
    Ans: A   Section: 4-2

54. The contribution of Copernicus to the development of astronomy was a mathematical model for
    A)   the solar system in which the planets move under the gravitational influence of the Sun.
    B)   a heliocentric cosmology in which the planets move in circular orbits.
    C)   a geocentric cosmology in which the planets move in circular orbits around Earth.
    D)   a heliocentric cosmology in which the planets move in elliptical orbits.
    Ans: B   Section: 4-2

55. Copernicus' nationality was
    A) Greek.   B) Italian.   C) Egyptian.   D) Polish.
    Ans: D   Section: 4-2

56. The book describing Copernicus' revolutionary work on planetary motions was published
    A)   in the year of his death.
    B)   when he was only a young man.
    C)   when he was in the prime of his life, age 45.
    D)   in the year that Newton was born.
    Ans: A   Section: 4-2

57. Copernicus used the fact that Mars can sometimes be seen high in our sky at midnight to conclude that
    A)   Earth can come between Mars and the Sun.
    B)   Mars and the Sun can never be on the same side of Earth at the same time.
    C)   Mars can come between Earth and the Sun.
    D)   the Sun can come between Earth and Mars.
    Ans: A   Section: 4-2

58. Which of the following statements correctly describes why Copernicus decided that the orbits of Mercury and Venus were smaller than the orbit of Earth?
    A)   Both planets show a complete cycle of phases, like the Moon.
    B)   Both planets can sometimes be seen high in our sky at midnight.
    C)   Both planets occasionally pass through conjunction with the Sun, as seen from Earth.
    D)   Both planets stay fairly close to the Sun in our sky.
    Ans: D   Section: 4-2

59. When Venus is at inferior conjunction,
    A)   it is at its greatest angle from the Sun, as seen from Earth.
    B)   it is at its greatest distance from Earth.
    C)   the time between sunset and the time at which Venus sets is a maximum.
    D)   it is at its smallest distance from Earth.
    Ans: D   Section: 4-2

60. When Venus is at superior conjunction,
    A)   it is at its smallest distance from Earth.
    B)   it is at its greatest distance from Earth.
    C)   it is at its greatest angle from the Sun, as seen from Earth.
    D)   the time between sunset and the time at which Venus sets is a maximum.
    Ans: B   Section: 4-2

61. In which direction is Venus moving when it is at greatest elongation?
    A)   directly toward or away from Earth
    B)   perpendicular to the line from Venus to Earth
    C)   It is not possible to say, since the direction is different from one greatest
          elongation to the next.
    D)   directly toward or away from the Sun
    Ans: A   Section: 4-2

62. When Mercury is at greatest elongation, what is the angle between the line from Earth to
    Mercury and the line from Mercury to the Sun?
    A)   0°
    B)   180°
    C)   between 0° and 180°, depending on the particular planetary alignment
    D)   90°
    Ans: D   Section: 4-2

63. What is the angle between the line from Earth to Jupiter and the line from the Earth to
    the Sun when Jupiter is at opposition?
    A)   0°
    B)   90°
    C)   180°
    D)   between 0° and 180°, depending on the particular planetary alignment
    Ans: C   Section: 4-2

64. When Saturn is at its farthest distance from Earth, it is at
    A)   greatest elongation (about 47° from the Sun).
    B)   inferior conjunction.
    C)   opposition.
    D)   conjunction.
    Ans: D   Section: 4-2

65. Which of the following objects cannot transit (pass in front of) the Sun when viewed from Earth?
    A) Mars   B) Venus   C) the Moon   D) Mercury
    Ans: A   Section: 4-2

66. Venus can occasionally pass in front of the Sun. It can only do so when it is at
    A)   greatest or maximum elongation.
    B)   opposition.
    C)   inferior conjunction.
    D)   superior conjunction.
    Ans: C   Section: 4-2

67. Which of the following planets passes between the Earth and the Sun?
    A) Pluto   B) Mars   C) Jupiter   D) Venus
    Ans: D   Section: 4-2

68. When Mercury is at its farthest distance from Earth, it is at
    A)   greatest elongation.
    B)   inferior conjunction.
    C)   superior conjunction.
    D)   opposition.
    Ans: C   Section: 4-2

69. At which configuration is Jupiter when it is in the middle of its retrograde motion?
    A)   Jupiter never undergoes retrograde motion since it is a superior planet.
    B)   conjunction
    C)   maximum eastern elongation
    D)   opposition
    Ans: D   Section: 4-2

70. As seen by an observer on Saturn (or one of its moons), which of the following planets can never pass through inferior conjunction?
    A) Jupiter   B) Venus   C) Neptune   D) Earth
    Ans: C   Section: 4-2

71. At what position in its orbit will an inferior planet appear to be moving, for a day or two, more or less directly toward Earth? (See Fig. 4-6, Freedman and Kaufmann, *Universe,* 7th ed., and draw a diagram if it will help.)
    A)   greatest western elongation
    B)   inferior conjunction
    C)   superior conjunction
    D)   greatest eastern elongation
    Ans: D   Section: 4-2

72. An inferior planet moves more or less directly toward Earth at greatest eastern elongation. What does this mean when you are watching the night-by-night motion of this planet against the background stars?
    A)   The planet appears to remain stationary for a few days.
    B)   The planet appears to be moving at its fastest motion against the background.
    C)   The planet is invisible in the sky because it is moving toward Earth.
    D)   Its motion against the background appears to be "direct" or constant eastward motion, because the planet is moving in a circular orbit.
    Ans: A   Section: 4-2

73. At which configuration is a planet whose angle of elongation is 0°?
    A)   conjunction
    B)   retrograde
    C)   opposition
    D)   It is not possible for a planet to have an elongation of 0°.
    Ans: A   Section: 4-2

74. A planet is observed (through a telescope) to have a crescent shape whenever it is close to
    A)   inferior conjunction.   C)   superior conjunction.
    B)   perihelion.   D)   opposition.
    Ans: A   Section: 4-2

75. A planet appears exactly half-lit (looking like the first- or last-quarter moon) when it is
    A)   in retrograde motion.   C)   at greatest elongation.
    B)   at inferior conjunction.   D)   at opposition.
    Ans: C   Section: 4-2

76. How will the illuminated side of Mars appear to us when it is at opposition?
    A)   quarter-phase or half-illuminated   C)   a full circle
    B)   gibbous   D)   crescent shaped
    Ans: C   Section: 4-2

77. How will the illuminated side of Venus appear to us when it is at its greatest eastern elongation?
    A)   a full circle   C)   gibbous
    B)   half-illuminated or quarter-phase   D)   crescent shaped
    Ans: B   Section: 4-2

78. A planet at inferior conjunction is always
    A)   below the horizon and therefore invisible.
    B)   farther away from us than is the Sun.
    C)   on the opposite side of the sky from the Sun, as seen from Earth.
    D)   closer to us than is the Sun.
    Ans: D   Section: 4-2

79. When a planet is seen at opposition, it is always near its
    A)   closest point to the Sun.   C)   closest point to Earth.
    B)   farthest point from Earth.   D)   farthest point from the Sun.
    Ans: C   Section: 4-2

80. Which of the following planetary configurations is not possible for the planet Mercury?
    A)   superior conjunction   C)   inferior conjunction
    B)   greatest elongation   D)   opposition
    Ans: D   Section: 4-2

81. When Saturn is closest to Earth, it is at
    A)   conjunction.
    B)   inferior conjunction.
    C)   greatest elongation (about 47° from the Sun).
    D)   opposition.
    Ans: D   Section: 4-2

82. The best time(s) to see inferior planets from Earth are when these planets are at positions of
    A)   greatest elongation.   C)   opposition.
    B)   inferior conjunction.   D)   superior conjunction.
    Ans: A   Section: 4-2

83. Where and when would Venus be seen from Earth when it is at greatest eastern elongation?
    A)   at midnight, in the south   C)   just after sunset, in the west
    B)   just before sunrise, in the east   D)   just after sunset, in the east
    Ans: C   Section: 4-2

84. When Jupiter is at opposition, it rises at
    A) midnight.   B) noon.   C) sunrise.   D) sunset.
    Ans: D   Section: 4-2

85. When Mars is at opposition, it
    A)   rises at about midnight.   C)   is high in the sky at sunset.
    B)   is high in the sky at midnight.   D)   is high in the sky at noon.
    Ans: B   Section: 4-2

86. In which part of the sky does Venus appear at sunset when it is at greatest eastern elongation?
    A)   It is not visible, because it is on the other side of the Sun.
    B)   western
    C)   southern
    D)   eastern
    Ans: B   Section: 4-2

87. When observed at greatest eastern elongation (see Fig. 4-6, Freedman and Kaufmann, *Universe,* 7th ed.), Venus is about 45° from the Sun. How long after sunset does Venus set on the western horizon?
    A)   about 3 hours
    B)   It does not set at this specific time in its orbit.
    C)   1 hour
    D)   about 10 minutes
    Ans: A   Section: 4-2

88. Which of the following planetary configurations can an inferior planet never reach?
    A)   opposition   C)   superior conjunction
    B)   greatest elongation   D)   inferior conjunction
    Ans: A   Section: 4-2

89. The planet Venus can never reach which planetary configuration, when viewed from Earth?
    A)   opposition   C)   superior conjunction
    B)   inferior conjunction   D)   greatest western elongation
    Ans: A   Section: 4-2

90. Which of the following planetary configurations or positions is impossible for a superior planet?
    A) inferior conjunction   B) conjunction   C) opposition   D) perihelion
    Ans: A   Section: 4-2

91. Greatest elongation in a planetary orbit occurs when the angle between
    A)   Sun-planet and Earth-planet lines is 90°.
    B)   Earth-planet and Sun-planet lines is a maximum.
    C)   Sun-Earth and planet-Earth lines is 90°.
    D)   Sun-Earth and Sun-planet lines is 90°.
    Ans: A   Section: 4-2

92. A superior planet is closest to Earth when it is near
    A)   the vernal equinox.   C)   conjunction.
    B)   opposition.   D)   maximum eastern elongation.
    Ans: B   Section: 4-2

93. A superior planet is farthest from Earth when it is near
    A)   the vernal equinox.   C)   maximum eastern elongation.
    B)   opposition.   D)   conjunction.
    Ans: D   Section: 4-2

94. An inferior planet is closest to Earth when it is near
    A) greatest eastern elongation.   C) opposition.
    B) superior conjunction.   D) inferior conjunction.
    Ans: D   Section: 4-2

95. An inferior planet is farthest from Earth when it is near
    A) greatest western elongation.   C) inferior conjunction.
    B) superior conjunction.   D) opposition.
    Ans: B   Section: 4-2

96. Where and when would Jupiter be seen from Earth when it is at opposition?
    A) on the eastern horizon just before sunrise
    B) high in the south at midnight
    C) on the western horizon just after sunset
    D) in the daytime sky
    Ans: B   Section: 4-2

97. What is the difference between the synodic and sidereal periods of a planet?
    A) There is no difference; they are one and the same time period. The synodic period
        is the name used in the geocentric theory, while the sidereal period is the name
        used in the heliocentric theory.
    B) The synodic period refers to the planet's period with respect to Earth's motion,
        while the sidereal period is the true period with respect to the background stars.
    C) The synodic period refers to the planet's rotation around its axis, while the sidereal
        period is the time for one orbit.
    D) The synodic period refers to the planet's motion with respect to the background
        stars, while the sidereal period is the true period with respect to Earth's motion.
    Ans: B   Section: 4-2

98. The sidereal period of a planet is defined as the time between
    A) two successive passages of the planet in front of a particular point in the sky (e.g.,
        a star) as seen from Earth.
    B) two successive identical configurations (e.g., opposition to opposition).
    C) two successive passages of the planet in front of a particular point in the sky (e.g.,
        a star) as seen from the Sun.
    D) two successive greatest elongations (e.g., greatest western elongation to greatest
        eastern elongation).
    Ans: C   Section: 4-2

99. The time period between two successive passages of a planet past a particular star as
    seen from the Sun is its
    A) precessional period.   C) synodic period.
    B) rotational period.   D) sidereal period.
    Ans: D   Section: 4-2

100. A planet's sidereal year is different from its synodic year because the
   A)   planet rotates about its own axis in addition to its orbital motion.
   B)   planet's speed in its orbit changes with time because the orbit is elliptical.
   C)   planet moves.
   D)   Earth moves.
   Ans: D   Section: 4-2

101. The synodic period of a planet is the time between
   A)   successive alignments of Sun, planet, and Earth (e.g., time between successive
        oppositions).
   B)   successive alignments of Sun, planet, and a particular point on the sky (e.g., a
        star).
   C)   its passage from conjunction to opposition in its orbit.
   D)   successive passages of the planet across the celestial equator.
   Ans: A   Section: 4-2

102. The synodic period of a planet is defined as the time between
   A)   two successive passages of the planet in front of a particular point in the sky (e.g.,
        a star) as seen from Earth.
   B)   two successive identical configurations (e.g., opposition to opposition).
   C)   two successive passages of the planet in front of a particular point in the sky (e.g.,
        a star) as seen from the Sun.
   D)   two successive greatest elongations (e.g., greatest western elongation to greatest
        eastern elongation).
   Ans: B   Section: 4-2

103. The time period between two successive passages of a planet through the position of
   opposition is
   A)   its sidereal period.   C)   one synodic month.
   B)   its synodic period.   D)   one year.
   Ans: B   Section: 4-2

104. The synodic period of a superior planet in motion around the sun, as viewed from Earth,
   is defined as the
   A)   time between two successive appearances of the planet at its highest point in the
        observer's sky.
   B)   time between two successive passages of Earth through the vernal equinox.
   C)   time between conjunction and opposition on any orbit.
   D)   time between two successive passages through identical configurations, for
        example, two opposition positions.
   Ans: D   Section: 4-2

105. The time it takes for a planet to return to the same position with respect to the Sun and Earth in its orbit, such as the time from opposition to the next opposition, is known as
    A)   1 year.   C)   1 day.
    B)   the planet's synodic period.   D)   the planet's sidereal period.
    Ans: B   Section: 4-2

106. How many more orbits around the Sun in 1 synodic period of that planet does an inferior planet cover compared to the Earth?
    A)   wrong way around—Earth does one more orbit compared to the planet
    B)   two
    C)   one
    D)   a fraction of an orbit
    Ans: C   Section: 4-2 and Box 4-1

107. An imaginary planet is orbiting the Sun in a circle at precisely the same average orbital distance as Earth (i.e., one AU). What is its sidereal period?
    A) about 8/10 of a year   B) infinitely long   C) 0   D) 1 year
    Ans: D   Section: 4-2 and Box 4-1

108. What will be the synodic period of a (hypothetical) planet that orbits the Sun at exactly the same distance as does Earth?
    A) 2 years   B) 0   C) 1 year   D) infinitely long
    Ans: D   Section: 4-2 and Box 4-1

109. A planet is imagined to be orbiting the Sun at precisely the same average distance as Earth (i.e., 1 AU). What will be its synodic period?
    A) 0   B) about 1 month   C) 1 year   D) infinitely long
    Ans: D   Section: 4-2 and Box 4-1

110. At what distance would a planet have to orbit the Sun to have its synodic period equal to its sidereal period, assuming circular orbits for Earth and the planet? (See Box 4-1, Freedman and Kaufmann, *Universe*, 7th ed.)
    A)   1.59 AU
    B)   2 AU
    C)   2.83 AU
    D)   1 AU, the same distance as Earth's orbit
    Ans: A   Section: 4-2 and Box 4-1

111. If a particular asteroid with a circular orbit is seen at opposition every 1.44 years, then its sidereal period is
    A) 0.59 years.   B) 1.44 years.   C) 0.44 years.   D) 3.27 years.
    Ans: D   Section: 4-2 and Box 4-1

112. A spacecraft that has been put into a circular orbit around the Sun (in the same plane as Earth's orbit) with a sidereal period of 2.25 years is unobservable behind the Sun once every
    A) 3.85 years.   B) 2.25 years.   C) 1.80 years.   D) 1.00 years.
    Ans: C   Section: 4-2 and Box 4-1

113. An asteroid in the asteroid belt orbits the Sun at a distance of 2.8 AU. Using Kepler's Laws and Box 4-1, Freedman and Kaufmann, *Universe,* 7th ed., determine the synodic period of this asteroid when observed from Earth.
    A) 2.01 years   B) 1.27 years   C) 1.56 years   D) 4.68 years
    Ans: B   Section: 4-2 and Box 4-1

114. What is the synodic period of Neptune? (See Table of Orbital Data in Appendix 1, and Box 4-1, *Universe*, Freedman and Kaufmann, 7th ed.)
    A) 367.5 days   B) 367.5 years   C) 84 years   D) 165 years
    Ans: A   Section: 4-2 and Box 4-1

115. Approximately how many of its sidereal periods has Neptune completed since its discovery? (See Table of Orbital Data in Appendix 1, and Box 4-1, Freedman and Kaufmann, *Universe,* 7th ed.)
    A) about 15   B) 212   C) less than 1   D) 147
    Ans: C   Section: 4-2 and Box 4-1

116. The greatest inaccuracy in Copernicus' theory of the solar system was that he
    A)   placed the planets in circular orbits.
    B)   placed the planets on epicycles, the centers of which followed orbits around Earth.
    C)   did not allow for retrograde motion.
    D)   assumed that the planets move in elliptical orbits with constant speeds rather than variable speeds.
    Ans: A   Section: 4-2

117. The reason why Copernicus' heliocentric theory soon came to be regarded as preferable to the geocentric theory of Ptolemy is that the heliocentric theory
    A)   accounted for the same observed motions of the planets as the geocentric theory but did so much more accurately.
    B)   used complex constructions called epicycles and deferents to account for the observed motions of the planets and so was considered more reliable than the geocentric theory.
    C)   accounted for the same observed motions of the planets as the geocentric theory but did so in a much simpler way.
    D)   accounted for retrograde motion, which the geocentric theory was unable to explain.
    Ans: C   Section: 4-2

118. The sidereal period of Mars is 1.9 years. Use the appropriate formula in Box 4-1 to find the time from the middle of one retrograde loop for Mars to the middle of the next retrograde loop (assuming circular orbits for Mars and Earth). This time is
A) 365 days.   B) 694 days.   C) 770 days.   D) 1059 days.
Ans: C   Section: 4-2 and Box 4-1

119. The Earth moves eastward in its orbit around the Sun, and so does Mars. Suppose Mars moved westward rather than eastward. What result would this have on the retrograde motion of Mars as observed from Earth? (You might need to make a drawing similar to Fig. 4-5 in Freedman and Kaufmann's *Universe*, 7th ed., to answer this question.)
A)   Mars would not exhibit retrograde motion.
B)   Mars would show retrograde motion, but less frequently than now.
C)   Mars would show retrograde motion, but more frequently than now.
D)   Mars would show retrograde motion with the same frequency it has now.
Ans: C   Section: 4-2

120. Which of the following planets shows the smallest maximum western elongation when viewed from Earth?
A) Mercury   B) Venus   C) Mars   D) Jupiter
Ans: A   Section: 4-2

121. The phenomenon of parallax is the
A)   change in the position of an object in the sky as a consequence of its motion.
B)   change in apparent position of a nearby object as the observer moves.
C)   apparent change in angular size of an object as it moves directly away from an observer.
D)   change in direction of motion of a planet from retrograde to direct motion.
Ans: B   Section: 4-3

122. The astronomer who used parallax to show that the supernova of 1572 occurred at a large distance from Earth was
A)   Nicolaus Copernicus.   C)   Johannes Kepler.
B)   Galileo Galilei.   D)   Tycho Brahe.
Ans: D   Section: 4-3

123. Tycho Brahe demonstrated that the supernova of 1572 was not a nearby (close to Earth) event by
A)   proving that it did not show parallax over the course of one night.
B)   showing that it did not get brighter and fainter as Earth moved toward and away from it over the course of a year.
C)   showing that it did not pass in front of the Sun at conjunction.
D)   proving that it did not move past the background stars like a planet in our solar system.
Ans: A   Section: 4-3

124. Tycho Brahe's most important contribution to the development of modern astronomy was the
    A) discovery of the satellites (moons) of Jupiter.
    B) proof that planetary orbits are ellipses.
    C) use of parallax to prove that Earth does not move.
    D) accurate measurement of planetary positions.
    Ans: D   Section: 4-3

125. Tycho Brahe
    A) built improved refracting telescopes that confirmed and extended Galileo's observations of the sky.
    B) made accurate measurements of planetary positions, which Kepler later used to find the shapes of planetary orbits.
    C) developed the first detailed heliocentric model for the solar system.
    D) developed a reflecting telescope, which used a curved mirror to focus the light.
    Ans: B   Section: 4-3

126. The person who compiled the large set of accurate observations of planetary positions that formed the basis for proving that planets move in elliptical orbits around the Sun was
    A) Nicolaus Copernicus.   C) Johannes Kepler.
    B) Ptolemy.   D) Tycho Brahe.
    Ans: D   Section: 4-3

127. How did Tycho Brahe use parallax in his observations?
    A) He did not attempt to measure parallax because he knew that it applied only to heliocentric systems; he believed the solar system was geocentric.
    B) He did not attempt to measure parallax because he knew that it applied only to geocentric systems; he believed the solar system was heliocentric.
    C) He successfully measured parallax for the supernova of 1572 and the comet of 1577.
    D) He tried but failed to measure parallax for the stars.
    Ans: D   Section: 4-3

128. Kepler as a young man became the assistant to
    A) Nicolaus Copernicus.   C) Tycho Brahe.
    B) Sir Isaac Newton.   D) Ptolemy.
    Ans: C   Section: 4-4

129. Before deriving the shapes of planetary orbits, Johannes Kepler worked as an assistant to
    A) Galileo Galilei.   B) Tycho Brahe.   C) Nicolaus Copernicus.   D) Ptolemy.
    Ans: B   Section: 4-4

130. The Danish astronomer Tycho Brahe had a young assistant who became famous himself some time later. His name was
    A)   Nicolaus Copernicus.   C)   Ptolemy.
    B)   Johannes Kepler.   D)   Isaac Newton.
    Ans: B   Section: 4-4

131. The major contribution of Johannes Kepler to the development of modern astronomy was to
    A)   develop the first mathematical heliocentric model of the solar system.
    B)   observe the satellites (moons) of Jupiter.
    C)   use parallax to prove that Earth moves around the Sun.
    D)   prove that planetary orbits are ellipses.
    Ans: D   Section: 4-4

132. The person who first showed that planetary orbits are ellipses was
    A) Kepler.   B) Newton.   C) Galileo.   D) Copernicus.
    Ans: A   Section: 4-4

133. The Kepler model of the solar system is
    A)   Sun-centered, with planets moving in circles around it.
    B)   Earth-centered, with Sun, Moon, and planets moving in ellipses in the sky.
    C)   Earth-centered, with planets describing epicycles in the sky.
    D)   Sun-centered, with elliptical planetary orbits.
    Ans: D   Section: 4-4

134. Kepler's laws describe the
    A)   motions of the planets around the Sun.
    B)   motion of the spin axis of Earth over long time periods.
    C)   motions of the planets around Earth.
    D)   motion of the Moon around the Sun.
    Ans: A   Section: 4-4

135. Kepler's first law states that the orbit of a planet about
    A)   the Sun is a circle with the Sun at the center.
    B)   the Sun is an ellipse with Earth at the center.
    C)   the Sun is an ellipse with the Sun at one focus.
    D)   the Sun is an ellipse with the Sun at the center.
    Ans: C   Section: 4-4

136. Kepler's first law states that a planet moves around the Sun in
    A)   an elliptical orbit, with the Sun on the minor axis of the ellipse.
    B)   an elliptical orbit, with the Sun at the center of the ellipse.
    C)   a circle, with the Sun at the center.
    D)   an elliptical orbit, with the Sun at one focus.
    Ans: D   Section: 4-4

137. Mars moves in an elliptical orbit around the Sun. The location of the Sun relative to this
     ellipse is at
     A)   the focus that is closer to the point where Mars is moving the slowest.
     B)   one end of the major axis of the ellipse.
     C)   the exact center of the ellipse.
     D)   the focus that is closer to the point where Mars moves the fastest.
     Ans: D   Section: 4-4

138. To which point in a planetary orbit does the word "perihelion" refer?
     A)   the "other" focus (the one not occupied by the Sun)
     B)   the precise center of the orbit
     C)   the point closest to the Sun
     D)   the point farthest from the Sun
     Ans: C   Section: 4-4

139. To which point in a planetary orbit does the word "aphelion" refer?
     A)   the precise center of the orbit
     B)   the point farthest from the Sun
     C)   the "other" focus (the one not occupied by the Sun)
     D)   the point closest to the Sun
     Ans: B   Section: 4-4

140. At which point in a planet's elliptical orbit is it farthest from the Sun?
     A) perihelion   B) aphelion   C) quadrature   D) superior conjunction
     Ans: B   Section: 4-4

141. At what point in its orbit is a comet closest to the Sun?
     A) perihelion   B) inferior conjunction   C) opposition   D) aphelion
     Ans: A   Section: 4-4

142. As it moves in its elliptical orbit, at what point is a planet at its farthest distance from
     the Sun?
     A) opposition   B) perihelion   C) superior conjunction   D) aphelion
     Ans: D   Section: 4-4

143. The eccentricity of a planet's orbit describes
     A)   its tilt with respect to the plane of Earth's orbit (the ecliptic plane).
     B)   its shape compared to that of a circle.
     C)   its motion at any specific point in its orbit as seen from Earth, i.e., whether direct,
           retrograde or stationary.
     D)   the tilt of the planet's spin axis with respect to its orbital plane.
     Ans: B   Section: 4-4 and Figure 4-16

144. If an object's orbit around the Sun has an eccentricity of 0.1, then the orbit is
    A)   almost circular.   C)   a straight line.
    B)   a long, thin ellipse.   D)   exactly circular.
    Ans: A   Section: 4-4 and Figure 4-16

145. If an object's orbit around the Sun has an eccentricity of 0.8, then the orbit is
    A)   a straight line.   C)   almost circular.
    B)   a long, thin ellipse.   D)   exactly circular.
    Ans: B   Section: 4-4 and Figure 4-16

146. The distance from the perihelion point to the aphelion point of a planetary orbit is
    A)   equal to the distance between the foci.
    B)   the minor axis.
    C)   the semimajor axis.
    D)   the major axis.
    Ans: D   Section: 4-4

147. An ellipse is a curve for which the
    A)   difference in distances between any point on the curve and two fixed points
         remains constant.
    B)   distance from any point on the curve to a single fixed point is constant.
    C)   distances between any point on the curve and two fixed points always maintain
         the same ratio to one another.
    D)   sum of the distances from any point on the curve to two other fixed points remains
         constant.
    Ans: D   Section: 4-4 and Figure 4-16

148. The semimajor axis of an ellipse is
    A)   the distance from one focus to any point on the circumference of the ellipse.
    B)   the distance from the center to one side of the ellipse along the shortest diameter
         of the ellipse.
    C)   the distance from the center of the ellipse to one end along the largest diameter of
         the ellipse.
    D)   half the distance between the foci of the ellipse.
    Ans: C   Section: 4-4

149. In an ellipse, the semimajor axis is a distance measured
    A)   along the circumference between the closest point to and the farthest point from
         one focus.
    B)   along the shorter diameter from the center to the ellipse.
    C)   from focus to focus.
    D)   along the longer diameter from the center through one focus to the ellipse.
    Ans: D   Section: 4-4

150. Kepler's second law states that a line joining a planet to the Sun
    A) sweeps through equal angles in equal times.
    B) points in the same direction at all times.
    C) sweeps out equal areas in equal times.
    D) moves equal distances along the planet's orbit in equal times.
    Ans: C   Section: 4-4

151. If the line joining a planet to the Sun sweeps out a particular area in one day, then in 2 days it will sweep out
    A) half the area.
    B) exactly twice the area.
    C) more than twice the area if the planet is approaching perihelion and less than twice the area if it is leaving perihelion.
    D) less than twice the area if the planet is approaching perihelion and more than twice the area if it is leaving perihelion.
    Ans: B   Section: 4-4

152. According to Kepler's second law, an object in an elliptical orbit around the Sun is traveling fastest when it is at what position?
    A) Since it travels at a constant speed throughout its orbit, there is no such position.
    B) when it is approaching the Sun, since attraction is greatest over this region
    C) aphelion, farthest from the Sun, since it has to move farther per day at that position
    D) perihelion, closest point to the Sun
    Ans: D   Section: 4-4

153. In any one day, the line joining a planet to the Sun will sweep through a certain angle as seen from the Sun. At what position is the planet when this angle has its smallest value?
    A) perihelion   B) greatest elongation   C) inferior conjunction   D) aphelion
    Ans: D   Section: 4-4

154. Kepler's second law states that a planet moves fastest when it
    A) passes through the minor axis.   C) is closest to the Sun.
    B) is furthest from the Sun.   D) is at conjunction.
    Ans: C   Section: 4-4

155. The planet Pluto moves fastest at what part of its elliptical orbit around the Sun?
    A) conjunction
    B) It always moves at a constant speed as required by Kepler's second law.
    C) aphelion
    D) perihelion
    Ans: D   Section: 4-4

156. Kepler's third law, the harmonic law, provides a relationship between a planet's
    A)   mass and orbital period.
    B)   orbital period and length of semimajor axis.
    C)   physical radius and its rotational period around its axis.
    D)   orbital eccentricity and length of semimajor axis.
    Ans: B   Section: 4-4

157. Kepler's third law states that
    A)   the orbital period of a planet is inversely proportional to the square of its mean distance from the Sun.
    B)   the cube of the orbital period is directly proportional to the square of its mean distance from the Sun.
    C)   the square of the orbital period is directly proportional to the cube of its mean distance from the Sun.
    D)   the orbital period of a planet is directly proportional to its mean distance from the Sun.
    Ans: C   Section: 4-4

158. Which of the following statements is true, according to Kepler's third law?
    A)   The smaller the orbit, the longer it takes for the planet to complete one revolution.
    B)   The smaller the radius of a planet, the more rapidly it rotates on its axis.
    C)   The larger the orbit, the longer it takes for the planet to complete one revolution.
    D)   The time to complete one revolution of its orbit depends on the size or radius of the planet.
    Ans: C   Section: 4-4

159. Kepler's third law of planetary motion relates the period P (in sidereal years) to the length of the semimajor axis a (in astronomical units) in which way?
    A) $P = 1/a^2$ B) $P^2 = a^3$ C) $P^3 = a^2$ D) $P = a^2$
    Ans: B   Section: 4-4

160. In the simplified version of Kepler's third law, $P^2 = a^3$, the units of the orbital period P and the semimajor axis a of the ellipses must be, respectively,
    A)   seconds and meters.   C)   years and meters.
    B)   years and light years.   D)   years and astronomical units.
    Ans: D   Section: 4-4

161. Kepler's third law in general applies
    A) accurately only close to the Sun, and becomes less accurate with increasing distance from the Sun.
    B) only to planets orbiting the Sun.
    C) to all situations where two objects orbit each other solely under the influence of their mutual gravitational attraction.
    D) only to situations similar to planets orbiting the Sun, where the mass of the orbiting body is small compared to the mass of the object being orbited.
    Ans: C   Section: 4-4

162. How closely do you expect Halley's Comet to obey Kepler's laws (particularly $P^2 = a^3$ with P in years and a in AU)?
    A) never, since it moves independently and is not related to the motions of the planets
    B) very closely only when it is close to the Sun (within Earth's orbital distance)
    C) closely only at very large distances
    D) fairly closely, since it is gravitationally bound to the Sun
    Ans: D   Section: 4-4

163. If a tenth planet (tentatively predicted to exist on the basis of perturbations in the orbits of Uranus and Neptune) were to be discovered with a sidereal period of 125 years, what would be the radius of its orbit (assumed to be circular)?
    A) 8.55 AU   B) 25 AU   C) 1 AU   D) 125 AU
    Ans: B   Section: 4-4 and Box 4-2

164. If a tenth planet (tentatively predicted to exist on the basis of perturbations in the orbits of Uranus and Neptune) were to be discovered with a sidereal period of 200 years, what would be the radius of its orbit (assumed to be circular)?
    A) 2828 AU   B) 34.2 AU   C) 200 AU   D) 342 AU
    Ans: B   Section: 4-4 and Box 4-2

165. According to Kepler's law, the approximate sidereal period of an asteroid moving around the Sun in the asteroid belt is
    A) 46.8 years.   B) 2.8 years.   C) 1.99 years.   D) 4.68 years.
    Ans: D   Section: 4-4 and Box 4-2

166. If a planet were to exist in our solar system in a circular orbit with a radius of 3 AU, about how long would it take to orbit the Sun once?
    A) 27 years   B) 3 years   C) 2.1 years   D) 5.2 years
    Ans: D   Section: 4-4 and Box 4-2

167. Suppose an asteroid is discovered in an elliptical orbit with a period of exactly one year and at perihelion it is 0.5 AU from the Sun. Using Kepler's third law, how far from the Sun is this asteroid when at aphelion? (Drawing a diagram of the orbit, including the Sun, will help.)
    A) 1.0 AU   B) 1.5 AU   C) 2.5 AU   D) 2.0 AU
    Ans: B   Section: 4-4 and Box 4-2

168. An asteroid orbits the Sun in a circle with a sidereal period of 11.9 years. Compare this with the orbital characteristics of the planets. At what equivalent distance will this asteroid orbit the Sun?
    A)   between the orbits of Saturn and Uranus
    B)   at an orbital distance beyond that of Pluto
    C)   at the same orbital distance as Jupiter
    D)   at the same orbital distance as Venus
    Ans: C   Section: 4-4 and Box 4-2

169. If an asteroid orbits the Sun in a circular orbit with a sidereal period of 11.9 years, how would this asteroid be classified? (See Ch. 17, Freedman and Kaufmann, *Universe,* 7th ed.)
    A)   normal asteroid, orbiting within the asteroid belt
    B)   meteoroid
    C)   Apollo asteroid
    D)   Trojan asteroid
    Ans: D   Section: 4-4, Box 4-2 and Chapter 17

170. Halley's Comet returns to the Sun's vicinity every 76 years in an elliptical orbit. (See Fig. 4-22, Freedman and Kaufmann, *Universe,* 7th ed.) What is the semimajor axis of this orbit?
    A) 17.5 AU   B) 0.59 AU   C) 1 AU   D) 50.000 AU
    Ans: A   Section: 4-4

171. If Halley's Comet has an elliptical orbit with a semimajor axis of 17.5 AU, approximately how far out into the planetary system does it reach at its furthest point (aphelion)? (Assume that perihelion distance from the Sun is negligible; be careful. The question needs some thought.)
    A)   between the orbits of Neptune and Pluto
    B)   between the orbits of Uranus and Neptune
    C)   beyond the orbit of Pluto
    D)   between the orbits of Saturn and Uranus
    Ans: A   Section: 4-4

172. A comet is observed to return to the vicinity of the Sun on a long elliptical orbit with a period of 31.7 years. What is the semimajor axis of its orbit?
    A) 178.5 AU   B) 1000 AU   C) 10 AU   D) 31.7 AU
    Ans: C   Section: 4-4

173. An asteroid-like object (or a cometary nucleus) is seen to be orbiting the Sun in a circular path with a period of 120 years. What is its distance of closest approach to Earth (the separation distance when the object is at opposition)? (Careful with your answer; a diagram might be helpful.)
A) 25.33 AU   B) 24.33 AU   C) 23.33 AU   D) 1314.5 AU
Ans: C   Section: 4-4

174. A distant asteroid is discovered that takes 50 years to orbit once around the Sun. According to Kepler's third law, what is the average distance of this asteroid from the Sun?
A)   50 AU   C)   353 AU (square root of 125,000)
B)   13.6 AU (cube root of 2500)   D)   2500 AU
Ans: B   Section: 4-4

175. The planet Jupiter travels in an elliptical orbit. The Sun is at one focus of this ellipse. What is at the other focus?
A)   the Earth
B)   Ganymede, the largest of Jupiter's moons
C)   the Trojan asteroids
D)   nothing
Ans: D   Section: 4-4

176. Consider a comet in a long, thin elliptical orbit with a semi-major axis of one AU. What can you say about the sidereal period of this comet?
A)   It will be less than one year.
B)   It will be one year.
C)   It will be more than one year.
D)   It is not possible to determine the comet's sidereal period without knowing the eccentricity of its orbit.
Ans: B   Section: 4-4

177. Who was the first astronomer to use a telescope for viewing the sky?
A) Newton   B) Brahe   C) Ptolemy   D) Galileo
Ans: D   Section: 4-5

178. Galileo's early observations of the sky with his newly made telescope included the
A)   fact that Venus showed phases similar to those of the Moon.
B)   discovery of the aurora, or northern lights.
C)   discovery of retrograde motion in planets.
D)   discovery of Pluto.
Ans: A   Section: 4-5

179. What did Galileo see when he observed Jupiter through his telescope?
    A)   phases like the Moon's phases
    B)   a set of rings
    C)   nothing interesting because Jupiter is perpetually cloud-covered
    D)   four satellites (moons) orbiting Jupiter
    Ans: D   Section: 4-5

180. How many moons of Jupiter were seen by Galileo?
    A) 4   B) 12   C) 1   D) 0
    Ans: A   Section: 4-5

181. Which of the following statements correctly states the significance of Galileo's observation that Jupiter has satellites (moons)?
    A)   It was interesting but had no particular significance.
    B)   It showed that bodies can orbit an object other than Earth.
    C)   It showed that Jupiter must be four times the size of Earth (since Jupiter has four moons and Earth has one).
    D)   It showed that Jupiter must orbit around the Sun, not around Earth.
    Ans: B   Section: 4-5

182. One of the major contributions of Galileo to the development of modern astronomy was to
    A)   discover the satellites (moons) of Jupiter.
    B)   prove that planetary orbits were ellipses.
    C)   use parallax to prove that Earth moved around the Sun.
    D)   develop the first mathematical heliocentric model of the solar system.
    Ans: A   Section: 4-5

183. In which country did Galileo make his astronomical discoveries?
    A) Poland   B) England   C) Greece   D) Italy
    Ans: D   Section: 4-5

184. Which of the following astronomers lived at the same time as Galileo?
    A) Copernicus   B) Ptolemy   C) Newton   D) Kepler
    Ans: D   Section: 4-5

185. What did Galileo see when he observed Venus through his telescope?
    A)   nothing interesting, because Venus is perpetually cloud-covered
    B)   four satellites (moons) orbiting Venus
    C)   a set of rings
    D)   phases like those of the Moon
    Ans: D   Section: 4-5

186. What did Galileo see when he observed Venus through his telescope?
    A)   Venus has phases like the Moon and has its largest angular diameter at gibbous phase.
    B)   Venus has an angular size that increases and decreases markedly, but it does not show phases (e.g., crescent, gibbous).
    C)   Like the Moon, Venus shows phases and its angular size remains almost constant.
    D)   Venus has phases like the Moon and has its largest angular diameter at crescent phase.
    Ans: D   Section: 4-5

187. As Venus orbits the Sun, by what factor, as viewed from Earth, does its angular size change from smallest to largest? (See Figs. 4-13 and 4-14, Freedman and Kaufmann, *Universe,* 7th ed.)
    A)   Only brightness changes; angular size does not.
    B) $1.72 \times$
    C) $58 \times$
    D) $5.8 \times$
    Ans: D   Section: 4-5

188. Which of the following statements correctly states the significance of Galileo's observation that Venus shows phases?
    A)   Since the phases were NOT correlated with angular size, they actually provided more support for the geocentric theory than for the heliocentric theory.
    B)   The phases were interesting but did not have any particular significance.
    C)   The phases showed that, like the Moon, Venus is always much closer to Earth than the Sun.
    D)   The phases were correlated with angular size in a way that supported the heliocentric theory.
    Ans: D   Section: 4-5

189. The one significant observation Galileo made through his home-built telescope that convinced him that the planets revolved around the Sun was
    A)   the appearance of the Milky Way as a mass of individual stars.
    B)   the discovery of rings around the planet Saturn.
    C)   the appearance of mountains and craters on the Moon.
    D)   that the appearance of Venus followed a cycle of phases, from crescent through quarter and gibbous phases to full phase.
    Ans: D   Section: 4-5

190. Venus shows changes in angular size and also shows phases similar to those of the Moon. When Galileo first saw these changes, he concluded that
    A)   Venus orbits the Moon.
    B)   Venus orbits the Sun.
    C)   the Moon really orbits Venus, not Earth after all.
    D)   Venus, like the Moon, orbits Earth.
    Ans: B   Section: 4-5

191. Galileo's observations suggested to him that the planets revolve around the Sun. This idea
    A)   was original with Galileo and had not been suggested before.
    B)   was similar to the teachings of the Roman Catholic Church.
    C)   was similar to the ideas of Ptolemy.
    D)   was similar to the ideas of Copernicus.
    Ans: D   Section: 4-5

192. In the geocentric model of the solar system, which one of the following phases of Venus should be visible from the Earth?
    A)   full
    B)   new
    C)   the gibbous phase between first quarter and full.
    D)   the gibbous phase between third quarter and full.
    Ans: B   Section: 4-5

193. In the heliocentric model of the solar system, which one of the following phases of Venus should *not* be visible from the Earth?
    A) full   B) gibbous   C) new   D) None of these. They are all visible.
    Ans: D   Section: 4-5

194. What was the MOST IMPORTANT difference in development between Isaac Newton's theory of planetary motion and that of Johannes Kepler?
    A)   Newton lived in a freer political climate, whereas Kepler risked house arrest if his theory opposed the Bible or Aristotle.
    B)   Newton lived in England, which is famous for clear skies, whereas Kepler lived on the Continent, which is notorious for bad weather.
    C)   Newton developed his theory from basic physical assumptions, whereas Kepler simply adjusted his theory to fit the data.
    D)   Newton based his theory on accurate telescopic observations, whereas Kepler used observations made by eye.
    Ans: C   Section: 4-6

195. Which one of the following relationships represents Newton's MOST IMPORTANT contribution to physics?
   A)   the relationship between gravity and distance
   B)   the relationship between velocity and acceleration
   C)   the relationship between mass and weight
   D)   the relationship between force and motion
   Ans: D   Section: 4-6

196. What was the MOST IMPORTANT contribution of Newton to the development of astronomy?
   A)   He showed that astronomical phenomena can be explained using only basic physics and mathematics.
   B)   He was the first person to observe the sky through a telescope.
   C)   He showed that planetary orbits are ellipses, with the planets moving fastest when closest to the Sun.
   D)   He invented the refracting telescope.
   Ans: A   Section: 4-6

197. Why were Newton's three laws so important to astronomy?
   A)   They showed that planets can move around the Sun by themselves forever, without coming to rest.
   B)   They provided a physical basis which did not conflict with the Bible, Aristotle, or Plato.
   C)   They showed that acceleration always results from a change in velocity.
   D)   They showed why objects released from rest always fall to the ground.
   Ans: A   Section: 4-6

198. Careful description of the velocity of a moving object at a particular time requires that one define
   A)   the mass, speed, and position of the object.
   B)   only the speed of the object.
   C)   the speed and the direction of the moving object.
   D)   the acceleration as well as the speed of the object.
   Ans: C   Section: 4-6

199. To specify an object's velocity completely, we need to specify
   A)   its speed.   C)   its direction of travel.
   B)   the rate of change of its acceleration.   D)   its speed and direction of travel.
   Ans: D   Section: 4-6

200. To define an object's velocity, we need to specify
  A)   how fast it is moving and also its mass.
  B)   only in which direction it is moving.
  C)   only how fast it is moving.
  D)   how fast it is moving and also in which direction it is moving.
  Ans: D   Section: 4-6

201. To specify an object's speed, we need to specify
  A)   only how fast it is moving.
  B)   only the direction in which it is moving.
  C)   how fast it is moving and also its mass.
  D)   how fast it is moving and also the direction in which it is moving.
  Ans: A   Section: 4-6

202. Acceleration of a moving body is defined as the rate of change of
  A)   position with time.   C)   mass with time.
  B)   kinetic energy with time.   D)   velocity with time.
  Ans: D   Section: 4-6

203. Acceleration of a body is the rate of change with time of its
  A) mass.   B) weight.   C) position.   D) velocity.
  Ans: D   Section: 4-6

204. An object orbiting the Sun in a circle can be said to be
  A)   always accelerating.
  B)   moving under the action of equal and opposite forces.
  C)   weightless.
  D)   moving at a constant velocity.
  Ans: A   Section: 4-6

205. An accelerating body must
  A)   have a changing direction of motion.   C)   be moving.
  B)   have a changing velocity.   D)   have an increasing velocity.
  Ans: B   Section: 4-6

206. Which of the following four objects or persons is not accelerating?
  A)   an olympic swimmer exerting considerable force to maintain a constant speed in a straight line through the water
  B)   an apple falling to the ground from an apple tree
  C)   a bicyclist gradually slowing down on a straight road while coasting toward a stop sign
  D)   a motorcyclist traveling around a circular racetrack at a constant speed
  Ans: A   Section: 4-6

207. A certain object in space is accelerating. From this, we know for certain that
    A)   its speed is changing.
    B)   both its speed and its direction of travel are changing.
    C)   its speed or its direction of travel is changing, but not both.
    D)   its speed, its direction of travel, or both are changing.
    Ans: D   Section: 4-6

208. A body whose velocity is constant
    A)   has a negative acceleration.   C)   can have any nonzero acceleration.
    B)   has zero acceleration.   D)   has a positive acceleration.
    Ans: B   Section: 4-6

209. Which of the following statements about an asteroid moving in a circular orbit around
    the Sun is untrue?
    A)   It is moving at a constant speed.   C)   It is moving at a constant velocity.
    B)   It is moving on a flat plane.   D)   It is accelerating.
    Ans: C   Section: 4-6

210. To which of these phenomena do Newton's laws of motion NOT apply?
    A)   a high jumper at the Olympic Games
    B)   a spacecraft in circular orbit around Earth, such as communication satellites
    C)   light travel between Sun and Earth
    D)   space vehicles on a journey to Jupiter (e.g., *Galileo*)
    Ans: C   Section: 4-6

211. Acceleration due to gravity on the Moon is
    A)   significantly smaller than that on Earth.
    B)   the same as on Earth.
    C)   twice that on Earth, because the Moon is smaller than Earth.
    D)   zero.
    Ans: A   Section: 4-6

212. If you were to be sent to the Moon, which of your physical properties would be altered
    noticeably?
    A) weight   B) height   C) mass   D) volume
    Ans: A   Section: 4-6

213. On the Moon, where gravity is 1/6 of that on Earth, which of the following activities
    would an astronaut not find easier to carry out?
    A) long jumping   B) running   C) slowing down and stopping   D) high jumping
    Ans: C   Section: 4-6

214. I have a massive purple object in my laboratory. If I were to take it to the Moon, which of its characteristics will be guaranteed to change?
    A) weight   B) color   C) mass   D) density (mass per unit volume)
    Ans: A   Section: 4-6

215. The strength of gravity on Mars is about 40% of that on Earth. If you were to take a standard red brick to Mars, which property of the brick would be significantly different on Mars than on Earth?
    A) weight   B) color   C) mass   D) volume
    Ans: A   Section: 4-6

216. The strength of gravity on Mars is about 40% of that on Earth. If your mass on Earth is 60 kg, what would your mass be on Mars?
    A) 24 kg   B) 60 kg   C) 150 kg   D) zero
    Ans: B   Section: 4-6

217. The strength of gravity on Mars is about 40% of that on Earth. If you were to visit Mars, what would happen to your mass and weight compared to when you were on Earth?
    A)   Your weight would be the same but your mass would be less.
    B)   Your weight and mass would both be unchanged from when you were on Earth.
    C)   Your mass would be the same but your weight would be less.
    D)   Your weight and mass would both be less than when you were on Earth.
    Ans: C   Section: 4-6

218. Compared with your mass on Earth, your mass out in space among the stars would be
    A) negligibly small.   B) huge.   C) zero.   D) the same.
    Ans: D   Section: 4-6

219. When several objects with different masses are dropped by an astronaut on the (airless) Moon where there is no air friction, their resultant motions
    A)   depend on densities of the objects, the one with the highest density falling fastest.
    B)   depend on masses of the objects, the lightest falling fastest.
    C)   depend on the masses of the objects, the most massive falling fastest.
    D)   are independent of the masses of the objects.
    Ans: D   Section: 4-6

220. Two objects of different mass when dropped by an astronaut on the Moon have
    A)   no acceleration at all in the airless space.
    B)   the same acceleration.
    C)   different accelerations proportional to their masses.
    D)   different accelerations, the more massive object having the smaller acceleration.
    Ans: B   Section: 4-6

221. According to Newton's first law,
    A)   an applied force always causes a change in the speed of an object.
    B)   an applied force always causes a change in the direction of travel of an object.
    C)   the rate of change of speed of an object is larger, the larger the force acting on the object.
    D)   if no force is acting on an object, then the object's speed and direction of travel will both be constant.
    Ans: D   Section: 4-6

222. Newton's second law of motion states that a
    A)   body acted on by a force will accelerate constantly while the force is applied.
    B)   force is always required to keep an object in motion.
    C)   body always moves in an elliptical orbit around the Sun.
    D)   body acted on by a force will move at a constant speed while the force is applied.
    Ans: A   Section: 4-6

223. Newton's second law states that acceleration produced by a force is
    A)   inversely proportional to the square of the mass on which the force acts.
    B)   independent of the mass on which the force acts.
    C)   proportional to the mass on which the force acts.
    D)   inversely proportional to the mass on which the force acts.
    Ans: D   Section: 4-6

224. According to Newton's laws, a force must be acting whenever
    A)   an object is moving with some speed.
    B)   an object's position changes.
    C)   time passes.
    D)   the direction of an object's motion changes.
    Ans: D   Section: 4-6

225. According to Newton's second law of motion, an object acted on by a constant force
    A)   does not move.
    B)   moves with constant speed, although the direction may vary.
    C)   moves with constant velocity.
    D)   moves with constant acceleration.
    Ans: D   Section: 4-6

226. An unbalanced force acting on an object will always cause it to change its
    A)   speed or its direction of travel or both.
    B)   acceleration.
    C)   direction of travel.
    D)   speed.
    Ans: A   Section: 4-6

227. Newton stated that if a force were applied to an object in space, the resultant acceleration would depend on the
    A)   initial speed of the object.   C)   initial position of the object.
    B)   mass of the object.   D)   size of the object.
    Ans: B   Section: 4-6

228. Newton, in his second law of motion, stated that any body of mass m acted on by a force F
    A)   will be given an acceleration a, of size $a = F/m$.
    B)   will also have acting on it an equal and opposite force, ma, where $F = ma$, and a is the acceleration.
    C)   will remain at rest, unless a second force also acts on the body.
    D)   moves with a constant velocity, in the direction of the force.
    Ans: A   Section: 4-6

229. Two spaceships that have different masses but rocket engines of identical force are at rest in space. If they fire their rockets at the same time, which ship will speed up fastest?
    A)   They will not speed up at all but will move at a constant speed since they are in space and the rocket has nothing against which to push.
    B)   the one with the lowest mass
    C)   They will increase speed at the same rate since they have identical rocket engines.
    D)   the one with the highest mass
    Ans: B   Section: 4-6

230. Which of the following statements is a correct version of Newton's third law?
    A)   Whenever object A exerts a force on some other object B, B must exert a force of equal magnitude on A in the same direction.
    B)   Whenever two forces act, they must be equal in magnitude and opposite in direction.
    C)   Whenever object A exerts a force on some other object B, B must exert a force of equal magnitude on A in the opposite direction.
    D)   Whenever any object feels some force it must also feel another force of equal magnitude in the opposite direction from some other source.
    Ans: C   Section: 4-6

231. According to Newton's third law, if a force is acting on an object then
    A)   the object must accelerate.
    B)   the object must move in a circular path.
    C)   there must be some other force acting on a different object, with the same magnitude but in the opposite direction.
    D)   there must be some other force also acting on the object, with the same magnitude but in the opposite direction.
    Ans: C   Section: 4-6

232. A horse is dragging a loaded sled across a field. Which of the following pairs of forces is an action-reaction pair by Newton's third law?
    A)   the force of the horse on the sled and the force of the ground on the horse
    B)   the force of the sled on the ground and the force of the horse's hooves on the ground
    C)   the force of the horse on the sled and the force of the sled on the horse
    D)   the force of the horse on the sled and the force of the ground on the sled
    Ans: C   Section: 4-6

233. The old story about the person who sneezed so hard that he fell off his barstool is an exaggerated illustration of which physical law?
    A)   the law forbidding the partaking of alcohol during physical experiments
    B)   Law of Inertia, Newton's first law
    C)   Law of Universal Gravitation
    D)   Newton's third law, of equal and opposite forces of action and reaction
    Ans: D   Section: 4-6

234. A person standing on a bathroom scale sees a reading on the scale of 148 pounds. This person is acted on by
    A)   no forces at all.
    B)   only one force, of 296 pounds (= 2 × 148 pounds).
    C)   two forces of equal size acting in opposite directions.
    D)   only one force (148 pounds, as shown by the reading on the scale).
    Ans: C   Section: 4-6

235. The action and reaction forces referred to in Newton's third law of motion
    A)   act on the same body.
    B)   must be equal in magnitude but need not act in the same straight line.
    C)   need not be equal in magnitude but must act in the same straight line.
    D)   act on different bodies.
    Ans: D   Section: 4-6

236. If you drop an object near the Earth's surface it will have an acceleration of 9.8 m/s^2. If, instead, you throw the object downward, its acceleration (after it leaves your hand) will be
    A)   less than 9.8 m/s^2.
    B)   9.8 m/s^2.
    C)   more than 9.8 m/s^2.
    D)   some value that depends on the velocity of the object as it leaves your hand.
    Ans: B   Section: 4-6

237. In which direction would Earth move if the Sun's gravitational force were suddenly removed from it?
A) in a straight line toward the Sun
B) It would continue in a circular orbit.
C) in a straight line directly away from the Sun
D) in a straight line along a tangent to its circular orbit
Ans: D   Section: 4-7

238. Which path would a planet (like Earth!) take if the force of gravity from the Sun were to be suddenly removed?
A) The planet would stop moving altogether since there would now be no gravity acting on it.
B) The planet would move in a straight line tangential to its present orbit.
C) The planet would move in a straight line outward, directly away from the Sun's position.
D) The planet would begin to move in a long ellipse with the Sun at one focus.
Ans: B   Section: 4-7

239. When an object moves uniformly at a constant speed in a circle, the acceleration of the object is always
A) outward, away from the center of the circle.
B) zero; the object is not accelerating, since it is moving uniformly at a constant speed.
C) inward, toward the center of the circle.
D) along the direction of the path, tangential to the circle.
Ans: C   Section: 4-7

240. If a planet moves around the Sun in a circular orbit, how many forces act on it?
A) two forces, one toward the Sun, the other along the direction of motion
B) one force toward the Sun
C) two equal and opposite forces along the direction to the Sun
D) one force in the direction of motion
Ans: B   Section: 4-7

241. How many forces need to be applied to a body in space to keep it moving with a constant velocity?
A) none
B) two unequal forces
C) one force in a direction opposite to the direction of motion
D) one force in the direction of motion
Ans: A   Section: 4-7

242. A body moves through space with a certain speed. How many forces are needed to make this object move in a circle?
    A)   two, one inward, the other outward away from the center of the circle
    B)   only one force along the circular path and tangential to it
    C)   two, one inward toward the center of the circle, the second tangential to the circle to keep the object moving
    D)   only one, toward the center of the circle
    Ans: D   Section: 4-7

243. Newton stated that a constant force continuously applied to a body in space would give it a
    A)   change of position from one state of rest to another state of rest.
    B)   constant acceleration.
    C)   headache.
    D)   constant velocity.
    Ans: B   Section: 4-7

244. If two massive bodies, initially held at rest in space, are released, then they will begin to
    A)   move in elliptical orbits around one another.
    B)   orbit one another in circles.
    C)   move away from each other with constant acceleration.
    D)   move toward one another.
    Ans: D   Section: 4-7

245. Which of the following pairs of forces is an example of an action-reaction pair by Newton's third law?
    A)   for a dog pulling on its leash, the force of the dog on the leash and the force of the leash on the dog
    B)   for a baseball player sliding into first base, the force of the baseball player on his shoes and the friction force of the ground on his shoes
    C)   for a tugboat pulling a barge, the force of the water on the barge and the force of the barge on the tugboat
    D)   for the solar system, the force of the Sun on Earth and the force of the Sun on Mars
    Ans: A   Section: 4-7

246. A diver weighing 138 pounds has just dived up and out from the high board and is doing a back flip before starting to descend towards the water. How much force does the diver exert on Earth while doing the back flip?
    A)   much more than 138 pounds, since Earth is so much more massive than the diver
    B)   138 pounds
    C)   much less than 138 pounds (but more than zero), because the diver has so much less mass than Earth
    D)   zero
    Ans: B   Section: 4-7

247. Earth exerts a force on you as you stand on its surface. What is the size of the force exerted on Earth by you, when compared to the above force?
    A)   zero, you do not exert a force on Earth
    B)   the same
    C)   very small, because your mass is small compared to that of Earth
    D)   twice as large, because of Earth's rotation
    Ans: B   Section: 4-7

248. A rocket that is accelerated by the force from the ejection of large quantities of hot gases represents an example of which physical law originally stated by Newton?
    A)   first law of motion, concerned with state of rest or uniform motion
    B)   law of elliptical motion of planets
    C)   third law of motion, concerning action and reaction forces
    D)   law of universal gravitation
    Ans: C   Section: 4-7

249. The law of gravitation expounded by Newton for the force F between two objects of masses M and m with separation (between centers) of R is given, with G being a constant, by
    A) $F = GMm/R^2$ B) $F = GMmR^2$ C) $F = Mm/GR^2$ D) $F = GM/mR^2$
    Ans: A   Section: 4-7

250. In Newton's law of universal gravitation, $F = GMm/R^2$, which defines the force between Earth with mass M and an orbiting satellite of mass m at a distance R from Earth, G
    A)   is variable, depending on the masses of the two objects.
    B)   depends on the material occupying the space between the two objects.
    C)   is a constant, throughout all measured space and time.
    D)   depends on the speed of motion of the satellite.
    Ans: C   Section: 4-7

251. Suppose that a planet of the same mass as Earth were orbiting the Sun at a distance of 10 AU. The gravitational force on this planet due to the Sun would be
    A)   100 times the gravitational force the Sun exerts on Earth.
    B)   10 times the gravitational force the Sun exerts on Earth.
    C)   1/10 of the gravitational force the Sun exerts on Earth.
    D)   1/100 of the gravitational force the Sun exerts on Earth.
    Ans: D   Section: 4-7

252. Suppose that a planet of 10 times the mass of Earth were orbiting the Sun at the same distance as Earth (1 AU). The gravitational force on this planet due to the Sun would be
    A)   100 times that on Earth due to the Sun.
    B)   1/10 of that on Earth due to the Sun.
    C)   1/100 of that on Earth due to the Sun.
    D)   10 times that on Earth due to the Sun.
    Ans: D   Section: 4-7

253. If the mass of the Sun were doubled, the gravitational force on Jupiter due to the Sun would
    A)   stay the same.
    B)   be four times its present value.
    C)   be sixteen times its present value.
    D)   be twice its present value.
    Ans: D   Section: 4-7

254. The force of gravity between two objects is proportional to the
    A)   difference of their masses.
    B)   product of their masses.
    C)   ratio of their masses.
    D)   sum of their masses.
    Ans: B   Section: 4-7

255. Suppose two asteroids are located at the same distance from the Sun. One asteroid has twice the mass of the other. According to Newton's law of gravitation (and ignoring all forces except those from the Sun),
    A)   the more massive asteroid feels half the force that the other does.
    B)   neither feel any force because they are weightless in space.
    C)   the more massive asteroid feels twice the force of that on the less massive asteroid.
    D)   both asteroids feel the same force, because gravity acts equally on all objects.
    Ans: C   Section: 4-7

256. The force of gravity between two objects is proportional to the
    A)   inverse cube of the distance between them.
    B)   inverse square of the distance between them.
    C)   inverse of the distance between them.
    D)   square of the distance between them.
    Ans: B   Section: 4-7

257. If an astronaut landed on a planet that had the same radius as Earth but four times its mass, then the astronaut's weight on the planet would be
    A)   twice her weight on Earth.
    B)   the same as on Earth, because weight is independent of location.
    C)   four times her weight on Earth.
    D)   sixteen times her weight on Earth.
    Ans: C   Section: 4-7

258. As a spacecraft such as *Voyager 2* moves away from the Sun, the gravitational force on it F varies with distance R from the Sun in which mathematical way? ($\propto$ means "proportional to.")
    A) $F \propto 1/R$
    B) $F \propto R$
    C) $F = $ constant, independent of distance
    D) $F \propto 1/R^2$
    Ans: D   Section: 4-7

259. How strong is the gravitational force that acts on an astronaut in the Space Shuttle in a circular orbit 300 km above Earth's surface?
    A)   exactly the same as when the astronaut is standing on the surface of Earth
    B)   almost zero
    C)   almost (but not quite) as strong as when the astronaut is standing on the surface of Earth
    D)   zero—the astronaut is weightless
    Ans: C   Section: 4-6

260. A person orbiting Earth in the Space Shuttle feels weightless because
    A)   only one force (gravity) acts on her, but gravity also accelerates the shuttle so that the shuttle does not push up on her to create the feeling of weight within it.
    B)   two forces are acting on her in opposite directions, so they cancel and produce the same effect as if no force at all were acting.
    C)   her mass is zero in space, and weight requires mass.
    D)   no forces act on her.
    Ans: A   Section: 4-6

261. If Earth were to be moved to a distance of 10 AU from the Sun, how much stronger or weaker would be the Sun's gravitational force on Earth?
    A)   10 times weaker   C)   100 times stronger
    B)   10 times stronger   D)   100 times weaker
    Ans: D   Section: 4-7

262. Newton's law of universal gravitation is so named because it
    A)   defines the forces between all the planets and the Sun and no other objects.
    B)   was first printed by Universal Press Ltd. of Cambridge, England.
    C)   holds for all objects on Earth, and nowhere else.
    D)   holds for all objects in the universe.
    Ans: D   Section: 4-7

263. Which of the following situations is not an acceptable orbital path for a body gravitationally bound to the Sun?
    A)   straight line ending at the Sun
    B)   parabolic path beginning at the center of the Galaxy
    C)   along ellipse with the Sun at one focus
    D)   circular path with the Sun on the circle
    Ans: D   Section: 4-7

264. Which of the following situations describes an acceptable path for a body gravitationally bound to the Sun?
    A) parabolic path passing through the center of the Sun
    B) circular path with the Sun on the circle
    C) long ellipse, with the Sun at one focus
    D) long ellipse, with the Sun at its center
    Ans: C   Section: 4-7

265. Suppose that an object is discovered moving around the Sun once every 120 years. Which of the following paths is a possible orbit for this object?
    A) hyperbola   B) ellipse   C) straight line   D) parabola
    Ans: B   Section: 4-7

266. Which objects are often found to follow parabolic orbits?
    A) comets
    B) asteroids
    C) no objects—all orbits have to be ellipses
    D) small satellites of the outer planets
    Ans: A   Section: 4-7

267. Which of the following conic sections can be considered to be a closed path in which an object could move in a stable long-term orbit around the Sun?
    A) parabola   B) straight line   C) ellipse   D) hyperbola
    Ans: C   Section: 4-7

268. A hyperbola is
    A) a very skinny ellipse.
    B) the shape of Jupiter's orbit.
    C) an ellipse with major and minor axes equal.
    D) an open curve of infinite length.
    Ans: D   Section: 4-7

269. The first person to derive the elliptical shape of planetary orbits from basic physics and mathematics (not from observations of planetary positions) was
    A) Kepler.   B) Newton.   C) Galileo.   D) Copernicus.
    Ans: B   Section: 4-7

270. Who was the discoverer of the planet Uranus? (As review, identify the planets or moons discovered by the other three astronomers.)
    A)   Galileo Galilei   C)   William Herschel
    B)   Clyde Tombaugh   D)   Johann Galle
    Ans: C   Section: 4-7

271. Who was the discoverer of the planet Uranus?
    A)   William Herschel, 1781   C)   Johann Galle, 1846
    B)   Galileo Galilei, 1610   D)   Clyde Tombaugh, 1930
    Ans: A   Section: 4-7

272. The planet whose discovery was initially made by using measured deviations of other
    planets from regular orbits and the application of Newton's laws of mechanics to predict
    its existence was
    A) Pluto.   B) Mercury.   C) Uranus.   D) Neptune.
    Ans: D   Section: 4-7

273. How was the planet Neptune discovered?
    A)   by mathematical prediction using Newton's laws
    B)   accidentally during a telescopic survey of the sky
    C)   It happened to pass close to Jupiter in the sky and was discovered by an
          astronomer studying Jupiter.
    D)   no one knows—it has been known since ancient times
    Ans: A   Section: 4-7

274. Which planet was "discovered" mathematically using Newton's laws before it was
    discovered observationally through the telescope?
    A) Pluto   B) Mercury   C) Neptune   D) Uranus
    Ans: C   Section: 4-7

275. In the years after Newton published his laws of motion, it was found that the observed
    positions of the planet Uranus did not match the predictions of Newton's theory. The
    reason for this turned out to be the
    A)   perturbing effect of Pluto, which at that time had not yet been discovered.
    B)   perturbing effects of Jupiter and Saturn, whose masses at that time were not
          accurately known.
    C)   perturbing effect of Neptune, which at that time had not yet been discovered.
    D)   weakening of gravity with increasing distance from the Sun.
    Ans: C   Section: 4-7

276. Who predicted the existence of the planet Neptune before it was discovered
    observationally?
    A)   Kepler and Brahe   C)   Newton and Halley
    B)   Adams and Leverrier   D)   Kepler and Galileo
    Ans: B   Section: 4-7

277. The first major astronomical prediction of Newton's theory of gravitation to be
    confirmed by observation was the
    A)   supernova of 1572.   C)   return of Halley's comet.
    B)   discovery of Pluto.   D)   discovery of Neptune.
    Ans: C   Section: 4-7

278. Titan, the largest satellite of Saturn, orbits Saturn with a semi-major axis of 1.22×10^9 meters and an orbital period of 1.38×10^6 seconds (about 16 days). Use the formula in Box 4-4 to compute the combined mass of Saturn and Titan. What is the result, in kilograms?
    A) 4.65×10^{17} B) 4.09×10^{20} C) 5.65×10^{26} D) 7.80×10^{32}
    Ans: C   Section: 4-7 and Box 4-4

279. The Moon produces tidal disturbances on the oceans of Earth. In general, there are
    A)   one high tide and one low tide per month.
    B)   one high tide and one low tide per day.
    C)   two equal high tides and one low tide per day.
    D)   two high and two low tides per day.
    Ans: D   Section: 4-8

280. Spring tides occur
    A)   once per month, at full moon.   C)   most often during springtime.
    B)   twice a month, at full and new moon. D)   once a year, in springtime.
    Ans: B   Section: 4-8

281. The highest of all tides on Earth's oceans occur at
    A)   full or new moon, at times when Moon and Sun are closest to Earth.
    B)   full moon but not new moon at times when Sun and Moon are closest to Earth.
    C)   any time, since they are driven by the action of winds in Earth's atmosphere.
    D)   quarter moon, at times when Sun and Moon are farthest from Earth.
    Ans: A   Section: 4-8

282. Neap tides occur
    A)   once a year, in the autumn, six months away from springtime.
    B)   once per month, at new moon.
    C)   twice a month, at first and third quarter moon.
    D)   twice a month, at full and new moon.
    Ans: C   Section: 4-8

283. The water on the side of Earth that faces away from the Moon experiences
    A)   a high tide because the Moon in effect pulls the solid Earth out from under the water on the far side.
    B)   a low tide because all Earth's water is pulled toward the side of Earth that faces the Moon.
    C)   no tidal force.
    D)   either a high tide or a low tide, depending on the angle to the Sun.
    Ans: A   Section: 4-8

284. How many "tidal bulges" are there on the Earth, due to the Moon's gravitational pull?
    A)   one, on the side of the Earth facing away from the Moon
    B)   four, one facing (almost) directly toward the Moon and the other three at 90 degree intervals from this one
    C)   one, facing (almost) directly toward the Moon
    D)   two, one facing (almost) directly toward the Moon and one facing (almost) directly away from the Moon
    Ans: D   Section: 4-8

285. Sometimes high tides are higher than at other times. What name is given to the highest high tides?
    A) spring tides   B) rip tides   C) neap tides   D) yule tides
    Ans: A   Section: 4-8

286. Sometimes high tides are lower than at other times. What name is given to the lowest high tides?
    A) neap tides   B) pep tides   C) spring tides   D) rip tides
    Ans: A   Section: 4-8

287. What are spring tides?
    A)   any low tide
    B)   any high tide
    C)   high tides that are significantly higher than the average high tide
    D)   high tides that are significantly lower than the average high tide
    Ans: C   Section: 4-8

288. What are neap tides?
    A)   high tides that are significantly higher than the average high tide
    B)   any low tide
    C)   high tides that are significantly lower than the average high tide
    D)   any high tide
    Ans: C   Section: 4-8

289. Suppose I am at the Earth's equator at a time when my location is experiencing a high tide that is higher than usual. What is happening one quarter of the way around the equator at this same time?
    A)   This location will also experience an exceptionally high tide.
    B)   This location will experience a high tide, but it will be lower than usual.
    C)   This location will experience a low tide, but it will be higher than usual.
    D)   This location will experience an exceptionally low tide.
    Ans: D   Section: 4-8

290. When do spring tides occur?
    A)   only when the Moon and Sun line up on the same side of the Earth
    B)   only when the Moon, Earth, and Sun form a straight line, with the Moon on the opposite side of Earth from the Sun
    C)   whenever the Earth-Moon line makes a 90° angle to Earth-Sun line
    D)   whenever the Earth, Moon, and Sun form a straight line, regardless of which side of Earth the Moon is on
    Ans: D   Section: 4-8

291. When do neap tides occur?
    A)   whenever the Earth-Moon line makes a 90° angle to the Earth-Sun line
    B)   only when the the Moon and Sun line up on the same side of the Earth
    C)   whenever the Earth, Moon, and Sun form a straight line, regardless of which side of the Earth the Moon is on
    D)   only when the Moon, Earth, and Sun form a straight line, with the Moon on the opposite side of the Earth from the Sun
    Ans: A   Section: 4-8

292. The Moon rotates synchronously as it orbits Earth, always keeping one side pointed toward Earth, because
    A)   it had precisely this rate of spin, equal to its revolution period around Earth, when it was formed.
    B)   of the effect of the magnetic field of Earth on the magnetic field of the Moon, much like the effect on a compass needle.
    C)   of frictional effects from micrometeoroids in its orbital plane, especially early in its history.
    D)   of the effect of the gravitational pull of Earth on the tidally induced bulge on the Moon.
    Ans: D   Section: 4-8

293. The reason the Moon always keeps one face toward Earth is that
    A)   the impact of asteroids on the Moon early in its history slowed its rotation rate.
    B)   gravitational forces from the Sun act on the tidal bulge of the Moon.
    C)   the Moon was spinning this way when it was formed and has maintained this rotation.
    D)   gravitational forces from Earth act on the tidal bulge of the Moon.
    Ans: D   Section: 4-8

Chapter 5: The Nature of Light

1. Who first showed that light does not travel at infinite speed?
   A) Isaac Newton in 1704
   C) James Clerk Maxwell in 1864
   B) Ole Romer in 1675
   D) Joseph von Fraunhofer in 1814
   Ans: B   Section: 5-1

2. In 1675, Romer measured the speed of light by
   A) timing eclipses of Jupiter's satellites, which appeared to occur later when Earth was farther from Jupiter.
   B) measuring how long it took the light from stars located at different distances to reach Earth.
   C) reflecting light from a mirror rotating at a known speed and measuring the angle of deflection of the light beam.
   D) opening a shutter on a lantern on a hilltop and measuring the time taken for light from an assistance's shuttered lantern to return.
   Ans: A   Section: 5-1

3. The first reliable method developed to measure the speed of light involved
   A) careful observation of the motions of the moons of Jupiter at different times in Jupiter's orbit.
   B) observing the opening and closing of shutters on lanterns on hilltops separated by a known distance.
   C) splitting of light into its spectrum in laboratory experiments.
   D) making careful measurements of the orbital path of the Moon around Earth.
   Ans: A   Section: 5-1

4. The first experiment in which the speed of light was measured precisely involved
   A) timing eclipses of Jupiter's satellites, which appeared to occur later when Earth was farther from Jupiter.
   B) measuring how long it took the light from stars located at different distances to reach Earth.
   C) reflecting light from a mirror rotating at a known speed and measuring the angle of deflection of the light beam.
   D) opening a shutter on a lantern on a hilltop and measuring the time taken for light from an assistance's shuttered lantern to return.
   Ans: C   Section: 5-1

5. The first experiment to measure the speed of light accurately was made by the
   A) French physicists Fizeau and Foucault.
   B) Danish astronomer Romer.
   C) Italian scientist Galileo.
   D) German/American physicist Einstein.
   Ans: A   Section: 5-1

6. A scientist reports the detection of an atomic particle that came toward his experiment from outer space at a speed of 4×10^5 km s^{-1}. What conclusion can we draw from this report?
    A) He has made an error in his experiment, since such a speed is considered to be impossible by all previous experiments.
    B) This "particle" must have been a photon or quantum of electromagnetic radiation of very high energy in order to have traveled this fast.
    C) This result is acceptable since atomic particles can travel this fast, whereas larger bodies are limited to 3×10^5 m s$^{-1.}$
    D) This is an acceptable result for a particle originating from outer space, since particle speed from such regions is unlimited.
    Ans: A   Section: 5-1

7. Assuming that Uranus was at opposition to Earth when *Voyager II* sent back its historic (and magnificent) pictures from Uranus in January 1986, how long did those signals take to arrive, after transmission by *Voyager?* (Use Fig. 4-6 and Table 7-1, Freedman and Kaufmann, *Universe*, 7th ed., and be careful!)
    A)   9066.7 minutes   C)   5 hours 2 minutes
    B)   151.1 hours   D)   2 hours 31 minutes
    Ans: D   Section: 5-1

8. The average distance of Pluto from the Sun is 40 AU. How long does it take for light to travel across the solar system from one side of Pluto's orbit to the other?
    A) 8 min   B) 22 hrs   C) 5½ hrs   D) 11 hrs
    Ans: D   Section: 5-1

9. No matter how close or how far Galileo was from his assistance, he always measured roughly the same time in doing the lantern experiment. Just what time *was* Galileo measuring?
    A)   the time for light to travel from his assistant to himself
    B)   the round trip time for light to travel between Galileo and his assistant
    C)   his own reaction time—that is, the time for him to open his shutter after observing his assistant's light
    D)   the combined reaction time of Galileo and his assistant
    Ans: D   Section: 5-1

10. Radio waves travel through space at what speed?
    A)   much faster than the speed of light
    B)   faster than the speed of light, since their wavelength is longer
    C)   slower than the speed of light
    D)   at the speed of light, 3×10^8 m/s
    Ans: D   Section: 5-2

11. When light passes through a prism of glass, the
    A) different colors are caused by multiple reflections in the prism and interference between the resulting beams.
    B) prism absorbs colors from different parts of the broad beam coming out of the prism, leaving the complementary colors that we see.
    C) prism adds colors to different parts of the broadly scattered beam coming out of it.
    D) different colors or wavelengths of light are separated in angle by the prism.
    Ans: D   Section: 5-2

12. Around 1670, Isaac Newton performed a crucial experiment on the nature of light when he
    A) showed the wave nature of light by passing light through two slits and obtaining a pattern of bright interference bands on a screen.
    B) showed that light that passes through a prism has a spectrum of colors added to it by the prism.
    C) proved mathematically that light can be described by oscillating electric and magnetic fields.
    D) demonstrated that the colors that make up white light are intrinsic, not produced by the glass through which the light passes.
    Ans: D   Section: 5-2

13. Who first proved that light is a wave?
    A) James Clerk Maxwell   C) Isaac Newton
    B) Albert Einstein   D) Thomas Young
    Ans: D   Section: 5-2

14. Around 1801, Thomas Young in England showed that light behaves as a wave by
    A) deriving a set of mathematical equations that described electromagnetic waves that could have different wavelengths.
    B) shining light through two closely spaced slits and observing the resulting pattern of light on a white screen.
    C) reflecting light from a rotating mirror and measuring the deflection in different directions.
    D) shining light through a glass prism and observing the resulting pattern of colors on a white screen.
    Ans: B   Section: 5-2

15. Who was the first person to suggest that light is an electromagnetic wave?
    A) Albert Einstein   C) Isaac Newton
    B) Thomas Young   D) James Clerk Maxwell
    Ans: D   Section: 5-2

16. In the 1860s, James Clerk Maxwell derived a set of mathematical equations that described electromagnetic waves that could have different wavelengths. These waves, which include visible light, have since been shown to
    A)   have no lower wavelength limit, but waves cannot exist with wavelengths longer than about the length of the diameter of Earth.
    B)   have no upper wavelength limit, but waves cannot exist with wavelengths smaller than an atom.
    C)   have no wavelength limit, either short or long.
    D)   exist only over a wavelength range from infrared to ultraviolet radiation.
    Ans: C   Section: 5-2

17. An electrical spark, such as lightning, generates electromagnetic radiations over a wide range of wavelengths. How much longer does a pulse of radio energy take to travel between two detector stations 100 m apart than a pulse of ultraviolet radiation from the same spark?
    A)   much longer, since radio waves have much longer wavelengths and therefore travel slower
    B)   much shorter, since long-wavelength radiations travel faster
    C)   just a little longer, since the high-frequency UV radiation travels faster than the low-frequency radio waves
    D)   The time is identical, since both pulses travel at the speed of light.
    Ans: D   Section: 5-2

18. Visible light occupies which position in the whole electromagnetic spectrum?
    A)   between radio and infrared radiation   C)   between infrared and ultraviolet
    B)   between ultraviolet and X rays   D)   between infrared and microwave
    Ans: C   Section: 5-2

19. In the full wavelength range of electromagnetic radiation, visible light occupies what proportion of the possible range?
    A)   about half the possible range
    B)   two narrow but separate ranges between ultraviolet and infrared radiation, the red and the blue, which mix to give all the other colors
    C)   a very narrow range
    D)   almost the full range between radio and X rays
    Ans: C   Section: 5-2

20. Which one of the following statements is true?
    A)   Visible light takes up only a very small part of the total range of wavelengths in the electromagnetic spectrum.
    B)   Visible light takes up most (but not all) of the total range of wavelengths in the electromagnetic spectrum.
    C)   Visible light takes up all of the electromagnetic spectrum.
    D)   Visible light is not part of the electromagnetic spectrum.
    Ans: A   Section: 5-2

21. Violet light differs from red light in that violet light
    A)   has a longer wavelength than red light.
    B)   travels more slowly (through a vacuum) than red light.
    C)   travels more quickly (through a vacuum) than red light.
    D)   has a shorter wavelength than red light.
    Ans: D   Section: 5-2

22. Visible wavelengths of electromagnetic radiation have a range of wavelengths of
    A) 90 to 130 nm.   B) 1 to 100 nm.   C) 800 to 1900 nm.   D) 400 to 700 nm.
    Ans: D   Section: 5-2

23. The wavelength of infrared radiation is longer than visible light and is usually measured
    in units of micrometers. One micrometer (μm) is
    A) 10^{-3} m.   B) 10^{6} m.   C) 10^{-6} m.   D) 10^{-9} m.
    Ans: C   Section: 5-2

24. Suppose an astronomical satellite observes the Orion Nebula at a wavelength of 1250
    nm. In what wavelength range is this satellite observing?
    A) X rays   B) ultraviolet   C) infrared   D) visible light
    Ans: C   Section: 5-2

25. Suppose an astronomical satellite observes the Crab Nebula at a wavelength of 0.85 nm.
    In what wavelength range is this satellite observing?
    A) ultraviolet   B) infrared   C) gamma rays   D) X rays
    Ans: D   Section: 5-2

26. Choose the correct sequence of electromagnetic radiations, in order of increasing
    wavelengths.
    A)   radio, IR, visible, UV   C)   UV, visible, IR, radio
    B)   UV, visible, radio, IR   D)   visible, UV, IR, radio
    Ans: C   Section: 5-2

27. In terms of wavelengths, gamma rays are
    A)   the shortest-wavelength electromagnetic waves.
    B)   intermediate between radio and infrared waves.
    C)   intermediate between X rays and ultraviolet waves.
    D)   the longest-wavelength electromagnetic waves.
    Ans: A   Section: 5-2

28. Which of the following is an electromagnetic wave?
    A) microwave   B) gravitational wave   C) cosmic ray proton   D) sound wave
    Ans: A   Section: 5-2

29. Which of the following wave effects is not electromagnetic in nature?
    A) microwaves   B) seismic waves   C) radio waves   D) gamma rays
    Ans: B   Section: 5-2

30. What is the one fundamental difference between X rays and radio waves?
    A)   They always come from different sources.
    B)   Their wavelengths are very different.
    C)   Radio waves are always wavelike, while X rays always behave like particles.
    D)   Their speeds in outer space are different.
    Ans: B   Section: 5-2

31. X rays and light are
    A)   different because X rays are made up of particles, whereas light is made up of
          waves.
    B)   the same thing except that X rays have a shorter wavelength than light.
    C)   the same thing except that X rays have a longer wavelength than light.
    D)   different because X rays are made up of waves, whereas light is made up of
          particles.
    Ans: B   Section: 5-2

32. Electromagnetic radiation emitted by a planet has a wavelength of 10 micrometers (1
    μm = 10^{-6} m). What is this radiation called?
    A) visible light   B) infrared radiation   C) radio radiation   D) gamma rays
    Ans: B   Section: 5-2

33. Electromagnetic radiation moving through space with the speed of light consists of
    oscillating
    A)   electric and magnetic fields, always inseparable, always having the same
          frequency and wavelength, and traveling in the same direction.
    B)   electric fields, with magnetic fields occasionally accompanying them, moving in
          the same direction.
    C)   electric and magnetic fields moving in opposite directions along the same line in
          space.
    D)   magnetic fields that over time and distance change to oscillating electric fields and
          back again.
    Ans: A   Section: 5-2

34. What is the wavelength of electromagnetic radiation whose frequency is 10^6 cycles per
    second (10^6 Hz or 1000 kHz, the frequency of ordinary AM radio)?
    A) 3 mm   B) 3 cm   C) 3 m   D) 300 m
    Ans: D   Section: 5-2

35. What is the wavelength of radiation emitted by an FM radio station transmitting at a frequency of 100 MHz?
    A) 300 m   B) 0.03 m   C) 1 m   D) 3 m
    Ans: D   Section: 5-2

36. In a radio wave transmitter (such as that used by a radio or TV station), when the frequency of the signals is increased, the
    A)   wavelength is decreased.
    B)   speed of transmission of the waves is increased.
    C)   wavelength and speed of transmission both increase.
    D)   wavelength remains constant.
    Ans: A   Section: 5-2

37. Which one of these scientists was the last to perform his investigation of electromagnetic radiation?
    A)   Newton (the prism experiment)
    B)   Hertz (production of radio waves)
    C)   Young (two-slit interference experiment)
    D)   Huygens (wave theory of light)
    Ans: B   Section: 5-2

38. White light passes through a prism and separates into a spectrum of colors. All of these colors are recombined into a single beam by means of a lens. What color is this beam?
    A)   white
    B)   black (there will be no light left)
    C)   It will be in the ultraviolet region of the spectrum.
    D)   It will be in the infrared region of the spectrum.
    Ans: A   Section: 5-2

39. White light passes through a prism and separates into a spectrum of colors. A second prism is placed so that only the green light from the first prism falls upon it. After passing through this second prism the light will be
    A) white.   B) green.   C) ultraviolet.   D) infrared.
    Ans: B   Section: 5-2

40. The temperature of a gas cloud in space is directly related to and representative of the
    A)   number of atomic collisions per second within the cloud.
    B)   average speed of its atoms.
    C)   density of the cloud.
    D)   color of the cloud.
    Ans: B   Section: 5-3

41. To what physical parameter is the temperature of a thin gas most closely related?
    A)   average number of collisions per second between molecules
    B)   pressure of the gas
    C)   average speed of the molecules
    D)   mean mass per unit volume, or density, of the gas
    Ans: C   Section: 5-3

42. On the absolute scale of temperature (in kelvins), the zero of the scale corresponds to the
    A)   freezing point of hydrogen.
    B)   melting point of ice.
    C)   mean temperature of space.
    D)   temperature at which motions of atoms and molecules essentially cease.
    Ans: D   Section: 5-3

43. At absolute zero temperature, which of the following conditions holds?
    A)   Electrons stop moving around the nuclei of atoms.
    B)   The motion of atoms ceases.
    C)   Electrons in all atoms move to their ground states.
    D)   The motion of atoms becomes the minimum possible (but not zero).
    Ans: D   Section: 5-3

44. The temperature scale most often used by scientists is the
    A) Celsius scale.   B) Fahrenheit scale.   C) Richter scale.   D) Kelvin scale.
    Ans: D   Section: 5-3

45. The Kelvin scale measures
    A)   temperature referenced to zero at the freezing point of water.
    B)   mass per unit volume, or density, with water having a value of 1.0.
    C)   temperature in Fahrenheit-sized degrees above absolute zero.
    D)   temperature in Celsius-sized degrees above absolute zero.
    Ans: D   Section: 5-3

46. What is the main reason that astronomers almost always use the Kelvin (absolute) temperature scale rather than the Celsius or Fahrenheit scales?
    A)   The temperature of freezing and boiling water are easier to remember.
    B)   Calculations are easier on the Kelvin scale.
    C)   The scale has a physically meaningful absolute zero of temperature.
    D)   The size of each degree (or unit) of temperature is more convenient.
    Ans: C   Section: 5-3

47. A typical but very cool star might have a temperature of 3100°C. On the Kelvin scale, this is about
    A)   2827 K.
    B)   3068 K.
    C)   3373 K.
    D)   3100 K, since Kelvin and Celsius degrees are the same.
    Ans: C   Section: 5-3 and Box 5-1

48. A scientist reports that his measurement of the temperature of the surface of a newly discovered planet is −20 K. What conclusion can you draw from this report?
    A)   The scientist measured only the dark side of the planet, away from the Sun.
    B)   The planet is a very long way from the Sun.
    C)   The planet has no atmosphere.
    D)   The result is erroneous since one cannot have negative absolute temperature.
    Ans: D   Section: 5-3

49. The temperature of a normal, healthy, human being (37°C) expressed on the Kelvin (absolute) scale is approximately
    A) 137 K.   B) 410 K.   C) 310 K.   D) 236 K.
    Ans: C   Section: 5-3 and Box 5-1

50. The normal temperature of the melting point of water ice is
    A) 293 K.   B) 100 K.   C) 0 K.   D) 273 K.
    Ans: D   Section: 5-3 and Box 5-1

51. The temperature of boiling water at ordinary pressures on the Kelvin (absolute) scale is
    A) 373 K.   B) 273 K.   C) 212 K.   D) 100 K.
    Ans: A   Section: 5-3 and Box 5-1

52. On the absolute Kelvin temperature scale, the temperature of freezing water is about
    A) −273 K.   B) +373 K.   C) +273 K.   D) 0 K.
    Ans: C   Section: 5-3 and Box 5-1

53. The range of temperatures in the Kelvin (absolute) scale between the freezing point and boiling point of water is
    A) 10 degrees.   B) 212 degrees.   C) 100 degrees.   D) 273 degrees.
    Ans: C   Section: 5-3 and Box 5-1

54. A scientist measures the temperature change between freezing water and boiling water with a thermometer calibrated in the Kelvin or absolute scale. How many degrees Kelvin (K) will he measure?
    A) 180   B) 273   C) 373   D) 100
    Ans: D   Section: 5-3 and Box 5-1

55. The temperature at the top of the clouds on Jupiter is about 165 K. In degrees Celsius, this is
    A) 0°C.   B) –108°C.   C) –165°C.   D) 438°C.
    Ans: B   Section: 5-3 and Box 5-1

56. The minimum temperature reached on the surface of Mars, –140°C, is represented on the absolute (Kelvin) temperature scale as
    A) –133 K.   B) 153 K.   C) 140 K.   D) 133 K.
    Ans: D   Section: 5-3 and Box 5-1

57. An example of an object that emits no radiation at all is
    A)   an object with the temperature of outer space.
    B)   a blackbody.
    C)   an object made of ice.
    D)   an object at a temperature of 0 K.
    Ans: D   Section: 5-3

58. An ideal blackbody in physics and astronomy is an object that
    A)   absorbs all electromagnetic radiation but emits none.
    B)   emits only infrared light and so looks black to the eye.
    C)   does not emit or absorb any electromagnetic radiation.
    D)   absorbs and emits electromagnetic radiation at all wavelengths.
    Ans: D   Section: 5-3

59. A blackbody is an idealized object that
    A)   reflects and emits light with the same intensity at all wavelengths.
    B)   neither reflects nor emits light.
    C)   both reflects and emits light in a manner determined by its temperature.
    D)   reflects no light and emits light in a manner determined by its temperature.
    Ans: D   Section: 5-3

60. A perfect blackbody is so named because it
    A)   reflects only the radiation falling on it and emits none of its own.
    B)   absorbs all radiation falling on it and reflects none.
    C)   never emits radiation.
    D)   always emits the same amount and color of radiation regardless of its temperature.
    Ans: B   Section: 5-3

61. Two physicists, one in Australia, the other in the United States, find that each has constructed an ideal blackbody in the laboratory. The two blackbodies are made from very different materials. Without conducting tests, they know that the radiation emitted by these two objects will be
    A) different because the amount of light falling on them is likely to be different in the two laboratories.
    B) identical to each other if the blackbodies have the same size, even if their temperatures are different.
    C) different from each other because of the difference in materials.
    D) identical to each other if the blackbodies are at the same temperature but not otherwise.
    Ans: D   Section: 5-3

62. If all stars are considered to be perfect blackbodies, then it should follow that all stars
    A) of the same composition (made of exactly the same material) emit the same energy flux.
    B) of the same size emit the same energy flux.
    C) traveling at the same speed emit the same energy flux.
    D) of the same temperature emit the same energy flux.
    Ans: D   Section: 5-3

63. Figure 5-10 in Freedman and Kaufmann's *Universe*, 7th ed., shows that a blackbody with a temperature of 3000 K emits radiation that peaks at a wavelength much longer than wavelengths in the visible part of the spectrum. This means that
    A) the object is not visible but might be detected with equipment sensitive to nonvisible radiation.
    B) the object, like all blackbodies, emits no radiation.
    C) the object emits visible radiation, but not as intensely as at longer wavelengths.
    D) no visible radiation is emitted, but visible radiation would be emitted if the temperature of the object were increased.
    Ans: C   Section: 5-3

64. Wien's law, relating the peak wavelength λ_{max} of light emitted by a dense object to its temperature T, can be represented by
    A) $\lambda_{max} = \text{constant} \times T^4$.
    C) $\lambda_{max} = \text{constant}/T^2$.
    B) $\lambda_{max}T = \text{constant}$.
    D) $\lambda_{max}/T = \text{constant}$.
    Ans: B   Section: 5-4

65. Cepheid-variable stars pulsate regularly in size. During the contraction part of the cycle, when the star's temperature is increasing, the peak wavelength of the emitted radiation
    A) shifts toward longer or shorter wavelengths at random as the temperature changes.
    B) remains unchanged.
    C) shifts from the visible to the UV part of the spectrum.
    D) shifts from the UV to the visible part of the spectrum.
    Ans: C   Section: 5-4

66. As a newly formed star continues to contract, its temperature increases while the chemical nature of the gas does not change. What happens to the peak wavelength of its emitted radiation?
    A) It moves toward shorter wavelengths (e.g., IR to visible).
    B) It moves toward longer wavelengths (e.g., visible to IR).
    C) It remains constant, since the chemical state of the gas does not change.
    D) It does not change, since it does not depend on temperature.
    Ans: A   Section: 5-4

67. As a new star evolves from cool dust and gas to a hot star, the peak wavelength of its spectrum of electromagnetic radiation
    A) changes from the ultraviolet to the visible range.
    B) changes from the infrared to the visible wavelengths.
    C) increases from the visible to infrared wavelengths.
    D) remains the same.
    Ans: B   Section: 5-4

68. The "color" or wavelength of maximum emission of radiation for a hot, solid body (or a dense gas such as a star) when the body cools from a temperature of several thousand degrees
    A) remains fixed, as the light fades and eventually becomes invisible to the eye.
    B) moves toward the red end of the spectrum.
    C) moves toward the blue end of the spectrum.
    D) remains absolutely constant, depending only on the original color of the body.
    Ans: B   Section: 5-4

69. The average temperature of Mars is lower than that of Earth. If a distant observer measures the infrared radiation from both Mars and Earth, then
    A) the emission from the two planets will peak at the same wavelength, but that from Mars will be less intense than that from Earth.
    B) the wavelength of peak emission from Earth will be longer than that from Mars.
    C) the wavelength of peak emission from Mars will be longer than that from Earth.
    D) it is not possible to predict the behavior of the radiation from the information given.
    Ans: C   Section: 5-4

70. Using Wien's law, which relates the peak wavelength λ_{max}, (1 μm = 10^{-6} m) emitted by a body to its temperature T, what is the peak wavelength of electromagnetic radiation emitted by a piece of iron that is just melting (1538°C)? (See Box 5-2 and Fig. 5-7, Freedman and Kaufmann, *Universe*, 7th ed.)
    A) 16 μm, intermediate infrared   C) 1.04 μm, very near infrared
    B) 1.89 μm, near infrared   D) 1.6 μm, near infrared
    Ans: D   Section: 5-4

71. A star whose surface temperature is 100,000 K emits a spectrum whose peak wavelength is at (see Box 5-2, Freedman and Kaufmann, *Universe*, 7th ed.)
    A) infrared wavelengths.   C) visible wavelengths.
    B) X-ray wavelengths.   D) ultraviolet wavelengths.
    Ans: D   Section: 5-4

72. The human eye has evolved over time so that its peak wavelength sensitivity is about 0.5 µm (1 µm = 10^{-6} m). Use Wien's law to calculate the temperature of blackbody radiation to which the eye is most sensitive.
    A) 14,240 K   B) 0.58 K   C) 580 K   D) 5,800 K
    Ans: D   Section: 5-4

73. You are asked to design a detection system for human beings (or animals) in darkness, using infrared detection. If human beings are at a temperature of about 310 K, what would need to be the wavelength of peak sensitivity of your equipment or cameras (1 µm = 10^{-6} m)? (Hint: Use Wien's law.)
    A) 9.35 µm   B) 0.935 µm   C) 0.00094 µm or 0.94 nm   D) 90 µm
    Ans: A   Section: 5-4 and Box 5-2

74. Using Wien's law (see Box 5-2, Freedman and Kaufmann, *Universe*, 7th ed.), what is the approximate peak wavelength of radiation emitted by (live) human beings, who are (normally) at a temperature of about 310 K (1 µm = 10^{-6} m)?
    A) 9.4 µm   B) 3.1 µm   C) 94 µm   D) 0.94 µm
    Ans: A   Section: 5-4

75. Large quantities of X rays are seen to come from the direction of Cygnus X-1 (see Chapter 24, Freedman and Kaufmann, *Universe*, 7th ed.) with a spectrum that looks similar to that of a blackbody, with a peak wavelength of 1.45 nm (1 nm = 10^{-9} m). These X rays are probably emitted by matter being heated as it falls into a black hole. What temperature is this gas?
    A) 4205 K   B) 2×10^4 K   C) 2×10^6 K   D) 2×10^{-2} K
    Ans: C   Section: 5-4

76. A small particle of interplanetary material is heated by friction from 400 K to 4000 K as it falls into the atmosphere of Earth and produces a meteor or a shooting star in our sky. If this object behaves like a perfect blackbody over this short time, how does its emitted radiation change as it is heated?
    A)   Its intensity rises by a factor of 10, while its peak wavelength becomes shorter by a factor of 10, moving from infrared to red visible light.
    B)   Its intensity rises by a factor of 100 while the peak wavelength of emitted light becomes shorter by a factor of 100, moving from infrared to ultraviolet.
    C)   Its emitted intensity rises by a factor of 10,000, while its peak wavelength becomes shorter by a factor of 10, from infrared to red visible light.
    D)   Its intensity rises by a factor of 10,000 while its peak wavelength becomes longer by a factor of 10, moving from the visible to infrared or heat radiation.
    Ans: C   Section: 5-4

77. The energy flux F from a star is the
    A)   amount of visible light energy emitted by each square meter of the star's surface each second.
    B)   amount of energy emitted by each square meter of the star's surface each second.
    C)   total energy emitted by the star over its lifetime.
    D)   amount of energy emitted by the entire star each second.
    Ans: B   Section: 5-4

78. The total energy flux F of radiation emitted per unit area by a blackbody (e.g., star) is related to its temperature T and a constant σ by which equation?
    A) $F = \sigma T^4$ B) $FT^4 = \sigma$ C) $F^4 = \sigma T$ D) $F = \sigma/T$
    Ans: A   Section: 5-4

79. When a solid body is heated to a temperature T, the total radiated energy flux F from this body per second per unit area is given by (where σ is a constant)
    A) $F = \sigma T$.   B) $F = \sigma/T^2$.   C) $F = \sigma T^4$.   D) $FT = \sigma$.
    Ans: C   Section: 5-4

80. The laws governing the energy flux F and wavelength of maximum intensity λ_{max} of emitted radiation from a hot, dense body whose temperature is T are given by (where σ and a are constants)
    A) $F = \sigma T^2$, $\lambda_{max}T = a$.   C) $F = \sigma T$, $\lambda_{max} = a/T^4$.
    B) $F = \sigma T^4$, $\lambda_{max}T = a$.   D) $F = \sigma T^4$, $\lambda_{max} = aT$.
    Ans: B   Section: 5-4

81. The total energy emitted per unit time at all wavelengths from an object increases by what factor if its temperature is increased by a factor of 3 (e.g., from room temperature to 900 K)?
    A) 27   B) 81   C) 3   D) 9
    Ans: B   Section: 5-4

82. A piece of iron is heated from 400 to 800 K (127 to 527°C). By what factor will the total energy per second emitted by this iron increase?
    A) 2   B) 296.5   C) 4   D) 16
    Ans: D   Section: 5-4

83. The temperature of the surface of the Sun is 5800 K. What would be the surface temperature of a star that emits twice the energy flux (watts per square meter) that the Sun emits?
    A) 11,600 K   B) 8200 K   C) 6900 K   D) 4880 K
    Ans: C   Section: 5-4

84. The energy flux arriving at the Earth from the Sun is known as the solar constant and has a value of 1.37×10^3 watts per square meter. Assuming that the atmosphere absorbs 50% of the energy and that a 5-m^2 roof collector is available to collect energy with a 30% efficiency, how much of this solar energy would then be available for use in the house for water or house heating, etc.? (1 KW = 1 kilowatt = 1000 W.)
    A) about 1 KW   B) about 46 KW   C) about 1 W   D) about 10 KW
    Ans: A   Section: 5-4

85. The Stefan-Boltzmann law relating energy per unit area F emitted by an object to its temperature T, $F = \sigma T^4$, is obeyed ideally by what type of object?
    A)   only hot gases, whose atoms emit and absorb only specific colors (e.g., neon tubes)
    B)   all objects, whatever their color or reflective properties
    C)   a red-colored object that absorbs blue light but reflects red light
    D)   a blackbody, a perfect absorber and emitter of energy at all wavelengths
    Ans: D   Section: 5-4

86. The star Vega has a higher surface temperature than the Sun; therefore (with IR = infrared and UV = ultraviolet)
    A)   Vega emits less IR and more UV flux than the Sun.
    B)   Vega emits less IR and less UV flux than the Sun.
    C)   Vega emits more IR and less UV flux than the Sun.
    D)   Vega emits more IR and more UV flux than the Sun.
    Ans: D   Section: 5-4

87. The star Betelgeuse has a lower surface temperature than the Sun; therefore (with IR = infrared and UV = ultraviolet)
    A)   Betelgeuse emits more IR and less UV flux than the Sun.
    B)   Betelgeuse emits less IR and more UV flux than the Sun.
    C)   Betelgeuse emits more IR and more UV flux than the Sun.
    D)   Betelgeuse emits less IR and less UV flux than the Sun.
    Ans: D   Section: 5-4

88. Pieces of metal are heated by varying amounts in a flame. The hottest of these is the one that shows which color most prominently?
    A) red   B) black   C) blue   D) yellow
    Ans: C   Section: 5-4

89. What changes would you expect to see in the resulting spectrum of emitted light from a piece of metal when it is heated slowly in an intense flame from 500 K to 1500 K?
    A)   The intensity of radiation would increase and the color would change from blue through white to red.
    B)   The intensity of radiation would increase and its color would change from red through white to blue.
    C)   The intensity of radiation would increase and the color would remain a dull red.
    D)   The intensity of radiation would remain constant while the color would change from red through white to blue.
    Ans: B   Section: 5-4

90. When a rod of metal is heated intensely, its predominant color
    A)   remains predominantly red as the intensity of light increases.
    B)   is white, all colors mixed together, as the intensity of light increases.
    C)   changes from red, through orange to white, and then to blue.
    D)   changes from blue through white, then orange and finally red, when it becomes red-hot at its hottest.
    Ans: C   Section: 5-4

91. The hot, dense gas existing in the Sun emits energy
    A)   at all wavelengths uniformly.
    B)   at all wavelengths, with a peak at one particular wavelength (color).
    C)   only at certain wavelengths and no others.
    D)   mostly at the longest and shortest wavelengths, less in between.
    Ans: B   Section: 5-4

92. The radius of the Sun is about 1/200 of an AU. What happens to the flux of solar energy as it travels from the Sun's surface to the Earth?
    A)   It remains constant.
    B)   It increases by a factor of 200.
    C)   It decreases by a factor of 200.
    D)   It decreases by a factor of $(200)^2 = 40,000$.
    Ans: D   Section: 5-4

93. The Sun's surface has a temperature of 5800 K. What will be the peak wavelength of the spectrum of a star that emits twice the Sun's flux of energy?
    A) 2.1×10^{-7} m.   B) 4.0×10^{-7} m   C) 5.0×10^{-7} m   D) 1.0×10^{-6} m
    Ans: B   Section: 5-4 and Box 5-2

94. The important breakthrough in theoretical physics that was first suggested by Planck to explain the shape of the spectrum of a hot body was the
    A) concept that electromagnetic energy was emitted in small packets or quanta.
    B) idea that light is a form of electromagnetic energy transmitted at a constant speed and that there is a continuous spectrum of electromagnetic waves from gamma rays to radio waves.
    C) idea that light traveled at a constant speed, whatever the speed of the source.
    D) formula $F = \sigma T^4$, which can be used to calculate the energy flux emitted by the body at all wavelengths.
    Ans: A   Section: 5-5

95. In the revolution that overtook physics around 1900, the assumption that Max Planck made to solve the problem concerning the spectrum of radiation emitted by a hot blackbody was that
    A) all radiation is emitted in small, discrete packets, or quanta, of energy, each quantum having an energy that is directly proportional to the wavelength of the light.
    B) radiation is emitted as continuous waves whose wavelength is inversely proportional to the temperature of the object.
    C) all radiation is emitted in small, discrete packets, or quanta, of energy, each quantum having an energy that is inversely proportional to the wavelength of the light.
    D) all radiation is emitted in small, discrete packets, or quanta, of energy, whose individual energies are all the same, independent of wavelength.
    Ans: C   Section: 5-5

96. In its interaction with matter, light behaves
    A) only as waves.
    B) alternatively as particles or as waves, switching its properties about once every second.
    C) as both waves and particles, depending on the type of interaction.
    D) only as small particles, photons.
    Ans: C   Section: 5-5

97. In comparing photons of different wavelengths, we find that the energy carried by a photon
    A) increases as the wavelength increases up to a wavelength equal to λ_{max}, then decreases again.
    B) does not depend on its wavelength.
    C) is larger if the wavelength is shorter.
    D) is larger if the wavelength is longer.
    Ans: C   Section: 5-5

98. In what way does a photon of blue light NOT differ from a photon of yellow light in a vacuum?
    A) wavelength   B) color   C) energy   D) speed
    Ans: D   Section: 5-5

99. The energy of a photon of X rays, compared to the energy of a photon of visible light, is
    A)   about the same.
    B)   much lower.
    C)   variable and can be higher or lower under certain circumstances and in certain positions in the universe.
    D)   much higher.
    Ans: D   Section: 5-5

100. Which is the correct sequence of electromagnetic radiation in order of increasing energy of the photons (or quanta)?
    A)   visible light, UV radiation, X rays, gamma rays
    B)   radio waves, microwaves, gamma rays, UV radiation
    C)   gamma rays, radio waves, X rays, infrared rays
    D)   visible light, microwave, radio waves, infrared rays.
    Ans: A   Section: 5-5

101. The energy E of a photon or quantum of electromagnetic radiation is related to the wavelength λ of the radiation by what relation (h = Planck's constant)?
    A) $E = hc/\lambda$ B) $E = h\lambda$ C) $E = hc\lambda$ D) $E = h/c\lambda$
    Ans: A   Section: 5-5

102. If two photons in a vacuum have different energies, what can we say about the wavelengths of these photons?
    A)   The wavelength depends only on color, not on energy.
    B)   The higher-energy photon has the shorter wavelength.
    C)   They have the same wavelength; all photons have the same wavelength, regardless of energy.
    D)   The higher-energy photon has the longer wavelength.
    Ans: B   Section: 5-5

103. A particular photon of ultraviolet (UV) light has a wavelength of 200 nm and a photon of infrared (IR) light has a wavelength of 2000 nm. What is the energy of the UV photon compared to the IR photon?
    A)   100 times more energy than the IR photon
    B)   1/10 of the energy of the IR photon
    C)   10 times more energy than the IR photon
    D)   1/100 of the energy of the IR photon
    Ans: C   Section: 5-5

104. The human eye is most sensitive to light with a wavelength near 550 nm. To what photon energy is the human eye most sensitive?
   A) 2.49 eV   B) 3.61×10^{-19} eV   C) 2.25 eV   D) 1.83 eV
   Ans: C   Section: 5-5 and Box 5-3

105. What is the energy in eV of a photon with the wavelength of Lyman Lα at 121.5 nm in the ultraviolet range?
   A) 1030 eV   B) 1.51×10^{-4} eV   C) 1.02×10^{-8} eV   D) 10.2 eV
   Ans: D   Section: 5-5 and Box 5-3

106. What is the wavelength of the radiation whose photons have 1 eV of energy?
   A) 8.1×10^{-4} nm
   B)   1240 nm in the infrared range
   C) 1.24×10^{-6} nm, gamma rays
   D)   124 nm in the ultraviolet range
   Ans: B   Section: 5-5 and Box 5-3

107. What is the energy in electron volts of a photon whose wavelength is the diameter of a typical atom, about 0.1 nm?
   A)   12.4 keV, or 12,400 eV
   B) 1.24×10^{-7} eV
   C)   1.24 keV, or 1,240 eV
   D)   8.061 MeV, or 8,061,000 eV
   Ans: A   Section: 5-5

108. The early workers in spectroscopy (Fraunhofer with the solar spectrum, Bunsen and Kirchhoff with laboratory spectra) discovered which very significant fact about the spectra produced by hot gases, such as elements heated in a flame?
   A)   The higher the temperature, the greater the red shift of the emitted spectral lines.
   B)   They produce their own characteristic pattern of spectral lines, which remain fixed as the temperature increases.
   C)   They emit spectral lines that move continuously toward the blue end of the spectrum as the gas temperature increases.
   D)   They produce the same set of spectral lines and are hence indistinguishable.
   Ans: B   Section: 5-6

109. Where and by what technique was the element helium first discovered?
   A)   in radioactive rocks from uranium deposits
   B)   in the upper atmosphere of Earth, by studying the aurora, or northern lights
   C)   in the laboratory, by heating chemicals in a flame
   D)   on the Sun, from spectroscopy during a solar eclipse
   Ans: D   Section: 5-6

110. The chemical makeup of a star's surface is obtained by
   A)   measuring the chemical elements present in the stellar wind.
   B)   theoretical methods, considering the evolution of the star.
   C)   taking a sample of the surface with a space probe.
   D)   spectroscopy of the light emitted by the star.
   Ans: D   Section: 5-6

111. Atoms in a thin, hot gas (such as a neon advertising sign) emit light at
    A)   specific wavelengths, depending on the element.
    B)   all wavelengths, with the shape of the continuum distribution depending on the temperature of the gas.
    C)   only visible wavelengths.
    D)   only a specific single wavelength.
    Ans: A   Section: 5-6

112. The spectrum of sunlight, when spread out by a spectrograph, has what characteristic appearance?
    A)   series of separate emission lines, characteristic of many elements, that overlap in certain regions of the spectrum to produce short sections of continuous color
    B)   continuous band of color, crossed by innumerable emission lines
    C)   continuous band of color, crossed by innumerable dark absorption lines
    D)   continuous and uniform band of color from violet to deep red
    Ans: C   Section: 5-6

113. The dark absorption lines in the solar spectrum are caused by absorption
    A)   of sunlight in a layer of pure hydrogen gas overlying the solar surface.
    B)   of sunlight in a cooler layer of gas overlying the hot solar surface.
    C)   entirely by atoms and molecules in Earth's cool atmosphere.
    D)   of sunlight in a hotter layer of gas overlying the cooler solar surface.
    Ans: B   Section: 5-6

114. An astronomer studying a particular object in space finds that the object emits light only in specific, narrow emission lines. The correct conclusion is that this object
    A)   cannot consist of gases but must be a solid object.
    B)   is made up of a hot, dense gas surrounded by a rarefied gas.
    C)   is made up of a hot, dense gas.
    D)   is made up of a hot, low-density gas.
    Ans: D   Section: 5-6

115. The gas in interstellar space between the stars is very tenuous ("thin"). Near a hot star, this gas is heated to a high temperature. Any such hot, tenuous gas emits light
    A)   at all wavelengths, peaking at a certain wavelength or color.
    B)   at no wavelength, since hot thin gases do not emit light.
    C)   only at specific wavelengths ("spectral lines"), and these spectral lines do not change in wavelength as the temperature changes.
    D)   only of specific colors ("spectral lines") whose wavelengths change as the temperature changes.
    Ans: C   Section: 5-6

116. Atoms in a hot, low-density gas (e.g., in a laboratory-type spectral source) emit a spectrum that is
A)   a series of specific colors at the same wavelengths, independent of the type of atom excited.
B)   a series of specific colors, whose positions change as the gas temperature changes.
C)   continuous over all visible wavelengths, with maximum intensity in the blue.
D)   a series of specific colors, unique to the type of atom in the tube, but fixed in position even when the gas temperature changes.
Ans: D   Section: 5-6

117. If light from a hot, dense star is viewed through a cool cloud of gas (see Fig. 5-14, Freedman and Kaufmann, *Universe,* 7th ed.),
A)   the spectrum of the star will still be seen unchanged because the gas cloud is cool.
B)   only specific wavelengths of light will be removed from the spectrum.
C) · the whole spectrum will be reduced in intensity.
D)   the atoms of the gas cloud will add energy to the overall spectrum, producing emission lines at specific wavelengths.
Ans: B   Section: 5-6

118. The star P Cygni (in the constellation Cygnus, the Swan) is surrounded by an extensive low-density atmosphere. Its spectrum is bright continuous,with many narrow, dark absorption lines and a few bright emission lines. The bright, continuous part of the spectrum is produced by
A)   all parts of the star, the stellar surface and the atmosphere, equally.
B)   the hot, dense, opaque gas of the star's surface.
C)   the low-density atmosphere of the star emitting light in all directions.
D)   only the part of the low-density atmosphere that is between us and the surface of the star.
Ans: B   Section: 5-6

119. The star P Cygni (in the constellation Cygnus, the Swan) is surrounded by an extensive low-density atmosphere. Its spectrum consists of a bright, continuous spectrum with many narrow, dark absorption lines and a few bright emission lines. The dark absorption lines are produced by
A)   all parts of the star, the stellar surface and the atmosphere, equally.
B)   only the part of the low-density atmosphere that is between us and the surface of the star.
C)   the hot, dense, opaque gas of the star's surface.
D)   the hot, low-density atmosphere of the star emitting light in all directions.
Ans: B   Section: 5-6

120. The star P Cygni (in the constellation Cygnus, the Swan) is surrounded by an extensive low-density atmosphere. Its spectrum consists of a bright, continuous spectrum with many narrow, dark absorption lines and a few bright emission lines. The bright emission lines are produced by
    A)   the low-density atmosphere of the star emitting light in all directions.
    B)   only the part of the low-density atmosphere that is between us and the surface of the star.
    C)   all parts of the star, the stellar surface and the atmosphere, equally.
    D)   the hot, dense, opaque gas at or near the star's surface.
    Ans: A   Section: 5-6

121. Why is the sky blue?
    A)   The air molecules absorb red light better than blue light, allowing more blue light to reach our eyes.
    B)   The air molecules scatter blue light better than red light, so more blue light reaches our eyes.
    C)   The air molecules scatter red light better than blue light, so less red light reaches our eyes.
    D)   The air molecules absorb blue light better than red light, making the sky appear bluer.
    Ans: B   Section: 5-6 and Box 5-4

122. Chemical pollution often results in large numbers of very small particles being emitted into the atmosphere. What effect, if any, will this have on the color of the sunset?
    A)   It should have no effect.
    B)   It should make the sunset look less red.
    C)   It should make the sunset look more red.
    D)   Its effect depends on the color of the pollutants.
    Ans: C   Section: 5-6 and Box 5-4

123. The basic makeup of an atom is
    A)   small, negatively charged particles orbiting around a central positive charge.
    B)   negative and positive charges mixed uniformly over the volume of the atom.
    C)   small, positively charged particles orbiting around a central negative charge.
    D)   miniature planets, possibly with miniature people, gravitationally bound in orbits around a miniature star.
    Ans: A   Section: 5-7

124. The physical structure of an atom is
    A)   neutrons orbiting an electrically neutral nucleus of protons and electrons under the influence of their intense gravitational field.
    B)   negatively charged electrons moving around a very small but massive, positively charged core.
    C)   positively and negatively charged particles orbiting a small but powerful black hole.
    D)   negatively charged electrons and positively charged protons mixed uniformly in the volume of the atom.
    Ans: B   Section: 5-7

125. An atom is now known to consist of a
    A)   crystalline structure of matter with electrons moving within it.
    B)   small, massive, electrically charged core with electrons surrounding it.
    C)   small black hole with electrons held around it by intense gravitational forces.
    D)   uniform distribution of matter with electrons embedded within it.
    Ans: B   Section: 5-7

126. The overall diameter of a typical atom is about
    A) 10^{-7} m, or 10^2 nm.   C) 10^{-14} m, or 10^{-5} nm.
    B) 10^{-5} m, or 10^4 nm.   D) 10^{-10} m, or 0.1 nm.
    Ans: D   Section: 5-7

127. The typical size of an atom is
    A) 10^{-6} m.   B) 10^{-8} m.   C) 1 m.   D) 10^{-10} m.
    Ans: D   Section: 5-7

128. The physical force that holds the components of an atom together is the
    A)   nuclear force from protons and neutrons.
    B)   centrifugal force on the electrons, caused by their orbital motion.
    C)   gravitational force between the nucleus and the electrons.
    D)   electromagnetic attraction between the nucleus and the electrons.
    Ans: D   Section: 5-7

129. The New Zealand physicist Lord Rutherford and his colleagues in England demonstrated the existence of the very small but massive nucleus inside every atom in which crucial experiment?
    A)   reflection of light from a thin metal sheet
    B)   detection of the motion of electrons around the nucleus by the use of a very powerful microscope
    C)   measurement of the spectrum of light emitted from metal atoms
    D)   deflection, and occasional reflection backward, of energetic nuclear particles from a beam aimed at a thin metal sheet
    Ans: D   Section: 5-7

130. Most of the mass of ordinary matter resides in the
    A)   electrons and the nuclei, shared equally.
    B)   nuclei of atoms.
    C)   electron cloud around the nuclei of atoms.
    D)   energy stored within the atom in electromagnetic forces.
    Ans: B   Section: 5-7

131. The diameter of the nucleus of a typical atom (as measured by Rutherford in the early 1900s) is
    A)   1/2000 of the diameter of the atom.   C)   about one half that of the atom.
    B) 10^{-3} of the diameter of the atom.   D) 10^{-4} of the diameter of the atom.
    Ans: D   Section: 5-7

132. The mass of a proton is
    A)   about twice as large as that of an electron.
    B)   almost 2000 times greater than that of an electron.
    C)   about the same as that of an electron.
    D)   about 1/2000 as large as that of an electron.
    Ans: B   Section: 5-7

133. The proton, the nucleus of the hydrogen atom, has a mass that exceeds that of the electron by approximately what factor?
    A) 10^4 B) 100   C) 2000   D) 2
    Ans: C   Section: 5-7

134. The mass of the neutron (the electrically neutral particle that is one component of the atomic nucleus, along with the proton) compared to the mass of the proton is
    A)   about twice as large.   C)   200 times greater.
    B)   2000 times less.   D)   about the same.
    Ans: D   Section: 5-7

135. By how much is a hydrogen atom heavier than a proton?
    A)   2 times
    B)   2000 times
    C)   1 part in 2000
    D)   A hydrogen atom is lighter than a proton.
    Ans: C   Section: 5-7

136. The majority of the naturally occurring elements in the periodic table that decay radioactively are
    A)   arranged randomly throughout the table, because stability is largely independent of nuclear mass.
    B)   at the low-mass end of the table, since the nuclear mass is too small to maintain stability.
    C)   in the center of the table.
    D)   at the high-mass end of the table, since the large atomic nuclei are unstable.
    Ans: D   Section: 5-7

137. The parameter of an atom that defines its unique position in the periodic table is
    A)   the total number of protons and neutrons in the nucleus.
    B)   its temperature.
    C)   the number of protons in the nucleus.
    D)   its size.
    Ans: C   Section: 5-7

138. The atomic number that designates the position of an element in the periodic table is equal to the
    A)   number of the column in which the element is placed in the periodic table.
    B)   number of protons in the nucleus of the atom.
    C)   number of neutrons in the nucleus of the atom.
    D)   sum of the number of neutrons and protons in the nucleus of the atom.
    Ans: B   Section: 5-7

139. The atomic number of one isotope of iron is 26. How many protons are in the nucleus of this iron atom?
    A)   The atomic number is not an indicator of the number of protons, which could be any number up to 25.
    B)   one less than 26, or 25
    C)   26
    D)   52
    Ans: C   Section: 5-7

140. The property of an atom that uniquely defines how it behaves chemically and fixes its position in the periodic table is
    A)   the total number of protons and neutrons.
    B)   the number of neutrons in the nucleus.
    C)   its physical size.
    D)   the number of protons in the nucleus.
    Ans: D   Section: 5-7

141. According to the arrangement of elements in the periodic table shown in Box 5-5 (Section 5-7 of Freedman and Kaufmann, *Universe*, 7th ed.), which of the following elements would be expected to have chemical properties MOST SIMILAR to those of nitrogen, N, whose atomic number is 7?
    A)   oxygen (O, atomic number 8)   C)   chlorine (Cl, atomic number 17)
    B)   phosphorous (P, atomic number 15)   D)   carbon (C, atomic number 6)
    Ans: B   Section: 5-7

142. Isotopes of a particular element in the periodic table have which nuclear property in common?
    A)   same number of neutrons but different numbers of protons
    B)   same number of neutrons, but different numbers of protons and electrons
    C)   same total number of protons and neutrons
    D)   same number of protons but different numbers of neutrons
    Ans: D   Section: 5-7

143. How many neutrons are there in the nucleus of the isotope ^{18}O of oxygen?
    A) 8   B) 18   C) 9   D) 10
    Ans: D   Section: 5-7

144. How many electrons surround the nucleus of an atom of the isotope ^{18}O of oxygen in its neutral state?
    A) 7   B) 10   C) 18   D) 8
    Ans: D   Section: 5-7

145. The isotope ^{15}N has an atomic number of 7. This isotope has
    A)   7 protons and 8 neutrons.   C)   7 protons and 15 neutrons.
    B)   7 neutrons and 8 protons.   D)   7 neutrons and 15 protons.
    Ans: A   Section: 5-7

146. An isotope of iron, ^{57}Fe, has an atomic mass of about 57 and iron occupies the 26th position in the periodic table. How many neutrons are in the nucleus of this atom?
    A) 26   B) 57   C) 83   D) 31
    Ans: D   Section: 5-7

147. The fissionable isotope of uranium used in nuclear weapons, ^{235}U, whose atomic number is 92, has what total number of protons and neutrons in its nucleus?
    A) 327   B) 235   C) 92   D) 143
    Ans: B   Section: 5-7

148. Which of the following properties is/are the same for both the isotopes ^{15}N of nitrogen and ^{15}O of oxygen?
    A)   the total number of neutrons and protons
    B)   the mass and the number of neutrons
    C)   only the number of protons
    D)   only the number of neutrons
    Ans: A   Section: 5-7

149. ^{12}C is an isotope of carbon. If in a particular nuclear reaction one neutron were added to a nucleus of ^{12}C, the result would be
    A) ^{13}C.   B) ^{11}C.   C) ^{13}O.   D) ^{12}O.
    Ans: A   Section: 5-7

150. One atom of ^{13}C has how many particles?
    A)   13:   6 protons, 1 neutron, 6 electrons
    B)   19:   6 protons, 7 neutrons, 6 electrons
    C)   20:   6 protons, 7 neutrons, 7 electrons
    D)   39:   13 protons, 13 neutrons, 13 electrons
    Ans: B   Section: 5-7 and Box 5-5

151. The specific colors of light emitted by an atom in a hot, thin gas (e.g., in a tube in a laboratory or a gas cloud in space) are caused by
    A)   the vibrations of the electrons within the atom.
    B)   an electron dropping into the nucleus and causing changes in the energy of the nucleus.
    C)   electrons jumping to lower energy levels, losing energy as they do so.
    D)   protons jumping from level to level.
    Ans: C   Section: 5-8

152. A hydrogen atom in a low-density, hot gas gives off what type of spectrum?
    A)   a series of emission lines at uniform wavelength spacings
    B)   a uniform spectrum crossed by numerous dark absorption lines
    C)   a series of emission lines spaced in a mathematical sequence
    D)   a uniform spectrum containing all colors
    Ans: C   Section: 5-8

153. When astronomers look for evidence of hydrogen gas in the spectra of the Sun, the planets, and nearby stars, the positions of the spectral features or "lines" due to hydrogen
    A) are in a very different pattern, depending on the location of the planet or star, and are reproduced only with difficulty in the laboratory.
    B) are always in the same pattern, characteristic of hydrogen gas, as seen in the laboratory.
    C) change systematically, depending on the distance from the source, starting with a laboratory pattern.
    D) are in the same pattern for solar and planetary sources but are very different for stars at larger distances because of absorption of light by the interstellar matter.
    Ans: B   Section: 5-8

154. The Balmer series of spectral lines at visible wavelengths are emitted by a hot hydrogen gas when the electrons fall from all higher atomic energy levels to the
    A) ionization level, or n = infinity.
    B) first excited level, $n = 2$.
    C) next level down for each level (e.g., $n = 4$ to $n = 3$).
    D) ground state, $n = 1$.
    Ans: B   Section: 5-8

155. Light that originates in hydrogen atoms in which electrons have jumped from high levels to the level $n = 2$ are part of which series of spectral lines?
    A) Paschen
    B) There would be a continuum of light, not a series of lines.
    C) Balmer
    D) Lyman
    Ans: C   Section: 5-8

156. The specific sequence of spectral line series emitted by excited hydrogen atoms, in order of increasing wavelength range, is
    A) Balmer, Lyman, Paschen.
    C) Lyman, Paschen, Balmer.
    B) Lyman, Balmer, Paschen.
    D) Paschen, Balmer, Lyman.
    Ans: B   Section: 5-8

157. The Balmer series of visible spectral emissions from hydrogen gas arises from transitions in which electrons jump between energy levels
    A) from higher levels to the second excited level, $n = 3$.
    B) between adjacent levels (e.g., $n = 2$ to $n = 1$, $n = 3$ to $n = 2$, $n = 4$ to $n = 3$, etc.)
    C) from higher levels to the first excited level, $n = 2$.
    D) from all levels to the ground state, $n = 1$.
    Ans: C   Section: 5-8

158. The temperature of hydrogen gas is such that electrons are excited by atomic collisions up to the $n = 3$ atomic energy levels. Emission lines from which spectral sequences result when electrons return to the ground state?
    A) Paschen (IR), Balmer (visible), and Lyman (UV) series
    B) Lyman (UV) series only
    C) Balmer (visible) and Lyman (UV) series
    D) Balmer (visible) series only
    Ans: C   Section: 5-8

159. The strong ultraviolet spectral line emitted by hot hydrogen gas is known as the
    A) 21-cm line.   B) Balmer α line.   C) Paschen α line.   D) Lyman α line.
    Ans: D   Section: 5-8

160. The Lyman series of ultraviolet spectral emission lines from hydrogen gas is produced by electrons jumping
    A) only from the first excited level to the ground state.
    B) to the ground state from all other energy levels.
    C) to the first excited level of the H atom.
    D) from the continuum level to all other levels.
    Ans: B   Section: 5-8

161. The Paschen series of spectral lines from hydrogen gas appear in which part of the electromagnetic spectrum?
    A) ultraviolet region, with wavelengths between 90 and 130 nm
    B) infrared region, with wavelengths longer than 700 nm
    C) radio range, with wavelengths longer than 0.01 m or 10 mm
    D) visible region, with wavelengths between 350 to 660 nm
    Ans: B   Section: 5-8

162. The series of spectral absorption lines in the infrared part of the spectrum that result from atomic transitions in hydrogen atoms in which electrons are lifted from the $n = 3$ level to all other atomic energy levels is known as
    A) the Paschen series.   C) the Lyman series.
    B) ionization transitions.   D) the Balmer series.
    Ans: A   Section: 5-8

163. The wavelengths λ of the emission lines from hot hydrogen gas depend on an integer n according to
    A) n.   B) $1/n^2$.   C) $1/n$.   D) n^2.
    Ans: B   Section: 5-8

164. If the wavelengths of H$_\alpha$ and H$_\beta$, the first two lines of the hydrogen Balmer series, are 656.3 nm and 486.2 nm, respectively, what is the wavelength of H$_\gamma$, the third line of the Balmer series?
    A) 486.2 nm   B) 1875 nm   C) 364.6 nm   D) 434.1 nm
    Ans: D   Section: 5-8

165. What type of radiation is emitted by hot hydrogen gas when electrons jump from the n = 8 level to the n = 7 level of the atoms?
    A)   52,489 m, in the radio
    B)   1.905 µm, in the near infrared
    C)   19.05 µm, in the infrared
    D)   38.9 nm, in the ultraviolet
    Ans: C   Section: 5-8

166. What happens in general when ultraviolet radiation passes through a tube of cool hydrogen gas?
    A)   Radiation at all wavelengths is absorbed, reducing the intensity at all wavelengths uniformly.
    B)   It is unhindered except at the specific wavelengths of the Lyman series, Lα, Lβ, etc, which are absorbed by the atoms.
    C)   It is unhindered except the Lyman Lα wavelength, which is absorbed by the atoms.
    D)   It is unhindered since the hydrogen gas is cool and cannot absorb energy.
    Ans: B   Section: 5-8

167. An atom of hydrogen undergoes a collision with another atom in a hot gas, the energy of collision being about 11 eV. What is the probable outcome of this collision in terms of the atom?
    A)   An electron is excited to the first excited level, n = 2. Its return to the ground state produces a Lα UV photon.
    B)   An electron is excited to the first excited level, and de-excitation to the ground state produces a visible photon of Balmer Hα light.
    C)   An electron is excited to the second excited level, n = 3, and de-excitation generates either a Lβ UV Lyman photon or an Hα visible and a Lα UV photon.
    D)   An electron is excited beyond the ionization level, the atom will be ionized and the electron leaves the atom completely.
    Ans: A   Section: 5-8

168. The Balmer series of hydrogen has a series limit (at 364.6 nm) because hydrogen in the n = 2 state
    A)   is excited by photons of shorter wavelength.
    B)   is ionized by photons of shorter wavelength.
    C)   cannot absorb photons of longer wavelength.
    D)   cannot absorb photons of shorter wavelength.
    Ans: B   Section: 5-8

169. An atom that has had one or more electrons removed is known as
     A) an ion.   B) a molecule.   C) an excited atom.   D) an isotope.
     Ans: A   Section: 5-8

170. Ionization of an atom occurs when
     A)   the nucleus undergoes fission or splitting.
     B)   an electron is removed from the atom.
     C)   an electron is lifted from the ground state to an excited level.
     D)   an electron is allowed to return to the ground state.
     Ans: B   Section: 5-8

171. An ionized hydrogen atom is simply
     A) a helium nucleus.   B) a neutron.   C) an electron.   D) a proton.
     Ans: D   Section: 5-8

172. Balmer constructed his formula for the hydrogen spectral lines by trial and error
     manipulations of large amounts of experimental measurement data. This is somewhat
     like the procedure followed by
     A)   Ptolemy in constructing his model of the universe.
     B)   Kepler in discovering his laws of planetary motion.
     C)   Newton in deriving Kepler's laws.
     D)   Bohr in deriving Balmer's formula.
     Ans: B   Section: 5-8

173. An electron is in the $n = 3$ energy level in a hydrogen atom. To ionize this atom it is
     necessary for the electron to gain a minimum of how much energy?
     A) 1.5 eV   B) 4.5 eV   C) 12.1 eV   D) 13.6 eV
     Ans: A   Section: 5-8

174. An electron is in the $n = 3$ energy level in a hydrogen atom. What can you say about the
     spectral series in which it can participate?
     A)   If it gains energy it can participate in the Lyman Series; if it loses energy it can
          participate in the Balmer Series.
     B)   If it gains energy it can participate in the Lyman Series or the Paschen Series; if it
          loses energy it can participate in the Balmer Series.
     C)   If it gains energy it can participate in the Balmer Series; if it loses energy it can
          participate in the Paschen Series.
     D)   If it gains energy it can participate in the Paschen Series; if it loses energy it can
          participate in the Lyman Series or the Balmer Series.
     Ans: D   Section: 5-8

175. The observed change in wavelength due to the Doppler effect occurs
    A)   whenever the light source is moving with respect to the observer (regardless of direction).
    B)   only when the light source has a radial velocity (toward or away from the observer).
    C)   only when the temperature of an object changes.
    D)   only when the light source has a proper motion (across the line of sight).
    Ans: B   Section: 5-9

176. According to the Doppler effect,
    A)   the wavelength of light is shifted to a shorter wavelength if the source of light is moving toward you.
    B)   the wavelength of light is shifted to a longer wavelength if the source of the light is moving toward you.
    C)   the wavelength of peak emission of light from a source changes as the temperature of the source changes.
    D)   spectral lines are split into two or more wavelengths when the source of the light is in a strong magnetic field.
    Ans: A   Section: 5-9

177. The spectrum of a star shows an equivalent set of dark absorption lines to those of the Sun, but with one exception: Every line appears at a slightly longer wavelength, shifted toward the red end of the spectrum. What conclusion can be drawn from this observation?
    A)   The star is moving rapidly toward Earth.
    B)   A cloud of dust surrounds the star and absorbs the light.
    C)   The star is moving rapidly away from Earth.
    D)   The temperature of the star's surface is higher than that of the Sun.
    Ans: C   Section: 5-9

178. When electromagnetic radiation (e.g., light) is Doppler-shifted by motion of the source away from the detector the
    A)   frequency remains the same, but the wavelength is shortened, compared to the emitted radiation.
    B)   detected wavelength is longer than the emitted wavelength.
    C)   speed of the radiation is reduced below the emitted speed.
    D)   measured frequency is higher than the emitted frequency.
    Ans: B   Section: 5-9

179. The Doppler effect is the change in the wavelength of light caused by the source
    A)   being within a high gravitational field.
    B)   being in an intense magnetic field.
    C)   being embedded in a cloud of dust and gas.
    D)   moving with respect to the observer.
    Ans: D   Section: 5-9

180. The Doppler shift, describing the way in which the wavelength λ_0 of light emitted by a moving object is detected as a different wavelength λ by a stationary observer (with v the object velocity, and c the velocity of light), is given by
 A) $(\lambda-\lambda_0)/\lambda_0 = v/c$.   B) $\lambda.\lambda_0 = vc$.   C) $\lambda - \lambda_0 = (v - c)$.   D) $\lambda/\lambda_0 = v/c$.
 Ans: A   Section: 5-9

181. Hydrogen gas emits a strong spectral line of red light with a wavelength of 656.3 nm (Balmer α line). This emission line is seen in the spectrum of a distant quasar but at a wavelength of 721.9 nm. Applying Doppler's relation, how fast is this object moving with respect to Earth, in terms of the velocity of light, c?
 A) $1/10\ c$ B) $1.1\ c$ C) $1/100\ c$ D) $10\ c$
 Ans: A   Section: 5-9 and Box 5-6

182. An astronomer photographs the spectrum of an object and finds a spectral line at 499 nm wavelength. In the laboratory, this spectral line occurs at 500 nm. According to the Doppler effect, this object is moving
 A)   away from the Earth at 499/500 the speed of light.
 B)   away from the Earth at 1/500 the speed of light.
 C)   toward the Earth at 499/500 the speed of light.
 D)   toward the Earth at 1/500 the speed of light.
 Ans: D   Section: 5-9 and Box 5-6

183. An astronomer observing the spectrum of the Sun finds that the Balmer H_β spectral line ($\lambda = 486$ nm) on the solar equator at one edge of the Sun's disk is blueshifted by 0.0033 nm compared to the same line at the center of the Sun's disk and is redshifted by the same amount on the equator at the other side of the Sun's disk. If this Doppler shift is due to the Sun rotating (try drawing a diagram), then the rotational speed of the Sun at its equator is
 A) 2 km/s.   B) 0.5 km/s.   C) 4 km/s.   D) 1 km/s.
 Ans: A   Section: 5-9 and Box 5-6

184. A police radar bounces radio waves of wavelength 3 mm from the front of a speeding car and measures the Doppler shift in wavelength of the reflected waves. The shift is doubled because of the reflection. What will be the wavelength shift if the speeding car is moving at 60 mph (80 km/h or 22.2 ms^{-1}) (in a 30 mph zone!)?
 A) 0.44 nm   B) 0.88 nm   C) 4.4 nm   D) 8.8 nm
 Ans: A   Section: 5-9 and Box 5-6

185. A star looks predominantly yellow to an observer who is at rest with respect to the star.
    To an observer moving away from the star at 1% of the speed of light
    A)   the star will look predominantly red.
    B)   the star will look predominantly blue.
    C)   the star will still look predominantly yellow, but each part of the spectrum will be
          shifted to slightly shorter wavelengths.
    D)   the star will still look predominantly yellow, but each part of the spectrum will be
          shifted to slightly longer wavelengths.
    Ans: D   Section: 5-9

Chapter 6: Optics and Telescopes

1. Compared to its speed in a vacuum (or in space), the speed of light in glass is
   A)   much greater.
   B)   greater.
   C)   less.
   D)   exactly the same, since the speed of light cannot vary.
   Ans: C   Section: 6-1

2. How does the speed of light in glass compare to the speed of light in a vacuum?
   A)   The speed of light is the same in both.
   B)   The speed of light in glass is faster.
   C)   Depending on the glass, the speed of light can be faster or slower.
   D)   The speed of light in glass is slower.
   Ans: D   Section: 6-1

3. Compared to the speed of visible light in a vacuum (or in space), its speed in glass is
   A) greater.   B) less.   C) exactly the same.   D) much greater.
   Ans: B   Section: 6-1

4. As light passes from air into a dense but transparent material it
   A)   speeds up.
   B)   slows down.
   C)   maintains its speed.
   D)   changes its speed to the speed of sound in glass.
   Ans: B   Section: 6-1

5. Light enters the smooth, flat surface of a glass from the vacuum of space (e.g., a
   spacecraft window). What is the speed of light inside the glass compared to that in a
   vacuum?
   A)   Since the speed of light is always constant by definition, it is the same.
   B)   Since the glass is denser than the vacuum, it is slower.
   C)   The speed will depend on the angle that the light ray makes with the perpendicular
         to the surface, becoming slower as the angle increases, because of refraction.
   D)   Since the glass is denser than the vacuum, it is faster.
   Ans: B   Section: 6-1

6. Light enters a plane-parallel block of glass from the vacuum of space and exits through
   the opposite side (e.g., in a space-borne instrument). What is the speed of light after it
   exits the glass?
   A)   Since it has passed through the glass it has been slowed.
   B)   faster than when it entered
   C)   The exit speed will depend on the thickness of the glass.
   D)   the same as when it entered the glass
   Ans: D   Section: 6-1

7. Which characteristic of a glass lens is the most important in bending light rays to form a focused image?
   A) curvature and shape of its surfaces
   C) diameter or size of the lens
   B) color of the glass
   D) thickness of the center of the lens
   Ans: A   Section: 6-1

8. What is the refraction of light?
   A) the change in direction of a light ray as it reflects from a more dense material than the one in which it is traveling
   B) the absorption of light as it traverses a dense, transparent material
   C) the breaking of white light into its composite colors
   D) the change in direction of a light ray as it crosses from a less dense, transparent material to a more dense one
   Ans: D   Section: 6-1

9. Refraction is the
   A) change in direction of light when it bounces off a smooth surface.
   B) change in the color of light when it enters a transparent material such as colored glass.
   C) bending of light around the sharp edge of an obstacle.
   D) bending of light as it enters a transparent material.
   Ans: D   Section: 6-1

10. Refraction of light at a surface between two transparent substances occurs because
    A) the speed of light is different in the two materials.
    B) some light is reflected at the surface.
    C) the amount of absorption of the light changes at the surface.
    D) the frequency of the light changes at the surface.
    Ans: A   Section: 6-1

11. The phenomenon of refraction, the change in direction of a light beam as it enters a dense but transparent material, is caused by the
    A) slowdown of light in denser material.
    B) speedup of light as it enters denser material.
    C) change in the color or wavelength of light as it enters denser material.
    D) reflection of part of the light at the surface.
    Ans: A   Section: 6-1

12. Which of the following statements correctly describes the refraction of light?
    A)   A ray of light spreads after passing through an opening because of the wave nature of light.
    B)   A ray of light is partially absorbed as it enters the denser material.
    C)   A light ray reverses its direction of travel after striking a mirror surface.
    D)   The path of a ray of light bends as the light enters or leaves a dense transparent medium such as glass.
    Ans: D   Section: 6-1

13. Which way does a light ray bend when it enters the smooth surface of a dense transparent material (from air or a vacuum) at an angle to the perpendicular?
    A)   it bends away from the perpendicular
    B)   it does not bend at all
    C)   it always bends to travel perpendicular to the surface
    D)   it bends toward the perpendicular
    Ans: D   Section: 6-1

14. When light enters the plane surface of a dense, transparent medium from a vacuum at an angle to the perpendicular to this surface, which way does the light ray bend?
    A)   Whatever the incoming angle, the light always travels along the perpendicular to the surface.
    B)   away from the perpendicular
    C)   It does not bend at all.
    D)   toward the perpendicular
    Ans: D   Section: 6-1

15. When a light ray in air or a vacuum enters the surface of a piece of perfectly smooth, flat glass at an angle, it
    A)   reverses its direction and returns back along its original path.
    B)   does not change its direction at all.
    C)   bends toward the perpendicular to the surface.
    D)   bends away from the perpendicular to the surface.
    Ans: C   Section: 6-1

16. As a light ray leaves a glass surface traveling from the glass back into air at an angle to the surface, the light ray
    A)   bends to travel along the perpendicular.
    B)   travels in a straight line.
    C)   bends toward the perpendicular.
    D)   bends away from the perpendicular.
    Ans: D   Section: 6-1

17. The main optical element in a refracting telescope is a
    A)   lens.
    B)   mirror.
    C)   combination of many small plane mirrors.
    D)   prism of glass.
    Ans: A   Section: 6-1

18. Which type of telescope uses a lens as the main optical element?
    A)   radio telescope   C)   Newtonian telescope
    B)   Cassegrain telescope   D)   refracting telescope
    Ans: D   Section: 6-1

19. A typical refracting telescope is made up of
    A)   a long-focal-length lens at the front and a short-focal-length lens at the rear (next to your eye as you look through the telescope).
    B)   a short-focal-length lens at the front and a long-focal-length lens at the rear (next to your eye as you look through the telescope).
    C)   a mirror which gathers and focuses the light, and a lens next to your eye to examine the image.
    D)   two mirrors, one concave in shape and the second one convex in shape.
    Ans: A   Section: 6-1

20. Who was the first astronomer to build and use a telescope to observe the night sky?
    A) Copernicus   B) Newton   C) Tycho Brahe   D) Galileo
    Ans: D   Section: 6-1

21. The major reason astronomers seek funds to build larger telescopes is to
    A)   bring stars closer to Earth.
    B)   measure a wider spectrum of light from stars.
    C)   provide magnified images of stars.
    D)   collect more light from distant objects.
    Ans: D   Section: 6-1

22. The main reason for building large optical telescopes on Earth's surface is
    A)   for national prestige with no scientific reason.
    B)   to collect more light from faint objects.
    C)   to bring astronomical objects closer for more detailed examination by scientists.
    D)   to magnify images of objects and produce higher resolution photographs.
    Ans: B   Section: 6-1

23. The light-gathering power of a telescope is related directly to the
    A)   image quality of its optics (resolution).
    B)   area of its primary mirror or lens.
    C)   focal length of its primary mirror or lens.
    D)   ratio of the focal lengths of its primary element (mirror or lens) and its eyepiece.
    Ans: B   Section: 6-1

24. A refracting telescope has an objective lens of focal length 80 cm, a diameter of 10 cm, and an eyepiece of focal length 5 cm and diameter 1 cm. How much more light will this telescope collect than the average unaided eye whose focal length is 2 cm and diameter is 0.5 cm?
    A) 4   B) 1600   C) 20   D) 400
    Ans: D   Section: 6-1

25. By what factor is the amount of light gathered by the 10-m diameter Keck telescope on Mauna Kea, Hawaii, greater than that gathered by the 2.5-m diameter Mount Wilson telescope?
    A) 4   B) 16   C) 256   D) 2
    Ans: B   Section: 6-1

26. How much more light will be collected by the optics of one side of a pair of binoculars (7×50, with magnification of 7 and an objective lens aperture diameter of 50 mm) compared to that collected by an average human eye with a typical aperture diameter of 5 mm?
    A) 10   B) 2500   C) 100   D) 1.4 or 7/5
    Ans: C   Section: 6-1

27. How many times more light can the 10-m diameter Keck telescope on Mauna Kea in Hawaii collect than an average unaided human eye which has a typical aperture diameter of 5 mm?
    A) 2×10^4 B) 2,000   C) 4×10^6 D) 4
    Ans: C   Section: 6-1

28. Many amateur astronomers have telescopes with mirrors 20 cm (1/5 m) in diameter. In comparison, the largest astronomical telescope in the world is the Keck telescope, with a diameter of 10 m. How much greater is the light-gathering power of the Keck telescope than that of a 20 cm telescope?
    A)   2,500 times larger   C)   7 times larger
    B)   125,000 times larger   D)   50 times larger
    Ans: A   Section: 6-1

29. For many years, the Palomar telescope (5 m diameter) in California was the largest fully steerable telescope in the world; now that honor falls to one of the two Keck telescopes (each of diameter 10 m) in Hawaii. How many times larger is the light-gathering power of the Keck telescope than the Palomar telescope?
A) 2 times larger   B) 4 times larger   C) 1.4 times larger   D) 8 times larger
Ans: B   Section: 6-1

30. A refracting telescope has an objective lens of focal length 80 cm, a diameter of 10 cm, and an eyepiece of focal length 5 cm and diameter 1 cm. What is the magnifying power of this telescope?
A) 10×   B) 8×   C) 16×   D) 80×
Ans: C   Section: 6-1

31. A particular reflecting telescope has an objective mirror with a focal length of 1.2 m and an eyepiece lens of focal length 6 mm. What is the magnifying power of this telescope?
A) 5×   B) 2000×   C) 20×   D) 200×
Ans: D   Section: 6-1

32. A department store sells an "astronomical telescope" with an objective lens of 30 cm focal length and an eyepiece lens of focal length 5 mm. What is the magnifying power of this telescope?
A) 150×   B) 6×   C) 15×   D) 60×
Ans: D   Section: 6-1

33. A particular reflecting telescope has a primary mirror 0.4 m in diameter, 2.0 m focal length, and an eyepiece lens 1.0 cm in diameter and 0.5 cm focal length. What is the magnifying power of this telescope?
A) 400×   B) 40×   C) 4×   D) 80×
Ans: A   Section: 6-1

34. In a correctly focused refracting telescope, the objective lens and the eyepiece lens are separated by a distance equal to the (see Fig. 6-5, Freedman and Kaufmann, *Universe,* 7th ed.)
A)   focal length of the eyepiece.
B)   focal length of the objective minus the focal length of the eyepiece.
C)   sum of the focal lengths of objective and eyepiece.
D)   focal length of the objective.
Ans: C   Section: 6-1

35. What happens when a beam of white light (containing all colors) is passed through a prism of glass?
    A)   Different colors are refracted at different angles to produce a spectrum.
    B)   Selected colors are absorbed so that the remaining light that leaves the prism is colored.
    C)   The speed of the red light that leaves the prism is higher than that of the blue light, leading to a colored beam.
    D)   Selected colors are reflected from the outer faces of the prism, and the light that passes through is colored.
    Ans: A   Section: 6-1

36. When white light passes through a prism or a lens, which wavelengths of light are deflected most by the glass? (See Figs. 5-3 and 6-21, Freedman and Kaufmann, *Universe*, 7th ed.)
    A)   The directions of all wavelengths are changed by the same amount.
    B)   intermediate wavelengths
    C)   longer wavelengths
    D)   shorter wavelengths
    Ans: D   Section: 6-1

37. In a telescope, to what does the term "aberration" refer?
    A)   the magnifying power of the telescope
    B)   the absorption of light by the glass in the lenses
    C)   a fundamental limitation of any telescope to resolve very small details in the image
    D)   a defect in design that blurs or distorts the image
    Ans: D   Section: 6-1

38. Which of the following types of telescope will suffer from chromatic aberration unless very expensive measures are taken to avoid it?
    A)   radio telescope   C)   reflecting telescope
    B)   cassegrain telescope   D)   refracting telescope
    Ans: D   Section: 6-1

39. Chromatic aberration is the failure of a telescope objective to bring all colors of light to the same focus and appears at the prime focus
    A)   in both reflecting and refracting telescopes.
    B)   only in a refracting telescope.
    C)   only in a reflecting telescope.
    D)   in all telescopes, since it is a basic property of light.
    Ans: B   Section: 6-1

40. Chromatic aberration occurs in a refracting telescope when
    A) some wavelengths are reflected from the front surface of the objective lens of the telescope.
    B) light from some wavelengths is absorbed by the lenses, thereby creating false colors of objects.
    C) the lenses bend under their own weight, thereby distorting the final image.
    D) all colors of light do not come to the same focal point.
    Ans: D   Section: 6-1

41. What causes chromatic aberration in the objective lens of a telescope?
    A) different colors refracting through different angles at each surface of the lens
    B) distortion of the image by the shape of the lens surface
    C) blurring of the image by reflection of light back and forth inside the lens
    D) different colors suffering different amounts of absorption by the glass in the lens
    Ans: A   Section: 6-1

42. What is chromatic aberration in a telescope?
    A) Light striking the lens at different distances from the center comes to a focus at different points inside the telescope.
    B) The light of different colors comes to a focus at different points inside the telescope.
    C) Light reflecting from the sides of the telescope comes to a focus at different points inside the telescope.
    D) The objective lens varies in thickness from center to edge, and light passing through these different thicknesses suffers different amounts of absorption.
    Ans: B   Section: 6-1

43. Chromatic aberration, the inability of a simple lens to focus all colors of light to the same focal point, is reduced in refracting telescopes by
    A) bending the lens in its mounting to correct the aberration.
    B) combining two lenses of different shape made from different kinds of glass.
    C) adding a carefully shaped mirror to the lens to produce a lens-mirror combination.
    D) combining two lenses of different shape made from the same kind of glass.
    Ans: B   Section: 6-1

44. Which of the following is not a defect or problem that occurs in a refracting telescope?
    A) opaqueness of the glass lens to certain wavelengths of light
    B) bubbles in the glass lens which scatters light
    C) chromatic aberration, focusing light of different wavelengths to different foci
    D) spherical aberration at the primary reflecting surface
    Ans: D   Section: 6-1

45. Chromatic aberration is corrected in a refracting telescope by
    A)   using a compound lens made of two different types of glass.
    B)   painting the inside of the telescope jet black to minimize reflections.
    C)   grinding the lens surfaces into a parabolic shape.
    D)   using a prism to recombine the colors into white light.
    Ans: A   Section: 6-1

46. When used for photography, which of the following simple telescopes (with film or detector placed at the appropriate focus) will suffer from chromatic aberration?
    A)   refracting   C)   reflecting, prime focus
    B)   Newtonian reflecting   D)   cassegrain reflecting
    Ans: A   Section: 6-1

47. Which of the following DOES NOT represent a major drawback when developing a refracting telescope for astronomy?
    A)   Lenses cannot be made with focal lengths that produce very high magnifications.
    B)   opacity of the glass lens to certain kinds of light, restricting the observable wavelength range
    C)   The lens brings different wavelengths of light to a focus at different positions.
    D)   the presence of defects in the glass lens through which the light must pass
    Ans: A   Section: 6-1

48. The largest refracting telescope in the world is the 102-cm (40 in.) diameter telescope at Yerkes Observatory, built in 1897. Refracting telescopes with larger diameter have never been built because they would
    A)   sag too much under their own weight.
    B)   give too much magnification.
    C)   have too little chromatic aberration.
    D)   be too thick, and suffer too much spherical aberration.
    Ans: A   Section: 6-1 and Figure 6-8

49. How can you increase the magnification of a refracting telescope without decreasing the light gathering power?
    A)   decrease both the diameter and the focal length of the objective lens
    B)   increase the focal length of the eyepiece
    C)   decrease the focal length of the eyepiece
    D)   increase the diameter of the eyepiece
    Ans: B   Section: 6-1

50. At what distance from the objective lens in a refracting telescope is the image formed (i.e., where would the photographic film or electronic detector be placed)?
    A)   immediately behind the lens to collect the most light
    B)   its diameter
    C)   its focal length
    D)   twice its focal length
    Ans: C   Section: 6-1

51. To correct for chromatic aberration in a refracting telescope a corrective lens is mounted next to the objective lens. In this corrective lens
    A)   red light bends more than blue light.
    B)   blue light bends more than red light.
    C)   all colors bend the same amount.
    D)   no bending is experienced by any of the colors.
    Ans: A   Section: 6-1 and Figure 6-7

52. If you want to build a telescope having the least possible amount of chromatic aberration, you should use
    A)   mirrors instead of lenses.
    B)   as thin a front lens as possible.
    C)   a front lens that has been coated with a special material to reduce refraction.
    D)   a front lens that is composed of two closely spaced lenses made of different kinds of glass.
    Ans: A   Section: 6-2

53. When a ray of light strikes a smooth mirror surface at an angle to the perpendicular, the ray is reflected
    A)   at various angles, depending on wavelength.
    B)   back along its original (incoming) path.
    C)   so that it travels along the perpendicular to the surface of the mirror.
    D)   on the "other" side of the perpendicular but at the same angle as the incoming ray.
    Ans: D   Section: 6-2

54. In the reflection of a light beam from a flat mirror, the angle between the incident and reflected beams relative to the perpendicular to the surface of the mirror is
    A)   equal to the angle between the incident beam and the perpendicular.
    B)   equal to ½ the angle between the incident beam and the perpendicular.
    C)   always a right angle, or 90°.
    D)   twice the angle between incident beam and the perpendicular.
    Ans: D   Section: 6-2

55. In the reflection of a beam of light from a flat surface, the relationship between the angle of incidence i between the perpendicular to the surface and the incident beam and the angle of reflection r between the perpendicular and the reflected beam is
   A) r is equal to $2i$.
   B)   The reflected ray always follows the perpendicular direction from the reflecting surface.
   C) r is equal to $i/2$.
   D) r is equal to i.
   Ans: D   Section: 6-2

56. A light ray strikes a smooth surface of glass at an angle α to the perpendicular. What angle will the reflected ray make with the perpendicular to the surface?
   A) 2α on the opposite side of the perpendicular to the incident ray
   B) $0°$, the ray will always reflect along the perpendicular, a condition necessary for the focusing of light.
   C)   the same angle α on the opposite side of the perpendicular to the incident ray
   D)   the same angle α on the same side of the perpendicular, returning along the incident direction
   Ans: C   Section: 6-2

57. The prime focus of a reflecting telescope is reached by light after
   A)   refraction through one lens and reflection at one mirror.
   B)   refraction at one lens.
   C)   reflection at two mirrors.
   D)   one reflection.
   Ans: D   Section: 6-2

58. A Newtonian telescope uses
   A)   two curved mirrors.
   B)   several mirrors; some curved, some flat, to guide light to a fixed focus with respect to Earth.
   C)   one curved mirror and one flat mirror at a 45° angle to the curved mirror.
   D)   only one mirror.
   Ans: C   Section: 6-2

59. A Newtonian telescope consists of which of the following combinations of optical elements?
   A)   one concave focusing mirror
   B)   two lenses, producing an image the correct way around
   C)   two curved mirrors, one concave, the second convex
   D)   one concave and one flat mirror
   Ans: D   Section: 6-2

60. How is a Newtonian reflecting telescope constructed?
    A)   A series of mirrors channel the light to a remote location.
    B)   It has a concave primary mirror and flat, diagonal secondary mirror.
    C)   A concave primary mirror, with a concave secondary mirror that reflects light back through a hole in the primary mirror.
    D)   A concave primary mirror, with a convex secondary mirror that reflects light back through a hole in the primary mirror.
    Ans: B   Section: 6-2

61. A reflecting telescope in which light is reflected by one curved mirror and a second plane mirror at 45° to the original beam, to reach a focus at the side of the telescope, is being used at its
    A)   Newtonian focus.   C)   prime focus.
    B)   out-of-focus position.   D)   Cassegrain focus.
    Ans: A   Section: 6-2

62. When light from the concave primary mirror of a telescope is reflected by a small secondary mirror through a hole in the primary, it is called
    A)   prime focus.   C)   Cassegrain focus.
    B)   Newtonian focus.   D)   Coude focus.
    Ans: C   Section: 6-2

63. A Cassegrain reflecting telescope is constructed from a
    A)   concave primary mirror and a convex secondary mirror that reflects light back through a hole in the primary mirror.
    B)   series of mirrors that channel the light to a remote location.
    C)   concave primary mirror and a concave secondary mirror that reflects light back through a hole in the primary mirror.
    D)   concave primary mirror and a flat, diagonal secondary mirror.
    Ans: A   Section: 6-2

64. The prime focus cage of a telescope whose primary mirror is 3 m in diameter has a diameter of 0.5 meters. What fraction of the incoming light is obstructed by this cage?
    A) about 3%   B) about 44%   C) about 1/6, or 17%   D) about 36%
    Ans: A   Section: 6-2

65. If part of the primary mirror of a reflecting telescope is blocked off by a small screen, which of the following characteristics of the final image is affected?
    A)   Although the brightness is unaffected, the size of the image will be reduced.
    B)   A part of the image is missing.
    C)   Only the brightness is reduced.
    D)   Depending on which part of the mirror is obscured, the color of the image is affected.
    Ans: C   Section: 6-2

66. A particular telescope is set up to use the Coude focus. What arrangement of mirrors is used to bring the light to this focus?
    A)   A concave primary mirror and concave secondary mirror reflect light back through a hole in the primary mirror.
    B)   A series of mirrors channel the light to a remote and fixed location.
    C)   a concave primary mirror and flat, diagonal secondary mirror
    D)   A concave primary mirror and convex secondary mirror reflect light back through a hole in the primary mirror.
    Ans: B   Section: 6-2 and Figure 6-11

67. The magnifying power of a reflecting telescope, in terms of the focal length F of the primary mirror and the focal length f the eyepiece, (with F and f measured in the same units), is
    A) fF.   B) f/F.   C) F/f^{2} D) F/f.
    Ans: D   Section: 6-2

68. What is the magnification of a Newtonian telescope with a primary mirror of diameter 0.25 m and focal length of 4 m when used with an eyepiece of focal length 25 mm and an optical diameter of 2.5 mm?
    A) 100   B) 160   C) 10   D) 1600
    Ans: B   Section: 6-2

69. Which of the following statements is NOT correct in describing a disadvantage of large refracting telescopes when compared to large reflecting telescopes?
    A)   Air bubbles in the lens are more of a problem in refracting than reflective telescopes.
    B)   Sagging of the primary optical element under its own weight is a problem with refracting telescopes but not with reflecting telescopes.
    C)   Refracting telescopes suffer from spherical aberration and reflecting telescopes do not.
    D)   Refracting telescopes suffer from chromatic abberation and reflective telescopes do not.
    Ans: C   Section: 6-2

70. A reflecting telescope used at prime focus does not suffer from chromatic aberration because
    A)   regardless of color, all wavelengths of light are reflected by the same amount.
    B)   the aluminum coating on the mirror absorbs light from all wavelengths except the range of interest to the astronomer.
    C)   the lens is perfectly formed so all colors of light travel through the lens along the same path.
    D)   the light has passed through only one lens.
    Ans: A   Section: 6-2

71. To produce the sharpest images of very distant objects, the best shape for the cross-section of a large astronomical mirror should be
    A) elliptical.   B) spherical.   C) perfectly flat and smooth.   D) parabolic.
    Ans: D   Section: 6-2

72. In order to produce images of distant objects, the best shape for the curvature of the polished surface of an astronomical mirror is
    A)   elliptical.
    B)   spherical.
    C)   flat, since the light comes from infinity.
    D)   paraboloidal.
    Ans: D   Section: 6-2

73. A spherical mirror suffers from spherical aberration because
    A)   the starlight is distorted by turbulence in the Earth's atmosphere.
    B)   the mirror sags under its own weight, distorting the image.
    C)   different parts of the mirror focus the light at different distances from the mirror.
    D)   different colors are focused at different distances from the mirror.
    Ans: C   Section: 6-2

74. Spherical aberration can be corrected in a reflecting telescope by
    A)   using light of only one color.
    B)   grinding the mirror to a parabolic shape.
    C)   grinding the mirror to an elliptical shape.
    D)   grinding the mirror to a more accurate spherical curve.
    Ans: B   Section: 6-2

75. The reason the primary mirror of an astronomical telescope is often polished to a parabolic shape is
    A)   to avoid the chromatic aberration that would be produced by an equivalent spherical mirror.
    B)   that it is lighter and easier to mount in a telescope.
    C)   that it is easier to produce, even though the resulting mirror will produce more spherical aberration than an equivalent spherical mirror.
    D)   to avoid spherical aberration.
    Ans: D   Section: 6-2

76. At the present time (2004), the largest optical telescope in the world has a primary mirror with a diameter of
    A) 6.0 m.   B) 11.0 m.   C) 10.0 m.   D) 6.5 m.
    Ans: B   Section: 6-2

77. At the present time (2004), the largest-diameter telescope mirror in the world is in the
    A)   Hobby-Eberly telescope in the Davis Mountains, Texas.
    B)   Hale telescope on Mt. Palomar, California.
    C)   Special Astrophysical Observatory, Russia.
    D)   Keck telescope on Mauna Kea, Hawaii.
    Ans: A   Section: 6-2

78. At the present time, the telescope with the largest-diameter mirror in the world that is fully steerable and can be pointed to essentially all parts of the sky is in the
    A)   Special Astrophysical Observatory, Russia.
    B)   Hale telescope on Mt. Palomar, California.
    C)   Hobby-Eberly telescope in the Davis Mountains, Texas.
    D)   Keck telescope on Mauna Kea, Hawaii.
    Ans: D   Section: 6-2

79. A Cassegrain telescope has a primary mirror with a 5-m diameter and a 5-cm diameter hole through the primary mirror. By what percent is the light gathering power of the mirror reduced because of the hole?
    A) 0.01 %   B) 1 %   C) 20 %   D) 50 %
    Ans: A   Section: 6-2

80. In order to correct for spherical aberration
    A)   a spherical mirror is used with a correcting lens.
    B)   a parabolic mirror is used with a correcting lens.
    C)   an elliptical mirror is used *without* a correcting lens.
    D)   an elliptical mirror is used with a correcting lens.
    Ans: A   Section: 6-2

81. In telescopes, the resolution is worse for
    A)   larger diameter lenses or mirrors and shorter wavelength light (or other electromagnetic radiation).
    B)   smaller diameter lenses or mirrors and longer wavelength light (or other electromagnetic radiation).
    C)   smaller diameter lenses or mirrors and shorter wavelength light (or other electromagnetic radiation).
    D)   larger diameter lenses or mirrors and longer wavelength light (or other electromagnetic radiation).
    Ans: B   Section: 6-3

82. Which of the following characteristics of an astronomical telescope is most important for determining the angular resolution?
    A)   the focal length of the eyepiece
    B)   the magnifying power of the telescope
    C)   the diameter of the objective lens or mirror
    D)   the focal length of the objective lens or mirror
    Ans: C   Section: 6-3

83. Assuming that all effects due to variations in Earth's atmosphere could be removed (with adaptive optics) from images produced by a telescope, what diameter of telescope would be needed to see two bright (laser) headlights of wavelength 650 nm separated by 2 m on a vehicle on the Moon? (Assume the Earth-Moon distance to be 400,000 km.)
    A) 0.2 m   B) 2000 m   C) 2 m   D) 200 m
    Ans: D   Section: 6-3 and Box 1-2

84. If all effects caused by Earth's atmospheric variations (seeing) could be removed from the visible image of a star on one of the 10-m diameter Keck telescopes on Hawaii, what would be the angular resolution achievable by this telescope in arcseconds for light of wavelength 500 nm? (1 nm = 10^{-9} m)
    A) 0.00125 arcsec   B) 0.125 arcsec   C) 12.5 arcsec   D) 0.0125 arcsec
    Ans: D   Section: 6-3

85. In single-telescope astronomical systems, either optical or radio, the
    A)   longer the focal length of the primary mirror, the sharper the image.
    B)   longer the wavelength, the sharper the image.
    C)   smaller the main-mirror aperture in general, the sharper the image.
    D)   larger the main mirror aperture in general, the sharper the image.
    Ans: D   Section: 6-3

86. At the extreme limit of magnification, the major cause of blurred and unsharp images of objects observed through very large telescopes is
    A)   the poor tracking capabilities of modern telescopes.
    B)   air turbulence in the Earth's atmosphere.
    C)   the poor optical polish achievable on large mirrors.
    D)   the clumsiness of the telescope operator.
    Ans: B   Section: 6-3

87. What does the word "seeing" mean to an astronomer using a telescope?
    A)   The twinkling and blurring of the image due to air currents in the Earth's atmosphere.
    B)   Blurring of images caused by wind-induced telescope vibrations.
    C)   The combined effects of aberrations in the telescope, particularly spherical and chromatic aberration.
    D)   The amount of haze or thin cloud in the atmosphere that affects the brightness of the telescope image.
    Ans: A   Section: 6-3

88. If one observatory site is described as having better seeing than another observatory site, what is it that is better?
    A)   winds are lighter, reducing vibrations in the telescope
    B)   clearer nights
    C)   sky is more transparent (less haze), giving brighter images
    D)   less air turbulence, causing less twinkling and blurring of the images
    Ans: D   Section: 6-3

89. It is difficult to improve the angular resolution of optical telescopes located on the surface of the Earth beyond a certain limit because
    A)   we would need to build larger telescopes and this is very expensive.
    B)   spherical mirrors suffer from too much aberration.
    C)   air turbulence distorts the star images more than does the telescope optics.
    D)   large telescopes are always reflecting telescopes and these suffer from too much chromatic aberration.
    Ans: C   Section: 6-3

90. The sharpest images of stars that can be formed by a single large ground-based visible-light telescope are of the order of what angular size?
    A)   about 10^{-3} arcsecond   C)   about 0.5 arcsecond
    B)   about 1 arcminute   D)   about 1 degree
    Ans: C   Section: 6-3

91. To reduce the effects of bad seeing on astronomical images, the best Earth-based sites for modern large astronomical telescopes are
    A)   at sea level. The air is less turbulent and the presence of water stabilizes the air.
    B)   the tops of high mountains.
    C)   the downwind side of mountain ranges. Smooth airflow produces clear air and stable images.
    D)   near large cities. The warm air from human activity serves to stabilize the overlying atmosphere.
    Ans: B   Section: 6-3

92. Why was adaptive optics developed?
    A)   to prevent distortion of mirrors by the vacuum of space
    B)   to prevent distortion by sagging in very thin, lightweight mirrors
    C)   to compensate for spherical aberration
    D)   to compensate for image distortion caused by Earth's atmosphere
    Ans: D   Section: 6-3

93. In a telescope that uses adaptive optics to correct for atmospheric distortion of images or "seeing,"
    A)   computer-controlled motors adjust the tilt and shape of mirrors within the telescope many times per second.
    B)   computer-controlled motors rapidly adjust the orientation of the individual mirrors in a multiple-mirror telescope (MMT).
    C)   a corrector lens compensates for image distortion by having its shape electronically controlled.
    D)   the light rays are focused electronically, without the use of lenses or mirrors.
    Ans: A   Section: 6-3

94. The technique used by astronomers to increase the amount of detail that can be seen or photographed through telescopes is
    A)   antireflective coatings, where the mirror is coated with a substance such as fluorite to reduce the amount of reflected light.
    B)   increased size, where mirrors are made far larger than was possible before, e.g., 8 to 10 meters in diameter and larger.
    C)   adaptive optics, where the tilt and shape of mirrors in the telescope are changed many times per second to compensate for atmospheric turbulence.
    D)   multiple-mirror telescopes, where several mirrors are mounted together in a single telescope to simulate the performance of a single, very large mirror.
    Ans: C   Section: 6-3

95. How is the VLT (Very Large Telescope), installed at the European Southern Observatory, designed?
    A)   A single, thin, 20-m-diameter primary mirror has its shape changed and controlled by a computer.
    B)   The light from four 8-m telescopes, which are spread over a distance of 200 m, will eventually be combined into a single image.
    C)   A dish of mercury 100 m in diameter is rotated and thus forms a very large parabolic mirror.
    D)   Six thin, 10-m-diameter mirrors are arranged in a circle to simulate a single, 30-m-diameter mirror.
    Ans: B   Section: 6-3

96. What angular resolution will eventually be possible with the European Southern Observatory's Very Large Telescope (VLT) when light from all four telescopes are combined?
    A)   1/10,000 arcsecond
    B)   1/100 arcsecond
    C)   1/1000 arcsecond
    D)   1/5 arcsecond (limited by atmospheric turbulence, or "seeing")
    Ans: C   Section: 6-3

97. What factor has seriously reduced the effectiveness of the telescopes around the world, such as those at Mt. Palomar in California and at Kitt Peak, near Tucson, Arizona, over the last few years?
    A)   tarnishing of the mirror surface by air pollution
    B)   cracking of the mirror by earthquakes
    C)   bending of the mirror surface from repeated exposure to the cold night air
    D)   light scattering in the atmosphere from nearby cities
    Ans: D   Section: 6-3

98. You are using a telescope with a diameter of 20 cm and you are observing with light of wavelength 650 nm. You are looking at the word "astronomy" on a distant signboard. What minimum angular spacing (in arcseconds) between adjacent letters will ensure that the entire word can be seen clearly?
    A) 0.25   B) 0.50   C) 0.75   D) 1.0
    Ans: D   Section: 6-3

99. Suppose the four 8.2-m mirrors of the VLT were replaced with 10-m mirrors, but they were still spread out over a distance of 200 m. The combined light-gathering power would be equivalent to that of a single telescope of what diameter?
    A) 16.4 m   B) 20 m   C) 40 m   D) 200 m
    Ans: B   Section: 6-3

100. The resolution in a telescope is best for which segment of the visible spectrum?
    A)   red
    B)   green
    C)   blue
    D)   The resolution is the same all across the visible spectrum.
    Ans: C   Section: 6-3

101. The detector that in many instances has replaced the photographic plate for astronomical photography is the
    A)   diffraction grating.   C)   interferometer.
    B)   CCD (charge-coupled device).   D)   PMT (photomultiplier tube).
    Ans: B   Section: 6-4

102. The CCD (charge-coupled device) is a(n)
    A) detector in which a small electric current is controlled by a bimetallic strip that expands and contracts in response to infrared radiation.
    B) array of small light-sensitive cells that can be used in place of photographic film to obtain a picture.
    C) electronic filter to single out one wavelength or set of wavelengths for studying astronomical objects.
    D) array of electrodes used on spacecraft to detect charged particles such as electrons and protons.
    Ans: B   Section: 6-4

103. The charged-coupled device (CCD), now used extensively for astronomical imaging, works on what principle?
    A) Light generates electrical charge on a computer-readable, multi-element array of detectors.
    B) Light from the image modifies the plastic material on a disk, which can then be read on a standard video compact disk (CD) player.
    C) Light from the image is detected by new, high-sensitivity, fine-grain, automatically processed film.
    D) A single optical detector generates an electrical signal as it is scanned quickly across the astronomical image.
    Ans: A   Section: 6-4

104. What percentage of the light falling on a piece of photographic film is typically wasted (does not contribute to the formation of the image)?
    A) 2%   B) 45%   C) 18%   D) 98%
    Ans: D   Section: 6-4

105. Approximately what percentage of the light falling on a typical photographic plate from a telescope is actually used to record an image on this plate?
    A) 25%   B) 50%   C) 98%   D) 2%
    Ans: D   Section: 6-4

106. The fraction of incoming photons recorded by a charge-coupled device (CCD) is greater than that recorded by a typical photographic plate by what factor?
    A) 10 times   B) twice   C) more than 100 times   D) 35 times
    Ans: D   Section: 6-4

107. What happens if adjacent pixels in a CCD become so close together that the angular separation between them is smaller than the resolution limit of the telescope being used?
    A)   The electronic signals from these adjacent pixels will really represent a single signal representing the average intensities of this two-pixel region.
    B)   The resolution of the picture will improve dramatically.
    C)   The CCD can no longer be used on this instrument.
    D)   Only the long-wavelength images will remain sharp.
    Ans: A   Section: 6-4

108. A spectrograph is usually used in astronomy to measure the
    A)   variation of the mass of an object as it moves through space.
    B)   distribution of light intensity among the various colors.
    C)   vibration of Earth following an earthquake.
    D)   brightness of light at one specific color.
    Ans: B   Section: 6-5

109. In a spectrograph, a glass prism has a number of disadvantages compared to a diffraction grating. Which of the following is not one of these disadvantages?
    A)   A prism cannot be used with a CCD detector and a computer.
    B)   A prism is opaque to ultraviolet light.
    C)   A prism reduces the light intensity unevenly over the spectrum.
    D)   A prism does not disperse the colors uniformly.
    Ans: A   Section: 6-5

110. In spectroscopy, a diffraction grating is a
    A)   screen placed at the focus of a telescope to provide a calibrated grid on photographs.
    B)   source of light that provides calibration lines alongside the measured spectrum.
    C)   piece of glass or metal on which many closely spaced grooves have been cut.
    D)   prism of very pure glass through which light can pass.
    Ans: C   Section: 6-5

111. One major difference between radio waves and light is that
    A)   radio waves have shorter wavelengths.
    B)   radio waves are electromagnetic, unlike light.
    C)   light waves are electromagnetic, unlike radio waves.
    D)   radio waves have lower frequencies.
    Ans: D   Section: 6-6

112. The first nonvisible radiation detected from outer space was
    A) X rays.   B) radio waves.   C) gamma rays.   D) ultraviolet (UV) light.
    Ans: B   Section: 6-6

113. The first person to detect and identify radio emissions coming from deep space was
     A) Karl Jansky.   B) Edwin Hubble.   C) Thomas Edison.   D) Galileo.
     Ans: A   Section: 6-6

114. The first astronomical radio source was detected and identified in the year
     A) 1932.   B) 1945.   C) 1897.   D) 1967.
     Ans: A   Section: 6-6

115. The first astronomical radio source, identified by Karl Jansky during measurements of sources of radio noise, was
     A) the Sun.   B) Jupiter.   C) the Orion Nebula.   D) the center of our galaxy.
     Ans: D   Section: 6-6

116. The first true radio telescope, built by Grote Reber to map radio emissions from the center of the Milky Way, was built in
     A) 1980.   B) 1946.   C) 1932.   D) 1936.
     Ans: D   Section: 6-6

117. The first extraterrestrial radio source detected was
     A) the Sun.   B) the Moon.   C) the center of our galaxy.   D) Jupiter.
     Ans: C   Section: 6-6

118. The first radio energy to be detected from outer space came from the direction of
     A)   a quasar.
     B)   the Moon.
     C)   the Sun.
     D)   the Milky Way galaxy, near Sagittarius.
     Ans: D   Section: 6-6

119. Astronomers began to use radio telescopes to investigate the universe
     A)   during the 1920s.
     B)   during the 1980s, with the development of CCD detectors.
     C)   in the early 1960s, with the development of satellites.
     D)   in the late 1940's, shortly after World War II.
     Ans: D   Section: 6-6

120. How does angular resolution for a given diameter of telescope depend on wavelength?
     A)   Angular resolution worsens as wavelength increases.
     B)   Angular resolution improves as wavelength increases.
     C)   Angular resolution may improve or worsen as wavelength increases, depending on other factors such as intensity and spectral range (e.g., optical, infrared, radio).
     D)   Angular resolution depends only on the diameter of the telescope and is independent of wavelength.
     Ans: A   Section: 6-6

121. The angular resolution attainable with a radio telescope, compared to that attainable with an optical telescope of the same diameter, is significantly inferior because
    A) the wavelength of radio waves is larger than that of visible light.
    B) it is difficult to make a reflector for radio waves since these waves penetrate most materials.
    C) the Earth's atmosphere disturbs radio waves from space much more than it does visible light.
    D) radio wavelengths are smaller than visible wavelengths, making it difficult to produce a reflector sufficiently smooth to produce images.
    Ans: A   Section: 6-6

122. What is the main reason that the angular resolution of a 20-m-diameter radio telescope is worse than that of a 0.5-m-diameter optical telescope?
    A) Angular resolution gets worse as mirror diameter increases.
    B) Optical mirrors suffer from chromatic aberration.
    C) Angular resolution gets worse as wavelength increases.
    D) Angular resolution gets worse as wavelength decreases.
    Ans: C   Section: 6-6

123. Why is the angular resolution of a 20-m-diameter radio telescope worse than that of a 0.5-m-diameter optical telescope?
    A) The ratio of wavelength to telescope diameter is larger for the radio telescope.
    B) It is difficult to make a radio dish sufficiently smooth to reflect radio waves.
    C) Atmospheric turbulence disturbs radio waves more than it does visible light.
    D) The ratio of wavelength to telescope diameter is smaller for the radio telescope.
    Ans: A   Section: 6-6

124. How does the angular resolution of the 305-m Arecibo radio telescope in Puerto Rico compare with the angular resolution of the 10-m Keck optical telescope on Mauna Kea, Hawaii?
    A) They have about the same angular resolution, since angular resolution is limited by turbulence in Earth's atmosphere, not by mirror diameter.
    B) The 305-m telescope has much worse angular resolution than the 10-m Keck telescope.
    C) It is not possible to compare their angular resolution, since they work in different wavelength ranges.
    D) The 305-m telescope has much better angular resolution than the 10-m Keck telescope.
    Ans: B   Section: 6-6

125. A 10-m-diameter radio telescope has worse angular resolution than a 1-m-diameter optical telescope because
    A)   radio waves have much longer wavelengths than visible light.
    B)   optical mirrors suffer from chromatic aberration.
    C)   angular resolution gets worse as mirror size increases.
    D)   radio waves have much shorter wavelengths than visible light.
    Ans: A   Section: 6-6

126. What is the main reason for combining many radio telescopes together into an interferometer with large distances between telescopes?
    A)   to obtain much sharper images of sources
    B)   to ensure that at least one of the telescopes is in a radio interference-free zone
    C)   to ensure that observations are uninterrupted by the failure of one or two telescopes
    D)   to collect more radiation from very faint sources
    Ans: A   Section: 6-6

127. How does the angular resolution (sharpness) of the images obtained from radio telescopes using very long baseline interferometry (VLBI), compare to the typical angular resolution of optical telescopes?
    A)   VLBI images are about 10 times less sharp than the best optical images.
    B)   VLBI images are much sharper.
    C)   VLBI images are very much less sharp because of the longer wavelength.
    D)   VLBI images have about the same resolution as the best optical images, about 0.2 arcsecond.
    Ans: B   Section: 6-6

128. The primary reason for spreading many radio telescopes across a large area and combining the signals at a central station is to
    A)   ensure that cloudy weather only affects a few of the telescopes, leaving the others to continue observing.
    B)   avoid interference between signals from the separate telescopes.
    C)   collect more radiation than would be possible with the same telescopes clustered together.
    D)   produce much sharper images of radio sources.
    Ans: D   Section: 6-6

129. What is the maximum angular resolution (sharpness of the image) obtainable with radio telescopes on Earth?
    A)   100 arcseconds using the 305-m Arecibo telescope in Puerto Rico
    B)   0.00001 arcsecond using Very Long Baseline Interferometry
    C)   0.1 arcsecond using the 27-dish Very Large Array of radio telescopes at Socorro, New Mexico
    D)   0.0001 arcsecond using the Very Long Baseline Array
    Ans: B   Section: 6-6

130. Using the combined signals from radio telescopes on opposite sides of Earth, the highest resolution attainable on astronomical images from Earth's surface by Very Long Baseline Interferometry, is
    A)   1 arcsecond.
    B)   0.00001 arcsecond (10^{-5} arcsecond).
    C)   0.1 arcsecond.
    D)   1 arcminute.
    Ans: B   Section: 6-6

131. The Very Large Array (VLA) built in New Mexico provides very sharp radio images of astronomical sources by combining the signals from many individual telescopes. It consists of
    A) 85 units.   B) 2 units.   C) 3 units.   D) 27 units.
    Ans: D   Section: 6-6

132. An optical telescope using 650 nm light has a diameter of 1 m. A radio telescope using radio waves of wavelength 6.5 cm has a diameter of 100 m. The resolution of the optical telescope is
    A)   better than that of the radio telescope by a factor of 1000.
    B)   worse than that of the radio telescope by a factor of 1000.
    C)   better than that of the radio telescope by a factor of 100,000.
    D)   worse than that of the radio telescope by a factor of 100,000.
    Ans: A   Section: 6-6

133. A radio telescope
    A)   is very similar to a refracting optical telescope.
    B)   is very similar to a reflecting optical telescope.
    C)   is completely different in design from any optical telescope.
    D)   combines major features of both refracting and reflecting optical telescopes.
    Ans: B   Section: 6-6

134. An electromagnetic wave has a wavelength of 80 cm. This wave is
    A) visible light.   B) ultraviolet radiation.   C) infrared radiation.   D) a radio wave.
    Ans: D   Section: 6-6

135. The two ranges of electromagnetic radiation for which Earth's atmosphere is reasonably transparent are
    A)   UV and radio waves.   C)   X rays and visible radiation.
    B)   visible and far infrared radiation.   D)   visible and radio radiation.
    Ans: D   Section: 6-7

136. Earth's atmosphere is transparent to which of the following types of electromagnetic radiation?
    A) X rays
    B) long, infrared wavelengths
    C) short, ultraviolet wavelengths
    D) radio waves
    Ans: D   Section: 6-7

137. Which substance in Earth's atmosphere is the main absorber of infrared radiation from space?
    A) ozone   B) carbon dioxide   C) water vapor   D) methane
    Ans: C   Section: 6-7

138. A high mountaintop such as Mauna Kea in Hawaii is a good site for an infrared observatory because it is
    A) above most of the moisture in Earth's atmosphere.
    B) farther from city lights.
    C) closer to the stratospheric ozone layer.
    D) above most of the turbulence in Earth's atmosphere.
    Ans: A   Section: 6-7

139. The main reason for mounting a telescope and scientific equipment in an aircraft to carry out infrared astronomy is to
    A) avoid the contaminating IR radiation from the warm Earth and its occupants.
    B) obtain photographs of higher resolution than are obtainable on the ground.
    C) obtain longer observing time by flying in a specific direction to extend nighttime (westward).
    D) avoid the absorbing effects of water vapor on IR radiation.
    Ans: D   Section: 6-7

140. The constituents of the atmosphere that absorb most strongly at infrared wavelengths, limiting our ability to observe astronomical infrared objects from the surface of Earth, is (are)
    A) dust.
    B) N_2 and O_2, the major constituents of the atmosphere.
    C) electrons and ionized atoms in Earth's ionosphere.
    D) water vapor, H_2O.
    Ans: D   Section: 6-7

141. Telescopes are placed in space to view distant galaxies primarily to
    A) get closer to the observed objects.
    B) avoid having to steer the telescope against Earth's motion.
    C) avoid the absorption of the light or other radiations in the atmosphere of Earth.
    D) avoid the light pollution from Earth's populated areas.
    Ans: C   Section: 6-7

142. The main reason for placing astronomical telescopes and detectors on satellites is to
    A) avoid dust and haze in Earth's atmosphere.
    B) avoid light pollution from cities and other built-up areas.
    C) get closer to the objects being viewed.
    D) get above the absorption in Earth's atmosphere.
    Ans: D   Section: 6-7

143. The first satellite to be dedicated to infrared astronomy was
    A) EUVE.   B) IUE.   C) IRAS.   D) the Hubble Space Telescope.
    Ans: C   Section: 6-7

144. Astronomy from space vehicles is particularly useful because the telescope
    A) is in a clean, dust-free environment and scattered light is much reduced.
    B) is above Earth's absorbing and distorting atmosphere and can measure radiation over a very wide wavelength range.
    C) is in a gravity-free state, its mirror is not distorted by gravitational stress, and it can produce sharper images.
    D) moves smoothly in a constant orbit and can produce sharp photographs.
    Ans: B   Section: 6-7

145. The IRAS satellite was placed in orbit in 1983 to survey the whole sky to detect
    A) visible light radiation.   B) X rays.   C) UV radiation.   D) infrared radiation.
    Ans: D   Section: 6-7

146. Which of the following wavelengths of electromagnetic radiation will not reach Earth's surface? (See Fig. 6-28 of Freedman and Kaufmann, *Universe,* 7th ed.)
    A) 10 m   B) 100 μm   C) 1 μm   D) 10 cm
    Ans: B   Section: 6-7

147. For which of the following spectral ranges is it essential that astronomical observations be made from space?
    A) visible   B) far UV   C) radio   D) near infrared
    Ans: B   Section: 6-7

148. The Hubble Space Telescope, placed in orbit from the Space Shuttle in 1990, has a primary mirror diameter of
    A) 6 m.   B) 2.4 m.   C) 57 m.   D) 1 m.
    Ans: B   Section: 6-7

149. After the Hubble Space Telescope was launched, it was found to suffer seriously from
    A) chromatic aberration.
    B) spherical aberration.
    C) too much angular resolution.
    D) jittery images caused by strong stratospheric winds.
    Ans: B   Section: 6-7

150. What is the present angular resolution of the Hubble Space Telescope for visible light?
    A) 0.001 arcsecond   B) 0.01 arcsecond   C) 1 arcsecond   D) 0.1 arcsecond
    Ans: D   Section: 6-7

151. Over what range of wavelengths does the Hubble Space Telescope operate?
    A)   only visible and ultraviolet   C)   infrared, visible, and ultraviolet
    B)   visible only   D)   only visible and infrared
    Ans: C   Section: 6-7

152. ROSAT was launched into Earth orbit in 1990 to study the universe using
    A) UV radiation.   B) X rays.   C) infrared.   D) visible light.
    Ans: B   Section: 6-7

153. Many of the telescopes sent into space have to be cooled to liquid helium temperatures. Why is this?
    A)   The telescope will expand to a distorted shape if it is not cooled to the temperature of its surroundings. This cooling would not be necessary if the telescope were on Earth.
    B)   The telescope will radiate as a blackbody, and this radiation will obscure the astronomical signal. This blackbody radiation is reduced at cooler temperatures.
    C)   The cooler temperatures reduce the wavelengths of the incoming radiation, thus increasing the resolution.
    D)   The liquid helium is vaporized and used to produce a reference spectrum for comparison with the spectra of the astronomical sources.
    Ans: B   Section: 6-7

Chapter 7: Comparative Planetology I: Our Solar System

1. Our planetary system consists of
   A) one large planet, and many small planets of about the same size, all accompanied by small moons.
   B) large and small planets, all of them accompanied by small moons, none of which are as large as a planet.
   C) large and small planets, some accompanied by moons as large as the smaller planets.
   D) a series of planets of about the same size, some of which are accompanied by moons, the largest of which are as big as the planets themselves.
   Ans: C   Section: 7-1

2. The main characteristics of our solar system are
   A) two large planets close to the Sun, three small planets next out, and four large planets farthest from the Sun.
   B) two small planets close to the Sun, six larger planets much farther from the Sun, and one small planet very far from the Sun.
   C) four small planets close to the Sun, four large planets far from the Sun, and one small planet farthest from the Sun.
   D) three small planets close to the Sun, five large planets far from the Sun, and one small planet farthest from the Sun.
   Ans: C   Section: 7-1

3. The correct sequence of planets in our solar system from the Sun outward is
   A) Mercury, Venus, Earth, Mars, Saturn, Uranus, Jupiter, Neptune, Pluto.
   B) Mercury, Earth, Venus, Mars, Jupiter, Saturn, Uranus, Pluto, Neptune.
   C) Mercury, Venus, Mars, Earth, Jupiter, Saturn, Uranus, Pluto, Neptune.
   D) Mercury, Venus, Earth, Mars, Jupiter, Saturn, Uranus, Neptune, Pluto.
   Ans: D   Section: 7-1

4. In our solar system, which of the following planets is not a member of the terrestrial group?
   A) Mercury   B) Jupiter   C) Venus   D) Mars
   Ans: B   Section: 7-1

5. In our solar system, which of the following planets is not a member of the Jovian group?
   A) Mars   B) Saturn   C) Neptune   D) Jupiter
   Ans: A   Section: 7-1

6. Suppose that in 2008, the Hubble Space Telescope discovers a series of planets with the following characteristics moving around a star resembling our Sun: spherical, solid surfaces; mean densities about 4 times that of H_2O; radii about 4000 km, low-density atmospheres. How would these planets be classified, in terms of our solar system?
   A) Jovian planets   B) cometary nuclei   C) asteroids   D) terrestrial planets
   Ans: D   Section: 7-1

7. Suppose that observers using the Hubble Space Telescope detect around several solar-type stars the presence of planets with the following characteristics: low density, large size, polar diameters shorter than equatorial diameters, fluid surfaces, rapid rotation. How would these planets be classified, in terms of our solar system?
   A) asteroids   B) terrestrial planets   C) comet nuclei   D) Jovian planets
   Ans: D   Section: 7-1

8. Compared to the orbital distance of the Earth from the Sun, the equivalent orbital distances for the Jovian planets are
   A)   more than 10 times greater.   C)   between 2 and 5 times greater.
   B)   more than 5 times greater.   D)   between 2 and 20 times greater.
   Ans: B   Section: 7-1

9. Which planet or planetary group occupies the next orbital position beyond Saturn?
   A) the asteroid belt   B) Jupiter   C) Neptune   D) Uranus
   Ans: D   Section: 7-1

10. The overall shape of the orbits of most of the planets in the solar system is
    A)   slightly elliptical but nearly circular.   C)   perfectly circular.
    B)   parabolic.   D)   elliptical, very elongated.
    Ans: A   Section: 7-1

11. Orbital eccentricity is a number that describes the
    A)   rate of rotation of the semimajor axis of the orbit because of precession.
    B)   orbital tilt with respect to the plane of Earth's orbit, in degrees.
    C)   mean diameter of the orbit.
    D)   shape of the orbital ellipse.
    Ans: D   Section: 7-1

12. The planets whose orbits have the greatest eccentricity are
    A)   Uranus and Mars.   C)   Mercury and Pluto.
    B)   Mercury and Earth.   D)   Uranus and Pluto.
    Ans: C   Section: 7-1

13. The planet with its orbit closest to a circle (least orbital eccentricity) in our planetary system is
    A) Pluto.   B) Neptune.   C) Earth.   D) Venus.
    Ans: D   Section: 7-1

14. Most of the planets orbit the Sun on or close to the
    A) plane containing both north and south celestial poles and the zenith at Greenwich, England.
    B) plane of the Milky Way galaxy.
    C) equatorial plane.
    D) ecliptic plane.
    Ans: D   Section: 7-1

15. The planet whose orbit is inclined at the greatest angle to the plane of the ecliptic is
    A) Saturn.   B) Uranus.   C) Pluto.   D) Mercury.
    Ans: C   Section: 7-1

16. One planet whose orbit carries it both inside and outside the orbital distance of another is
    A) Uranus.   B) Pluto.   C) Mars.   D) Mercury.
    Ans: B   Section: 7-1

17. How many orbits of the Sun (sidereal periods) has Neptune completed since its discovery? (See Table 7-1, Freedman and Kaufmann, *Universe*, 7th ed.)
    A) just more than 1   B) fewer than 1   C) about 147   D) more than 2
    Ans: B   Section: 7-1

18. The mass of a planet is determined primarily by what method?
    A) measurement of its orbital eccentricity
    B) measurement of its diameter by photography
    C) observation of its gravitational influence on an orbiting moon
    D) measurement of its average temperature by remote sensing
    Ans: C   Section: 7-1

19. What observations permit the mass of a planet to be most easily determined?
    A) measurement of its albedo (reflectivity) and brightness in the sky
    B) observation of its gravitational interaction with its moon
    C) measurement of its excess infrared radiation as a measure of its gravitational shrinkage
    D) measurement of its volume and density
    Ans: B   Section: 7-1

20. The best way to measure the mass of a planet is to measure the
    A) gravitational pull of the planet on an orbiting satellite or a nearby spacecraft.
    B) speed of the planet in its orbit around the Sun.
    C) size and rotational speed of the planet.
    D) composition of the planet using spectroscopy.
    Ans: A   Section: 7-1

21. The mean density of a planet is
    A)   another way of describing its total mass.
    B)   the amount of mass in one cubic meter of material at the planet's surface.
    C)   the amount of mass in one cubic meter of material in the planet's core.
    D)   its total mass divided by its volume.
    Ans: D   Section: 7-1

22. The average density of the massive Jovian planets is
    A)   very much lower than the density of water because of the amount of hydrogen
          they contain.
    B)   much higher than the density of Earth rocks due to the great gravitational
          compression of their interiors.
    C)   close to the density of basaltic rocks on Earth.
    D)   close to the density of water.
    Ans: D   Section: 7-1

23. The average density of the outer "giant" planets compared to that of liquid water is
    A)   much less than that of water.   C)   about 5 times.
    B)   about 1.2 times.   D)   greater than 10 times.
    Ans: B   Section: 7-1

24. The average density of which of the following planetary groups is close to that of water
    (1000 kg/m^3)?
    A)   Mercury and Venus, because they are close to the Sun
    B)   terrestrial planets, because they are of relatively low mass and have been
          compressed very little by gravitational forces
    C)   asteroids, because they are very small objects
    D)   Jovian planets, because of their H and He composition
    Ans: D   Section: 7-1

25. A curious fact about the structure of the planet Jupiter, compared to that of Earth, is that
    it has
    A)   much greater mass but much lower average density.
    B)   about the same mass but much greater density.
    C)   much greater mass and greater average density.
    D)   much greater mass but about the same density.
    Ans: A   Section: 7-1

26. The low average densities of the Jovian planets, which have high masses and hence high
    gravitational fields, is an indication that their interiors are
    A)   gaseous and have not condensed to liquid or solid form.
    B)   composed mainly of very light elements, such as H and He.
    C)   composed of very porous rock (many small, empty cavities).
    D)   composed of H_2O, CH_4 (methane), and NH_3 (ammonia).
    Ans: B   Section: 7-1

27. In order of increasing density, the Jovian planets are
    A) Neptune, Saturn, Uranus, Jupiter.   C) Jupiter, Saturn, Uranus, Neptune.
    B) Saturn, Uranus, Jupiter, Neptune.   D) Neptune, Uranus, Saturn, Jupiter.
    Ans: B   Section: 7-1

28. The Jovian planets have high masses and hence generate powerful gravitational fields, yet they have low average densities. What does this indicate about their interiors?
    A) They are composed mainly of water.
    B) The interiors are hot and gaseous, like those of cool stars.
    C) They have not condensed to liquid or solid form.
    D) They are composed mainly of very light elements, such as H and He.
    Ans: D   Section: 7-1

29. Which planet in our solar system has the lowest average density?
    A) Saturn   B) Uranus   C) Jupiter   D) Earth
    Ans: A   Section: 7-1

30. The planet whose average density is less than that of water is
    A) Jupiter.   B) Neptune.   C) Saturn.   D) Earth.
    Ans: C   Section: 7-1

31. The planet with the highest mean density is
    A) Earth.   B) Mercury.   C) Jupiter.   D) Neptune.
    Ans: A   Section: 7-1

32. The Earth has an average density of 5500 kg/m^3, whereas the density of rock on its surface is about 3000 kg/m^3. What conclusion can be reached about the Earth's core from this observation?
    A) The core is composed of material with density about twice that of the surface material.
    B) The core consists of lower density material than surface rock.
    C) The core is very hot.
    D) The core is made of material far denser than surface rock.
    Ans: D   Section: 7-1

33. Based on its mean density, Pluto is
    A) similar to the terrestrial planets in composition, but much larger in size.
    B) denser than the Jovian planets but lighter than the terrestrial planets.
    C) similar to the terrestrial planets in composition, but much smaller in size.
    D) similar to the Jovian planets in composition, but much smaller in size.
    Ans: B   Section: 7-1

34. Based on its mean density, Pluto appears to be composed of
    A)   the very lightest elements, H and He.
    B)   gases such as methane and ammonia, possibly with a small, liquid core.
    C)   rock and iron.
    D)   a mixture of rock and ice.
    Ans: D   Section: 7-1

35. Which of the following general statements about all of the planets in the planetary
    system is true?
    A)   They have hard, rocky surfaces, which can be seen and photographed.
    B)   They orbit the Sun in the same direction.
    C)   They have satellites or moons.
    D)   They have very dense atmospheres.
    Ans: B   Section: 7-1

36. The smallest of the planets is
    A) Neptune.   B) Mars.   C) Mercury.   D) Pluto.
    Ans: D   Section: 7-1

37. Which is the largest planet in our solar system?
    A) Saturn   B) Earth   C) Uranus   D) Jupiter
    Ans: D   Section: 7-1

38. The smallest terrestrial planet is
    A) Mars.   B) Ganymede.   C) Mercury.   D) Neptune.
    Ans: C   Section: 7-1

39. The largest of the terrestrial planets is
    A) Jupiter.   B) Venus.   C) Mars.   D) Earth.
    Ans: D   Section: 7-1

40. Which planet in our solar system has the highest mass?
    A) Uranus   B) Saturn   C) Earth   D) Jupiter
    Ans: D   Section: 7-1

41. Which of the following statements is true?
    A)   Jupiter has the highest average density among the planets.
    B)   The average mass of terrestrial planets is close to the average mass of the Jovian
         planets.
    C)   Earth is the most massive of terrestrial planets.
    D)   Earth is the biggest planet.
    Ans: C   Section: 7-1

42. Which of the following characteristics is not typical of our planetary system?
    A) The orbits of most planets are almost circular.
    B) Most planets have about the same physical size.
    C) The spin axes of most planets are aligned to within 30° to the perpendicular to the orbital plane.
    D) Most planets orbit the Sun in the same direction.
    Ans: B   Section: 7-1

43. Which planets do not have natural satellites (moons)?
    A) Jupiter and Uranus   C) Mars and Venus
    B) Uranus and Mars   D) Venus and Mercury
    Ans: D   Section: 7-1

44. The next planet beyond Saturn is Uranus. The distance from the orbit of Saturn to the orbit of Uranus is about the same as
    A) the distance from Saturn to the Sun.
    B) the distance from the Earth to the Sun.
    C) the distance from the orbit of the Earth to the orbit of Mars.
    D) the distance from the orbit of Saturn to the orbit of Jupiter.
    Ans: A   Section: 7-1 and Table 7-1

45. Viewed from the Earth, which planet has the smallest *angular* size?
    A) Mercury   B) Mars   C) Jupiter   D) Pluto
    Ans: D   Section: 7-1 and Box 1-1

46. The average number of natural satellites (moons) per planet for the terrestrial planets is
    A) less than one.   B) exactly one.   C) at least eight.   D) just over two.
    Ans: A   Section: 7-2 and Appendix 3

47. The natural satellites (moons) of the planets in our solar system
    A) fall into three main classes: four larger than our Moon, five others slightly larger than Pluto, and the rest less than 300 km in diameter.
    B) fall into two main classes: seven larger than Pluto, the rest much smaller.
    C) are all small, less than 2000 km in diameter.
    D) are all approximately the size of our Moon or larger.
    Ans: B   Section: 7-2 and Appendices

48. Table 7-2 describes the seven largest satellites in the solar system. From these data it can be seen that the presence of an atmosphere correlates with
    A)   diameter. The largest satellites have atmospheres, the smaller ones do not.
    B)   mass. The more massive the satellite, the more likely the satellite is to have an atmosphere.
    C)   average density. The satellites with the larger average densities are more likely to have atmospheres.
    D)   none of the above.
    Ans: D   Section: 7-2 and Table 7-2

49. The seven largest satellites in the solar system, in their size and physical characteristics, most resemble
    A) the terrestrial planets.   B) the Jovian planets.   C) Mercury.   D) Pluto.
    Ans: D   Section: 7-2 , Table 7-1, Table 7-2

50. Determination of the chemical composition of the atmospheres of the planets is carried out most effectively by what type of study?
    A)   photometry—the measurement of the fading of light from their moons as they pass behind the planet's atmosphere
    B)   measurement of their relative mean densities
    C)   measurement of their atmospheric temperature
    D)   spectroscopy—the measurement of absorption features in their spectra
    Ans: D   Section: 7-3

51. When astronomers look for evidence of hydrogen gas in the spectra of the Sun, planets, and nearby stars, the positions of the spectral features or "lines" due to hydrogen
    A)   are always in the same pattern, characteristic of hydrogen gas, as seen in the laboratory.
    B)   change systematically, depending on the distance from the source, starting with a laboratory pattern.
    C)   are in the same pattern for solar and planetary sources but very different for stars at larger distances because of absorption of light by the interstellar matter.
    D)   are in a very different pattern, depending on the location of the planet or star, and reproduced only with difficulty in the laboratory.
    Ans: A   Section: 7-3

52. The wide absorption features in the optical spectrum of Titan's atmosphere (see Figure 7-3, Freedman and Kaufmann, *Universe*, 7th ed.) are produced by
    A)   water vapor, H_2O.   C)   hydrogen gas, H_2.
    B)   methane gas, CH_4.   D)   oxygen gas, O_2.
    Ans: B   Section: 7-3

53. The discovery of nitrogen gas (N_2) in the atmosphere of Titan (see Table 7-2, Freedman and Kaufmann, *Universe*, 7th ed.) was made by
    A) direct sampling of the atmosphere by a probe as it descended to Titan's surface.
    B) ultraviolet spectroscopy from Earth.
    C) measurement of microwave emission from N_2 molecules by radio telescopes on Earth.
    D) infrared spectroscopy from the *Cassini* spacecraft.
    Ans: B   Section: 7-3

54. The composition of the solid surfaces of planets and satellites (moons) that do not have substantial atmospheres can be found by
    A) measuring the thermal emission from the surface at several wavelengths in the microwave and infrared regions of the spectrum.
    B) comparing the spectrum of the sunlight reflected from the surface with the spectrum of direct sunlight from the Sun.
    C) comparing very broad absorption features in their spectra with spectra of known substances on Earth.
    D) measuring the wavelengths of narrow absorption lines in their spectra.
    Ans: C   Section: 7-3

55. A ground-based telescope is pointed at the atmosphere of Titan and a spectrum is made. The spectral lines observed in this spectrum
    A) can only be features of Titan.
    B) can be characteristic of the Earth's atmosphere as well as Titan's atmosphere.
    C) can be characteristic of the cooler, outer layers of the Sun's atmosphere as well as of Titan's atmosphere.
    D) can be characteristic of the atmospheres of Titan and the Earth and also of the cooler, outer layers of the Sun's atmosphere.
    Ans: D   Section: 7-3

56. To an astronomer, the word "ice" can mean any one or more of
    A) water (H_2O), carbon dioxide (CO_2), methane (CH_4), or ammonia (NH_3).
    B) hydrogen (H_2), water (H_2O), carbon dioxide (CO_2), methane (CH_4), or ammonia (NH_3).
    C) only water (H_2O).
    D) water (H_2O) or carbon dioxide (CO_2).
    Ans: A   Section: 7-4

57. If the atmosphere of a particular planet is at a temperature of 213 K (−60°C), then molecules of methane (CH_4) and molecules of carbon dioxide (CO_2) in this atmosphere have
    A) different average speed and kinetic energy.
    B) the same average kinetic energy (but different average speed).
    C) the same average speed (but different average kinetic energy).
    D) the same average speed and kinetic energy.
    Ans: B   Section: 7-4 and Box 7-2

58. A nitrogen molecule (N_2) has a mass of 4.7×10^{-26} kg, and a carbon dioxide molecule (CO_2) has a mass of 7.3×10^{-26} kg. On a day when the temperature is 18°C (64°F), the N_2 molecules will have a
    A) greater average kinetic energy and greater average speed than the CO_2 molecules.
    B) smaller average kinetic energy but greater average speed than the CO_2 molecules.
    C) smaller average speed than the CO_2 molecules but the same average kinetic energy.
    D) greater average speed than the CO_2 molecules but the same average kinetic energy.
    Ans: D   Section: 7-4 and Box 7-2

59. Each type of molecule has the same average kinetic energy in a planetary atmosphere. As a result (and knowing that an oxygen [O_2] molecule has twice the mass of a methane [CH_4] molecule), we can say that in this atmosphere the average speed of an oxygen molecule is
    A) 1.4 times less than that of a methane molecule.
    B) half that of a methane molecule.
    C) twice that of a methane molecule.
    D) 1.4 times greater than that of a methane molecule.
    Ans: A   Section: 7-4 and Box 7-2

60. An oxygen (O_2) molecule has twice the mass of a methane (CH_4) molecule. In a planet's atmosphere at some particular temperature, the AVERAGE KINETIC ENERGY of an oxygen molecule is
    A) the same as that of a methane molecule (i.e., all molecules have the same average kinetic energy).
    B) 1.4 times greater than that of a methane molecule (i.e., the average kinetic energy increases in proportion to the square root of the mass).
    C) four times greater than that of a methane molecule (i.e., the average kinetic energy increases in proportion to square of the mass).
    D) twice that of a methane molecule (i.e., the average kinetic energy increases in the same proportion as the mass).
    Ans: A   Section: 7-4 and Box 7-2

61. The average speed of methane molecules (CH_4, molecular mass = 2.66×10^{-26} kg) in the atmosphere of Neptune (temperature = 63 K = –210°C) is
    A) 313 m/s.   B) 327,000 m/s.   C) 572 m/s.   D) 98,000 m/s.
    Ans: A   Section: 7-4 and Box 7-2

62. Most of the ammonia on Jupiter is in the form of a
    A) gas.   B) liquid.   C) solid.   D) plasma.
    Ans: B   Section: 7-4

63. On Mars, the temperature can reach 290 K and the escape speed is 5.0 km/sec. What is the average speed of a carbon dioxide molecule (mass = 7.31×10^{-26} kg) at this temperature, and what can you say about the retention of carbon dioxide on Mars?
    A)   The average speed is 0.4 km/sec, so Mars should retain its carbon dioxide.
    B)   The average speed is 0.4 km/sec, so Mars should lose its carbon dioxide.
    C)   The average speed is 1.9 km/sec, so Mars should retain its carbon dioxide.
    D)   The average speed is 1.9 km/sec, so Mars should lose its carbon dioxide.
    Ans: A   Section: 7-4 and Box 7-2

64. The asteroid Vesta, located in the main asteroid belt between the orbits of Mars and Jupiter, is spherical in shape with a radius of 265 km and a mass of 3.0×10^{20} kg. What is the minimum speed at which you could propel yourself upward and not fall back down?
    A) 285,000 m/s   B) 0.28 m/s   C) 388 m/s   D) 534 m/s
    Ans: C   Section: 7-4 and Box 7-2

65. What relationship must exist between a certain molecule's average speed, v, in a planetary atmosphere and the escape velocity, V_{esc}, from the planet's surface for this particular molecular species to be retained by the planet?
    A) v should not exceed V_{esc} C) v must be less than about 1/6 V_{esc}
    B) v must be less than about $6 \times V_{esc}$ D) v should not exceed $2 \times V_{esc}$
    Ans: C   Section: 7-4 and Box 7-2

66. The mass of the planet Jupiter is high and its atmosphere is relatively cool. What are the chances for the retention of gases within its atmosphere?
    A)   good for light (H_2 and He) molecules but poor for heavier (CH_4, NH_3, H_2O) molecules
    B)   good for all gases, including light (H_2 and He) and heavier (CH_4, NH_3, H_2O) molecules
    C)   poor for all gases because of the low temperature, thus all gases will be leaving Jupiter continuously
    D)   good for heavier (CH_4, NH_3, H_2O) molecules but poor for light (H_2 and He) molecules
    Ans: B   Section: 7-4 and Box 7-2

67. A typical asteroid is (see Figure 7-7, Freedman and Kaufmann, *Universe*, 7th ed.)
   A)   spherical and densely covered with craters.
   B)   potato shaped with large and small craters.
   C)   potato shaped with a smooth, metallic surface.
   D)   spherical but distorted by seismic and volcanic activity.
   Ans: B   Section: 7-5

68. A typical asteroid is made of
   A)   ices of water, methane, and ammonia or perhaps ices with dust-sized grains of rock mixed in.
   B)   ice with a liquid water core.
   C)   rock and metal.
   D)   rock and ice.
   Ans: C   Section: 7-5

69. The asteroid belt exists between the orbits of which planets?
   A)   Jupiter and Saturn   C)   Venus and Earth
   B)   Mars and Jupiter   D)   Earth and Mars
   Ans: B   Section: 7-5

70. The asteroid belt is made up of
   A)   large, rocky bodies typically about the size of our Moon.
   B)   rocky bodies from a few meters to tens of kilometers in diameter.
   C)   several planet-sized objects with dense methane atmospheres.
   D)   irregularly shaped bodies composed primarily of ices.
   Ans: B   Section: 7-5

71. Comets are typically
   A)   chunks of ice that begin to vaporize if they pass close to the Sun.
   B)   chunks of rock a few tens to hundreds of kilometers in diameter.
   C)   slushy mixtures of liquid and ice.
   D)   gaseous bodies from which some of the gas is pushed out by the Sun to form a long tail.
   Ans: A   Section: 7-5

72. What is the basic difference between comets and asteroids?
   A)   Comets always emit their own light, while asteroids only reflect sunlight.
   B)   Comets always move in open orbits around the Sun, visiting the Sun only once in their lifetime, while asteroids move in closed orbits.
   C)   Comets are mostly composed of ices, while asteroids are mainly composed of rocks.
   D)   Comets are spherical, while asteroids are mostly irregular in shape.
   Ans: C   Section: 7-5

73. The region outside the orbit of Neptune in which a large number of objects composed of rock and ice circle the Sun not far from the plane of the ecliptic is called
    A)   the Outer Solar System.   C)   the Kuiper belt.
    B)   the asteroid belt.   D)   the Oort comet cloud.
    Ans: C   Section: 7-5

74. Which one of the following planets shows the greatest amount of cratering on its surface?
    A) Mercury B) Earth C) Mars D) Jupiter
    Ans: A   Section: 7-6

75. Planets and satellites with a large amount of surface cratering generally have insignificant atmospheres. Why are these two conditions correlated?
    A)   The impacts that create the craters also tend to vaporize the atmosphere.
    B)   A large amount of cratering implies a small size, and this, in turn, implies a low escape speed.
    C)   A large amount of cratering implies a small size, and this, in turn, implies a high escape speed.
    D)   Most of the solar system debris that caused cratering was near the Sun. Thus heavily cratered planets and satellites are near the Sun where high temperatures result in high average molecular speeds.
    Ans: B   Section: 7-6 and Box 7-2

76. The craters on the Moon are all nearly circular. Why is this?
    A)   Most of the craters on the Moon were formed by volcanoes, and this results in circular craters.
    B)   It is believed that the objects that formed the impact craters on the Moon's surface all struck the Moon approximately perpendicular to its surface, and this would result in circular craters.
    C)   The objects that produced the impact craters came in at a variety of angles, but the craters were actually made by the shock waves generated by impact—and this results in circular craters.
    D)   The objects that produced the impact craters had been rounded by many previous collisions in space, and round objects produce circular craters regardless of their direction of impact.
    Ans: C   Section: 7-6

77. In order to produce a planet-wide magnetic field, a planet must have in its interior some material capable of carrying the electric current to produce a dynamo effect. All of the following substances appear to be able to fill this role, *except one*. Which is the exception?
    A)   molten iron
    B)   solid iron
    C)   liquid metallic hydrogen
    D)   a liquid water-ammonia mixture under high pressure
    Ans: B   Section: 7-7

78. In general, a heavily cratered surface should imply a solid interior. Lack of a planet-wide magnetic field should also imply a solid interior. Which one of the following bodies actually possesses both a heavily cratered surface and no planet-wide magnetic field?
    A) Mercury B) Venus C) the Moon D) Mars
    Ans: C   Section: 7-7

79. All of the following conditions *except one* appear to be necessary in order for a planet or satellite to produce a planet-wide magnetic field by the dynamo effect. Which is the exception?
    A)   an interior that is at least partially liquid
    B)   an interior containing material that can conduct an electric current
    C)   relatively rapid rotation around its axis
    D)   a rotation axis that tilts only slightly with respect to the ecliptic
    Ans: D   Section: 7-7

80. A general summary of the planets in the solar system is that
    A)   despite differences in size, the planets are remarkably similar.
    B)   the magnetic fields are all produced in the same way, but differences in planet size result in different field strengths.
    C)   the planets are remarkably different in size, magnetic field strength, and magnetic field generation method.
    D)   the terrestrial planets vary dramatically, but the Jovian planets are remarkably similar.
    Ans: C   Section: 7-8

Chapter 8: Comparative Planetology II: The Origin of Our Solar System

1. A theory of the origin of the solar system must take into account all important general properties of the planets. These include three of the four properties listed below. Which one is *not* an important general property of the planets?
   A) The planets are grouped by size and composition into two general groups: terrestrial and Jovian.
   B) The outermost planet, Pluto, does not fit easily into either one of these groups.
   C) The terrestrial planets all orbit much closer to the Sun than do any of the Jovian planets.
   D) All of the planets orbit the Sun in the same direction and nearly in the same plane.
   Ans: B   Section: 8-1

2. The most abundant elements in the universe, as revealed by spectroscopic analysis, in order of decreasing abundance (number of atoms) are
   A) nitrogen, oxygen, carbon, helium.
   C) helium, carbon, oxygen, hydrogen.
   B) hydrogen, helium, oxygen, carbon.
   D) hydrogen, helium, oxygen, nitrogen.
   Ans: B   Section: 8-2

3. The most common elements in the universe are
   A) large quantities of heavy elements, with smaller quantities of hydrogen and helium.
   B) equal amounts of hydrogen and helium with small amounts of heavier elements.
   C) equal amounts of all elements up to iron but very little of any heavier elements.
   D) hydrogen, smaller quantities of helium, and very small quantities of heavier elements.
   Ans: D   Section: 8-2

4. Together, hydrogen and helium account for what percentage of the total mass of all matter in the universe?
   A) 98%   B) about 50%   C) 90%   D) 75%
   Ans: A   Section: 8-2

5. The composition of matter in the universe can be summarized by which statement?
   A) About half of the mass of the universe is in the form of rocks, molecules, and planetary material, visible by infrared radiation.
   B) All but 2% of the mass in the universe is hydrogen and helium.
   C) 2% of the mass of the universe is hydrogen and helium, the rest is heavier elements.
   D) All but 2% of the mass of the universe is hydrogen.
   Ans: B   Section: 8-2

6. What fraction of the mass of the universe is in the form of atoms other than hydrogen and helium?
   A) much less than 1%   B) 50%   C) 2%   D) 10%
   Ans: C   Section: 8-2

7. The most abundant material in the universe is
   A) hydrogen.   B) carbon dioxide.   C) water.   D) helium.
   Ans: A   Section: 8-2

8. The fractional abundance of hydrogen by mass in the solar system is about
   A) 99.9%   B) 98%   C) only 20%   D) 75%
   Ans: D   Section: 8-2

9. Which of the following chemical elements is relatively rare in the universe?
   A) carbon   B) oxygen   C) nitrogen   D) gold
   Ans: D   Section: 8-2

10. Where in the universe are heavy elements with masses greater than that of helium being produced at this time?
    A)   dark clouds of dust and gas
    B)   central cores of stars
    C)   event horizons of massive black holes
    D)   surface layers of stars
    Ans: B   Section: 8-2

11. Most of the elements beyond H and He in the periodic table in our Sun and solar system probably originated
    A)   in the original Big Bang.
    B)   from the center of our own Sun, through fusion and later ejection as solar wind.
    C)   from chemical reactions in planetary atmospheres.
    D)   from fusion reactions in the centers of earlier stars.
    Ans: D   Section: 8-2

12. How has the present mix of chemical elements in the universe been produced?
    A)   All the known elements have been formed by the radioactive breakup of the heavy elements formed in the initial Big Bang.
    B)   All of the known elements were formed in the Big Bang.
    C)   H and He were formed in the Big Bang, while the heavier elements have been slowly forming by collisions in cold interstellar gas clouds.
    D)   H and some He were formed in the Big Bang, while the heavier elements have been slowly formed in the centers of stars over the life of the universe.
    Ans: D   Section: 8-2

13. Just after the original Big Bang the abundance of elements heavier than helium was
    A) about the same as it is now.
    B) much greater than it is now.
    C) much smaller than it is now.
    D) about the same as the abundance of helium at that time.
    Ans: C   Section: 8-2

14. In the solar system the distribution of light and heavy elements is as follows:
    A) The heavy elements are generally within a few astronomical units of the center while the light elements are generally farther from the center than this.
    B) The light elements are generally within a few astronomical units of the center while the heavy elements are generally farther from the center than this.
    C) Both the light and heavy elements are generally within a few astronomical units of the center.
    D) Both the light and heavy elements are generally farther than a few astronomical units from the center.
    Ans: C   Section: 8-2

15. Suppose the ratio of radiogenic ^{40}K to nonradiogenic ^{39}K was 1:10 at the time a rock was formed, and that at that time also the ratio between radiogenic ^{40}Ar to ^{39}K was 1:20. Now, when the rock is analyzed, it is found that the ratios are ^{40}K/^{39}K = 1:20 and ^{40}Ar/^{39}K = 1:10. How old is the rock (in billions of years)?
    A) 0.13   B) 1.3   C) 13   D) 26
    Ans: B   Section: 8-3 and Box 8-1

16. The oldest rocks, as measured by radioactive age-dating, have been found
    A) on the Earth.   C) in the maria of the lunar lowlands.
    B) in the lunar highlands.   D) in meteorites.
    Ans: D   Section: 8-3

17. The half-life of radiogenic ^{14}C is 5730 years. How long must you wait until 90% of the original sample remains?
    A) less than 5730 years   C) $9 \times 5730 = 51{,}570$ years
    B) 5730 years   D) more than 51,570 years
    Ans: A   Section: 8-3 and Box 8-1

18. It is found by the radioactive age-dating technique that only one-quarter of the original sample of a radiogenic element remains, so the time is calculated to be two half-lives. What does this time represent?
    A) the age of the universe
    B) the age of the solar system
    C) the time since the formation of the elements
    D) the time since the rock was formed
    Ans: D   Section: 8-3

19. In order to employ the radioactive age-dating technique on a sample of rock, it is necessary to know all of the following *except one*. Which is the exception?
    A) the amount of the radioactive element in the rock
    B) the amount in the rock of the stable element into which the radioactive element decays
    C) the amount in the rock of some nonradiogenic element for reference
    D) the mass of the rock when it was formed
    Ans: D   Section: 8-3 and Box 8-1

20. Radioactive decay in an atom occurs because
    A) the atom has more protons than electrons.
    B) the atom has more protons than neutrons.
    C) the nucleus contains a mix of neutrons and protons which is not stable.
    D) the nucleus, originally stable, has been made unstable by exposure to the nuclear reactions in a nearby star.
    Ans: C   Section: 8-3

21. The idea that the Sun and planets formed from a large cloud of gas and dust was first proposed by
    A)   Edwin Hubble.   C)   Sir William Herschel.
    B)   Aristotle.   D)   Kant and Laplace.
    Ans: D   Section: 8-4

22. The birthplace of the Sun and planets (and of other stars and maybe their planets) is thought to have been
    A) in cool gas and dust clouds.
    B) at the centers of supernova explosions.
    C) in the centers of galaxies.
    D) in black holes dotted about the universe.
    Ans: A   Section: 8-4

23. What was the form of the material from which the solar system formed?
    A)   a nebula made mostly of hydrogen and helium gas, but enriched in heavier elements from supernova explosions
    B)   a nebula made mostly of heavy elements, but enriched in hydrogen and helium from the supernova explosions
    C)   a nebula made entirely of hydrogen and helium gas
    D)   debris from the explosion of a massive star
    Ans: A   Section: 8-4

24. The temperature began to rise at the center of the solar nebula because
    A)   the nebula was contracting, increasing the speed of motion of the atoms.
    B)   supernova explosions were stirring up the material there and causing turbulence.
    C)   fusion reactions were beginning in the core, releasing tremendous amounts of heat.
    D)   massive stars nearby were heating the nebula with their ultraviolet radiation.
    Ans: A   Section: 8-4

25. What process heated the early solar nebula as it slowly condensed toward a central protosun?
    A)   rotational energy transferred to heat by friction between particles as the nebula slowly revolved around its center
    B)   release of heat by collisions of particles as they gain kinetic energy in falling toward the center of the nebula
    C)   release of heat as molecules formed and as gases condensed into ices
    D)   thermonuclear fusion in the protosun, followed by radiated heating of the nebula
    Ans: B   Section: 8-4

26. Which of the following statements is an example of Kelvin-Helmholtz contraction?
    A)   A contraction of the planet Mercury as it cooled, with consequent buckling of the surface.
    B)   A contraction of a dense cloud of gas slowly gets hotter due to the release of gravitational energy.
    C)   the condensation of ices (e.g., ammonia) onto dust particles in the early solar nebula
    D)   A contraction of a thin cloud of gas, in which the temperature remains constant due to the escape of infrared radiation.
    Ans: B   Section: 8-4

27. What name is given to the concentration of mass that formed at the center of the solar nebula, eventually becoming the Sun?
    A) antisun   B) protosun   C) nebular core   D) pseudosun
    Ans: B   Section: 8-4

28. The most likely mechanism for the solar system's formation is that the
    A)   Sun captured the planets as they drifted through space.
    B)   planets were spun out of the Sun as smaller gas clouds and subsequently condensed.
    C)   solar system was once a galaxy, from which the Sun and planets are the remnants.
    D)   Sun and planets slowly condensed to their present form from a gas and dust cloud.
    Ans: D   Section: 8-4

29. The most probable theory for the solar system's formation is
    A)   a capture theory in which the Sun captured objects moving through space which then became the planets.
    B)   an encounter, in which a passing star ripped off material from the Sun to form the planets.
    C)   gas and dust clouds condensed to form the Sun, while planets formed later within a nebular disk.
    D)   condensation of a slowly contracting nebula of hot gas, first into planets in the outer region, then into the Sun at the center.
    Ans: C   Section: 8-4

30. In a rotating physical system (e.g., a star formation region, or a skater), what happens to the rotation rate (or angular speed) when the mass of the system condenses toward the center of rotation?
    A)   It varies periodically.
    B)   It decreases.
    C)   Since rotation depends only on the initial rotation speed, it remains the same.
    D)   It increases.
    Ans: D   Section: 8-4

31. A proplyd is
    A)   a primitive organism thought to exist on Jupiter's moon, Europa.
    B)   a protoplanetary disk, such as is observed around some stars in the Orion nebula, for example.
    C)   any planet of greater mass than Jupiter.
    D)   a planet orbiting a star beyond the Sun.
    Ans: B   Section: 8-4

32. As the early Sun got smaller in a Kelvin-Helmholtz Contraction, its interior became hotter and gained thermal energy. What was the source of this energy?
    A)   the tidal pull of a passing star
    B)   gravitational potential energy released by inward-falling material
    C)   nuclear energy from the interior
    D)   energy released by radioactive decay
    Ans: B   Section: 8-4

33. Which one of the following is *not* an example of the conservation of angular momentum?
    A)   A figure skater spins faster as she brings her arms in close to her body.
    B)   The Earth moves faster in its orbit at those times of the year when it is closer to the Sun (Kepler's Second Law).
    C)   The particles in the nebula around a protostar move faster in their orbits as the nebula collapses inward.
    D)   The Moon always keeps one face pointed toward the Earth.
    Ans: D   Section: 8-4

34. The protosun became a full fledged star when
    A)   thermonuclear fusion reactions began at its center.
    B)   the temperature began to rise at its center.
    C)   it became hot enough to emit light and heat.
    D)   planetary formation was complete.
    Ans: A   Section: 8-4

35. The most probable process for the formation or acquisition of the Sun's planets is
    A)   the breakup of one single large companion body to the Sun, by tidal distortion.
    B)   the freezing of immense gas clouds by the cold temperature of space.
    C)   capture of planets from outer space by gravity.
    D)   relatively slow growth of smaller objects by collisions and mutual gravitational attraction.
    Ans: D   Section: 8-5

36. The most probable time sequence for the solar system's formation was that the
    A)   Sun formed initially, and the planets and major moons were captured much later as they drifted by the Sun.
    B)   planets formed first out of the cold gas and dust nebula, followed by the Sun, which formed when the gas had become much hotter.
    C)   Sun formed first, the planets were spun off from the Sun, and the moons in turn were spun off from the planets.
    D)   Sun contracted first as a gas ball, and the planets and moons formed shortly afterward by accretion and condensation.
    Ans: D   Section: 8-5

37. The three common substances believed to have been important in planet formation are
    A)   water, carbon dioxide ice (dry ice), and iron.
    B)   solid, liquid, and gaseous hydrogen.
    C)   hydrogen, helium, and neon gases.
    D)   rocks, ices, and gas.
    Ans: D   Section: 8-5

38. The planetary system was probably formed from three different categories of material with different condensation temperatures (the temperature at which the material melts), gases, ices, and rocks. Which is the correct order of these materials, in increasing condensation temperature?
    A)   rocks, gases, ices   C)   gases, rocks, ices
    B)   rocks, ices, gases   D)   gases, ices, rocks
    Ans: D   Section: 8-5

39. Which of the following types of material has the highest condensation temperature in the planetary system?
    A) hydrogen
    B) rocks and dust grains
    C) nitrogen gas
    D) gases such as methane, ammonia, water vapor
    Ans: B   Section: 8-5

40. More than any other, which physical parameter probably controlled the early evolution of the planetary system and dictated the characteristics of the planets that eventually formed?
    A) overall rotation of the nebula
    B) density of hydrogen gas in the nebula
    C) mix of chemical constituents
    D) temperature distribution within the nebula
    Ans: D   Section: 8-5

41. The most common ices in the early solar nebula were
    A) hydrogen and helium.   C) hydrogen, methane, and ammonia.
    B) water ice and carbon dioxide.   D) water ice, methane, and ammonia.
    Ans: D   Section: 8-5

42. Which substances form ice in the outer solar system?
    A) carbon dioxide, iron oxides
    B) hydrogen and helium
    C) water, carbon dioxide, and minerals rich in iron, silicon, magnesium, and sulfur
    D) water, ammonia, methane
    Ans: D   Section: 8-5

43. Suppose you were to go back in time and explore the early solar nebula (during the formation of the solar system). If you were to travel outward from the protosun, the first solid material you would encounter would be
    A) dust-sized grains of iron and rocky material.
    B) dust-sized grains of frozen hydrogen, water, ice, and rocky minerals.
    C) snowflakes made of frozen water, methane, ammonia, and carbon dioxide.
    D) snowflakes of frozen hydrogen and helium.
    Ans: A   Section: 8-5

44. Various ices condense at temperatures less than 300 K. What is the smallest distance from the Sun in the early solar nebula at which these ices would have condensed to form solid particles? (See Figure 8-7 of Freedman and Kaufmann, *Universe*, 7th ed.)
    A) 2 AU   B) 5 AU   C) 1 AU   D) 1.5 AU
    Ans: A   Section: 8-5

45. In the early solar nebula, iron sulfide condensed into solid form at a temperature of about 750 K. What is the smallest distance from the Sun at which this would have happened? (See Figure 8-7 of Freedman and Kaufmann, *Universe*, 7th ed.)
    A) 0.5 AU   B) 1.6 AU   C) 0.2 AU   D) 0.9 AU
    Ans: D   Section: 8-5

46. The early phases of planetary formation into protoplanets were characterized by
    A)   slow accretion of small particles by gravitational attraction and collision.
    B)   condensation of hot gas clouds.
    C)   the shattering collision of very large objects into planet-sized fragments.
    D)   violent collapse and heating of gas and dust grains by gravity.
    Ans: A   Section: 8-5

47. The process of accretion in planetary formation is the
    A)   slow accumulation of solid particles by gravity and collision into larger, solid objects.
    B)   slow acquisition from deep space by the giant planets of their complement of moons, by gravitational capture.
    C)   slow condensation by gravity of gas atoms into large dense gas clouds, which become the planets.
    D)   relatively rapid gravitational collapse (in less than 10^6 years) of gas clouds to form planets.
    Ans: A   Section: 8-5

48. The formation of terrestrial-type planets around a star is most likely to have occurred by what process?
    A)   breakup of a large disk of matter which formed around the star
    B)   condensation of gas from the original star nebula
    C)   capture by the star of objects traversing the depths of space
    D)   accretion, or slow accumulation of smaller particles by mutual gravitational attraction
    Ans: D   Section: 8-5

49. The manner in which the terrestrial planets formed was
    A)   accretion of planetesimals to form a core, followed by gravitational capture of gas from the solar nebula.
    B)   gravitational condensation of hydrogen, helium, and dust in eddies or vortices in the solar nebula.
    C)   gravitational condensation of gas followed by capture of solid planetesimals.
    D)   accretion of solid planetesimals containing mostly rocky material.
    Ans: D   Section: 8-5

50. What is the process of chemical differentiation?
    A) the separation of different chemical compounds into different regions of the solar nebula; e.g., rocky grains in the inner nebula, icy grains in the outer nebula
    B) the sinking of heavy material to the center of a planet or other object and the rising of lighter material toward the surface
    C) the condensation of different chemical compounds at different temperatures and therefore at different times—iron first, rock next, and ices last.
    D) a separation of different chemical compounds into different types of grains in any given part of the solar nebula; e.g., grains of ice, rock, and iron
    Ans: B   Section: 8-5

51. The reason most of the terrestrial planets have dense, iron cores is because
    A) iron solidifies at the highest temperatures, so the iron core condensed first from the solar nebula. The rocky material then condensed directly onto the iron core as the nebula cooled.
    B) terrestrial planets were initially molten or partially molten, and the iron sank to the center.
    C) iron is magnetic, so there was a rapid accretion of iron dust grains into a core, followed by a slow accretion of rocky grains.
    D) iron solidifies at the highest temperatures, so the iron core condensed first from the solar nebula. Rocky planetesimals then formed as the nebula cooled further, and gradually impacted onto the iron core.
    Ans: B   Section: 8-5

52. The reason for the vast amount of hydrogen in the interior of Jupiter is probably that
    A) Jupiter formed from mutual gravitational contraction of the primordial hydrogen gas.
    B) the mass of the initial condensation of rocks at Jupiter's orbit was sufficient to attract vast amounts of gas to it.
    C) nuclear fission of atoms in Jupiter's interior split all nuclei down to hydrogen nuclei early in its history.
    D) Jupiter became so hot in its interior that all kinds of atoms and molecules were melted down and dissociated into the fundamental atom—hydrogen.
    Ans: B   Section: 8-5

53. According to modern theories, the most significant difference between the formation of the terrestrial and Jovian planets is that
    A) both formed by accretion of planetesimals, but the Jovian planets became massive enough to attract gas onto them directly from the solar nebula.
    B) both formed by accretion of rocky and icy planetesimals, but the terrestrial planets were close enough to the Sun that almost all of ices escaped back to space after the planets formed.
    C) the terrestrial planets formed close to the Sun where there was lots of rock but no ice, whereas the Jovian planets formed far from the Sun where there was lots of hydrogen and ice but no rocky material.
    D) the terrestrial planets formed by accretion of planetesimals, whereas the Jovian planets formed from streamers of hot gas which shot out of the protostar.
    Ans: A   Section: 8-5

54. The steps in the process of formation of the large, outer planets were
    A) gravitational condensation of hydrogen, helium, and dust in eddies or vortices in the outer solar nebula.
    B) accretion of cold planetesimals containing large quantities of hydrogen and helium.
    C) gravitational condensation of methane and ammonia gas, followed by capture of planetesimals.
    D) accretion of planetesimals to form a core, followed by gravitational capture of hydrogen and helium gas.
    Ans: D   Section: 8-5

55. The timescale over which material in the solar nebula accreted to form planets was about
    A) 100 thousand years.   C) 4.6 billion years.
    B) 4.6 million years.   D) 100 million years.
    Ans: D   Section: 8-5

56. How are many of the satellites of the Jovian planets thought to have formed?
    A) They are small planets in their own right but were captured by the Jovian planets early in the solar system's history.
    B) They are fragments of one large satellite orbiting around each of the planets.
    C) from a disk of material around the planet, similarly to the way the planets formed around the Sun
    D) from material thrown off the planet when one or more large planetesimals or small planets collided with it
    Ans: C   Section: 8-5

57. A Tauri wind is
    A)   the rapid condensation of gas onto a Jovian-type protoplanet.
    B)   a slow expulsion of the outer layers of a solar-type star, extending over a large part of its life.
    C)   a wind created by the orbital motion of protoplanets through a young solar-type nebula.
    D)   a rapid expulsion of the tenuous outer layers of a young star.
    Ans: D   Section: 8-5

58. In order for the disk instability model to be able to account for the formation of the Jovian planets
    A)   the rocky material would have to be confined completely to the inner part of the solar system.
    B)   the gas in the nebular disk would have to be at a very high temperature.
    C)   the gas in the nebular disk would have to be clumpy rather than smooth.
    D)   the gas in the nebular disk would have to be mostly methane and ammonia rather than hydrogen and helium.
    Ans: C   Section: 8-5

59. The Oort cloud is
    A)   a spherical solar system halo of icy objects far beyond the orbit of Pluto.
    B)   a flat region just outside the orbit of Neptune in which icy and rocky objects circle the Sun.
    C)   the collection of rocky objects orbiting the Sun between the orbits of Mars and Jupiter.
    D)   the swarm of small satellites around Jupiter.
    Ans: A   Section: 8-5

60. Strong evidence for the existence of planetary systems in the process of formation around other stars comes from
    A)   periodic wobbling of the positions and spectral line positions of several nearby stars.
    B)   direct photography of actual planets near other stars.
    C)   spectroscopic evidence of large quantities of molecules such as ammonia and methane, which can only exist in planetary atmospheres.
    D)   detection of very regular pulses of radio energy from some stars.
    Ans: A   Section: 8-6

61. Astrometry is the branch of astronomy dealing with the measurement of the
    A)   ages of stars and galaxies.
    B)   accurate motions of stars with respect to the Sun.
    C)   precise positions of stars and galaxies.
    D)   precise surface temperatures of stars.
    Ans: C   Section: 8-6

62. Astrometry is the very precise measurement of
    A)   a star's brightness (e.g., to measure light variations).
    B)   a star's blackbody curve (e.g., to measure the star's temperature).
    C)   a star's position in the sky (e.g., to measure its motion).
    D)   lines in a star's spectrum (e.g., to measure the Doppler shift).
    Ans: C   Section: 8-6

63. What is the astrometric method used in searches for planets orbiting stars other than the Sun?
    A)   a search for excess infrared radiation from the star, caused by the presence of planets that are cool and thus emit primarily in the infrared
    B)   a search for tiny wobbles in the position of the star due to the gravitational pull of a planet orbiting around it
    C)   a search for tiny wobbles in the positions of absorption lines in the star's spectrum, caused by radial velocity variations of the star due to a planet orbiting around it
    D)   a search for tiny "bumps" on images of the star, due to the light from a planet located close to the star
    Ans: B   Section: 8-6

64. What type of search technique has discovered the largest number of planets around the stars other than the Sun?
    A)   Looking for tiny variations in the star's position in the sky, caused by the gravitational pull of one or more planets orbiting the star.
    B)   Looking for tiny variations in the star's radial velocity, caused by the gravitational pull of one or more planets orbiting the star.
    C)   Looking for excess infrared radiation from the star, caused by the presence of planets that are cool and thus emit primarily in the infrared.
    D)   Using space-based telescopes to search for tiny pinpoints of light that follow circular or elliptical paths around the star.
    Ans: B   Section: 8-6

65. We measure the mass of an extrasolar planet by
    A)   using spectra to measure the planet's temperature and photometry to measure its brightness.
    B)   We cannot make a useful estimate of the mass of an extrasolar planet with present technology.
    C)   measuring the planet's angular diameter and its size, using spectra to find its composition and hence density.
    D)   using Newton's law of gravity, using the measured distance from the star and its gravitational pull on the star.
    Ans: D   Section: 8-6

66. So far, what is the typical mass of the majority of extrasolar planets discovered?
    A)   between the the mass of Saturn and a few times the mass of Jupiter
    B)   about the mass of the Earth
    C)   large, between ten and a hundred times Jupiter's mass
    D)   small, between a tenth and a few tenths of the mass of the Earth
    Ans: A   Section: 8-6

67. In general, what are the characteristics of the planets that have been found so far around other stars?
    A)   They are the mass of Saturn or larger, and are therefore Jovian-type planets.
    B)   They are larger than the mass of Jupiter, and are probably a new type of planetary object.
    C)   between the mass of Mercury and Earth, and are therefore terrestrial-type planets.
    D)   They have masses between the mass of Earth and about three times the mass of Jupiter.
    Ans: A   Section: 8-6

68. What is surprising about the extrasolar planets that have been discovered?
    A)   More than half of them have strong lines of molecular oxygen in their spectra, a possible indication of life on these planets.
    B)   The majority of them rotate much faster than the planets in our solar system.
    C)   Many of them are giant planets like Jupiter, orbiting at distances characteristic of terrestrial planets.
    D)   Many of them are terrestrial planets like Earth but orbiting at distances characteristic of giant planets.
    Ans: C   Section: 8-6

69. What is surprising about the planet orbiting the star 51 Pegasi?
    A)   It has a mass similar to that of Saturn, but its orbital radius is similar to that of Mars.
    B)   It has a mass almost as large as Jupiter, but its orbital radius is smaller than that of Mercury.
    C)   Its mass is similar to that of Mercury, but its orbital radius is similar to that of Jupiter.
    D)   Its mass and orbital radius are almost identical to that of Jupiter, indicating that 51 Pegasi may have a planetary system that is a twin of our own.
    Ans: B   Section: 8-6

70. Of the extrasolar planets that have been found, many have masses comparable to that of Jupiter but orbits smaller than Earth. What is believed to be the most likely explanation for this surprising combination?
    A) The protoplanetary disk was much denser than that of the Sun, and larger planets formed. Collisions between these planets then sent some of them into much smaller orbits.
    B) Friction with the protoplanetary disk caused the planets to migrate inward from much larger orbital distances.
    C) "Planets," are in fact low-mass objects that formed separately in the same manner as stars, and were later captured into the orbits in which we now see them.
    D) The protoplanetary disk was much denser than that of the Sun, allowing large planets to form very close to the star.
    Ans: B   Section: 8-6

71. Some extrasolar planets appear to have very surprising characteristics (Jupiter-like masses but very small orbital radii). What observational uncertainty may render this observation meaningless?
    A) The radial velocity method can only give a lower limit for a planet's mass, so they could be massive brown dwarf or low-mass stars.
    B) The astrometric method can only give an upper limit for a planet's mass, so they could be terrestrial planets.
    C) The astrometric method can only give a lower limit to the orbital radius, so they could be orbiting at the proper distance expected for a Jovian planet.
    D) The radial velocity method cannot distinguish between orbital variations due to a planet and stellar pulsations where the radial velocity variations are caused by motion of the star's surface. Thus, there may be no planets at all.
    Ans: A   Section: 8-6

72. Observers in a distant solar system are watching our Sun and using the radial velocity method to try to determine whether the Sun has planets. Because of the gravitational pull of Jupiter, these observers will see the Sun's spectrum slowly redshift and then blueshift by a tiny amount. How long must they observe in order to see a full cycle?
    A) 25 days
    B) one year
    C) almost 12 years
    D) It depends on how far away the observers are.
    Ans: C   Section: 8-6

73. Interaction between newly formed planets and gas and dust left over in the stellar nebula may account for our observation of
    A) large planets in orbits near their stars, but not the large eccentricities of their orbits.
    B) the large eccentricities of the orbits, but not the existence of large planets so close to their stars.
    C) both the existence of large planets in near orbits and the large eccentricities of the orbits.
    D) neither the existence of large planets in near orbits nor the large eccentricities of the orbits.
    Ans: C   Section: 8-6

Chapter 9: The Living Earth

1. When seen by astronauts traveling to the Moon, the noticeable color(s) of Earth was (were)
   A) gray and white.
   B) green and brown.
   C) brown.
   D) blue, white, and green.
   Ans: D   Section: 9-1

2. One distinct difference between Earth and its neighboring planets, Venus and Mars, is the presence of
   A) evidence of volcanic action both earlier in history and at present.
   B) desert regions.
   C) a gaseous atmosphere.
   D) liquid water on its surface and water molecules chemically locked into rocks.
   Ans: D   Section: 9-1

3. Earth's atmosphere differs from those of near-neighbor planets, Venus and Mars, in one important respect in that
   A) the atmospheric temperature at the surface is much higher than those of the other two planets.
   B) it has a much larger fraction of CO_2 than either of the other two atmospheres.
   C) it has a higher pressure than these other planetary atmospheres.
   D) it has a significant fraction of oxygen in it.
   Ans: D   Section: 9-1

4. The age of Earth is considered to be
   A) about 100 million years.
   B) about 4.6 billion years.
   C) about 4.6 million years.
   D) 93 million years.
   Ans: B   Section: 9-1

5. Which of the planets fits the following description: "cool solid surface with an atmosphere of N_2 and O_2 and H_2O clouds"?
   A) Mercury   B) Venus   C) Earth   D) Mars
   Ans: C   Section: 9-1

6. Which of the following is the major power source that drives the dynamics of Earth's atmosphere?
   A) outflow of the original heat of production from Earth's interior
   B) tidal effects from the Moon and Sun
   C) the burning of fossil fuels such as coal, oil, and natural gas on Earth's surface
   D) solar radiation
   Ans: D   Section: 9-1

7. The albedo of a planet is the fraction of energy that is
    A)   reradiated into space as infrared radiation by the planet.
    B)   reflected by the whole planet, including atmosphere and surface.
    C)   absorbed.
    D)   reflected by clouds in the atmosphere.
    Ans: B   Section: 9-1

8. What is the main mechanism by which the lower atmosphere of Earth is heated?
    A)   Sunlight heats Earth's surface and the resultant heat is transferred to the
         atmosphere by infrared radiation and convective gas motions.
    B)   Conduction carries heat from Earth's interior to the surface where conduction in
         the lower atmosphere transfers this heat to the higher layers.
    C)   friction between the winds in the atmosphere and the mountain ranges and land
         masses of Earth
    D)   absorption of sunlight by molecules of the gases of the atmosphere
    Ans: A   Section: 9-1

9. Energy calculations that simply equate the influx of solar energy on Earth with the
    outflow of energy from Earth lead to a very low average equilibrium temperature for
    Earth, of around −27°C or −16°F, which is much lower than the actual average surface
    temperature of Earth, +9°C or 48°F. What mechanism explains this discrepancy
    between the simple prediction and observation?
    A)   kinetic energy of meteoritic material that is dissipated in the atmosphere as the
         particles are stopped by friction
    B)   chemical action between molecules in Earth's atmosphere
    C)   the greenhouse effect—the capture by gases in the atmosphere of heat radiation
         that would otherwise escape
    D)   extra energy conducted outward from the hot interior of Earth
    Ans: C   Section: 9-1

10. The greenhouse effect is the
    A)   absorption of solar ultraviolet radiation by gases in planetary atmospheres leading
         to atmospheric heating.
    B)   absorption of solar infrared radiation by the atmosphere and the subsequent
         heating of a planet's surface.
    C)   protection of the surface of a planet from harmful infrared rays by atmospheric
         gases.
    D)   absorption by atmospheric gases of infrared radiation emitted by a planet that has
         been heated by solar visible and ultraviolet radiation.
    Ans: D   Section: 9-1

11. The surface temperature of Earth is actually warmer than expected from the amount of sunlight received. This is a result of
    A)   Earth's magnetic field.
    B)   the greenhouse effect.
    C)   a large outflux of heat from Earth's interior.
    D)   the force of gravity on Earth's atmosphere.
    Ans: B   Section: 9-1

12. The greenhouse effect is the
    A)   trapping of infrared radiation from Earth by the atmosphere.
    B)   accentuated growth of plants near the equator, compared to the growth in temperate regions.
    C)   capturing of visible and ultraviolet radiation from the Sun by the atmosphere.
    D)   shielding of life-forms from solar ultraviolet radiation by the ozone layer.
    Ans: A   Section: 9-1

13. Which of the following molecular species plays a major role in the greenhouse effect in planetary atmospheres?
    A) ozone   B) nitrogen   C) carbon dioxide   D) oxygen
    Ans: C   Section: 9-1

14. The Earth has a temperature and thus emits radiation somewhat like a blackbody. What is the source of the energy for this radiation?
    A)   incoming radiation received from the Sun
    B)   heat retained by the Earth's interior since it was created by the collisions of planetesimals
    C)   heat from radioactive decay deep within the Earth
    D)   tidal friction
    Ans: A   Section: 9-1

15. The Earth's albedo is 0.39. The total amount of radiant energy emitted (rather than reflected) by the Earth is thus
    A)   39% of the incoming radiation from the Sun.
    B)   61% of the incoming radiation from the Sun.
    C)   100% of the incoming radiation from the Sun.
    D)   actually slightly more than 100% of the incoming radiation from the Sun because of the Greenhouse effect.
    Ans: B   Section: 9-1

16. Suppose the Earth's albedo were greater than 0.39. This would mean that
    A) less radiant energy would be emitted by the Earth, and its temperature would be colder.
    B) more radiant energy would be emitted by the Earth, and its temperature would be warmer.
    C) the radiant energy emitted by the Earth would be 100% of the incoming radiation from the Sun, as it is now.
    D) the Greenhouse effect would be stronger, resulting in a higher surface temperature.
    Ans: A   Section: 9-1

17. Earth has an average density of
    A) three times that of water.   C) that of water.
    B) greater than 10 times that of water.   D) 5.5 times that of water.
    Ans: D   Section: 9-2

18. The mean density of Earth in terms of that of water (1000 kg/m^3 or 1 gm/cm^3) is
    A) smaller.   C) a little larger.
    B) more than 10 times greater.   D) 5.5 times greater.
    Ans: D   Section: 9-2

19. Which one of the following processes was important for melting the entire Earth about 4.6 billion years ago?
    A) radioactivity, or the spontaneous breaking apart of heavier nuclei into lighter nuclei
    B) tidal heating of Earth due to the combined gravitational pulls of the Sun and the Moon
    C) heat released by the condensation of water vapor into liquid water to form the oceans
    D) nuclear fusion, or the combining of lighter nuclei to form heavier nuclei
    Ans: A   Section: 9-2

20. "Chemical differentiation" in planetary sciences refers to
    A) the formation of rocky planets in the hotter, inner solar system and gas giants in the colder, outer regions.
    B) the circulation of iron in the core of a planet, resulting in the generation of a magnetic field.
    C) the large-scale convection of rock in the mantle of a planet, that on Earth causes continental drift.
    D) the sinking of heavier elements toward the center of a planet and the floating of lighter elements toward the surface.
    Ans: D   Section: 9-2

21. To form the present structure of Earth, which of the following mechanisms is most likely to have taken place while Earth was molten?
    A)   Heavy elements sank to the center under gravity, while lighter materials rose to the surface and solidified into rocks.
    B)   Lighter elements sank to the center leaving the heavier material to form the rocky surface after cooling.
    C)   Hydrogen and helium became highly compressed by gravity and sank to the core below a layer of heavier rocky material.
    D)   All materials were thoroughly mixed by convection in the molten state, and Earth remained mixed as it cooled.
    Ans: A   Section: 9-2

22. The process by which heavier materials sank into the centers of terrestrial planets while lighter material rose to the surfaces early in the history of these planets is known as
    A)   seafloor spreading.   C)   chemical differentiation.
    B)   plate tectonics.   D)   subduction.
    Ans: C   Section: 9-2

23. Terrestrial planets are thought to have dense iron cores because
    A)   the accumulation of material into planets in the original solar system nebula would have begun with the heavier elements, to be followed later by lighter materials.
    B)   magnetism in iron would be sufficiently powerful to pull more iron into the center of the forming planet.
    C)   thermonuclear processes produced iron in the earlier phases of planetary formation.
    D)   in earlier molten states the heavy elements sank and lighter materials floated to the surface by chemical differentiation.
    Ans: D   Section: 9-2

24. Where is the mantle of Earth located?
    A)   between the stratosphere and the thermosphere
    B)   outside of, but in contact with, the crust; i.e., the oceans and atmosphere
    C)   in the outermost atmosphere and beyond, where the planet's magnetic field captures solar wind particles
    D)   between core and crust
    Ans: D   Section: 9-2

25. The mantle of Earth is composed of
    A) water.   B) iron.   C) atmospheric gases.   D) rock.
    Ans: D   Section: 9-2

26. The core of Earth occupies what fraction of its radius?
    A) about 25%   B) roughly half   C) less than 10%   D) almost 80%
    Ans: B   Section: 9-2

27. What is the basic structure of Earth's interior?
    A) solid iron inner core, molten iron outer core, rocky mantle, lighter rocky crust
    B) molten iron inner core, molten rocky outer core, solid rocky mantle, lighter rocky crust
    C) molten iron core, molten rocky mantle, solid rocky crust
    D) molten iron inner core, solid iron outer core, rocky mantle, lighter rocky crust
    Ans: A   Section: 9-2

28. The internal structure of Earth is a
    A) core of solid rock extensively enriched in iron, surrounded by a solid mantle of pure rock.
    B) large core of iron, partly solid and partly molten, surrounded by a thick, flexible mantle of rock.
    C) large, solid iron core surrounded by a thick, flexible mantle of rock.
    D) core of rock and iron, surrounded by a mantle of liquid hydrogen.
    Ans: B   Section: 9-2

29. The core of Earth is composed of
    A) mostly iron.
    B) titanium and nickel.
    C) roughly half rock and half iron.
    D) rock of similar composition to that in the crust.
    Ans: A   Section: 9-2

30. Which scientific approach gives us the most information about the deep interior of Earth?
    A) deep drilling of exploratory holes for science and mineral recovery (e.g., oil)
    B) study of lava flows from volcanoes
    C) worldwide measurement of low-frequency seismic waves produced by earthquakes
    D) measurement of cosmic neutrinos, which pass very easily through Earth
    Ans: C   Section: 9-2

31. Which of the following techniques is used by geologists and geophysicists to probe the structure of Earth's core and mantle?
    A) direct sampling of interior rock by deep drilling through the ocean floor
    B) extrapolation of surface features (e.g., mountain chains) into the deep interior
    C) study of the deflection of seismic waves produced by earthquakes
    D) X-ray analysis from satellites
    Ans: C   Section: 9-2

32. A "Slinky" toy is made up of a long flexible spring. The analogous wave to the (P) or primary wave produced in an Earthquake would be generated by moving the end of the spring
    A) round and round, in a circular motion perpendicular to the axis of the spring.
    B) in a twisting motion back and forth, thereby tightening and loosening the spiral of the spring.
    C) side to side, in a direction perpendicular to the spring.
    D) back and forth in a direction along the spring.
    Ans: D   Section: 9-2

33. The waves that geologists and geophysicists use to probe the inside of Earth are
    A) seismic waves.   B) gravitational waves.   C) radio waves.   D) microwaves.
    Ans: A   Section: 9-2

34. The vibrations in the primary (P) and secondary (S) seismic waves caused by earthquakes are
    A) along the direction of travel for both waves.
    B) perpendicular to the direction of travel for P waves and along the direction of travel for S waves.
    C) at right angles to the direction of travel for both waves.
    D) perpendicular to the direction of travel for S waves and along the direction of travel for P waves.
    Ans: D   Section: 9-2

35. Secondary (S) seismic waves in the Earth have the following characteristics:
    A) vibrations perpendicular to the direction of travel of the waves; cannot traverse liquids.
    B) vibrations perpendicular to the direction of travel; only travel along the surface of the Earth.
    C) vibrations along the direction of travel of the waves; cannot traverse liquids.
    D) vibrations perpendicular to the direction of travel of the waves; can traverse liquids.
    Ans: A   Section: 9-2

36. Why do transverse seismic S waves not traverse Earth's deep interior?
    A) They cannot travel through the liquid part of the core.
    B) Earth is not transparent to these electromagnetic waves.
    C) They cannot travel through the dense, solid core.
    D) They are surface waves and travel only along the surface of Earth.
    Ans: A   Section: 9-2

37. The point on Earth's surface directly above an earthquake is known as its
    A) focus.   B) shadow zone.   C) epicenter.   D) discontinuity.
    Ans: C   Section: 9-2

38. The shadow zone, in which seismic waves from an earthquake cannot be detected, is caused by
    A) S and P waves being refracted at the boundary of Earth's core and P waves being absorbed by the core.
    B) both P and S waves being refracted into Earth's core, thus concentrating the waves on the far side of Earth.
    C) all seismic waves being absorbed by Earth's molten core, so that none reach the far side of Earth.
    D) S and P waves being refracted at the boundary of Earth's core and S waves being absorbed by the core.
    Ans: D   Section: 9-2

39. Seismic waves inside Earth
    A) travel at a constant speed but change direction (refract) as they travel through materials of different densities or compositions.
    B) travel at different speeds in materials of different densities or compositions and change direction (refract) as they move from one material to another.
    C) travel in straight lines with speeds that change as the waves move through materials of different densities or compositions.
    D) always travel in a straight line at a constant speed.
    Ans: B   Section: 9-2

40. The main reason that deep P and S seismic waves do not travel in straight lines inside Earth is that
    A) Earth is spherical, and the waves follow the shape of the surface of Earth.
    B) they cannot travel through molten regions, and thus reflect back toward the surface of Earth.
    C) they reflect and scatter off numerous irregularities and faults inside Earth.
    D) their speed changes with changing density, causing the waves to refract.
    Ans: D   Section: 9-2

41. The temperature of the deep interior of Earth is approximately
    A) 5000°C.   B) 50,000°C.   C) 1.5×10^6°C.   D) 500°C.
    Ans: A   Section: 9-2

42. The material of Earth's interior (see Fig. 9-9, Freedman and Kaufmann, *Universe*, 7th ed.) becomes molten at a certain depth below the surface. This depth is
    A) 5200 km.
    B) 300 km.
    C) This statement is erroneous, because nowhere is the interior molten.
    D) 2900 km.
    Ans: D   Section: 9-2

43. The depth from the surface of Earth to the top of its liquid core is about (see Fig. 9-9, Freedman and Kaufmann, *Universe*, 7th ed.)
    A) 30 km. B) 6400 km. C) 5000 km. D) 2900 km.
    Ans: D   Section: 9-2

44. Earth's solid inner core results from the fact that the
    A) temperature of the inner core is lower than the temperature of the outer core, producing a "temperature inversion."
    B) melting temperature of an iron-nickel mixture increases with increasing pressure and rises above the actual temperature in the inner core.
    C) outer core is heated and melted by friction between the core and the mantle, and this heating does not extend to the inner core.
    D) inner core has a different composition than the outer core, with a higher melting temperature.
    Ans: B   Section: 9-2

45. What effect does an increase in pressure have on the temperature at which rock melts?
    A) We do not know yet. Temperatures needed to melt rock have not yet been achieved in the laboratory.
    B) It increases the melting temperature.
    C) It lowers the melting temperature.
    D) It has no effect on the melting temperature, because the melting temperature is independent of pressure
    Ans: B   Section: 9-2

46. The outer core of Earth is molten, but the inner core is solid. The reason for this is that the
    A) actual temperature is below the melting point of iron-nickel mixture at the high pressure of the interior.
    B) lower pressure in the inner core allows the material to freeze out of the molten rock.
    C) inner core has a different composition than the outer core, with a higher melting point.
    D) temperature is lower in the inner core than in the surrounding region.
    Ans: A   Section: 9-2

47. Which of the following statements correctly describes the mantle of Earth?
    A) molten iron
    B) molten rock
    C) solid rock that is hot enough to become semimolten and be able to flow
    D) solid, immovable but smooth rock on which the crustal plates can slide
    Ans: C   Section: 9-2

48. The Earth's mantle is composed largely of what chemical materials?
    A)   almost pure iron   C)   solid hydrogen and helium
    B)   silicon-rich rocks and minerals   D)   minerals rich in iron and magnesium
    Ans: D   Section: 9-2

49. What is believed to be the composition of Earth's core?
    A)   about 1/4 iron and 3/4 lighter elements
    B)   about half iron and half lighter elements
    C)   about 80% iron and 20% lighter elements
    D)   essentially pure iron
    Ans: D   Section: 9-2

50. The chemical makeup of the central core of Earth is considered to be
    A)   very close to that at the surface, silicon-rich rocks and minerals.
    B)   iron-rich minerals.
    C)   mainly solid hydrogen and helium similar to that of the giant planets.
    D)   almost pure iron.
    Ans: D   Section: 9-2

51. The internal structure of Earth is a
    A)   core of solid rock extensively enriched in iron surrounded by a solid mantle of
         pure rock.
    B)   core of rock and iron surrounded by a mantle of liquid hydrogen.
    C)   large, mostly molten, core of iron and nickel surrounded by a thick flexible mantle
         of rock.
    D)   large solid core of iron and nickel surrounded by a thick flexible mantle of rock.
    Ans: C   Section: 9-2

52. Earth's interior received its heat energy from the impacts of planetesimals and from
    radioactivity. This heat energy is gradually radiating into space. As the Earth's interior
    continues to cool, we can expect that, in the distant future,
    A)   the inner core will become molten like the outer core.
    B)   the outer core will become solid like the inner core.
    C)   the mantle will become molten while the core will become solid.
    D)   the entire interior will become one homogeneous solid.
    Ans: B   Section: 9-2

53. We have found that the upper layers of the mantle are "plastic." Why is this important?
    A)   Plastic is an important resource for the future.
    B)   These layers can easily crack to allow pent-up heat and energy to escape.
    C)   These layers can easily bend to accommodate oceans and mountains.
    D)   The continents are able to float and drift on these layers.
    Ans: D   Section: 9-2 and 9-3

54. "Continental drift" on the Earth is now thought to be caused by
    A) earthquakes.
    B) precession of the Earth's spin axis.
    C) tidal forces from the the Moon and Sun acting on the continental land masses.
    D) circulation currents in the deep interior causing slabs of the Earth's crust to move slowly.
    Ans: D   Section: 9-3

55. Continental drift on the Earth is a result of
    A) large-scale circulation of partly molten or plastic rock in Earth's interior.
    B) water percolating down through geological fault zones, acting as a lubricant.
    C) the momentum of impacts from giant asteroids or planetoids hitting the early Earth.
    D) flexing of the Earth's surface by lunar and solar tides.
    Ans: A   Section: 9-3

56. Who first postulated that continents drift around over the Earth's surface?
    A) Alfred Wegener   C) James Van Allen
    B) Jules Pangaea   D) Bruce C. Heezen
    Ans: A   Section: 9-3

57. Which fact first gave Alfred Wegener the idea that continents had drifted over Earth's surface?
    A) The ocean floors were much younger than the continents, indicating that they were still being formed.
    B) Volcanoes and earthquakes were localized into a well-defined "ring of fire" around the Pacific Ocean and other areas.
    C) A system of mountains and faults running up the middle of the Atlantic sea floor showed evidence that the crust was spreading apart.
    D) The east coasts of north and south America fit nicely against the west coasts of Europe and Africa.
    Ans: D   Section: 9-3

58. Approximately how many tectonic plates make up Earth's surface?
    A) seven (one under each continent)
    B) two (the eastern and western hemispheres)
    C) about ten
    D) hundreds
    Ans: C   Section: 9-3

59. Which of the following statements correctly describes the surface of Earth?
    A) a thin, deformable crust that allows the continents to slide over it
    B) individual, solid crustal plates that are pushed around by Earth's rotation and the tidal forces of the Moon and Sun
    C) individual and separate solid crustal plates floating on, and being pushed around by, the underlying semimolten mantle
    D) a thick, solid crust that holds the continents and ocean floors fixed in position
    Ans: C   Section: 9-3

60. What is the relationship between the mantle and the crust of Earth?
    A) The crust sits motionless on top of the mantle and does not interact with it.
    B) Convection in the mantle moves the continents around, but there is no transfer of material from the mantle to the crust or vice-versa.
    C) New crust is formed by magma rising from the mantle in some places, and old crust is pushed back down into the mantle in other places.
    D) New layers of crust are formed when magma from the mantle flows out over old crust and old crust is pushed back down into the mantle by the weight of the magma on top of it.
    Ans: C   Section: 9-3

61. The supercontinent Pangaea was apparently
    A) the original continent that was created after Earth formed and broke up 200 million years ago.
    B) a myth, part of the Atlantis legend.
    C) a random assemblage of continents that occurred earlier in Earth's history but appears to be part of no cyclic pattern.
    D) the result of a collision of continents, of a type that occurs roughly every 500 million years.
    Ans: D   Section: 9-3

62. The name "Pangaea" refers to the
    A) supercontinent that split into the present North and South America, Europe, and Africa.
    B) tectonic plate on which most of North America is riding.
    C) ocean that covered most of North America millions of years ago.
    D) outer life-bearing layer of Earth, including the soil, oceans, and atmosphere.
    Ans: A   Section: 9-3

63. In what way are the supercontinents Laurasia, Pangaea, and Gondwanaland related?
    A) An earlier, larger supercontinent split into Laurasia, Pangaea, and Gondwanaland.
    B) Pangaea split into Gondwanaland and Laurasia.
    C) Gondwanaland split into Pangaea and Laurasia.
    D) Laurasia split into Gondwanaland and Pangaea.
    Ans: B   Section: 9-3

64. In the modern theory of crustal motion on Earth's surface, the process of seafloor spreading is described as the
    A) motion of plates away from mid-oceanic ridges and toward continental boundaries.
    B) upward motions of some plates and the downward motions of others while remaining in fixed positions on Earth.
    C) rotation of plates around axes that remain stationary on Earth, causing plate-edge collisions.
    D) motion of plates toward mid-oceanic ridges and away from continental boundaries.
    Ans: A   Section: 9-3

65. The African and South American continents are separating at a rate of about 3 cm per year according to the ideas of plate tectonics. If they are now 5000 km apart and have moved at a constant speed over this time, how long ago is it since they were in contact?
    A) 1.6 million years   C) 1.6 billion years
    B) 0.16 billion years   D) 0.16 million years
    Ans: B   Section: 9-3

66. The average speed of motion of the plates on Earth's surface is
    A) about 10 meters per year.
    B) very small, less than a millimeter per century.
    C) a few centimeters per century.
    D) a few centimeters per year.
    Ans: D   Section: 9-3

67. What is a typical speed of drift for a continent sliding over Earth's surface?
    A) a few meters per year   C) a few centimeters per year
    B) a few centimeters per million years D) a few centimeters per century
    Ans: C   Section: 9-3

68. The process of seafloor spreading and plate tectonic movement on Earth's surface takes place at a speed of
    A) a few meters per year.   C) a few centimeters per year.
    B) a few centimeters per century. D) less than a millimeter per year.
    Ans: C   Section: 9-3

69. The Mid-Atlantic Ridge in Earth's crust is a region where
    A) two tectonic plates are slowly spreading apart.
    B) a single hot plume is pushing molten magma or lava through a hole in the crust.
    C) two tectonic plates are pushing against one another, forcing the ridge upward.
    D) one tectonic plate is moving below another (subducting).
    Ans: A   Section: 9-3

70. The Mid-Atlantic Ridge is being produced by
    A)   two tectonic plates pushing together and producing upthrust.
    B)   volcanic upflow pushing two tectonic plates apart.
    C)   the tidal flow of ocean water meeting in the mid-Atlantic.
    D)   the weight of the Atlantic Ocean bending the thin crust on the seabed.
    Ans: B   Section: 9-3

71. The long and high mountain ranges found in the centers of several major oceans on
    Earth, such as the Mid-Atlantic Ridge, are caused by
    A)   continuous and steady erosion of the seabed on either side of the mountains by
          powerful sea currents flowing across the oceans, such as the Gulf Stream in the
          Atlantic.
    B)   lava upflow as the tectonic plates on the seafloor split apart and separate.
    C)   the rebounding of the surface of Earth in the centers of the large craters that
          became the ocean basins after the impacts of the large planetesimals or asteroids
          early in Earth's history.
    D)   upthrust and buckling caused by seafloor motions from the continents toward the
          ocean centers, equivalent to the production of continental mountain ranges such as
          the Rockies.
    Ans: B   Section: 9-3

72. The Mid-Atlantic Ridge has been formed by
    A)   two crustal plates sliding past each other in a transverse fault.
    B)   the weight of sediments causing the ocean floor to sink and slump toward the
          center of this ocean basin.
    C)   two crustal plates colliding, one plate moving under the other, causing the upper
          plate to buckle.
    D)   molten rock pushing up from Earth's interior and forcing two crustal plates apart.
    Ans: D   Section: 9-3

73. Which of the following places on Earth experiences frequent earthquakes and volcanic
    activity because of its location? (See Figs. 9-12 and 9-13, Freedman and Kaufmann,
    Universe, 7th ed.)
    A) Central Canada   B) Iceland   C) Australia   D) Brazil
    Ans: B   Section: 9-3

74. Which two tectonic plates are slowly separating from each other along the Mid-Atlantic
    Ridge in the south Atlantic? (See Fig. 9-12, Freedman and Kaufmann, *Universe,* 7th ed.)
    A)   Nazca and Pacific plates   C)   Pacific and Australia-India plates
    B)   African and Eurasian plates   D)   South American and African plates
    Ans: D   Section: 9-3

75. The Australia-India tectonic plate (See Fig. 9-12, Freedman and Kaufmann, *Universe*, 7th ed.) is pushing against which plate to form the Himalayan mountains?
    A)   Antarctic Plate
    C)   African Plate
    B)   Eurasian Plate
    D)   North American Plate
    Ans: B   Section: 9-3

76. The San Andreas fault in California is an example of
    A)   an upthrust due to a hot spot in Earth's mantle.
    B)   a subduction zone, where one plate is pushed back down into Earth.
    C)   a spreading center, where two tectonic plates are being pushed away from each other.
    D)   two tectonic plates sliding past each other.
    Ans: D   Section: 9-3

77. All the boundaries of the major moving tectonic plates on Earth's surface coincide with
    A)   the edges of the continental shelves around the major continents.
    B)   regions where ocean depths are greatest.
    C)   the occurrence of major auroral activity.
    D)   the positions of maximum earthquake occurrence.
    Ans: D   Section: 9-3

78. On Earth, the majority of earthquakes occur
    A)   along the zone of maximum tidal stress around the equator.
    B)   in the arctic and antarctic regions.
    C)   in the centers of tectonic plates (e.g., North American continent).
    D)   along the boundaries of major tectonic plates.
    Ans: D   Section: 9-3

79. Most earthquakes occur
    A)   only where crustal plates are sliding past each other, as in the San Andreas fault.
    B)   where crustal plates are colliding, separating or sliding past each other.
    C)   more or less evenly over the entire Earth's surface.
    D)   only where crustal plates are colliding head-on.
    Ans: B   Section: 9-3

80. The motions of large portions of Earth's surface, or "plates," are caused by
    A)   tidal forces from the Moon and the Sun, acting on continental landmasses.
    B)   the varying pressure of Earth's atmosphere, both daily and seasonally.
    C)   flexing of the surface due to solar heating and nighttime cooling.
    D)   convective flow of matter in Earth's interior.
    Ans: D   Section: 9-3

81. The asthenosphere is
    A)   the layer of Earth's atmosphere that lies above the stratosphere.
    B)   a layer below the Earth's crust.
    C)   a layer in the atmosphere of Venus containing the densest clouds.
    D)   one of the colored layers in the atmosphere of Jupiter.
    Ans: B   Section: 9-3

82. The lithosphere of Earth is the
    A)   solid outer layer that is divided into rigid, moving plates.
    B)   molten outer core, composed of iron and nickel.
    C)   atmospheric layer between the stratosphere and the thermosphere, where
         temperature decreases with height.
    D)   soft layer under the outer crust that allows the rigid crustal plates to move around
         and collide.
    Ans: A   Section: 9-3

83. Deep oceanic trenches on Earth are locations where
    A)   volcanic material comes out from the deep interior at volcanic islands.
    B)   molten lava oozes out between two tectonic plates that are spreading apart.
    C)   dense material sank while lighter material rose to the surface during the early
         geological history.
    D)   cool surface material sinks below or subducts other material at a tectonic plate
         boundary.
    Ans: D   Section: 9-3

84. The deepest parts of Earth's oceans are
    A)   subduction zones, where one tectonic plate is flowing under an adjacent plate.
    B)   at the two poles, near the ends of the spin axis, where tidal distortion from the
         Moon and Sun is least.
    C)   in the centers of the oceans, where deep and fast ocean currents such as the Gulf
         Stream have scooped out the troughs.
    D)   where large asteroids or planetoids have impacted in the past and have produced
         deep craters.
    Ans: A   Section: 9-3

85. Subduction in the Earth is the process by which
    A)   dense material sank while lighter material rose to the surface during the early
         geological history.
    B)   molten lava oozes out between two tectonic plates that are spreading apart.
    C)   cool surface material sinks below other material at a tectonic plate boundary.
    D)   volcanic material flows from the deep interior to produce volcanic islands.
    Ans: C   Section: 9-3

86. The Rocky Mountains of North America were formed by
    A)   asteroid impacts during the first billion years of Earth's history.
    B)   folding of Earth's crust where two crustal plates collided along a subduction zone.
    C)   giant dinosaurs dragging their tails along the ground, gouging out the valleys.
    D)   an ancient mid-ocean ridge, now uplifted to become dry land.
    Ans: B   Section: 9-3

87. What caused the great mountain ranges on Earth, such as the Rocky Mountains and the Andes?
    A)   collisions of two tectonic plates, where one is folded into mountains while the other is thrust underneath
    B)   two tectonic plates being pushed apart by molten rock that is being forced up between them
    C)   heat from Earth's interior causing Earth's crust to expand and then crumple
    D)   the carving of continents by ice sheets during ice ages, with the mountains left behind as "islands" in a sea of glaciers
    Ans: A   Section: 9-3

88. The great mountain ranges of Earth have been produced by
    A)   volcanic eruptions.
    B)   wrinkling of the crust as the interior cools and contracts.
    C)   asteroid impacts, because they are just worn-down crater walls.
    D)   collisions between tectonic plates.
    Ans: D   Section: 9-3

89. Craters as seen on the Moon are not apparent on Earth at the present time because
    A)   the Moon protected Earth from impacts, and this resulted in the craters and maria on the Moon.
    B)   interplanetary objects have avoided Earth during its history.
    C)   plate tectonics has returned cratered surface layers into Earth's interior, and weathering has obliterated the more recent craters.
    D)   all the potentially damaging interplanetary bodies were stopped by Earth's atmosphere.
    Ans: C   Section: 9-3

90. In planetary geology, a mineral is defined as a particular
    A)   chemical element or chemical combination of elements in a rock.
    B)   type of rock, such as granite.
    C)   rock having undergone a specific formation process, such as an igneous or metamorphic rock.
    D)   chemical element in a rock.
    Ans: A   Section: 9-3

91. Chemical elements are rarely found in their pure states in Earth's crust. Which of the following groups of elements are often found in their pure states rather than always in chemical compounds in Earth's crust?
    A) copper, silver and gold
    B) silicon and iron
    C) hydrogen and oxygen
    D) magnesium and calcium
    Ans: A   Section: 9-3

92. On Earth, you would expect to find metamorphic rocks
    A) at the boundaries of colliding tectonic plates, where upthrust has brought them to the surface.
    B) on the ice of the Antarctic, since they come only from outer space.
    C) around new volcanoes, these rocks having recently set from new molten lava.
    D) in layers on the sea floor.
    Ans: A   Section: 9-3

93. On the big island of Hawaii, the most common rocks are
    A) sedimentary rocks.
    B) meteoritic rocks.
    C) igneous rocks.
    D) metamorphic rocks.
    Ans: C   Section: 9-3

94. Sedimentary rocks commonly form from
    A) rocks being carried deep below a planetary surface and being modified by heat and pressure.
    B) minerals precipitating out of the oceans and accumulating on the ocean bottom.
    C) molten rock (lava) solidifying as it flows downward from volcanoes.
    D) mineral crystals solidifying in magma (molten rock) and settling down to the bottom of the molten region.
    Ans: B   Section: 9-3

95. Which of the following geological materials originated as molten lava?
    A) sandstone   B) marble rock   C) limestone   D) igneous rock
    Ans: D   Section: 9-3

96. Suppose that an astronaut trained in geology lands on the surface of a distant planet and finds that most of the rock at the landing site is composed of limestone. The astronaut can immediately surmise that the location of the landing site
    A) was once subjected to enormous pressure and high temperature deep under the planet's surface, causing the original rock to change structure.
    B) solidified from molten rock close to the surface of the planet.
    C) solidified from molten rock deep beneath the surface of the planet.
    D) was once the bed of an ancient ocean.
    Ans: D   Section: 9-3

97. What is the difference between minerals and rocks?
    A)   A mineral is formed of a single element or compound; rocks can be composed of more than one mineral.
    B)   A rock is formed of a single element or compound; minerals can be composed of more than one rock.
    C)   Minerals exist only deep in the Earth's core; rocks exist in the mantle and crust.
    D)   Minerals occur only in lava flows; rocks are formed only in nonvolcanic regions.
    Ans: A   Section: 9-3

98. Sedimentary rocks are found
    A)   only on the present-day ocean floor.
    B)   only on the floors of ancient oceans.
    C)   only in the volcanic regions.
    D)   just about everywhere on the Earth's surface.
    Ans: D   Section: 9-3

99. Earth's magnetic field is thought to be caused by
    A)   the flow of solar wind particles around and within its outer atmospheric region—the magnetosphere.
    B)   electric currents flowing in the liquid core.
    C)   localized magnetic anomalies near the Earth's surface.
    D)   a magnetized solid iron core in the interior.
    Ans: B   Section: 9-4

100. Earth's magnetic field is generated by
    A)   permanent magnetism in Earth's crustal rocks.
    B)   electric currents in Earth's core.
    C)   electric currents in Earth's mantle.
    D)   the flow of electrons and ions in Earth's magnetosphere.
    Ans: B   Section: 9-4

101. Earth's magnetic field is caused by
    A)   electric currents flowing in the molten core.
    B)   the motion of the electrically charged particles of the solar wind as they pass the Earth.
    C)   a solid iron magnet in its interior.
    D)   electric currents flowing in the ionospheric layer of its atmosphere.
    Ans: A   Section: 9-4

102. Earth's magnetic field originates in
    A)   a solid, permanently magnetized core in the interior of Earth.
    B)   intense electric currents flowing in the Van Allen belts within the magnetosphere of Earth.
    C)   the tidal ebb and flow of electrically conducting seawater in Earth's oceans.
    D)   slowly moving currents of molten iron which produce electric currents in the deep interior of Earth.
    Ans: D   Section: 9-4

103. Earth is not thought to have a permanent magnet in its interior because the
    A)   magnetic field reverses direction over periods of tens of thousands of years.
    B)   magnetic field distribution in space around Earth does not match that of a permanent magnet.
    C)   rotation of Earth quickly destroys the properties of a permanent magnet.
    D)   core is not made of magnetic material.
    Ans: A   Section: 9-4

104. Earth's magnetosphere is
    A)   a cavity in the solar wind carved out and controlled by the Earth's magnetic field.
    B)   Earth's molten core where motion of electrically charged particles produces the magnetic field.
    C)   a layer in the atmosphere between stratosphere and thermosphere where motions are governed by magnetic effects.
    D)   a region of the Earth's surface near the magnetic poles.
    Ans: A   Section: 9-4

105. Earth's magnetosphere is the
    A)   molten core, whose motions produce the magnetic field.
    B)   region beyond the atmosphere, where the magnetic field protects us from solar wind.
    C)   atmospheric layer between the stratosphere and thermosphere, where motions are governed by the magnetic field.
    D)   region in the crust near each magnetic pole.
    Ans: B   Section: 9-4

106. Suppose that the Earth was somehow put into orbit around a cool star (cooler than our Sun) at the right distance for our oceans to remain liquid so that life could still exist but the star emitted no UV radiation. Which of the following statements would most likely be FALSE?
    A)   Our ozone layer would disappear.
    B)   Our magnetosphere would disappear.
    C)   Our thermosphere would disappear.
    D)   We would be closer to the star than we are to our present sun.
    Ans: B   Section: 9-4 and 9-5

107. Which of the following is not a region of the Earth's atmosphere?
A) stratosphere   B) chromosphere   C) magnetosphere   D) troposphere
Ans: B   Section: 9-4

108. What mechanism forms the magnetospheres around several of the planets?
A)   the gravitational force of attraction of the other planets on the planetary upper atmosphere
B)   the very rapid spin of these planets, spinning the atmosphere outward
C)   repulsion of solar electromagnetic radiation by the planetary magnetic field
D)   repulsion of the solar wind by the planetary magnetic field
Ans: D   Section: 9-4

109. The magnetopause is the part of the magnetosphere where
A)   high-energy electrons and protons collide with gases in the planet's upper atmosphere, producing fluorescence.
B)   supersonic particles in the solar wind are suddenly slowed to subsonic speeds.
C)   high-energy charged particles are trapped by the planet's magnetic field.
D)   the inward pressure of the solar wind is balanced by the outward magnetic pressure of the planet's magnetic field.
Ans: D   Section: 9-4

110. What protects us from the damaging radiation effects of the high-speed solar wind that flows through interplanetary space?
A)   the rapid rotation of the Earth, which deflects most of the solar wind
B)   the Moon, whose gravitational field shields us from the solar wind
C)   Earth's atmosphere
D)   the Earth's magnetic field
Ans: D   Section: 9-4

111. The Van Allen belts are
A)   regions of the Earth in which no seismic activity is detected from earthquakes.
B)   dense collections of small rocks surrounding the major planets.
C)   two doughnut-shaped rings of charged particles, surrounding the equatorial regions of Earth at very high altitudes.
D)   undersea mountain ranges in the centers of the oceans.
Ans: C   Section: 9-4

112. What are the Van Allen belts?
A)   Regions of high-energy charged particles in the Earth's magnetosphere.
B)   Regions in the outer solar system beyond Pluto, where comets are thought to originate.
C)   Regions of intense earthquake activity along tectonic plate boundaries on the Earth.
D)   Dark regions in Jupiter's atmosphere, circling the planet parallel to the equator.
Ans: A   Section: 9-4

113. What are the Van Allen belts?
    A)   Two donut-shaped regions of high-energy charged particles in the Earth's magnetosphere.
    B)   An oval-shaped region around each of the Earth's magnetic poles where charged particles collide with ions in the Earth's atmosphere.
    C)   The inner and outer parts of the asteroid belt.
    D)   Regions of high ion concentration in the Earth's upper atmosphere, where radio waves are reflected back toward the surface of the Earth.
    Ans: A   Section: 9-4

114. The Van Allen belts are
    A)   zones on the Earth where seismic waves from an earthquake are not felt.
    B)   faint halos of interplanetary dust between Moon and Earth.
    C)   layers of the Earth's atmosphere between troposphere and stratosphere.
    D)   regions of high-energy charged particles trapped within the Earth's magnetosphere.
    Ans: D   Section: 9-4

115. The Van Allen belts associated with the Earth are
    A)   layers of meteoritic dust in the Earth's atmosphere, trapped in regions where the temperature reaches a minimum.
    B)   regions of intense radiation of protons and electrons trapped within the magnetosphere above the Earth.
    C)   rings of dust surrounding Earth, similar to the rings of Saturn.
    D)   zones of varying depths below the Earth's surface in which the speed of sound has distinctly different values.
    Ans: B   Section: 9-4

116. Van Allen radiation belts are located in the
    A)   stratosphere.
    B)   molten iron core.
    C)   magnetosphere.
    D)   auroral regions over the north and south magnetic poles.
    Ans: C   Section: 9-4

117. Aurorae on the Earth are caused by
    A)   electrical currents in the ionosphere, generated by dynamo action in Earth's core.
    B)   charged particles from the sun moving through Earth's magnetic field and striking the upper atmosphere.
    C)   the reflection of sunlight from arctic and antarctic ice into the polar night skies
    D)   ultraviolet radiation from the Sun ionizing atoms in the upper atmosphere.
    Ans: B   Section: 9-4

118. The auroral display of northern and southern lights in the atmosphere is caused by
    A)   reflection of sunlight from the ice in the polar regions.
    B)   solar wind electrons hitting the high atmosphere after being accelerated by the magnetosphere.
    C)   sunlight scattered by very high atmospheric clouds.
    D)   fluorescence from solar ultraviolet light.
    Ans: B   Section: 9-4

119. Auroras, or northern and southern lights, are caused by
    A)   solar ultraviolet light exciting ozone molecules in the ozone layer.
    B)   charged particles emitting light as they spiral along magnetic field lines in the magnetosphere.
    C)   light from solar flares reflecting from high-altitude clouds in Earth's atmosphere.
    D)   charged particles from the magnetosphere, striking atoms in the upper atmosphere and causing the gases to emit light.
    Ans: D   Section: 9-4

120. Auroral displays are most often
    A)   directly above the North and South geomagnetic poles.
    B)   in two bands on either side of the equator in the tropics.
    C)   at the North and South geographical poles.
    D)   in circular regions around the North and South geomagnetic poles.
    Ans: D   Section: 9-4

121. In you were able to measure the Earth's magnetic field at some time, say, 100,000 to 200,000 years ago, you would
    A)   find the field to be zero because the Earth's field is a relatively recent development.
    B)   certainly find the field to be exactly what it is today.
    C)   most likely find the field to be quite different in magnitude from what it is today.
    D)   certainly find the field to be the same magnitude it is today, but exactly opposite in direction.
    Ans: C   Section: 9-4

122. Which one of the following statements about the solar wind is true?
    A)   It consists almost entirely of hydrogen and helium.
    B)   The "solar wind" is another name for the Sun's magnetic field when it extends far beyond the Sun.
    C)   It originates in the Van Allen Radiation Belts.
    D)   Its particles travel at very high speeds.
    Ans: D   Section: 9-4

123. The presence of oxygen in Earth's atmosphere is thought to result directly from what type of process?
    A)   volcanic eruptions
    B)   original condensation of interplanetary gas clouds
    C)   outgassing of the oceans
    D)   biological activity of plants and animals
    Ans: D   Section: 9-5

124. The large amount of free oxygen in Earth's present atmosphere is primarily a result of
    A)   splitting of CO_2 into carbon and oxygen by solar ultraviolet light.
    B)   a biological process such as photosynthesis.
    C)   the outgassing by volcanoes and other geological processes.
    D) CO_2 becoming dissolved in the oceans, releasing O_2.
    Ans: B   Section: 9-5

125. The molecular oxygen in the Earth's present atmosphere was most probably produced
    A)   from seawater by outgassing.
    B)   from volcanic eruptions as the primitive Earth cooled down.
    C)   by biological activity, such as photosynthesis from living things.
    D)   from condensation of interstellar gas clouds during the formation of Earth.
    Ans: C   Section: 9-5

126. One of the major differences between Earth and its neighboring planets, Venus and Mars, is the lack of large quantities of CO_2 in its atmosphere. If all three planets were originally formed with significant quantities of this gas in their atmospheres, where is the majority of this CO_2 on Earth at the present time?
    A)   It is dissociated by UV and visible sunlight into carbon and oxygen that now exist in abundance as separate chemicals.
    B)   It is concentrated high in the atmosphere where it contributes to the greenhouse effect.
    C)   It is dissolved in seawater, a situation that cannot arise on the neighboring planets.
    D)   It is locked up in carbonate, and carbon-rich rocks and minerals formed in the sea and on Earth's surface.
    Ans: D   Section: 9-5

127. If carbon dioxide (CO_2) was much more abundant in the Earth's early atmosphere, what happened to most of this gas?
    A)   It was dissociated by lightning into its components, carbon and oxygen, which then escaped from Earth's gravity.
    B)   It escaped into space because of its low molecular weight.
    C)   It combined with other substances to produce carbonate rocks in limestone.
    D)   It was dissociated by the ultraviolet radiation in sunlight, the carbon settling onto Earth while the oxygen remained in the atmosphere to support life.
    Ans: C   Section: 9-5

128. Billions of years ago, Earth's atmosphere was composed primarily of carbon dioxide. Where might you go to find a large fraction of this carbon dioxide today?
    A)   nowhere; most of the carbon dioxide escaped into space
    B)   Rocky Mountains of North America, which are composed largely of limestone
    C)   extinct volcanoes composed of rock from Earth's interior
    D)   anywhere; most of the carbon dioxide is still in the atmosphere, but nitrogen and oxygen have since been added to it
    Ans: B   Section: 9-5

129. Billions of years ago, Earth's atmosphere was composed primarily of carbon dioxide. What happened to much of this carbon dioxide?
    A)   It is still in the atmosphere.
    B)   It was broken into carbon and oxygen by solar ultraviolet light.
    C)   It dissolved into Earth's oceans.
    D)   It was lost to space.
    Ans: C   Section: 9-5

130. Which of the following was not an important process in helping to remove carbon dioxide from Earth's early atmosphere?
    A)   biological activity
    B)   dissolving of carbon dioxide into rainwater and thence into the oceans
    C)   escape of carbon dioxide into space
    D)   sedimentation of carbon compounds onto the ocean floors
    Ans: C   Section: 9-5

131. Which one of the following statements is true for Earth?
    A)   The oxygen in our atmosphere was created by evaporation of seawater, allowing life to move from the seas onto dry land.
    B)   Earth has always had an oxygen-rich atmosphere, which was one reason life could develop.
    C)   Outgassing by volcanic eruptions converted the carbon-dioxide-rich atmosphere into an oxygen-rich atmosphere, thus creating conditions in which life could develop.
    D)   Life developed in a carbon-dioxide-rich atmosphere, and it converted this into an oxygen-rich atmosphere.
    Ans: D   Section: 9-5

132. Which major constituent of the atmosphere of Venus and Mars is present in only very small amounts in Earth's atmosphere?
    A) carbon dioxide, CO_2 B) oxygen, O_2 C) methane, CH_4 D) nitrogen, N_2
    Ans: A   Section: 9-5 and Table 9-4

133. Which is the most abundant gas in Earth's atmosphere?
    A) oxygen   B) hydrogen   C) carbon dioxide   D) nitrogen
    Ans: D   Section: 9-5

134. What is the ratio of nitrogen to oxygen in the atmosphere?
    A)   equal parts nitrogen and oxygen   C)   1 part nitrogen to 2 parts oxygen
    B)   4 parts nitrogen to 1 part oxygen   D)   1 part nitrogen to 4 parts oxygen
    Ans: B   Section: 9-5

135. The major constituents of the atmosphere are
    A)   methane, ammonia, water vapor, and carbon dioxide in about equal amounts.
    B)   77% nitrogen, 21% oxygen.
    C)   77% oxygen, 21% nitrogen.
    D)   95% carbon dioxide and some water vapor.
    Ans: B   Section: 9-5 and Table 9-4

136. The planet whose atmosphere is composed primarily of nitrogen is
    A) Earth.   B) Jupiter.   C) Mars.   D) Venus.
    Ans: A   Section: 9-5

137. Why did Earth's earliest atmosphere, composed primarily of hydrogen, not last long?
    A)   Hydrogen is a very light gas, and it soon escaped into space.
    B)   Biological activity very quickly combined the hydrogen with oxygen to form
          water.
    C)   Hydrogen soon dissolved in Earth's oceans.
    D)   Hydrogen is highly reactive, and it became bound into chemical compounds in
          Earth's rocks.
    Ans: A   Section: 9-5

138. Pressure is
    A)   force times the distance over which the force acts.
    B)   force divided by the area over which the force acts.
    C)   the same as force, but expressed in different units.
    D)   force times the area over which the force acts.
    Ans: B   Section: 9-6

139. The pressure in the atmosphere of Earth varies with height by
    A)   decreasing smoothly with height, dropping by about half for every 5.5 km in
          height.
    B)   increasing over a small height range the surface of Earth (about 1 km), and then
          decreasing smoothly with increasing height.
    C)   remaining a constant up to the height of the highest mountains, then decreasing
          rapidly.
    D)   decreasing and increasing several times with increasing height, following the
          temperature variation.
    Ans: A   Section: 9-6

140. How does the temperature of Earth's atmosphere vary with height over the range 0 to 120 km?
    A)   It remains approximately constant at room temperature over the whole range.
    B)   It always remains well below the surface temperature.
    C)   It decreases and then increases two or three times.
    D)   It rises steadily until it reaches a high and constant value above 120 km.
    Ans: C   Section: 9-6 and Figure 9-22

141. What is the basic structure of Earth's atmosphere?
    A)   smoothly decreasing temperature with increasing altitude
    B)   four layers of alternating temperature profiles: temperature decreasing, then increasing, then decreasing, then increasing with altitude
    C)   smoothly increasing temperature with increasing altitude
    D)   two layers: temperature decreasing with increasing altitude in the lower layer, then increasing with increasing altitude in the upper layer
    Ans: B   Section: 9-6 and Figure 9-22

142. The major layers of Earth's atmosphere from the surface upward in correct order are
    A)   stratosphere, mesosphere, thermosphere, troposphere.
    B)   mesosphere, troposphere, thermosphere, stratosphere.
    C)   thermosphere, mesosphere, troposphere, stratosphere.
    D)   troposphere, stratosphere, mesosphere, thermosphere.
    Ans: D   Section: 9-6

143. The troposphere of a terrestrial planet is the
    A)   atmospheric layer closest to the ground.
    B)   atmospheric layer which contains the highest concentration of ozone.
    C)   uppermost layer of solid rock below the planet's surface.
    D)   atmospheric layer above the mesosphere.
    Ans: A   Section: 9-6

144. In which layer of Earth's atmosphere does all weather occur?
    A) thermosphere   B) stratosphere   C) mesosphere   D) troposphere
    Ans: D   Section: 9-6

145. At the altitude of the boundary between the troposphere and the stratosphere in Earth's atmosphere, the temperature is approximately (see Fig. 9-22, Freedman and Kaufmann, *Universe,* 7th ed.)
    A) +20°C.   B) −58°C.   C) −80°C.   D) +10°C.
    Ans: B   Section: 9-6

146. Ozone is
    A)   ionized oxygen atoms.
    B)   a combination of oxygen, nitrogen, and electrons.
    C)   one of a number of chlorofluorocarbons (CFCs).
    D)   a molecule made of three oxygen atoms.
    Ans: D   Section: 9-6

147. The chemical constituent that absorbs UV radiation in the intermediate layers of Earth's atmosphere (the stratosphere and mesosphere), thereby heating these layers to relatively high temperatures, is
    A) ozone, O_3.   B) N_2.   C) H_2O, water vapor.   D) CO_2.
    Ans: A   Section: 9-6

148. In the stratosphere, the gas temperature of Earth's atmosphere reaches a maximum at about 50 km. The cause of this is
    A)   heating by auroral activity higher in the atmosphere.
    B)   absorption of ultraviolet radiation by ozone, O_3.
    C)   ionization of O_2 and N_2 by solar ultraviolet radiation.
    D)   turbulence and friction caused by wind and weather.
    Ans: B   Section: 9-6

149. Earth's stratosphere is warmer than the layers above and below it because
    A)   warm air heated by contact with the ground rises into the stratosphere, thereby heating it.
    B) CO_2 in the stratosphere absorbs infrared light radiated outward by the ground.
    C)   the methane released when we burn fossil fuel absorbs infrared light in this layer.
    D)   ozone in the stratosphere absorbs ultraviolet radiation from the Sun.
    Ans: D   Section: 9-6

150. The temperature in the stratosphere increases with increasing altitude because
    A)   it is heated by solar infrared radiation absorbed by carbon dioxide and water vapor.
    B)   it is heated by the absorption of solar ultraviolet radiation by ozone.
    C)   charged particles from the magnetosphere collide with atoms in the stratosphere, depositing energy.
    D)   these higher altitudes are closer to the Sun.
    Ans: B   Section: 9-6

151. In which layer of Earth's atmosphere is the ozone layer located?
    A) stratosphere   B) mesosphere   C) thermosphere   D) troposphere
    Ans: A   Section: 9-6

152. We need the ozone layer because it
    A)   allows long-distance radio communication by reflecting radio waves back to Earth's surface.
    B)   protects us from the solar wind.
    C)   provides a convenient dumping site for chlorofluorocarbon chemicals that are harmful to life.
    D)   shields us from harmful solar ultraviolet radiation.
    Ans: D   Section: 9-6

153. The coldest layer of Earth's atmosphere exists between which two main regions?
    A)   troposphere and Earth's surface   C)   mesosphere and thermosphere
    B)   stratosphere and mesosphere   D)   troposphere and stratosphere
    Ans: C   Section: 9-6

154. The lowest temperature in Earth's atmosphere is about
    A)   −58°C or 215 K.   C)   −80°C or 193 K.
    B)   0°C or 273 K.   D)   1000°C or 1273 K.
    Ans: C   Section: 9-6

155. The lowest temperature in Earth's atmosphere occurs at an altitude of about
    A) 80 km.   B) 10 km.   C) 50 km.   D) 0 km (the surface of Earth).
    Ans: A   Section: 9-6

156. Earth's thermosphere is the
    A)   outermost atmospheric layer, in which ultraviolet light from the Sun is absorbed by nitrogen and oxygen atoms, stripping them of one or more electrons.
    B)   region of the magnetosphere that contains trapped high-energy charged particles.
    C)   intermediate atmospheric layer, in which ultraviolet light from the Sun is absorbed by ozone (O_3) molecules.
    D)   layer of molten iron and nickel below the mantle in the Earth's interior.
    Ans: A   Section: 9-6

157. Each of the following is one mechanism for heating various parts of Earth's atmosphere *except one*. Which one is the exception?
    A)   Greenhouse gases in the lower troposphere absorb infrared radiation emitted by the Earth's surface.
    B)   Ozone in the stratosphere absorbs ultraviolet radiation from sunlight.
    C)   Atomic oxygen and nitrogen in the thermosphere absorb ultraviolet radiation from sunlight.
    D)   Ions in the ionosphere absorb gamma rays from natural radioactivity on and within the Earth.
    Ans: D   Section: 9-6

158. If the Earth did not rotate on its axis, most surface winds would blow
    A)   from the poles toward the equator.   C)   from east to west.
    B)   from the equator toward the poles.   D)   from west to east.
    Ans: A   Section: 9-6 and Figure 9-22

159. The hottest part of the Earth's atmosphere is
    A)   the lowest layer of the troposphere (near the Earth's surface).
    B)   the boundary of the upper troposphere with the stratosphere.
    C)   the upper mesosphere.
    D)   the upper thermosphere.
    Ans: D   Section: 9-6

160. The lowest pressure in the Earth's atmosphere occurs where?
    A)   the lowest layer of the troposphere (near the Earth's surface)
    B)   the boundary of the upper troposphere with the stratosphere
    C)   the upper mesosphere
    D)   the upper thermosphere
    Ans: D   Section: 9-6

161. The circulation in Earth's atmosphere is dominated by
    A)   a random distribution of transient storms and high-pressure areas, with no
         permanent overall pattern.
    B)   one large convection cell in each hemisphere, with air rising at the equator due to
         solar heating, moving toward the poles at high altitude and returning along the
         surface.
    C)   three large convection cells in each hemisphere, with surface winds toward the
         equator in the tropics and away from the equator at temperate latitudes.
    D)   bands of winds blowing parallel to the equator, from the east in the tropics and
         from the west at temperate latitudes.
    Ans: C   Section: 9-6 and Figure 9-23

162. One might expect the dominant circulation in Earth's atmosphere to be one large
    convection cell in each hemisphere, with air rising at the equator due to solar heating,
    moving toward the poles at high altitude, cooling and sinking, then returning toward the
    equator along the surface. The actual circulation is more complicated than this primarily
    because of the
    A)   speed of rotation of Earth.
    B)   uneven heating of oceans and continents by the Sun.
    C)   escape of heat outward through Earth's crust.
    D)   uneven heating of the different atmospheric layers by the Sun.
    Ans: A   Section: 9-6

163. Which of the following roles played by the massive rain forests of Earth is perhaps the most important in the maintenance of the entire world's living environment?
    A) absorption of H_2O as rain and the production of vital timber for fuel and other uses
    B) absorption of sunlight and the prevention of its reflection back into space, preventing massive worldwide cooling
    C) support of a vast variety of wildlife, which is essential for the maintenance of an adequate gene pool for mammals and insects on Earth
    D) absorption of CO_2 and production of O_2, renewing our atmosphere and reducing the greenhouse effect
    Ans: D   Section: 9-7

164. The El Niño phenomenon refers to which natural pattern on Earth?
    A) periodic cooling of the equatorial Pacific Ocean surface
    B) periodic north-south movement of the region of maximum hurricane occurrence track over North America
    C) slow but apparently continuous rise in overall global temperature over the past century
    D) periodic warming of the equatorial Pacific Ocean surface
    Ans: D   Section: 9-7

165. Which of the following areas of human endeavor and development is having the most impact on Earth at the present moment?
    A) rapid increase in human population
    B) development of mental telepathy, or communication without speech, between selected human beings
    C) growth in the use of solar energy for heating, lighting, and power
    D) exploration of the Moon and its exploitation for mineral resources
    Ans: A   Section: 9-7

166. Since 1900, how much has the global temperature risen? (See Fig. 9-28, Freedman and Kaufmann, *Universe*, 7th ed.)
    A) 0.7°C   B) 2°C   C) 0.2°C   D) 1°C
    Ans: A   Section: 9-7

167. Which of the following is NOT a major factor in the influence of humans on global warming?
    A) increase in heat added by the bodies of humans and animals as their populations increase rapidly
    B) use of gasoline (petrol) and natural gas in transportation vehicles, such as cars and aircraft
    C) burning of wood, coal, and oil for heating and cooking
    D) slash-and-burn methods that are destroying forests in South America
    Ans: A   Section: 9-7

168. Which of the following would NOT happen if we destroyed the ozone layer?
    A)   drastic increase in ultraviolet radiation at the Earth's surface
    B)   large-scale (perhaps total) destruction of life on Earth
    C)   elimination of the rise in temperature in the stratosphere
    D)   large-scale freezing of the oceans
    Ans: D   Section: 9-7

169. If the CO_2 content of our atmosphere was 280 ppm in 1850, how has this value changed in the century and a half through 2000?
    A)   It has decreased to about 50% of its 1850 value.
    B)   It has remained roughly constant.
    C)   It has increased by about one-third of its 1850 value.
    D)   It has doubled.
    Ans: C   Section: 9-7 and Figure 9-27

170. In the 25 years between 1975 and 2000, the world's population increased by two billion people. How many more years are estimated to be necessary for the world's population to increase by another two billion?
    A) 5 B) 10 C) 25 D) 50
    Ans: C   Section: 9-7

Chapter 10: Our Barren Moon

1. The terminator on the Moon is a line
    A) joining north and south lunar poles, passing through the center of the largest mare, Imbrium, representing 0° of lunar longitude.
    B) between the near and far sides of the Moon.
    C) between the solar-illuminated and dark hemispheres.
    D) along the equator, between northern and southern hemispheres.
    Ans: C   Section: 10-1

2. The diameter of the Moon is
    A) less than 1/100 of the diameter of the Earth.
    B) about 1/10 of the diameter of the Earth.
    C) about 1/4 of the diameter of the Earth.
    D) just over 1/2 the diameter of the Earth.
    Ans: C   Section: 10-1

3. People on Earth see
    A) only the sunlit side of the Moon.
    B) the same side of the Moon at all times.
    C) the entire Moon once each month as it rotates.
    D) the entire surface of the Moon once per year as the Earth revolves around the Sun.
    Ans: B   Section: 10-1

4. To observers on Earth, the Moon shows
    A) only its northern half because of the tilt of the Moon's rotational axis.
    B) its whole surface once per month as it rotates.
    C) only one side to Earth at all times.
    D) its whole surface once per year as Earth moves around the Sun.
    Ans: C   Section: 10-1

5. In its orbit around Earth, the Moon
    A) always keeps the sunlit side toward Earth.
    B) always keeps the same side toward the Sun.
    C) always keeps the same side toward Earth.
    D) rotates once every 24 hours to keep in step with Earth.
    Ans: C   Section: 10-1

6. The rotation period of the Moon on its axis with respect to space (its absolute rotation) is
    A) infinitely long, because the Moon never rotates.
    B) 27.3 days, the sidereal revolution period.
    C) 365.25 days, to match Earth's revolution period.
    D) 29.5 days, the synodic period.
    Ans: B   Section: 10-1 and Table 10-1

7. If viewed from a point directly above the plane of the planetary system, how would the Moon appear to rotate on its axis?
    A)   It would rotate once per year as Earth and Moon orbit the Sun together.
    B)   It would not rotate at all, because we always see the same face on Earth.
    C)   It would rotate once per day, to maintain its direction toward Earth.
    D)   It would rotate once per month, or once per revolution about Earth.
    Ans: D   Section: 10-1

8. If you were on the Moon, how long would it take between two crossings of a star in the sky through your zenith?
    A)   infinite time, because the Moon does not rotate on its axis
    B)   27.3 days
    C)   23 hours 56 minutes
    D)   29.5 days
    Ans: B   Section: 10-1 and Table 10-1

9. How long is a "lunar day," or the time between two successive sunrises or sunsets on the Moon?
    A)   about 1 month
    B)   infinitely long, because the Moon does not rotate about its axis with respect to the Sun
    C)   about 1 year
    D)   about 1 day
    Ans: A   Section: 10-1

10. Which of the following general statements about the Moon is true?
    A)   There is one side of the Moon from which Earth can never be seen.
    B)   The Moon does not rotate on its axis.
    C)   There is one side of the Moon from which the Sun can never be seen.
    D)   One side of the Moon is always in darkness.
    Ans: A   Section: 10-1

11. If you were standing on the Moon with Earth in view, how much time would elapse between two successive "Earthrises"?
    A)   about 1 synodic month
    B)   about 1 day
    C)   about 1 sidereal month
    D)   infinite time, because the same side of the Moon always faces toward Earth
    Ans: D   Section: 10-1

12. Which of the following is not true concerning the view from a Moon base that can be seen from Earth?
    A)   The Earth is always in view at approximately the same position in the sky.
    B)   The Sun is not always in the sky.
    C)   The Earth shows all the phases of crescent, quarter, gibbous, and full in a period of one month.
    D)   The Earth rises, sets, and moves across the lunar sky.
    Ans: D   Section: 10-1

13. Suppose you lived on the rim of the lunar crater Copernicus, which is visible from Earth. How often would Earth set below your horizon?
    A)   once every 24 hours   C)   once every 29.5 days
    B)   once every 27.5 days   D)   never
    Ans: D   Section: 10-1

14. If astronauts set up a permanent settlement at Tranquility Base on the Moon, how many times each year would Earth rise and set as seen by a resident of this base?
    A)   13 times each year
    B)   once each year
    C)   never—Earth would remain essentially motionless in the sky
    D)   12 times each year
    Ans: C   Section: 10-1

15. If astronauts set up a permanent settlement at Tranquility Base on the Moon, how many times each year would the Sun rise and set as seen by a resident of this base?
    A)   365 times each year
    B)   once each year
    C)   never—the Sun would remain motionless in the sky
    D)   about once per month
    Ans: D   Section: 10-1

16. Astronauts at a Moon base visible from Earth will NOT see
    A)   one side of Earth, because the Moon revolves at the same rate as Earth rotates.
    B)   sunrise or sunset, because the Sun will always remain in their sky.
    C)   the stars moving through their sky, because the Moon does not rotate.
    D)   Earthrise or Earthset.
    Ans: D   Section: 10-1

17. More detail is seen on the Moon at quarter phases than at full phases because (see Figure 10-3, Freedman and Kaufmann, *Universe,* 7th ed.)
    A) surface mists that are prominent at full phase have cleared at quarter phases.
    B) parts of the Moon that are visible at these phases show more craters in general.
    C) features on the Moon cast distinct shadows to produce high contrast at these phases.
    D) the Moon is closer to Earth at these phases.
    Ans: C   Section: 10-1 and Figure 10-3

18. If the angular resolution of detail on astronomical objects is limited to about 0.5 arcsecond by seeing fluctuations in Earth's atmosphere, what is the smallest lunar crater that can be seen from Earth? (Hint: Use the small-angle formula in Chapter 1, Freedman and Kaufmann, *Universe,* 7th ed.)
    A) about 100 m   B) about 3.8 km   C) about 250 m   D) about 1 km
    Ans: D   Section: 10-1

19. Libration is
    A) apparent wobbling of the Moon due to the shape and orientation of its orbit and rotation axis.
    B) a custom of toasting astronauts with champagne when they touch down on the Moon.
    C) exact synchronicity between orbital motion of the Moon and its rotation about its own axis.
    D) gradual movement of the terminator across the visible face of the Moon.
    Ans: A   Section: 10-1

20. Over time, what fraction of the Moon's surface can we see from Earth?
    A) about 60%, because of the shape and orientation of the Moon's orbit and rotation axis
    B) 52%, because two observers on Earth see the Moon from slightly different angles
    C) 100%, because of the rotation of the Moon about its axis
    D) exactly 50%, because the Moon is in synchronous rotation around Earth
    Ans: A   Section: 10-1

21. Estimates of the heights of lunar mountains can be made by measuring the lengths of their shadows when the Sun angle on them is relatively low. If a shadow length on a photograph of an isolated mountain on a flat plain is measured at 5 km when the solar elevation angle (angle above the horizon as seen by someone on the Moon) is about 6°, what is the mountain height above the plain? (A diagram might help, and the small-angle formula in Chapter 1, Freedman and Kaufmann, *Universe,* 7th ed. will be useful.)
    A) 500 m   B) 5 km   C) 2 km   D) 50 km
    Ans: A   Section: 10-1 and Box 1-1

22. The Moon has
    A)   an atmosphere of CO_2, but no evidence of water.
    B)   a lot of evidence for an atmosphere and the presence of liquid water (e.g., wind erosion and winding river valleys).
    C)   no measurable atmosphere or liquid water.
    D)   no measurable atmosphere, but plenty of groundwater.
    Ans: C   Section: 10-1

23. The so-called maria, or "seas" on the lunar surface, do not and could not contain water because
    A)   the water would boil and evaporate away rapidly in the vacuum of space.
    B)   any water falling on the porous surface would soak into it.
    C)   the water would have frozen into permafrost in the intense cold on the lunar surface.
    D)   the water would react chemically with the surface rocks.
    Ans: A   Section: 10-1

24. Most of the craters on the Moon were formed by
    A)   slumping of the surface following the outflow of lava from below the region.
    B)   bombardment by interplanetary meteoritic material.
    C)   wind and water erosion of mountains and hills in the distant past.
    D)   volcanic action; the craters are the old calderas of volcanoes.
    Ans: B   Section: 10-1

25. What is the origin of the majority of lunar craters?
    A)   impacts by space probes
    B)   surface collapse after loss of groundwater by evaporation
    C)   volcanic explosions
    D)   impacts by meteoric material
    Ans: D   Section: 10-1

26. Most lunar craters by far were caused by
    A)   lunar quakes, under gravitational tidal disturbance from Earth.
    B)   bombardment from space by meteoritic material.
    C)   the explosion of rocks caused by thermal shock from alternating intense sunlight and the cold of space.
    D)   volcanic eruptions from within the Moon's interior.
    Ans: B   Section: 10-1

27. Which of the following processes has played the greatest role in shaping the surface of the Moon?
    A)   erosion by wind and atmospheric gases
    B)   impacts of interplanetary bodies of all sizes
    C)   motions of tectonic plates, producing mountain ranges wherever they collide
    D)   recent volcanic activity, producing large numbers of crater-like volcanic calderas
    Ans: B   Section: 10-1

28. What are the most common shapes of lunar craters and why?
    A)   round, because the shock wave from the impact that produced them spread out uniformly in all directions
    B)   random shapes, because mantle convection has deformed the surface and distorted the craters since their production by impacts of meteoroids
    C)   all shapes from round to long and thin, depending on the angle at which the projectile hit the surface
    D)   round, because most of the craters were produced by volcanic explosions which formed calderas, not by meteoroid impacts
    Ans: A   Section: 10-1

29. Maria are
    A)   bright streaks radiating away from young, fresh craters.
    B)   isolated regions of heavily cratered highland terrain.
    C)   long, sinuous valleys formed by ancient lava rivers.
    D)   ancient lava floodplains.
    Ans: D   Section: 10-1

30. Maria are
    A)   large impact craters in-filled by lava.
    B)   ancient lake beds, now dry.
    C)   uplifted regions surrounding large shield volcanoes.
    D)   heavily cratered highland regions.
    Ans: A   Section: 10-1

31. A mare on the Moon is a
    A)   large crater with a central peak terracing along the crater walls.
    B)   crater shaped like a horse.
    C)   large area of dark material on the lunar surface.
    D)   large area of light material on the lunar surface.
    Ans: C   Section: 10-1

32. What is the diameter of Mare Imbrium, the largest lunar sea, compared to the diameter of the Moon itself?
    A)   about 1/3 the diameter   C)   just over 1/2 the diameter
    B)   about 1/10 the diameter   D)   about 1/100 the diameter
    Ans: A   Section: 10-1

33. The smooth, dark maria on the Moon are
    A)   areas that were still molten at the time of the early, heavy bombardment.
    B)   immense impact basins that are smooth because they were covered by lava flows after a period of heavy bombardment early in the Moon's history.
    C)   immense impact basins that are smooth because earlier craters were wiped out by shock waves from the impacts.
    D)   regions that are as old as the cratered highlands but escaped a period of heavy bombardment by being on the "wrong" side of the Moon.
    Ans: B   Section: 10-1 and Figure 10-5

34. What is the most likely cause of the smooth and relatively crater-free surfaces of lunar maria?
    A)   volcanic ash that rained on the surfaces of the basins in recent geological times
    B)   dust storms that eroded and smoothed the surface
    C)   sediments left behind after water flowed into the basins and evaporated
    D)   lava flows relatively late in the geological history of the Moon
    Ans: D   Section: 10-1

35. The lunar maria appear smooth because they are
    A)   ancient sea beds, now dry, dating back to when the Moon had a denser atmosphere and rainfall was abundant.
    B)   recent lava flows, occurring within the last billion years, which have obliterated earlier craters.
    C)   regions where craters have been obliterated by crustal deformation caused by hot spots and volcanic lava flow from the underlying molten mantle.
    D)   ancient lava flows that occurred soon after the end of an early period of intense bombardment and have had relatively few impacts since then.
    Ans: D   Section: 10-1

36. The Moon's appearance, when its whole surface is examined, could be described as
    A)   craters only on the near side, smooth surface on the far side.
    B)   surface features uniformly distributed.
    C)   many maria distributed uniformly on both the near and far sides.
    D)   maria only on the near side, no major maria on the far side.
    Ans: D   Section: 10-1

37. Examination of the whole surface of the Moon shows us that
    A)   craters exist only on one side of the Moon.
    B)   the Moon appears to have two distinctly different sides, that seen from Earth and that hidden from Earth.
    C)   surface features are distributed uniformly over the whole Moon.
    D)   the northern hemisphere is distinctly different from the southern hemisphere.
    Ans: B   Section: 10-1

38. Maria on the Moon exist
    A)   uniformly all over the surface of the Moon.
    B)   only in a zone around the equator.
    C)   only in the north and south polar regions.
    D)   only on the Earth-facing side of the Moon.
    Ans: D   Section: 10-1

39. The near and far sides of the Moon are particularly different in that
    A)   the far side is always in darkness.
    B)   the average height of the overall terrain is much lower on the far side.
    C)   the far side has no maria.
    D)   the number of craters differs markedly, with fewer on the far side.
    Ans: C   Section: 10-1

40. Which of the following statements is NOT true of the Moon?
    A)   It shows no evidence of ever having liquid water on its surface.
    B)   Parts of its surface are completely saturated with craters (i.e., no uncratered
         surface left in these regions).
    C)   It has extensive lava floodplains over most of its surface, near side and far side.
    D)   It has large basins that were carved out by asteroid impacts.
    Ans: C   Section: 10-1

41. Taken over the entire surface of the Moon, the older, lighter-colored and heavily
    cratered highlands (terrae) take up
    A)   more than 4/5 of the lunar surface.
    B)   between 1/3 and 1/2 of the lunar surface.
    C)   less than 1/5 of the lunar surface.
    D)   between 1/2 and 3/4 of the lunar surface.
    Ans: A   Section: 10-1

42. The smooth, dark maria take up what fraction of the entire surface of the Moon?
    A)   less than 1/5   C)   more than 4/5
    B)   between 1/2 and 3/4   D)   between 1/3 and 1/2
    Ans: A   Section: 10-1

43. Why are the lunar maria concentrated almost entirely on the near side of the Moon?
    A)   The apparent concentration of maria on the near side is merely an illusion caused
         by the fact that the near side is the only side that we can see.
    B)   The crust is thicker on the far side of the Moon, restricting massive lava flows
         after asteroid impact.
    C)   Earth's gravity concentrated asteroid impacts on the near side of the Moon.
    D)   Earth's gravity has concentrated meteoroid impacts on the far side of the Moon,
         erasing the ancient, smooth lava plains.
    Ans: B   Section: 10-1

44. The mountain ranges on the Moon are
    A)   lines of extinct volcanoes similar to the Hawaiian Islands, caused by hot-spot vulcanism.
    B)   the hard-rock remnants of geological features severely eroded by wind and weather.
    C)   the walls of craters caused by impacts of large objects early in the geological history of the Moon.
    D)   the upthrust caused by collisions of moving tectonic plates.
    Ans: C   Section: 10-1

45. Most of the mountain ranges on the Moon are the
    A)   result of water flow and erosion on the Moon's soft surface.
    B)   circular edges and rims of large maria, caused by impacts from large objects.
    C)   result of the buildup of meteoritic dust from winds on the Moon.
    D)   result of plate tectonic movement, similar to that on Earth.
    Ans: B   Section: 10-1

46. The mountains on the Moon were mostly caused by
    A)   tidal distortion and uplift.
    B)   volcanic eruption and buildup similar to terrestrial volcanoes.
    C)   impacts from meteoroids from outer space.
    D)   collisions of crustal plates under tectonic motion.
    Ans: C   Section: 10-1

47. How were the mountain ranges on the Moon formed?
    A)   They are "spreading centers," where magma from the mantle is rising and pushing tectonic plates apart.
    B)   They were rims of ancient craters, thrust up by impacts of large asteroids.
    C)   They were wrinkles in the crust, created when the Moon cooled and shrunk slightly in size.
    D)   They were pushed up by the collisions of tectonic plates on the lunar surface.
    Ans: B   Section: 10-1

48. What is the current state of plate tectonics on the Moon?
    A)   just in the process of beginning; the rilles (or sinuous valleys) are the first signs of continental rifting
    B)   very active, causing mountain uplift around the edges of several lunar maria
    C)   dying out; only the lunar maria show signs of tectonic movement today
    D)   absent; the Moon is a geologically dead world
    Ans: D   Section: 10-1

49. Earth has several lithospheric plates that gradually move in a process called plate tectonics. How many such plates are there on the Moon?
    A)   one; the entire lithosphere is a single plate
    B)   five; one for each of the major lunar seas (maria)
    C)   six; one for the highlands (terrae) and one for each of the major lunar seas (maria)
    D)   two; the region of the near side occupied by the seas (maria) forms one plate, and the rest of the Moon (the bulk of the highlands, or terrae) forms the other
    Ans: A   Section: 10-1

50. How many impact craters are there on Earth?
    A)   about 150, all less than a few hundred million years old
    B)   only one very recent crater, about 25,000 years old, found in Arizona
    C)   thousands, their times of formation extending from present times to more than 3 billion years ago
    D)   about 20, the oldest of which became Chesapeake Bay and resulted in the extinction of the dinosaurs 65 million years ago.
    Ans: A   Section: 10-1

51. The impact craters on Earth are younger than a few million years old, whereas ages of lunar craters extend back billions of years. Why is this?
    A)   Earth escaped the heavy bombardment that pelted the Moon early in its history.
    B)   Earth's surface has been covered by lava flows several times in its history, whereas such activity ceased on the Moon several million years ago.
    C)   Weathering by rain and melting snow gradually erases craters on Earth, and this does not happen on the Moon.
    D)   Plate tectonics has erased older craters on Earth, whereas this process has not occurred on the Moon.
    Ans: D   Section: 10-1

52. The major features on the near side of the Moon were named
    A)   in prehistoric times.   C)   in the 17th century.
    B)   by the ancient Greeks.   D)   in the 20th century.
    Ans: C   Section: 10-1

53. What actually moves around the Sun along the path we usually call the Earth's orbit?
    A)   the center of the Earth
    B)   the point midway between the Earth and the Moon
    C)   the center of mass of the Earth-Moon system
    D)   the center of mass of the Earth-Moon-Sun system
    Ans: C   Section: 10-1

54. How many times have human beings landed on the Moon?
    A) seven   B) five   C) six   D) four
    Ans: C   Section: 10-2

55. How many human beings have walked on the Moon?
    A) 1   B) 12   C) 6   D) 22
    Ans: B   Section: 10-2

56. Which was the first country to send a space probe past the Moon?
    A) China   B) France   C) the Soviet Union   D) the United States
    Ans: C   Section: 10-2

57. What kind of landing did the first spacecraft make in order to reach the surface of the Moon?
    A)   manned landing by *Apollo* spacecraft
    B)   crash landing by *Ranger* spacecraft
    C)   "drop and bounce" landing by *Pathfinder* spacecraft
    D)   soft landing by *Surveyor* spacecraft
    Ans: B   Section: 10-2

58. Which was the first country to land humans on the Moon?
    A) China   B) France   C) the United States   D) the Soviet Union
    Ans: C   Section: 10-2

59. Which was the first spacecraft to land humans on the Moon?
    A) *Apollo 13*   B) *Ranger 9*   C) *Apollo 11*   D) *Soyuz 5*
    Ans: C   Section: 10-2

60. How many countries have soft-landed spacecraft on the Moon and returned lunar samples to Earth?
    A)   one—the Soviet Union
    B)   To avoid the possibility of contaminating the Earth, no country has brought lunar samples to Earth.
    C)   one—the United States
    D)   two—the United States and the Soviet Union
    Ans: D   Section: 10-2

61. Can regions of ice exist on the surface of the Moon?
    A)   no, because the Moon never had water from which ice could form
    B)   no, because all parts of the Moon are heated by the Sun at one time or another during each orbit, and all ice would evaporate
    C)   no, because the Moon has no atmosphere, and ice would quickly evaporate (or "sublime") into space and be lost
    D)   yes, because the floors of craters at the north and south poles can be permanently shaded from the Sun
    Ans: D   Section: 10-2

62. Where is ice believed to have been discovered on the Moon?
    A)   in the floors of craters at the north and south poles, which are permanently shaded from the Sun
    B)   No ice has ever been discovered on the Moon, because water cannot exist there in any form.
    C)   in permafrost under the surface of the lunar highlands
    D)   as subsurface deposits in maria, from water released by molten lava and trapped under solidified crust
    Ans: A   Section: 10-2

63. What is considered to be the most likely source for the deposits of ice that have been discovered at the lunar poles?
    A)   the Moon's original shallow oceans
    B)   comets that have crashed onto the lunar surface
    C)   evaporation of subsurface water from lower latitudes on the Moon, which are heated by the Sun, and subsequent condensation at the poles
    D)   molten lava, which releases water as it cools
    Ans: B   Section: 10-2

64. Water may have been discovered recently on the Moon in the form of
    A)   fluid water flowing in deep protected tunnels, some of which have collapsed to form rilles on the lunar surface.
    B)   thin, hazy clouds overlying the dark polar regions, where they are shaded from the Sun's heat.
    C)   permafrost embedded in the centers of the large, dark maria, the color showing the presence of frost.
    D)   ice, in deep craters at the north and south poles, perpetually shaded from sunlight.
    Ans: D   Section: 10-2

65. It was originally thought questionable whether a manned lunar landing could take place because
    A)   of the extreme temperatures on the lunar surface.
    B)   the lunar surface might be too soft to land upon.
    C)   of extreme levels of radiation from the decay of radioactive elements and the lack of a shielding atmosphere.
    D)   the low atmospheric pressure would adversely affect human beings.
    Ans: B   Section: 10-2

66. The spacecraft *Clementine* observed the Moon in 1994 and provided evidence for ice near the South Pole. How was this information gathered?
    A)   A soft landing was made near an ice field.
    B)   Radar waves were sent out and their reflection from the lunar surface was detected.
    C)   Reflections of ultraviolet, visible, and infrared from the lunar surface were analyzed.
    D)   Sensitive heat detectors monitored the lunar surface temperature.
    Ans: C   Section: 10-2

67. Detailed examination of the overall surface of the Moon and of the rocks brought back by *Apollo* astronauts reveals that
    A)   unlike Earth's rocks, there is no evidence of water locked into crystal structures in lunar rocks, but there are significant quantities of ice in cold lunar polar regions.
    B)   no water exists in either liquid form or ice now but, like terrestrial rocks, some water is contained within the crystal structure of lunar rocks.
    C)   there have been short periods in recent history when water existed on the Moon, during which the rilles or river valleys were formed.
    D)   water probably existed on the Moon earlier and formed lake beds or maria, but it has evaporated.
    Ans: A   Section: 10-2 and 10-4

68. Most surface rocks on Earth are younger than a few million years old, whereas ages of lunar rocks have been measured in billions of years. Why is this?
    A)   The complete surface of Earth has been covered periodically by younger material from intense volcanic eruptions in the last few million years. No such activity has occurred on the Moon.
    B)   Earth's surface undergoes continuous recycling through the underlying mantle because of plate tectonic activity, and this does not occur on the Moon.
    C)   The ages of Earth and Moon are fundamentally different, the Moon being an old object captured from deep space by a younger Earth.
    D)   Most of the early surface rocks of Earth have been washed into the sea by weathering and rainwater, and this does not happen on the Moon.
    Ans: B   Section: 10-2 and 10-4

69. The Moon has
    A)   a global magnetic field which deflects the solar wind, but is not strong enough to trap high-energy charged particles.
    B)   no global magnetic field, although weak magnetism in lunar rocks does show that a magnetic field existed earlier in the Moon's history.
    C)   no detectable magnetism of any kind, either global or in individual rocks.
    D)   a very weak global field which is not strong enough to deflect the solar wind before it hits the lunar surface.
    Ans: B   Section: 10-3

70. The Moon apparently has
    A)   a small iron-rich core that was entirely molten in the Moon's history, as shown by magnetic measurements.
    B)   an iron core that takes up about half the volume of the Moon, as shown by the very high average density of the Moon.
    C)   no dense iron-rich core of any kind, as indicated by gravity measurements using orbiting spacecraft.
    D)   a small, molten iron-rich core at the present time, as indicated by the Moon's weak global magnetic field.
    Ans: A   Section: 10-3

71. Moonquakes occur
    A)   at a rate of about 3000 per year, less than the rate of terrestrial earthquakes.
    B)   at a similar rate to quakes on Earth, hundreds of thousands per year.
    C)   at a rate of only a few per year.
    D)   only very rarely; the Moon is almost seismically quiet because it has no molten core.
    Ans: A   Section: 10-3

72. Compared to earthquakes, moonquakes are
    A)   much more frequent but significantly weaker, occurring at any time.
    B)   much less frequent but significantly stronger, occurring mostly at full moon.
    C)   much weaker and less frequent, occurring mostly when the Moon is at perigee.
    D)   nonexistent, the Moon being seismically quiet.
    Ans: C   Section: 10-3

73. Moonquakes
    A)   never occur; the Moon is seismically quiet.
    B)   occur but are much weaker and much less frequent than earthquakes.
    C)   are much more violent and occur much more often than earthquakes.
    D)   occur, but only from the impact of meteoroids from space.
    Ans: B   Section: 10-3

74. Moonquakes occur
    A)   most often at full moon, not at new or quarter moons.
    B)   most often when the Moon is near perigee.
    C)   randomly at all times, at a uniform rate.
    D)   most often when the Moon is near apogee.
    Ans: B   Section: 10-3

75. Moonquakes occur most often when the Moon is near perigee. The reason for this is
    A) increased tidal distortion of the Moon by Earth.
    B) the higher probability of impacts on the Moon of meteoroids that have been accelerated by Earth at these lunar phases.
    C) increased speed of rotation of the Moon at these times and the consequent reduction of the gravitational force on the surface.
    D) increased sunlight on the Moon's surface at these times.
    Ans: A   Section: 10-3

76. The number of meteoroids with masses between 100 g and 1000 kg (between that of a bag of sugar and that of an automobile!) that hit the Moon each year is
    A) about 1000.   B) less than 10.   C) about 1 million.   D) about 100.
    Ans: D   Section: 10-3

77. About 100 meteroids of masses between 100 g and 1000 kg hit the Moon each year. The Moon is spherical with a total surface area given by $4\pi R^2$ (where R = radius). If a future lunar settler owns a parcel of land 1 km by 1 km in size, approximately how often, on average, will a meteoroid strike somewhere in the parcel?
    A) once every 4000 years   C) four times per year
    B) once every 40,000,000 years   D) once every 400,000 years
    Ans: D   Section: 10-3

78. If we think about two rocks of equal mass on the Moon, one on the near side and one on the far-side, then we can think of the tidal force as the difference between the gravitational force by Earth on the near-side rock and the gravitational force by Earth on the far-side rock. How quickly does this tidal force decrease with increasing distance from Earth?
    A) $1/r^3$ B) $1/r^4$ C) $1/r^2$ D) $1/r$
    Ans: A   Section: 10-3

79. Considering two rocks of equal mass on the Moon, one on the near-side and one on the far-side, we can think of the tidal force as the difference between the gravitational force by Earth on the near-side rock and on the far-side rock. If the Moon were orbiting at three times its present distance from Earth, what would the tidal force be, compared to its present value?
    A) 0.58   B) 1/81   C) 1/9   D) 1/27
    Ans: D   Section: 10-3

80. What is the primary cause of Moonquakes?
    A) the collision of tectonic plates
    B) meteoroid impact
    C) tidal forces due to the gravitational pull of the Earth
    D) tidal forces due to the gravitational pull of the Sun
    Ans: C   Section: 10-3

81. The gravitational pull of the Sun on the Moon is stronger than the gravitational pull of the Earth on the Moon. Which of these is more important in raising tides on the Moon?
    A) Because the Moon has no oceans it cannot experience tides.
    B) Because the Sun has the stronger pull it is clearly more important in raising tides.
    C) The Earth is more important in raising tides on the Moon because the *difference* between the near-side and far-side forces caused by the Earth is greater than the *difference* between the near-side and far-side forces caused by the Moon.
    D) The Moon is in a stable orbit because the gravitational effects of the Earth and the Sun just balance. Thus they are equally important in raising tides on the Moon.
    Ans: C   Section: 10-3

82. What kinds of large-scale changes have occurred on the Moon in the last billion years?
    A) None. The Moon is exactly as it was a billion years ago.
    B) tectonic activity
    C) volcanic activity and large scale lava flows
    D) Constant meteoroid impact has gently sculpted the landscape.
    Ans: D   Section: 10-3

83. Which of the following techniques is *not* used to gather information about the Moon's interior?
    A) detection of seismic waves which travel through the Moon's interior
    B) studies of the Moon's magnetism
    C) studies of tides raised on the earth by the Moon
    D) measurements of changes in the Moon's atmosphere
    Ans: D   Section: 10-3

84. Which one of the following influences has had the most effect on the "weathering" of the surface rocks of the Moon?
    A) wind erosion by the fine dust particles
    B) bombardment by the solar wind
    C) expansion and contraction because of intense temperature changes
    D) meteoritic bombardment
    Ans: D   Section: 10-4

85. Lunar rocks brought back by *Apollo* astronauts and remote-controlled Russian spacecraft are basically
    A) igneous rocks, formed from cooling lava.
    B) mostly metamorphic rocks, changed by pressure and heat from their original volcanic lava state.
    C) sedimentary rocks, with layered structure from repeated deposition and subsequent compression.
    D) a mixture of igneous, volcanic, and sedimentary rocks.
    Ans: A   Section: 10-4

86. The lunar maria are composed of which of the following rock types?
    A) basalt   B) limestone   C) anorthosite   D) granite
    Ans: A   Section: 10-4

87. The dominant rock type found on the lunar maria
    A)   solidified quickly on the surface of the Moon, as shown by gas bubbles frozen
         into the rock.
    B)   is metamorphic rock created from igneous rock by the intense heat and pressure of
         impacts by meteoroids.
    C)   is made up of volcanic ash thrown out by lunar eruptions and compressed into
         rock by later deposits of ash.
    D)   solidified slowly in the interior of the Moon, as shown by large crystals in the
         rock.
    Ans: A   Section: 10-4

88. The type of rock making up the lunar highlands is
    A)   old, low-density rocks—anorthosite.
    B)   young volcanic rocks—basalt.
    C)   deposited rocks—limestone.
    D)   volcanic rocks transformed by subsequent heat and pressure—granite.
    Ans: A   Section: 10-4

89. The oldest material found on the Moon during manned and unmanned exploration was
    A)   water ice locked into permafrost on the surface of the Moon.
    B)   anorthositic rocks from the highlands.
    C)   smooth, dark glass formed by meteoritic impact.
    D)   basalt rocks from the mare basins.
    Ans: B   Section: 10-4

90. The best method for estimating the age of the surface of a celestial body with a solid
    surface such as a terrestrial planet or a moon (other than bringing rock samples back to
    Earth) is based on the idea that
    A)   volcanic activity occurs at a known rate, so the fewer volcanoes observed, the
         younger the surface.
    B)   planets and other bodies are subject to impacts from space at a known rate, so the
         fewer the number of craters, the younger the surface.
    C)   lithospheric plates form at a known rate, so the more plates observed, the older the
         surface.
    D)   craters are weathered at a known rate, so the more eroded the craters, the older the
         surface.
    Ans: B   Section: 10-4

91. What is the approximate age of the oldest rocks brought back from the Moon by astronauts during the *Apollo* program?
    A)   4.3 billion years   C)   3.5 billion years
    B)   10 billion years   D)   4.3 million years
    Ans: A   Section: 10-4

92. The age of Moon rocks has been determined primarily by what method?
    A)   careful chemical analysis of the constituents
    B)   measurements of radioactive decay products
    C)   careful examination of the site and surroundings, and particularly the measurement of the crater density, from which the rocks were acquired
    D)   counting the numbers of micrometeoroid craters on the rock surface
    Ans: B   Section: 10-4

93. The age of the moon is determined by
    A)   measurements of radioactive elements and radioactive dating.
    B)   measurements of the relative concentrations of easily melted and evaporated substances—the "volatiles," and the less volatile materials—the "refractory" elements.
    C)   careful crater counts over different regions of the Moon and comparison to known meteoroid densities in space.
    D)   radiocarbon dating of remnants of living material such as plant life.
    Ans: A   Section: 10-4

94. A regolith is
    A)   a layer of pulverized rock on the surface of a planet or other object.
    B)   an extremely large, isolated rock on the surface of a planet or other object.
    C)   a heavily cratered region on a planet or other object.
    D)   a lithospheric plate, moved slowly by geologic processes.
    Ans: A   Section: 10-4

95. The texture of the surface of the Moon may be described as
    A)   eroded basalt held together by subsurface ice (permafrost).
    B)   hard bedrock almost everywhere, because there is very little erosion on the Moon.
    C)   regolith (pulverized rock) in and near craters but hard bedrock everywhere else.
    D)   regolith (pulverized rock) covering the entire lunar surface.
    Ans: D   Section: 10-4

96. The lunar regolith is the
    A)   part of the lunar surface not covered with lava flows.
    B)   layer of fine powder covering the lunar surface.
    C)   lower part of the lunar crust not extensively cracked by impacts.
    D)   lunar crust and mantle together.
    Ans: B   Section: 10-4

97. How old are the lunar maria?
    A)   less than 1 billion years old
    B)   1.8 to 2.6 billion years old
    C)   3.1 to 3.8 billion years old
    D)   4.0 to 4.3 billion years old
    Ans: C   Section: 10-4

98. How old are the lunar highlands?
    A)   3.1 to 3.8 billion years old
    B)   1.8 to 2.6 billion years old
    C)   less than 1 billion years old
    D)   4.0 to 4.3 billion years old
    Ans: D   Section: 10-4

99. In what fundamental way do lunar rocks differ from terrestrial rocks?
    A)   Lunar rocks are meteoric in origin.
    B)   All lunar rocks are rich in calcium and aluminum.
    C)   Lunar rocks contain no water within their crystal structure.
    D)   Lunar rocks all originate in ancient lava flows.
    Ans: C   Section: 10-4

100. What appears to be the "impact history" of cratering on the Moon?
    A)   more or less constant bombardment from the earliest times to the present
    B)   heaviest bombardment when the Moon first formed, gradually decreasing to light
          bombardment today
    C)   short periods of heavy bombardment alternating with long periods of light
          bombardment throughout the Moon's life
    D)   an early period of heavy bombardment followed by very light bombardment to the
          present
    Ans: D   Section: 10-4

101. Suppose that two regions on the Moon have ages, respectively, of 3.7 and 4.3 billion
     years. Based on these ages, we expect to find that
    A)   the older region has fewer craters than the younger region because the cratering
          rate was lower at earlier times.
    B)   both regions have roughly the same amount of cratering because they have
          approximately the same age.
    C)   the older region has 16% more craters than the younger region because its age is
          16% greater than that of the younger region.
    D)   the older region has far more craters than the younger region because of changes
          in the cratering rate over that time.
    Ans: D   Section: 10-4

102. After the initial formation of the solar system, rocky debris
    A)   was essentially absent, having been used up in the formation of the planets.
    B)   was quickly vaporized by the heat of the young Sun.
    C)   continued to bombard the planets and satellites for almost another billion years.
    D)   was quickly swept out of the solar system by the Sun's T Tauri wind.
    Ans: C   Section: 10-4

103. Which of the following kinds of rocks are *not* found on the Moon?
    A) basalt   B) anothosite   C) limestone   D) breccias
    Ans: C   Section: 10-4

104. By dating the Moon rocks we can determine its age. How long ago did the Moon form?
    A)   The maria are about 3.8 billion years old, suggesting that the entire Moon was molten at that time—so that is its probable age.
    B)   The oldest rocks in the lunar highlands are about 4.3 billion years old, so that must be the age of the Moon.
    C)   We believe the Moon was formed molten and then cooled. Because the oldest rocks are about 4.3 billion years old, the formation of the Moon must have occurred around 4.5 billion years ago.
    D)   Because it cooled and solidified almost to its core, the Moon must be at least a billion years older than the Earth. Its age, therefore, must be at least 5.5 billion years.
    Ans: C   Section: 10-4

105. One effect of the ocean water's tidal drag on Earth is to
    A)   tilt its spin axis farther and farther away from the perpendicular to the ecliptic.
    B)   speed up its rate of spin, thereby gaining energy from the Moon's orbital motion.
    C)   slow down Earth's spin rate.
    D)   speed up Earth in its orbital motion around the Sun.
    Ans: C   Section: 10-5

106. Which of the following statements is a correct description of the Moon's orbit?
    A)   The Moon is gradually spiraling away from Earth.
    B)   The Moon's distance from Earth remains constant from year to year, on average.
    C)   The Moon's distance to Earth increases and then decreases cyclically once every 26,000 years.
    D)   The Moon is gradually spiraling toward Earth.
    Ans: A   Section: 10-5

107. How quickly is the Moon spiraling away from Earth?
    A)   a few centimeters per million years   C)   a few centimeters per year
    B)   a few meters per year   D)   a few centimeters per century
    Ans: C   Section: 10-5

108. Because of the tides on Earth's oceans, the Moon is
    A)   shrinking.
    B)   unaffected and continues to orbit in a constant elliptical path.
    C)   moving slowly toward Earth.
    D)   spiraling outward away from Earth.
    Ans: D   Section: 10-5

109. If the rate at which the Moon is moving away from Earth remains approximately constant at 4 cm per year, how long will it take for the distance between Earth and the Moon to increase by 10%?
    A)   1 billion years   C)   10 million years
    B)   10 billion years   D)   100 million years
    Ans: A   Section: 10-5

110. Which of the following statements is a correct description of the rotation of Earth?
    A)   The average length of a day varies unpredictably from one year to the next because of the combined effects of solar and lunar tides.
    B)   The average length of a day is gradually getting longer because Earth's rate of rotation is slowing down.
    C)   The average length of a day is constant from year to year because nothing can change the speed of rotation of Earth.
    D)   The average length of a day is gradually getting shorter because Earth's rate of rotation is speeding up.
    Ans: B   Section: 10-5

111. One effect of the tidal drag of the ocean waters on Earth is to
    A)   speed up Earth in its orbital motion around the Sun.
    B)   speed up its rate of spin, thereby gaining energy from the Moon's orbital motion.
    C)   slow down Earth's spin rate.
    D)   tilt its spin axis farther and farther away from the perpendicular to the ecliptic.
    Ans: C   Section: 10-5

112. Which statement best describes the average relationship between passage of the Moon through a observer's meridian and the occurrence of high tide in the open ocean? (Hint: See Fig. 10-19, Section 9-5, Freedman and Kaufmann, *Universe*, 7th ed., and think about what you would experience on Earth.)
    A)   High tides occur at random and are not related to the time of the Moon's meridian crossing at any position on Earth.
    B)   High tide occurs at about the same time as the moon passes through the meridian.
    C)   The Moon passes through an observer's meridian about one hour before high tide at this position.
    D)   The Moon passes through the meridian about one hour after high tide has occurred.
    Ans: C   Section: 10-5

113. Earth's rotation is slowing down because of the tidal interaction between Earth and the Moon at a rate of 2 msec per century. If this rate remains constant at the present value, how long will it take for one day on Earth to become 2 seconds longer than it is now?
    A) 1 million years   B) 100 million years   C) 1000 years   D) 100,000 years
    Ans: D   Section: 10-5

114. Moon rocks contain no water in their crystal structure and contain far less volatile material than those on Earth. Which theory of the origin of the Moon provides the most likely explanation for these differences?
    A) formation of Earth and the Moon at about the same time from the preplanetary nebula. The gravity of this proto-moon was insufficient to hold water and lighter volatile materials.
    B) collision of a large meteoroid with Earth and the ejection of very hot material, depleted in volatiles, into orbit around Earth
    C) breaking away by tidal stress of material depleted in volatiles from the Earth's surface
    D) capture theory, in which an object with different chemical composition was captured by Earth's gravity from outer space
    Ans: B   Section: 10-5

115. Compared to rocks on Earth, lunar rocks are
    A) slightly depleted in elements that melt at low temperatures, enriched in elements that melt at high temperatures, and contain no water of crystallization.
    B) slightly enriched in elements that melt at low temperatures, depleted in elements that melt at high temperatures.
    C) composed of the same elements but in very different proportions.
    D) identical in composition, except for having no water of crystallization
    Ans: A   Section: 10-5

116. One theory about the origin of the Moon says that the Moon was formed from debris thrown out when a Mars-sized object collided with Earth. One fact that strongly supports this theory is that
    A) the Moon has several smooth plains formed by ancient lava flows.
    B) the Moon always turns the same side toward Earth.
    C) impact breccias (rock fragments cemented together by an impact) are common on the Moon.
    D) Moon rocks are very similar to those of Earth but are depleted in elements that melt at relatively low temperatures.
    Ans: D   Section: 10-5

117. What factor is now thought to have played a major role in such diverse events as the formation of the Moon, the tilting of Earth's spin axis, and even the extinction of the dinosaurs?
    A) passage of the solar system through gigantic gas clouds in space
    B) sudden change in the orbital path of Earth
    C) major volcanic eruptions on Earth
    D) collisions between asteroid-like bodies and Earth
    Ans: D   Section: 10-5

118. The theory that seems to account most satisfactorily for the origin of the Moon at the present time is that
     A)   the Moon formed from material spun off from Earth when Earth was molten and spinning rapidly, early in its history.
     B)   a large object collided with Earth and ejected the material that formed the Moon.
     C)   the Moon formed by accretion elsewhere in the solar system and was captured later by Earth.
     D)   the Moon formed from material already in orbit around Earth.
     Ans: B   Section: 10-5

119. Although we do not yet know precisely how the Moon was formed, an important clue is provided by the fact that
     A)   moon rocks resemble material similar to that in the interior of Earth.
     B)   the Moon is heavily cratered.
     C)   moon rocks resemble rocks close to the surface of Earth.
     D)   moon rocks contain significant amounts of water and other volatile substances.
     Ans: C   Section: 10-5

120. Which is the most probable heat source that produced extensive and possibly total melting of the Moon at an early stage in its history?
     A)   tidal flexing and distortion caused by its motion around Earth
     B)   decay of radioactive elements within it and the impact energy of meteoritic bombardment
     C)   intense sunlight from the early and very active Sun
     D)   nuclear fusion reactions occurring in its core
     Ans: B   Section: 10-5

121. Which one of the following four theories about the origin of the Moon is now believed to be correct?
     A)   An object about the size of Mars crashed into Earth and debris from the collision formed the Moon.
     B)   Earth and the Moon formed together, already orbiting each other.
     C)   The Moon formed separately in a different part of the solar nebula and was later captured by Earth.
     D)   Earth was spinning so rapidly while still molten that a piece "spun off" to form the Moon.
     Ans: A   Section: 10-5

122. Most of the craters on the Moon were created by
    A)   debris flying out to the Moon from asteroid impacts on Earth.
    B)   volcanic activity during the early part of the Moon's history which left old
          calderas.
    C)   impacts of fragments of asteroids more or less evenly and continuously over the
          history of the Moon.
    D)   impacts of rocky debris during the first billion years of the Moon's history.
    Ans: D   Section: 10-5

123. Most of the craters on the Moon are thought to have been caused by
    A)   the intense bombardment by large and small bodies over an early and specific
          period in the Moon's history.
    B)   volcanic activity, leaving behind volcano craters similar to those on Earth.
    C)   the continuous bombardment throughout the Moon's life, including the present
          and recent past, by large and small asteroids.
    D)   the collapse of volcanic domes, leaving central peaks in the craters.
    Ans: A   Section: 10-5

124. Before the Mars-sized impactor struck the Earth to cause ejecta which formed he Moon,
    the Earth probably had a
    A)   smaller density and slower rotation rate than it does now.
    B)   smaller density and faster rotation rate than it does now.
    C)   greater density and slower rotation rate than it does now.
    D)   greater density and faster rotation rate than it does now.
    Ans: A   Section: 10-5

125. Which of the following is believed to be the correct explanation for the origin of the
    Moon?
    A)   The Moon was formed elsewhere in the solar system (which is why its
          composition differs from that of the Earth) and was later captured by the Earth's
          gravity.
    B)   Shortly after its formation, the Earth was spinning so fast in its molten state that a
          large piece of material was thrown off, and this coalesced to form the Moon—
          leaving the Pacific Ocean Basin in the place where it was thrown off.
    C)   The Earth and Moon were formed separately at the same time, while in orbit
          around their common center of mass, by the accretion of planetesimals.
    D)   The Earth was struck by a large planetesima, which caused material to be ejected.
          This material coalesced to form the Moon.
    Ans: D   Section: 10-5

Chapter 11: Sun-Scorched Mercury

1. Mercury can be characterized as having
   A)   a Moon-like surface and an Earth-like interior.
   B)   both surface and interior like that of the Moon.
   C)   an Earth-like surface and a Moon-like surface.
   D)   a surface and interior significantly different from either the Moon or Earth.
   Ans: A   Section: Chapter 11, Introductory Section

2. The inner planets, in order of increasing planetary radius, are
   A)   Mercury, Venus, Earth, Mars.   C)   Mercury, Venus, Earth, Mars.
   B)   Mercury, Mars, Venus, Earth.   D)   Mercury, Earth, Venus, Mars.
   Ans: B   Section: Chapters 9, 11, 12 and 13

3. When Mercury is at its greatest western elongation, it is seen to the
   A)   east of the Sun in our post-sunset sky.
   B)   west of the Sun in our predawn sky.
   C)   east of the Sun in our predawn sky.
   D)   west of the Sun in our post-sunset sky.
   Ans: B   Section: 11-1

4. Mercury can be seen most easily from Earth
   A)   near the Sun, just after sunset or just before sunrise.
   B)   during a lunar eclipse, when the sky is sufficiently dark near the Moon, because
        Mercury is always close to the Moon in our sky.
   C)   in the winter, when the ecliptic plane is high in the sky at night.
   D)   at midnight, when it is high in the sky.
   Ans: A   Section: 11-1

5. A friend who says that he is an astronomer claims that he was outside at midnight a few
   weeks ago looking at Mercury. What should be your response?
   A)   Oh, you must have been in Australia or South America since Mercury can be seen
        at midnight only from the southern hemisphere."
   B)   "You must be mistaken, because Mercury NEVER appears in our midnight sky."
   C)   "Really! Have you just purchased a new telescope? Mercury can be seen at
        midnight only through a telescope."
   D)   "Congratulations, you have been fortunate enough to see Mercury on a very rare
        occasion."
   Ans: B   Section: 11-1

6. It is relatively difficult to observe details on the surface of Mercury from Earth because
   A)   detail is obscured by bright glows from hot regions of molten surface heated by the intense sunlight.
   B)   its orbit always keeps it on the opposite side of the Sun from Earth.
   C)   it is a small object that always appears close to the Sun in the sky.
   D)   its surface is always completely covered in clouds.
   Ans: C   Section: 11-1

7. The surface of Mercury is difficult to see from Earth because it
   A)   is shrouded in thick clouds for most of the time.
   B)   does not receive much light from the Sun.
   C)   appears in our sky in daylight.
   D)   remains relatively close to the Sun in our sky.
   Ans: D   Section: 11-1

8. If angular resolution of detail on Mercury is limited to about 1.0 arcsecond by "seeing" fluctuations in Earth's atmosphere, approximately what is the diameter of the smallest surface feature that can be seen on Mercury at greatest eastern or western elongation? (Hint: Assume a circular orbit for Mercury with a radius of mean distance from the Sun.)
   A) about 430 km   B) about 180 km   C) about 1250 km   D) about 770 km
   Ans: D   Section: 11-1 and Box 11-1

9. How large would the Sun appear to be in the sky (in angular diameter) as seen by someone on Mercury, compared to what we see from here on Earth?
   A)   the same size, because it is the same Sun
   B)   about 2.5 times larger
   C)   about 1.5 times larger
   D)   about 6.25 times larger
   Ans: B   Section: 11-1 and Table 11-1

10. Approximately how many times in one Earth year will Mercury actually go completely around the Sun, as viewed with respect to the distant stars? (See Table 11-1, Freedman and Kaufmann, *Universe*, 7th ed.)
    A) three times   B) twice   C) four times   D) once
    Ans: C   Section: 11-1

11. Approximately how many times in one Earth year will Mercury appear at its point of greatest eastern elongation (i.e., in the western sky at sunset) when viewed from Earth? (Review synodic period, Chapter 4, Freedman and Kaufmann, *Universe*, 7th ed.)
    A) twice   B) four times   C) three times   D) once
    Ans: C   Section: 11-1

12. How often does a solar transit of Mercury—Mercury passing directly across the face of the Sun as seen from Earth—occur?
    A)   regularly, once every synodic period of Mercury, or every 116 days
    B)   never
    C)   regularly, every sidereal period of Mercury, or every 88 days
    D)   relatively infrequently—between 10 and 20 times per century
    Ans: D   Section: 11-1

13. When is Mercury best seen from Earth with the unaided eye?
    A)   at midnight, when Mercury is at opposition
    B)   close to dawn or dusk, when Mercury is at positions of greatest elongation
    C)   near midday, when it is seen through the least amount of Earth's atmosphere
    D)   during the daytime, when Mercury is at superior conjunction
    Ans: B   Section: 11-1

14. Mercury is difficult to observe from Earth because
    A)   its orbit is very elliptical and is tilted at a large angle to the ecliptic, only appearing low in our sky at midnight.
    B)   it is a very small object which orbits a long way from the Sun, thereby reflecting very little light back to Earth.
    C)   it orbits around the Sun rapidly and moves across our sky very quickly.
    D)   it remains close to the Sun in its orbit and is seen in a dark sky only close to the horizon at sunrise or sunset.
    Ans: D   Section: 11-1

15. It is relatively difficult to observe Mercury from Earth because
    A)   it is a small object that always appears close to the Sun in the sky.
    B)   at best, it only appears very close to the horizon, near midnight.
    C)   its orbit is always on the opposite side of the Sun from Earth.
    D)   its surface is always completely covered in clouds.
    Ans: A   Section: 11-1

16. Telescopic views of Mercury are generally best at what time of day?
    A)   at sunset near inferior conjunction, when Mercury is closest to Earth
    B)   at sunset near superior conjunction, when Mercury is fully lit as seen from Earth
    C)   just before sunrise or just after sunset, when Mercury is visible in a reasonably dark sky
    D)   near midday, when Mercury is high in the sky and seeing fluctuations are least likely to occur
    Ans: D   Section: 11-1

17. Suppose that on a certain day both Mercury and Venus are at greatest eastern elongation. After some time has elapsed, Venus will again be at greatest eastern elongation. During this period, how many times will Mercury have been at greatest eastern elongation? (Hint: Review synodic period, Chapter 4, Freedman and Kaufmann, *Universe,* 7th ed.)
    A) three times   B) five times   C) twice   D) once
    Ans: B   Section: 11-1 and Table 4.1

18. The albedo or fraction of light reflected from Mercury is
    A)   very high because of its light-colored surface materials.
    B)   very low because of its dark rocky surface and absence of an atmosphere.
    C)   about the same as that of Earth.
    D)   variable and relatively high because of variable cloud cover.
    Ans: B   Section: 11-1

19. Mercury is much closer than Venus to the Sun, and yet it never appears brighter than Venus, even when both are at maximum brightness, because
    A)   Mercury is larger than Venus, but it has a thick atmosphere which impedes reflection from its surface, making it appear dark.
    B)   we never see more of Mercury than a thin crescent because of its orbital path relative to that of Earth.
    C)   Mercury has average reflectivity but is very small and hence appears relatively dark.
    D)   Mercury is small, has a dark surface, and has no reflecting clouds.
    Ans: D   Section: 11-1

20. When Mercury is at greatest elongation it is sometimes at a more favorable position for viewing and sometimes at a less favorable position for viewing. What can change from one occurrence of greatest elongation to the next to cause this difference?
    A)   the eccentricity of Mercury's orbit
    B)   the inclination of Mercury's orbit relative to the ecliptic
    C)   the position of Mercury in its orbit
    D)   the direction in space of the semimajor axis of Mercury's orbit
    Ans: C   Section: 11-1

21. When Mercury is at its least value of greatest elongation it is 18° from the Earth-Sun line. How long before sunrise (or after sunset) will Mercury be visible at this time?
    A) 18 minutes   B) about an hour   C) two hours   D) four hours
    Ans: B   Section: 11-1

22. Suppose you observe Mercury at each of the following phases and you extrapolate the full angular diameter from the part that you can see. At which phase will the angular diameter appear greatest?
    A) full   B) first quarter   C) third quarter   D) crescent
    Ans: D   Section: 11-1

23. How many times will Mercury rotate with respect to the Sun in one sidereal orbital period? (See Table 11-1 and Figure 11-7, Freedman and Kaufmann, *Universe*, 7th ed.)
    A)   1/2 rotation
    B)   once
    C)   many times, because Mercury rotates rapidly
    D)   1 1/2 rotations
    Ans: D   Section: 11-2

24. What surface features on Mercury can astronomers see when they use telescopes from Earth?
    A)   only a few indistinct markings
    B)   none at all
    C)   three or four roundish, dark areas similar to the lunar maria
    D)   extensive cratering and one large, multiringed impact basin
    Ans: A   Section: 11-2

25. The atmosphere of Mercury
    A)   is almost nonexistent.
    B)   is only sulfur dioxide and hydrogen sulfide from volcanoes.
    C)   consists mostly of nitrogen (80%) and oxygen (20%).
    D)   is made up of carbon dioxide with small quantities of nitrogen and argon.
    Ans: A   Section: 11-2

26. Because it has no atmosphere, Mercury shows extreme temperature changes on its surface between night and day with a range of about
    A) 60 K.   B) 20 K.   C) 700 K.   D) 600 K.
    Ans: D   Section: 11-2

27. The highest daytime temperature reached on the surface of Mercury is
    A)   430°C, high enough to melt lead and tin.
    B)   0°C, high enough to melt ice.
    C)   961°C, high enough to melt silver.
    D)   100°C, high enough to boil water.
    Ans: A   Section: 11-2

28. Tomorrow's weather forecast for Caloris Basin on Mercury is
    A)   lead and zinc melting by noon; temperatures well below freezing overnight.
    B)   hot and humid by mid-afternoon; cooling to near freezing overnight.
    C)   overcast, light winds, occasional acid rain.
    D)   sunny with scattered clouds, possible afternoon dust storms.
    Ans: A   Section: 11-2

29. Mercury's 59-day sidereal rotation period was first measured in
    A) 1965 using radar.   C) 1883 by Schiaparelli.
    B) 1974 by the *Mariner 10* spacecraft. D) 1610 by Galileo.
    Ans: A   Section: 11-2

30. Mercury's true rotation period was first determined by
    A) monitoring surface features using optical telescopes on Earth.
    B) radar measurements from Earth.
    C) direct photography from *Mariner 10*.
    D) measuring the temperature on Mercury's dark side using radio telescopes.
    Ans: B   Section: 11-2

31. The correct rotation period of Mercury around its axis was first measured
    A) by radar, using Doppler shifts of reflected returns from opposite sides of the
       planet's disk.
    B) by comparison of temperatures of the dark side of Mercury, measured by radio
       observations, with calculated temperatures, assuming various rotation periods.
    C) from observations from a passing spacecraft, because it is impossible to see detail
       on this small planet from Earth.
    D) by visible observations of varying patterns on the planet's surface by astronomers
       using early telescopes.
    Ans: A   Section: 11-2

32. The first person to try to measure the rotation period of Mercury around its own axis
    was the Italian astronomer Schiaparelli. He reached the conclusion that Mercury
    A) does not rotate with respect to the stars.
    B) rotates synchronously with its orbital period, keeping one face always toward the
       Sun.
    C) rotates three times for every two orbits around the Sun.
    D) rotates once for every two orbits around the Sun.
    Ans: B   Section: 11-2

33. To what does the phrase "synchronous rotation" for an astronomical object (e.g., planet
    or moon) refer?
    A) It has a rotation rate that is precisely maintained (e.g., 23 h 56 m 4.096 s for
       Earth).
    B) For an object in an elliptical orbit, the rotation rate increases and decreases to
       match the changes in its orbital speed.
    C) It completes precisely one rotation around its own axis for every orbit (1-1 spin-
       orbit coupling).
    D) It has any rotation period that is in simple proportion to its orbital period (1-1
       spin-orbit coupling, 3-2 spin-orbit coupling, etc.).
    Ans: C   Section: 11-2

34. What method first showed that Mercury does not rotate synchronously (one rotation about its own axis for every orbit around the Sun)?
    A)   Surface temperatures on Mercury's dark side, measured by radio telescopes, were compared to calculated temperatures.
    B)   individual surface features were monitored visually by Schiaparelli in the 1880s
    C)   rotational speed was measured by radar from Earth
    D)   rotation period was measured by direct photography from *Mariner 10*
    Ans: A   Section: 11-2

35. The reason the temperature on the dark side of Mercury is warmer than originally expected is that
    A)   Mercury's large iron core conducts heat through the planet.
    B)   Mercury does not rotate synchronously with its orbital period.
    C)   several very active volcanoes on Mercury, produced by tidal stresses from the Sun, produce excess heat.
    D)   winds in Mercury's tenuous atmosphere carry heat from the daytime side to the night side.
    Ans: B   Section: 11-2

36. Temperatures on the surface of Mercury fluctuate between a very cold 100 K (−173°C) and an extremely hot 700 K (427°C).This measurement indicates that
    A)   the planet is close to the Sun, has no atmosphere to maintain heat on its dark side, and is rotating.
    B)   Mercury has a very elliptical orbit, and the varying distance from the Sun produces large temperature fluctuations, because intensity varies as the inverse square of the distance from the Sun.
    C)   erupting volcanoes occasionally heat the planet's surface to extreme temperatures.
    D)   the planet has an atmosphere in which the greenhouse effect captures solar radiation to heat the sunlit hemisphere of the planet.
    Ans: A   Section: 11-2

37. In one orbit around the Sun, Mercury rotates around its axis
    A) twice.   B) 3 times.   C) 1½ times.   D) once, in a synchronous orbit.
    Ans: C   Section: 11-2

38. What kind of relationship is maintained between Mercury's rotation around its spin axis and its revolution about the Sun? (See Fig.11-7, Freedman and Kaufmann, *Universe,* 7th ed.)
    A)   It completes three rotations for every two revolutions.
    B)   It completes three rotations for every one revolution.
    C)   It completes two rotations for every three revolutions.
    D)   It completes one rotation for every one revolution (synchronous rotation).
    Ans: A   Section: 11-2

39. If you are on Mercury and the time is noon (Sun directly overhead), what time of day will it be one Mercurian year later (after Mercury has orbited the Sun once)? (See Fig.11-7, Freedman and Kaufmann, *Universe,* 7th ed.)
    A) noon
    B) It could be any time, because Mercury rotates independently of its revolution.
    C) midnight
    D) just after sunset
    Ans: C   Section: 11-2

40. If you were watching the sunrise on Mercury when Mercury was near perihelion, what would you see?
    A) The Sun would rise, turn back and set, then rise again a day or two later.
    B) The Sun would rise, cross the sky, and set again, all in a few days, then spend the rest of Mercury's "year" below the horizon.
    C) The Sun would rise, slowly come to a standstill, then start rising again.
    D) The Sun would rise slowly, gradually speed up over a period of a few days, then slow down again.
    Ans: A   Section: 11-2

41. Mercury rotates once with respect to the distant stars in 59 days and has a sidereal period of 88 days. A star is overhead to an observer on Mercury at midnight. How many times will Mercury orbit the Sun before this star is again above the observer's head in a nighttime sky? (Draw a diagram to help in this exercise.)
    A) It will never again reach this specific position.   B) 1   C) 3   D) 2
    Ans: D   Section: 11-2

42. How long, in Earth days, is one solar day (e.g., noon to noon) on Mercury? (See Fig. 11-7, Freedman and Kaufmann, *Universe,* 7th ed.)
    A) 132 days   B) 88 days   C) 176 days   D) 59 days
    Ans: C   Section: 11-2

43. Suppose Mercury had 5-to-3 spin-orbit coupling and that its sidereal period remained 88 days, as it is now. What would be the time from noon to noon on Mercury, in days?
    A) 88   B) 147   C) 264   D) 440
    Ans: C   Section: 11-2

44. Suppose Mercury had 5-to-3 spin-orbit coupling and that its sidereal period remained 88 days, as it is now. You observe the Sun directly overhead in the Mercurian sky and then observe again from the same location 88 days later. Where will the Sun be in the sky? (Mercury, like Earth, rotates toward the east.)
    A) below the eastern horizon
    B) below the western horizon
    C) directly overhead again
    D) directly on the opposite side of the planet
    Ans: A   Section: 11-2

45. Of the facts listed below, three contribute to the unusual 3-to-2 spin-orbit coupling of Mercury's motion. Which one does *not* contribute?
    A)   The gravitational attraction between two masses decreases as the distance between the two masses increases.
    B)   Mercury's orbit is inclined at an unusually large angle to the ecliptic.
    C)   Mercury's orbit has an unusually large eccentricity.
    D)   Mercury is slightly oblong rather than perfectly round.
    Ans: B   Section: 11-2

46. The *Mariner 10* spacecraft produced images of only one hemisphere of Mercury because
    A)   it was placed into orbit around Mercury with precisely the same orbital period as Mercury's rotation period for scientific reasons and thus saw only one hemisphere during the entire mission.
    B)   its orbital period around the Sun was twice that of Mercury and thus it always arrived at Mercury when the same side was illuminated because of the planet's rotation.
    C)   it was placed into exactly the same orbit around the Sun as Mercury's orbit but just behind it and, because of the planet's rotation synchronous to its orbital period, the cameras viewed only one hemisphere.
    D)   it passed by the planet only once before leaving the solar system and saw only one hemisphere on this single passage.
    Ans: B   Section: 11-3

47. The *Mariner* spacecraft was placed in an elliptical orbit with the period of its orbit around the Sun twice that of Mercury. What was the length of the semimajor axis of *Mariner's* orbit? (Careful with units.)
    A) 0.39 AU   B) 0.61 AU   C) 0.48 AU   D) 0.0125 AU
    Ans: B   Section: 11-3, Box 4-2, and Table 11-1

48. Which planet most resembles the Moon in visible surface features and atmosphere?
    A) Venus   B) Mercury   C) Mars   D) Uranus
    Ans: B   Section: 11-3

49. Craters on Mercury appear to have been produced by
    A)   impacts by objects from space continuously throughout the planet's history, including very recently in geological time.
    B)   volcanic eruptions early in the planet's history.
    C)   successive expansion and contraction of the planet's surface, caused by intense heating by the Sun and severe cooling during rotation, because the craters appear to be in irregular lines across the surface.
    D)   impacts from objects early in the planet's history.
    Ans: D   Section: 11-3

50. The best estimate for the time of production of most craters on both Mercury and the Moon is
    A)   during the first 700 million years after planet formation.
    B)   very early in the lives of these planetary bodies, or within the first billion years after planet formation.
    C)   relatively recently, or about 4 billion years after planet formation.
    D)   about halfway into the lives of these planetary bodies, or about 2.3 billion years after planet formation.
    Ans: A   Section: 11-3

51. What evidence would a planetary geologist use to identify a "young" crater on Mercury?
    A)   infrared and photographic results showing evidence of water released recently from the permafrost by the impact
    B)   sharper rim and central peak compared to older craters, whose features would have suffered significant erosion by wind and dust
    C)   lighter-colored central region, because older craters would have acquired a layer of dark dust over time
    D)   few if any smaller craters within it or on its rim
    Ans: D   Section: 11-3

52. The surface of Mercury, unlike the highland regions of the Moon, has extensive plains between the craters. The reason for this is thought to be that
    A)   the older craters were worn down and obliterated by the solar wind.
    B)   Mercury is larger than the Moon, and it cooled more slowly, leaving lava to flow more recently across its surface than it has over the lunar highlands.
    C)   Mercury is closer to the Sun and did not receive as many crater-forming impacts as the Moon.
    D)   Mercury has a thinner mantle because of its large iron core and therefore experienced less volcanism.
    Ans: B   Section: 11-3

53. Mercury appears from spacecraft photographs to resemble the Moon in its surface features. One important difference between these planetary bodies is
    A)   the presence of a measurable and significant atmosphere and clouds on Mercury.
    B)   evidence of active volcanoes on Mercury.
    C)   the presence of extensive plains between craters on Mercury in contrast to the surface of the Moon.
    D)   Mercury's retrograde direction of spin compared to the Moon and most other planets and moons.
    Ans: C   Section: 11-3

54. What is believed to be the cause of the long, meandering scarps (cliffs) observed on Mercury?
    A)   shrinkage of the planet as Mercury cooled
    B)   large impacts near the end of the early period of heavy bombardment
    C)   volcanic eruptions along crustal faults over hot spots in the mantle
    D)   crustal movement due to convection in the mantle, similar to continental drift on Earth but to a much smaller extent
    Ans: A   Section: 11-3

55. The Caloris impact basin is found on
    A)   the Moon.
    B)   Jupiter's outer Galilean satellite, Callisto.
    C)   Mercury.
    D)   Mars.
    Ans: C   Section: 11-3

56. The Caloris basin is a
    A)   multiringed impact basin on Mercury.
    B)   large, lowland area on Mars.
    C)   volcanic caldera on Mount Maxwell on Venus.
    D)   lunar mare on the far side of the Moon.
    Ans: A   Section: 11-3

57. Caloris Basin, a huge circular region on Mercury surrounded by rings of mountains, appears to have been produced by
    A)   the impact of a massive object in the early phases of the planet's formation, soon after the initial cratering period.
    B)   wind erosion from huge atmospheric storms, similar to super-hurricanes on the Earth or the Red Spot on Jupiter.
    C)   successive expansion and contraction of the planet's surface by intense solar heating and severe cooling as the planet rotated, causing buckling in a similar way to the formation of the North American Rocky Mountains or the South American Andes.
    D)   the lava flow from a large and long-lived volcano that formed the mountains in a similar manner to the formation of the Hawaiian Islands on Earth.
    Ans: A   Section: 11-3

58. The age of Mercury's Caloris basin been estimated by
    A) residual radioactivity inside the basin compared to that outside, as measured by the *Mariner 10* spacecraft
    B) comparing the number of craters per unit area inside the basin to areas outside the basin
    C) comparing the albedo inside the basin to areas outside, because material becomes lighter as it gets older, as it does on the Moon
    D) radioactive dating of rocks returned to Earth by the *Mariner 10* spacecraft
    Ans: B   Section: 11-3

59. The huge impact of an object that produced the circular Caloris Basin and its ring of mountains on Mercury also produced
    A) melting of permafrost causing massive floods that produced the deep valleys on Mercury's surface.
    B) a very localized region of intense magnetic field, the only magnetic field possessed by Mercury.
    C) a very thick dusty atmosphere that still obscures the planet's surface.
    D) a broken pattern of mountains diametrically opposite the basin, caused by the focused seismic waves from the original impact.
    Ans: D   Section: 11-3

60. Which of the following statements about the similarities of Mercury and our Moon is not true?
    A) Both have very dark surfaces and low reflectivities or albedos.
    B) Neither has an atmosphere.
    C) Both have heavily cratered surfaces.
    D) Both have large, circular, and relatively flat basins or maria on parts of their surfaces.
    Ans: D   Section: 11-3

61. Although Mercury's surface differs from that of the Moon in several ways, there are several characteristics that occur on both Mercury and the Moon. Which of the following occur on both?
    A) craters usually separated from each other by smooth plains (craters not densely overlapping)
    B) winding, branched valleys indicating flowing water at some early time
    C) numerous long, meandering scarps (cliffs) created by global shrinkage at some early time
    D) a large multi-ringed basin with a set of jumbled hills diametrically opposite it, raised by seismic waves from the impact
    Ans: D   Section: 11-3

62. A distinct area of unusually jumbled, hilly terrain has been found on Mercury. This terrain was formed by
    A)   upwelling of magma while Mercury was still hot enough for its mantle to be tectonically active.
    B)   the impact of a large comet.
    C)   an intense shower of meteoroids near the end of the heavy bombardment era.
    D)   the focusing of seismic waves generated by the Caloris impact.
    Ans: D   Section: 11-3

63. The history of Mercury can be summarized by
    A)   thin crust at first, with lava covering all but the latest craters during the early bombardment, thus producing extensive crater-free plains between the craters.
    B)   rapid cooling to form a thick crust during the early bombardment, with a few isolated lava flows but very dense cratering everywhere else.
    C)   volcanic activity and crustal deformation over most of its history, with only the craters formed during the most recent billion years surviving.
    D)   early cooling to form a thick crust, with no evidence of volcanism or lava flows at any time in its history.
    Ans: A   Section: 11-3

64. Recent radar observations of Mercury have suggested that Mercury may
    A)   not be precisely locked into its hypothesized 3-2 spin-orbit coupling.
    B)   have one or more tectonic rift valleys.
    C)   have ice inside craters at its north and south poles.
    D)   have geologically recent lava flows on the side that was not photographed by *Mariner 10*.
    Ans: C   Section: 11-3

65. Which unexpected chemical compound has recently been discovered on Mercury?
    A)   ammonia escaping from fissures in Caloris Basin
    B)   cyanide, poisonous to humans, in the troposphere
    C)   nitrogen dioxide in Mercury's upper atmosphere
    D)   water ice at the north and south poles
    Ans: D   Section: 11-3

66. On Mercury, water ice has been found
    A)   in a recently formed crater, probably from a comet impact.
    B)   suspended as microscopic crystals in the stratosphere.
    C)   in deep fissures on the night side.
    D)   in permanently shadowed crater floors at the north and south poles.
    Ans: D   Section: 11-3

67. Despite the planet's close proximity to the Sun, water ice remains on the surface of Mercury because it
    A) is permanently shielded from the Sun by crater walls at the north and south poles.
    B) exists as permafrost below the thermally insulating surface, being exposed only by occasional impacts.
    C) is continuously replenished by fresh impacts from comets.
    D) is continuously replenished by condensation of water vapor from volcanoes.
    Ans: A   Section: 11-3

68. On its first orbit after launch *Mariner 10* flew past both Venus and Mercury, and on its next two orbits it flew past Mercury only. The orbital period of *Mariner* was 176 days and that of Venus is 225 days. How many additional orbits (beyond the first) would *Mariner* have had to complete to pass close to Venus a second time at the same spot in its orbit?
    A) 3   B) 7   C) 9   D) 11
    Ans: C   Section: 11-3

69. When were most of the existing lava plains formed on the surface of Mercury?
    A) Never. There is no evidence of lava flows on the surface of Mercury.
    B) when Mercury was first formed, about 4.5 billion years ago
    C) at the end of the era of heavy bombardment, about 3.8 billion years ago
    D) when the crust wrinkled to form the scarps
    Ans: C   Section: 11-3

70. The Caloris Basin is an immense impact crater on Mercury, which is unusual in that the opposite side of the planet shows jumbled terrain which resulted from shock waves created by the impact. This combination has also been found
    A) nowhere else in the solar system.   C) on the Earth.
    B) on the Moon.   D) on Saturn.
    Ans: B   Section: 11-3

71. Earth has a slightly higher average density (5520 kg/m^3) than Mercury (5430 kg/m^3). This is because
    A) Earth has a denser atmosphere than has Mercury.
    B) Mercury's interior has expanded slightly due to radioactive heating, reducing its density.
    C) Earth has a larger iron core in proportion to its size than has Mercury.
    D) Earth is more massive than Mercury and is therefore more gravitationally compressed.
    Ans: D   Section: 11-4

72. Mercury's iron core takes up approximately what fraction of the volume of the planet?
    A) 10%   B) 40%   C) 95%   D) 65–70%
    Ans: B   Section: 11-4

73. The central core of Mercury is probably composed of
    A)   molten rock.   C)   ices of H_2O and CH_4.
    B)   solid rocks of relatively low density. D)   solid and/or molten iron.
    Ans: D   Section: 11-4

74. Mercury's average density and the fact that it has a (weak) magnetic field leads to the
    conclusion that its central core is probably composed of
    A)   solid and/or molten iron.   C)   solid rocks of relatively low density.
    B)   molten rock.   D)   ices of H_2O and CH_4.
    Ans: A   Section: 11-4

75. Mercury's average density is similar to that of Earth, even though its mass is 18 times
    less than Earth's mass. What conclusion can be drawn from this situation?
    A)   Mercury must contain a greater proportion of heavier elements, particularly iron,
         in its interior.
    B)   Mercury's rocks must have been compressed into a smaller volume by a massive
         impact with another object sometime in its history to form the higher density.
    C)   A gravitational anomaly such as a black hole exists inside Mercury, similar to
         those detected among stars or at the centers of galaxies.
    D)   Mercury must have a larger molten core than does Earth because liquid rocks are
         denser than solids at the pressures found inside planets.
    Ans: A   Section: 11-4

76. Mercury is unique among the terrestrial planets in having
    A)   an iron core that takes up almost half its volume.
    B)   extensive volcanic activity and crustal deformation over most of its history but no
         evidence of plate tectonics.
    C)   one hemisphere with many craters and few volcanoes, the other hemisphere with
         few craters and many volcanoes.
    D)   no evidence of an iron core.
    Ans: A   Section: 11-4

77. The internal structure of Mercury is a
    A)   rocky core, a hydrogen-helium atmosphere, and liquid metallic hydrogen in
         between.
    B)   thick, rocky mantle taking up most of the volume of the planet, overlying a small
         but dense iron core.
    C)   dense iron core taking up almost half of the volume of the planet and a rocky
         mantle surrounding the core.
    D)   rocky core with a liquid (or perhaps frozen) water mantle and icy surface.
    Ans: C   Section: 11-4

78. The interior of Mercury contains
    A)   mostly ices and very low-density material, because the planet's average density is close to that of water.
    B)   very little iron in contrast to Earth, so the planet has no magnetic field.
    C)   significant amounts of water as permafrost, because occasional melting has produced deep water-formed valleys that criss-cross the planet's surface.
    D)   an iron core that occupies a large fraction of the volume of the overall planet and produces a magnetic field.
    Ans: D   Section: 11-4

79. Mercury's magnetic field, compared with that of Earth, is
    A)   of equivalent strength.
    B)   weak, but strong enough to deflect the solar wind.
    C)   extremely weak, so it cannot prevent the solar wind from hitting the surface of Mercury.
    D)   much more powerful.
    Ans: B   Section: 11-4

80. The magnetic field of Mercury appears to be caused by
    A)   a solid magnetized iron core.
    B)   the motion of high-speed solar wind particles around the planet.
    C)   electric currents in a region of liquid metallic hydrogen in the core.
    D)   electric currents in a molten iron core.
    Ans: D   Section: 11-4

81. According to modern dynamo theory, the production of a planet-wide magnetic field around a terrestrial-type planet requires
    A)   both a molten outer core and a solid inner core.
    B)   a permanently magnetized solid metallic core.
    C)   a molten core with or without a solid inner core.
    D)   a strong solar wind.
    Ans: A   Section: 11-4

82. Two conditions appear to be necessary for the generation of a powerful magnetic field in planets that are not present simultaneously on Mercury. These conditions are
    A)   rapid rotation and a molten iron core.
    B)   a molten core and a significant atmosphere.
    C)   rapid rotation and a conducting atmosphere.
    D)   a solid surface and a significant iron content.
    Ans: A   Section: 11-4

83. Mercury's average density and the fact that it has a (weak) magnetic field lead to the conclusion that its central core is probably composed of
    A) ices of H_2O and CH_4. C) molten rock.
    B) solid rocks of relatively low density. D) solid and/or molten iron.
    Ans: D Section: 11-4

84. When the solar wind (mostly protons and electrons, emitted continuously at relatively high speeds by the Sun) approaches Mercury it
    A) is guided around the planet by its magnetic field.
    B) is absorbed and stopped by the atmosphere of the planet.
    C) hits its surface directly, causing heat and a continuous fluorescent glow.
    D) is repelled by the high electrostatic charge on the planet.
    Ans: A Section: 11-4

85. Which physical feature of the planet Mercury causes the deflection of solar wind particles away from its surface?
    A) the gravitational field of the planet
    B) a magnetosphere surrounding the planet, created by an internal magnetic field
    C) a stream of ionized atoms heated by the intense sunlight that are emitted continuously by the planet
    D) a dense, ionized atmosphere surrounding the planet
    Ans: B Section: 11-4

86. The density of Mercury is about the same as that of Earth, but Mercury contains a larger proportion of iron. How is this possible?
    A) The iron in Mercury's core is accompanied by a very low-density crust. The *average* density is thus comparable to the density of Earth.
    B) The inner core of Mercury is hollow, thus reducing the overall density much below that of iron.
    C) Mercury has only one eighteenth the Earth's mass. Thus it must be composed of heavier materials (like iron) in order to match Earth's density.
    D) The Earth contains, proportionally, a smaller volume of iron, but because of Earth's greater mass this iron has been compressed to a larger density than the iron on Mercury.
    Ans: D Section: 11-4

87. Which one of the following is *not* a reasonable explanation for Mercury's high iron content?
    A)   Mercury was formed in the iron-rich outer region of the solar system and later drifted in to its present location.
    B)   Mercury was struck by a planetesimal early in its history, and this ejected much of the iron-poor mantle.
    C)   The low-density mantle was stripped from Mercury by the intense solar wind in the early solar system.
    D)   The high temperatures in the inner solar system were favorable for the solidification of materials like iron with high condensation temperatures.
    Ans: A   Section: 11-4

88. All of the following properties are usually thought necessary for the creation of a planet-wide magnetic field. Which one does Mercury *not* have?
    A)   some liquid in the core
    B)   some solid in the core
    C)   some electrically conducting material in the core
    D)   a relatively rapid rotation rate
    Ans: D   Section: 11-4

Chapter 12: Cloud-Covered Venus

1. Which of the planets fits the following description: "a hot solid surface, cloud-shrouded, with a dense CO_2 atmosphere"?
   A) Venus   B) Mars   C) Mercury   D) Jupiter
   Ans: A   Section: Chapter 12, Opening Paragraph

2. Which of the following planets has no moon?
   A) Venus   B) Neptune   C) Jupiter   D) Pluto
   Ans: A   Section: Chapter 21, Appendix 3: Satellites of the Planets

3. When Venus is at its brightest as seen from Earth (near greatest elongation), it is
   A)   the brightest celestial object in the sky other than the Sun and Moon.
   B)   brighter than the full Moon but not as bright as the Sun.
   C)   just bright enough to be seen with the unaided eye if one knows exactly where to look for it.
   D)   too faint to see without binoculars or a telescope.
   Ans: A   Section: 12-1

4. Venus appears to be very bright in our skies at certain times because
   A)   even though its surface is very dark, it is relatively close to the Sun.
   B)   it is glowing from the heat of its surface, where the temperature is 750 K.
   C)   its rocky surface is shiny, like the surface of new volcanic lava.
   D)   it is relatively close to the Sun, Earth is close to it, and it is covered by very reflective clouds.
   Ans: D   Section: 12-1

5. What is the angle between the Earth-Venus line and the Sun-Venus line when Venus is at greatest eastern elongation?
   A) nearly 180°   B) approximately 90°   C) acute angle less than 90°   D) 0°
   Ans: B   Section: 12-1

6. Use the data on times of specific configurations of Venus in Table 12-2, Freedman and Kaufmann, *Universe*, 7th ed., to determine its synodic period. (Use the formula in Box 4-1 to verify this value, but be careful with units.)
   A)   139 days or 0.38 year   C)   584 days or 1.6 years
   B)   224.7 days or 0.615 year   D)   116 days or 0.317 year
   Ans: C   Section: 12-1

7. Why are there are so few solar transits of Venus across the Sun's face as it revolves in its orbit and passes through inferior conjunction?
   A)   The orbital plane of Venus is inclined at 3.4° to the ecliptic plane.
   B)   The synodic period of Venus is very long because of the relative orbits of Earth and Venus.
   C)   Venus revolves around the Sun in a retrograde direction compared to the other terrestrial planets.
   D)   Venus rotates on its axis in a retrograde direction compared to the other terrestrial planets.
   Ans: A   Section: 12-1

8. On the basis of appearance and general properties, which planetary body could be described as Earth's twin?
   A)   Pluto—similar in size and density, with a large moon and probably life on its surface
   B)   Venus—about the same mass and diameter, with a dense and cloud-shrouded atmosphere
   C)   Mars—somewhat smaller but with a similar surface, a thin atmosphere, and clouds
   D)   the Moon—somewhat smaller but with the same average density and geology, orbiting at the same distance from the Sun but with no atmosphere
   Ans: B   Section: 12-1

9. When Venus is seen at inferior conjunction, a ring of light is seen around it, as shown in Fig. 12-2 of Freedman and Kaufmann, *Universe,* 7th ed. What does this tell us about Venus?
   A)   Venus has auroral displays similar to those on Earth which extend over the whole planet.
   B)   Venus has a thick atmosphere that scatters sunlight toward us.
   C)   The surface of Venus is so hot that it glows, even on its dark side.
   D)   Venus is sufficiently massive that its gravitational field bends sunlight around the planet toward us.
   Ans: B   Section: 12-1

10. Why does Venus experience fewer transits of the Sun than does Mercury?
   A)   The orbit of Venus has a larger incline angle to the ecliptic than does the orbit of Mercury.
   B)   Mercury is closer to the Sun and thus orbits more frequently.
   C)   The retrograde rotation of Venus inhibits transits of the Sun.
   D)   The large eccentricity of Venus's orbit results in fewer transits.
   Ans: B   Section: 12-1

11. We can see evidence of the atmosphere of Venus when it is backlit by the Sun. This occurs when Venus is at
    A)   inferior conjunction.   C)   greatest eastern elongation.
    B)   superior conjunction.   D)   greatest western elongation.
    Ans: A   Section: 12-1

12. Which three planets rotate in the retrograde direction?
    A)   Mercury, Venus, Uranus   C)   Mercury, Neptune, Pluto
    B)   Venus, Uranus, Pluto   D)   Venus, Saturn, Neptune
    Ans: B   Section: 12-2

13. The one terrestrial planet that rotates in the "wrong" direction (opposite to the planet's direction of revolution around the Sun) is
    A) Mars.   B) Earth.   C) Venus.   D) Mercury.
    Ans: C   Section: 12-2

14. Which of the following planets rotates on its axis in the retrograde direction, opposite to that of most of the planets and opposite to the direction of revolution of the planets?
    A) Moon   B) Mercury   C) Saturn   D) Venus
    Ans: D   Section: 12-2

15. Venus rotates in
    A)   the same direction as Earth but very rapidly (in a few hours).
    B)   a "lock-in" situation to the Sun, maintaining one side toward the Sun at all times (synchronous rotation).
    C)   the same direction as Earth but very slowly.
    D)   the opposite direction to Earth but very slowly.
    Ans: D   Section: 12-2

16. The rotation rate of the planet Venus was first determined by measuring
    A)   the time delay of radio pulses after reflection from the planet's surface.
    B)   the Doppler shift in radio waves reflected from the planet's surface.
    C)   photography from the Hubble Space Telescope at infrared wavelengths that penetrate the planet's clouds.
    D)   sequential photography of Venus from Earth.
    Ans: B   Section: 12-2

17. An observer on the surface of Venus, looking upward during the daytime, would be likely to see
    A)   thin, high clouds near mountains, otherwise clear skies, the Sun moving from east to west.
    B)   a solid cloud deck, with a lighter area toward the Sun that moves from west to east.
    C)   scattered, billowy clouds, with clear sky between them, the Sun moving from west to east.
    D)   a solid cloud deck, with a lighter area toward the Sun that moves from east to west.
    Ans: B   Section: 12-2

18. A reasonable explanation for the retrograde rotation (in a direction opposite to that of most other planets) of Venus is the
    A)   frictional drag of its very dense atmosphere on the rotating planet throughout its history.
    B)   uneven pull of the Sun's gravitation due to the oblate shape of the Sun.
    C)   frictional slowing-down and eventual reversal of Venus's rotation by tidal forces at a time when the planet had deep oceans over its surface.
    D)   combined gravitational effects of its neighboring planets, Mercury and Earth.
    Ans: A   Section: 12-2

19. If one were on the planet Venus viewing the Sun through the clouds, where would the Sun appear to rise as Venus rotated?
    A)   the east
    B)   the north, because the spin axis of Venus is parallel to the plane of its orbit.
    C)   The Sun would not rise or set because Venus rotates synchronously, keeping one side always toward the Sun.
    D)   the west
    Ans: D   Section: 12-2

20. The length of one solar day on Venus (i.e., time between successive sunrises) is
    A)   243 Earth days.   C)   88 Earth days.
    B)   224 Earth days.   D)   117 Earth days.
    Ans: D   Section: 12-2

21. The length of one solar day (i.e., time between successive sunrises) on Venus is
    A)   about the same as that on Earth.
    B)   much longer than that on Earth.
    C)   much shorter than that on Earth, about an hour.
    D)   about half as long as that on Earth, about 10 hours.
    Ans: B   Section: 12-2

22. In one synodic period of Venus (584 Earth days), this planet rotates five times synodically (with respect to the Sun) because its synodic rotation period is 116.8 Earth days ($5 \times 116.8 = 584$). What does this mean in terms of the relative positions of Earth and Venus at successive inferior conjunctions? (A diagram might help.)
    A) At every inferior conjunction, Venus passes across the face of the sun (solar transit) as seen from Earth.
    B) The same side of Earth faces Venus at each inferior conjunction.
    C) Venus turns the same side toward Earth at every inferior conjunction.
    D) Venus keeps the same side toward the Sun at all times (synchronous rotation).
    Ans: C   Section: 12-2

23. Venus's orbital period is 225 days and its rotation period is 243 days, retrograde. Suppose you could observe the Sun from Venus when it is at your zenith. And suppose you observe it from the same location 225 days later. Where would the Sun be in the sky?
    A) to the east of your zenith
    B) to the west of your zenith
    C) at your zenith
    D) behind you on the opposite side of the planet
    Ans: B   Section: 12-2

24. In order to measure Venus's rotation it was necessary to send a beam of electromagnetic radiation through the cloud layer. This electromagnetic radiation was
    A) ultraviolet. B) visible. C) infrared. D) radio.
    Ans: D   Section: 12-2

25. The gas that is the major constituent of the atmospheres of Venus and Mars and a minor constituent of Earth's atmosphere is
    A) H_2O. B) N_2. C) CO_2. D) O_2.
    Ans: C   Section: 12-3

26. The component of Venus's atmosphere that is responsible for the greenhouse effect, or excess heating, is
    A) H_2SO_4 or sulfuric acid droplets. B) N_2. C) H_2O vapor. D) CO_2.
    Ans: D   Section: 12-3

27. The surface temperature of Venus was first measured by
    A)   direct temperature measurement at the planet's surface by the Soviet lander *Venera 7*.
    B)   infrared emission from the lower atmosphere of Venus by astronomers at the Canada-France-Hawaii telescope on Mauna Kea.
    C)   radio emission from the planet's surface by the Arecibo radio telescope in Puerto Rico.
    D)   microwave emission from the planet's surface by the American spacecraft *Mariner 2*.
    Ans: D   Section: 12-3

28. The surface temperature of Venus was first measured in
    A)   1957 by British astronomers at the Jodrell Bank Radio Telescope in England.
    B)   1962 during a flyby by the American spacecraft *Mariner 2*.
    C)   1978 by atmospheric descent probes released by the American *Pioneer Venus* orbiter.
    D)   1970 by the Soviet lander *Venera 7*.
    Ans: B   Section: 12-3

29. The surface temperature of Venus has been found by radio observations and by remote exploration by American and Soviet spacecraft to be approximately
    A) 190 K.   B) 273 K.   C) 460 K.   D) 730 K.
    Ans: D   Section: 12-3

30. The surface and near-surface atmospheric conditions on Venus are
    A)   no atmosphere, very variable temperature.
    B)   dense methane, ammonia, and H_2O atmosphere, low temperature.
    C) CO_2 atmosphere, low pressure, and low temperature.
    D) CO_2 atmosphere, high pressure, and high temperature.
    Ans: D   Section: 12-3

31. The main reason for the very high temperature (750 K) on the surface of the planet Venus is thought to be
    A)   the intense and continuous volcanic action on the surface and the radiation from hot lava.
    B)   chemical reactions between the constituents of the atmosphere.
    C)   the continuous bombardment of the surface by meteoroids and solar wind particles.
    D)   the absorption of visible radiation by the surface and clouds and the trapping of re-radiated infrared radiation by the atmosphere.
    Ans: D   Section: 12-3

32. The mechanism of the greenhouse effect, which has resulted in very high temperatures on the surface of Venus (and moderate temperatures on Earth), can be described as
    A)   solar UV and visible radiation heating the planet surface, the infrared emissions of which are then trapped by CO_2 in the atmosphere.
    B)   solar infrared radiation heating the planet surface, which then emits visible and UV radiation that is trapped by CO_2 in the atmosphere.
    C)   solar UV and visible radiation entering the clouds and triggering chemical reactions in the CO_2 and sulfur compounds, the released energy then heating the atmosphere.
    D)   solar UV and visible radiation being absorbed by the CO_2 of the atmosphere, thereby heating it.
    Ans: A   Section: 12-3

33. Why has the greenhouse effect been much more effective in raising the surface temperature on Venus than on Earth?
    A)   The solar wind, the major cause of heating in the greenhouse effect, is far more intense at Venus's distance from the Sun and Venus has no magnetic field to deflect it.
    B)   The oceans on Earth have acted as a thermostat in absorbing much of the heat that would otherwise have raised Earth's temperature significantly.
    C) CO_2, which traps heat from the planet's surface, is the major component in the very dense Venusian atmosphere but only a minor constituent of Earth's atmosphere.
    D)   The surface of Venus is much more effective than that of Earth in absorbing solar visible and UV radiation.
    Ans: C   Section: 12-3

34. Why is the surface of Venus hotter than that of Mercury, even though Mercury is much closer to the Sun?
    A)   Chemical reactions within the thick clouds and dense atmosphere are continuously supplying heat to the surface.
    B)   Continuous volcanic activity releases large quantities of hot lava onto the surface.
    C)   Venus rotates rapidly, thereby ensuring that its entire surface is being heated regularly and uniformly.
    D)   The thick CO_2 atmosphere prevents re-emission into space of the heat absorbed from sunlight.
    Ans: D   Section: 12-3

35. The surface pressure of the atmosphere of Venus compared to that of Earth is
    A)   about 90 atmospheres.   C)   extremely small.
    B)   about the same as Earth.   D)   about 1/100 atmosphere.
    Ans: A   Section: 12-3

36. The highest temperature in the atmosphere of Venus occurs
    A)   in the clear atmospheric layers below the cloud level at an altitude of about 30 km.
    B)   at the height of the thickest clouds, 48–52 km, where infrared absorption is highest.
    C)   at the cloud tops, which are heated by sunlight.
    D)   at the planet's surface.
    Ans: D   Section: 12-3 and Figure 12-5

37. What is the average temperature gradient in the atmosphere of Venus from the surface to the top of the clouds at 70 km above the surface? (See Fig. 12-5, Freedman and Kaufmann, *Universe,* 7th ed.)
    A)   about 11 K/km   C)   about 0.8 K/km
    B)   about 8 K/km   D)   about 80 K/km
    Ans: B   Section: 12-3

38. The temperature in the atmosphere of Venus (see Fig. 12-5, Freedman and Kaufmann, *Universe*, 7th ed.)
    A)   is almost constant with altitude.
    B)   decreases smoothly with increasing altitude.
    C)   has a complicated structure, passing through several maxima and minima at various altitudes.
    D)   increases smoothly with increasing altitude.
    Ans: B   Section: 12-3

39. The sulfuric acid clouds on Venus
    A)   extend from the surface to a height of 70 km and cover the whole planet.
    B)   are confined to a narrow layer about 60 km above the planet's surface and cover the whole planet.
    C)   are confined to a layer just above the surface about 1 km thick and completely opaque, rendering the surface invisible from above.
    D)   are in a layer about 70 km above the planet's surface but are patchy, so the surface can be seen occasionally from above.
    Ans: B   Section: 12-3

40. The highest altitude to which clouds extend above the surface of Venus is
    A)   thousands of kilometers.   C)   68 km.
    B)   There are no clouds on Venus.   D)   48 km.
    Ans: C   Section: 12-3

41. The clouds in the atmosphere of Venus consist primarily of
    A)   dust particles.
    B)   droplets of liquid methane and ammonia.
    C)   droplets of H_2SO_4 or sulfuric acid.
    D) H_2O.
    Ans: C   Section: 12-3

42. The chemical element that plays a major role in the color and chemistry of the Venusian atmosphere and clouds is
    A)   chlorine, as gas, hydrogen chloride, and hydrochloric acid droplets.
    B)   sulfur, as dust and as sulfur dioxide, and sulfuric acid droplets.
    C)   iron, as red dust, iron oxides, and iron sulfides.
    D)   nitrogen, as gas, nitric oxide, and nitric acid droplets.
    Ans: B   Section: 12-3

43. A ground-based visual telescopic view of Venus reveals
    A)   a completely cloud-shrouded planet with high atmospheric wind speeds.
    B)   a dark smooth surface with few mountain ranges.
    C)   evidence of ice-covered polar caps and huge dust storms.
    D)   a crater-covered surface of reddish color.
    Ans: A   Section: 12-3

44. The cloud structure of Venus can best be described as
    A)   a perpetual thick cloud layer extending almost to ground level.
    B)   a perpetual thick cloud layer with a haze layer under it and clear air below the haze layer down to the surface.
    C)   mostly clear sky with occasional thin H_2O and dust clouds.
    D)   isolated cloud systems constantly forming and dissipating with clear sky between them.
    Ans: B   Section: 12-3

45. The atmosphere of Venus immediately above the surface of the planet, as discovered by the *Venera* spacecraft, can best be described as
    A)   very dense, corrosive, and opaque clouds.
    B)   quite dusty.
    C)   very clear.
    D)   foggy.
    Ans: C   Section: 12-3

46. What phenomenon causes the V-shaped patterns that are a prominent feature on Venus?
    A)   circulation patterns of winds in clouds around the north pole of the planet, which points toward Earth once every synodic period of Venus
    B)   clouds blown by strong winds, dividing into north and south components around Maxwell Montes, the high mountain on the Ishtar Terra range
    C)   patterns in the sulfur dust storms on the surface of Venus
    D)   strong winds blowing from east to west, combining with north-south convection currents at cloud altitudes
    Ans: D   Section: 12-3

47. The retrograde rotation of Venus and its atmosphere (opposite that of most other planets) can be described as
    A)   planet and atmosphere rotating together, like Earth, but somewhat more slowly (4 days).
    B)   very slow planet rotation (243 days) with faster atmospheric rotation (4 days).
    C)   both planet and atmosphere rotating together, like Earth, but very slowly (243 days).
    D)   relatively fast planet rotation (4 days) with slow atmospheric rotation (243 days).
    Ans: B   Section: 12-3

48. The relative rotation patterns of the Venusian atmosphere and Venus itself are
    A)   fast (4 days) retrograde rotation of planet and slow (243 days) retrograde rotation of the upper cloud bank.
    B)   slow (243 days) prograde or direct planetary rotation and fast (4 days) retrograde rotation of the cloud tops.
    C)   slow (243 days) retrograde rotation of planet and rapid (4 days) retrograde rotation of upper atmospheric clouds.
    D)   no rotation of Venus itself, but atmospheric cloud tops rotate slowly (243 days) in a retrograde direction.
    Ans: C   Section: 12-3

49. There are many reasons why a multiday hiking trip on foot across Aphrodite Terra on Venus would not be advisable, at least not without suitable protection. Which of the following is NOT one of the reasons?
    A)   water not available
    B)   very cold nighttime temperatures
    C)   corrosive atmosphere
    D)   predominantly carbon dioxide atmosphere
    Ans: B   Section: 12-3

50. Tomorrow's weather report for Venus would be
    A)   snow and cold.   C)   overcast and hot.
    B)   hot and humid, with clear skies.   D)   cold and clear.
    Ans: C   Section: 12-3

51. Spacecraft from which country or countries have landed on the surface of Venus?
    A)   No country has yet successfully landed spacecraft on the surface of Venus.
    B)   the United States
    C)   the United States and the Soviet Union
    D)   the Soviet Union
    Ans: D   Section: 12-3

52. The *Venera* series of spacecraft landed on which planet or moon?
    A) Mercury   B) Venus   C) Mars   D) Earth's Moon
    Ans: B   Section: 12-3

53. Why did the *Venera* series of spacecraft survive for only a few minutes on Venus's surface?
    A) They landed very fast because there was insufficient atmosphere to slow down their descent.
    B) Conditions of extreme pressure, corrosive atmosphere, and high temperatures caused severe damage.
    C) They were attacked and destroyed by native inhabitants, but the space agency is not telling the world of this.
    D) They landed in very rugged terrain and were not able to land upright; they became damaged when they toppled over.
    Ans: B   Section: 12-3

54. The severe atmospheric conditions that quickly destroyed spacecraft, which were soft-landed on the surface of Venus, were
    A) high temperatures, high pressures, and corrosive acid clouds and mist.
    B) high temperatures, low atmospheric pressure, and intense UV radiation from the Sun.
    C) very low temperatures, a near vacuum, and corrosive alkaline clouds and mist.
    D) intense sunlight, including UV, very high pressures, and very low temperatures.
    Ans: A   Section: 12-3

55. Convection is the process in which
    A) hotter gases rise and cooler gases sink.
    B) the Coriolis force causes winds to veer to the right in the northern hemisphere and to the left in the southern hemisphere.
    C) gases such as water vapor or carbon dioxide condense directly to a solid form ("ice") in the fall and winter and sublimate back to a gas in spring and summer.
    D) winds blow from regions of high pressure to regions of low pressure.
    Ans: A   Section: 12-3

56. The circulation pattern in Venus's atmosphere consists of
    A) one main convection cell in each of the northern and southern hemispheres, which extends from the equator almost to the poles and drives weaker cells above and below it.
    B) three cells in each of the northern and southern hemispheres, resulting from upwelling at the equator combined with the Coriolis force due to the planet's rotation.
    C) one main convection cell extending across the equator from near the pole in the "summer" hemisphere to subtropical latitudes in the "winter" hemisphere.
    D) several individual convection cells in regions where the time of day is noon to late afternoon, moving around the planet to keep pace with the Sun as Venus rotates.
    Ans: A   Section: 12-3

57. What is the difference in temperature between the equator and the poles on Venus?
    A) large but less than on Earth, because a very dense atmosphere on Venus conducts heat more efficiently than does our own atmosphere
    B) almost none, because of a very efficient pattern of circulation in Venus's atmosphere
    C) much larger than on Earth, because Venus lacks an ocean. On Earth, ocean currents such as the Gulf Stream transport heat from the equator to the poles
    D) extreme, because of a lack of any appreciable atmosphere on Venus results in extreme solar heating at the equator and uninhibited heat loss at the poles
    Ans: B   Section: 12-3

58. To measure the surface temperature of Venus, *Mariner 2* measured emissions with wavelengths of 1.35 cm and 1.9 cm. The temperature of Venus is 730 K. What is the peak wavelength in the emission spectrum of Venus?
    A) 1.35 cm   B) 1.9 cm   C) 4 μm   D) 6 nm
    Ans: C   Section: 12-3 and Box 5-2

59. How do surface temperatures vary on Venus?
    A) The poles are significantly cooler than the equator and the night side is significantly cooler than the day side.
    B) The poles are about the same temperature as the equator at the terminator, but the night side is significantly cooler than the day side.
    C) The day and night sides are about the same temperature at the equator, but the poles are significantly cooler than the equator.
    D) There is little temperature variation over the whole surface.
    Ans: D   Section: 12-3

60. Which particular chemical associated with volcanic emissions has been detected by various techniques in amounts that appear to vary significantly over short time scales, indicating the presence of active volcanoes on Venus at the present time?
    A) carbon in CO_2 and CO   C) silicon and silicate dusts
    B) ammonia and methane gases   D) sulfur and sulfur compounds
    Ans: D   Section: 12-4

61. The sulfur compounds that are detected in the clouds above the surface of Venus have most probably come from
    A) recent eruptions of volcanoes, spewing gases and dust high into the atmosphere.
    B) meteoritic material that burned up as it fell into Venus's atmosphere.
    C) intense wind storms that have carried surface dust high into the atmosphere.
    D) the solar wind, having been captured by the intense magnetic field of the planet.
    Ans: A   Section: 12-4

62. A shield volcano is a
    A)   volcanic dome on the side of a larger volcano that shields the surrounding plains from inundation by lava from the main vent.
    B)   very broad volcano with gently sloping sides, similar in shape to an ancient Greek shield.
    C)   tall volcano with steep sides, similar in shape to the central ornament of an ancient Roman shield.
    D)   vast lava flood-plain originating from a ground-level fissure, similar in size and topography to the Canadian Shield rock formation.
    Ans: B   Section: 12-4

63. Hot-spot volcanism is a process that
    A)   produces gigantic volcanoes on Venus and Mars but produces chains of smaller volcanoes on Earth (e.g., the Hawaiian Islands).
    B)   produces dome-shaped rises on Venus and Mars and mid-ocean ridges on Earth (e.g., the Mid-Atlantic Ridge).
    C)   does not operate on Venus or Mars but produces subduction zones on Earth (e.g., along the west coast of North and South America).
    D)   produces large rift valleys on Mars, Venus, and Earth (e.g., the Great Rift Valley of Africa).
    Ans: A   Section: 12-4

64. The Hawaiian Islands experience continuous volcanic activity because they
    A)   lie right on a boundary between tectonic plates.
    B)   happen to be at a focal point for seismic waves from earthquakes around the Pacific Ocean.
    C)   are in the center of a major ocean.
    D)   lie directly above a hot-spot plume in Earth's interior.
    Ans: D   Section: 12-4

65. In what way was the production of the Hawaiian Islands on Earth similar to the production of some of the major mountains on Mars and Venus?
    A)   They were produced by hot-spot volcanism and upflow of heat from below.
    B)   They were produced by impacts of massive asteroids during the ancient heavy bombardment period, and are now being eroded by wind and water.
    C)   They were produced by slow buildup of coral reefs in ancient oceans.
    D)   They were formed by upthrust from collisions of two tectonic plates.
    Ans: A   Section: 12-4

66. Evidence of hot-spot volcanoes caused by hot, rising plumes under the planet's surface is present on Venus and Mars as well as on Earth. What distinguishes those on Earth from those on the other planets?
    A)   This type of volcano occurs near the spin axes or poles of Venus and Mars where tidal stress is greatest, whereas on Earth they occur near the equator.
    B)   Those on Venus and Mars occur on tectonic plate boundaries, and they therefore form long chains of volcanoes extending around the planet's surface, whereas on Earth they form large, stationary shield-type volcanoes.
    C)   Plate tectonics on all three planets has formed chains of small volcanic cones, but those on Earth have all occurred under the sea and now appear as islands.
    D)   Plate tectonics moves Earth's crust continuously, creating lines of individual volcanoes or islands, whereas no such movement has occurred on Venus or Mars.
    Ans: D   Section: 12-4

67. Which spacecraft and technique have given us our most detailed information about the overall surface of Venus?
    A)   photography by the four *Viking* spacecraft (two landers and two orbiters)
    B)   photography by the *Venera* landers from the former Soviet Union
    C)   photography from the Space Shuttle at UV wavelengths that penetrate the Venusian clouds
    D)   radar mapping by the U.S.A. *Magellan* orbiter
    Ans: D   Section: 12-4

68. The surface features and topology of Venus have been determined primarily by
    A)   radar methods from Earth and from Venus-orbiting spacecraft detecting reflected radio waves from the surface.
    B)   surface lander vehicles that have explored the surface.
    C)   visible light and UV photography from the Hubble Space Telescope and Earth-bound telescopes.
    D)   balloon-borne spacecraft launched into the Venus atmosphere by spacecraft.
    Ans: A   Section: 12-4

69. The overall geography of the Venus surface has been determined largely by
    A)   manned exploration by Russian cosmonauts.
    B)   visible light photography.
    C)   unmanned spacecraft that landed on the surface.
    D)   radar techniques from Earth and from orbiting spacecraft.
    Ans: D   Section: 12-4

70. The surface features and topology of Venus have been mapped primarily by what physical technique?
    A)   radar exploration from Earth and from orbiting spacecraft
    B)   unmanned exploration by robotic vehicles
    C)   ultraviolet photography from Earth
    D)   balloon-borne cameras mapping the planet surface
    Ans: A   Section: 12-4

71. The best images of the overall topology of Venus have been produced by
    A)   visible wavelength images from cameras on board an orbiting spacecraft.
    B)   photography from the Hubble Space Telescope at UV wavelengths to which the Venus atmosphere and clouds are transparent.
    C)   imaging cameras on board two spacecraft that soft-landed on the surface of Venus.
    D)   reflection of microwave and short radio wave radiation from the surface by an orbiting spacecraft.
    Ans: D   Section: 12-4

72. In the mapping of Venus by the orbiting *Magellan* spacecraft, what parameter was measured by the sensors to produce three-dimensional maps of the planet's surface?
    A)   time delay of the return of reflected radio waves
    B)   pairs of photographs, taken from different angles, that were then combined stereoscopically to produce contour maps
    C)   precise photographs of the extreme limb of the planet, taken at UV wavelengths to which the atmosphere is transparent, which showed detailed profiles of the planet's surface
    D)   wavelength and hence the Doppler shift of reflected radio waves
    Ans: A   Section: 12-4

73. Radar observations are used to evaluate mountain heights by measuring the time difference between echoes from mountain peaks and from the surrounding plains. In this technique, what would be the time delay from Maxwell Montes, which rises 12 km above the plain? (Hint: Think about the geometry and total path length.)
    A)   800 μs, or 8×10^{-7} s   C)   80 μs, or 8×10^{-5} s
    B)   80 ns, or 8×10^{-8} s   D)   80 ms, or 8×10^{-2} s
    Ans: C   Section: 12-4

74. Direct chemical analysis of surface material on Venus by the Soviet *Venera 13* lander indicates that the surface is dominated by
    A) granite, a plutonic rock formed when lava solidifies deep below the surface.
    B) sandstone, a sedimentary rock formed on Venus by sand grains deposited by wind.
    C) schist, a metamorphic rock formed by the deformation of other rocks by pressure and heat.
    D) basalt, a volcanic rock formed when lava solidifies on the surface.
    Ans: D   Section: 12-4

75. Which of the following bodies show evidence of currently active volcanoes?
    A) Earth and the Moon   C) the Moon and Mercury
    B) Mercury and Venus   D) Earth and Venus
    Ans: D   Section: 12-4

76. What evidence do we have of volcanic activity on Venus?
    A) none
    B) We have only the evidence of lava flows, which suggests active volcanoes as recently as 10 million years ago.
    C) In addition to old lava flows we have measured variability of sulfur compounds during the past half century. This suggests active volcanoes now.
    D) One of the *Venera* landers photographed a volcano in the act of erupting.
    Ans: C   Section: 12-4

77. How did the inner planets, Venus and Earth, acquire their original atmospheres?
    A) capture of solar wind gases from the Sun as they stream past the planets
    B) the impact and melting of icy comets and asteroids from the planetary system and perhaps beyond
    C) gravitational capture of material from the original solar nebula by the planets
    D) outgassing of the planets through volcanoes and other vents
    Ans: D   Section: 12-5

78. The atmosphere of Venus is observed to contain almost no water. This is apparent because
    A) the water is locked up as ice (permafrost) beneath the surface of the planet.
    B) Venus is so hot that whatever water there was simply evaporated into space because it was lighter than the major constituent, carbon dioxide.
    C) solar UV light dissociated the water into hydrogen and oxygen; the hydrogen then escaped into space and the oxygen combined with other substances.
    D) Venus has never had a significant amount of water, having formed closer to the Sun than did Earth, where water in the solar nebula could not condense.
    Ans: C   Section: 12-5

79. What do we understand about the presence of H_2O on Venus?
    A)   There has probably never been a significant amount of water on Venus.
    B)   In the past, the atmosphere of Venus held significant amounts of water vapor, but it has always been too hot for liquid water to exist on the surface.
    C)   Oceans of liquid water once existed on the surface, but these evaporated and the water vapor was dissociated by ultraviolet radiation from the Sun.
    D)   Oceans of liquid water once existed, but this water is now locked up in various rocks on the surface.
    Ans: C   Section: 12-5

80. On both Earth and Venus some sulfur dioxide is removed from the atmosphere to be locked up in various rocks and minerals. On Earth this SO_2 is recycled deep beneath the surface to be outgassed by volcanoes and again become part of the atmosphere. On Venus this SO_2 is not recycled. Why this difference?
    A)   There are no active volcanoes on Venus.
    B)   Venus does not experience the movement of tectonic plates.
    C)   On Venus, the sulfur dioxide minerals are dissolved by acids in the atmosphere.
    D)   Because of the higher temperature on Venus, the SO_2 minerals formed there are different from those on Earth, and they are essentially permanent and nonrecyclable.
    Ans: B   Section: 12-5

81. At what point did the greenhouse effect cease to raise the temperature of Venus?
    A)   when all the greenhouse gases evaporated
    B)   when the radiation from Venus balanced the radiation absorbed by Venus
    C)   when the CO_2 was dissolved in the early Venusian oceans
    D)   when the greenhouse gases combined with other chemicals
    Ans: B   Section: 12-5

82. Venus has
    A)   no magnetic field.
    B)   a very powerful magnetic field.
    C)   a magnetic field about the strength of that of Earth.
    D)   a weak magnetic field about 1/100 the strength of Earth's magnetic field.
    Ans: A   Section: 12-6

83. Spacecraft measurements near Venus indicate that the planet has
    A)   a very powerful magnetic field, much stronger than that of Earth.
    B)   no magnetic field.
    C)   a magnetic field that varies in concert with the 11-year solar activity cycle, and is linked to it via the solar wind.
    D)   a weak and variable magnetic field.
    Ans: B   Section: 12-6

84. Solar wind particles approaching the planet Venus
    A)   are stopped by the clouds, producing intense auroras.
    B)   collide directly with the planet's surface.
    C)   are deflected by the magnetosphere.
    D)   are stopped by the ionosphere, producing a shock wave.
    Ans: D   Section: 12-6

85. The geology and geography of the surface of Venus is best described as
    A)   mostly volcanic plains, with two continent-sized uplands and a number of large volcanoes.
    B)   heavily cratered, with no major volcanoes or lava flows.
    C)   volcanoes and volcanic uplifts in the northern hemisphere and cratered plains in the southern hemisphere.
    D)   colliding surface plates with long mountain chains, rift valleys, and deep subduction trenches.
    Ans: A   Section: 12-6

86. Compared to the surface of Earth, that of Venus is
    A)   extremely rugged, with deep valleys and many high volcanic mountains.
    B)   completely covered with innumerable, overlapping craters and old crater walls that constitute mountain ranges.
    C)   very smooth and flat, with no mountains or structure.
    D)   almost completely flat and relatively smooth, apart from two high volcanic mountain ranges.
    Ans: D   Section: 12-6

87. On a topographical map of Venus, how many "continents" of high ground above the flat plains are apparent?
    A) one   B) none   C) seven   D) two
    Ans: D   Section: 12-6

88. The highest mountain range detected on Venus is called
    A) Olympus Mons.   B) Alpha Regio.   C) Ishtar Terra.   D) Maxwell Montes.
    Ans: D   Section: 12-6 and Figure 12-14

89. The most common surface features on Venus are
    A)   ancient river valleys and huge floodplains.
    B)   impact craters.
    C)   volcanoes and lava flows.
    D)   evidence of plate tectonic motion, including long mountain ranges and subduction troughs.
    Ans: C   Section: 12-6

90. Tectonic activity on Venus differs from that on Earth in that
    A)   active crustal deformation appears to be completely absent.
    B)   the lithosphere appears to be softer or more plastic and cannot support the creation
         and motion of solid plates.
    C)   the lithosphere appears to be cooler and thicker and is therefore too rigid to break
         up into moving plates.
    D)   mantle convection appears to be more vigorous and has broken the lithosphere
         into a multitude of small plates instead of a few large ones.
    Ans: B   Section: 12-6

91. The surface of the planet Venus
    A)   has several large volcanoes, but no extensive ridged or mountainous regions.
    B)   shows long mountain ranges similar to the Rockies/Andes ranges and the mid-
         ocean ridges on Earth.
    C)   has ridged and mountainous regions but no long, connected mountain ranges like
         the mid-ocean ridges on Earth.
    D)   is very smooth, with no mountains.
    Ans: C   Section: 12-6

92. Tectonic activity on Venus is characterized by
    A)   large-scale convection currents in the mantle, which push several hard,
         lithospheric plates around on the surface.
    B)   constant resurfacing of the crust by lava floods, without separately identifiable
         upward and downward-flowing magma currents in the mantle.
    C)   a cool, solid mantle that has not driven any crustal deformation for the last 3.2
         billion years.
    D)   hot-spot volcanism and localized regions of downwelling magma.
    Ans: D   Section: 12-6

93. Areas of ridges and valleys on Venus are caused by
    A)   compression of the crust above regions of downwelling magma in the mantle.
    B)   compression of the crust as Venus's iron core cooled and shrank.
    C)   upward pressure from magma rising beneath the planet's crust.
    D)   the collision of moving tectonic plates.
    Ans: A   Section: 12-6

94. The age of the surface of Venus appears to be
    A)   uniformly about 500 million years, compared to very variable ages across Earth's
         surface.
    B)   3 to 4 billion years, almost as old as the surfaces of the Moon and Mercury.
    C)   100 million years, about half the average age of most of Earth's surface.
    D)   less than 10 million years, due to constant resurfacing of the planet by lava flows.
    Ans: A   Section: 12-6

95. The average age of the surface of Venus has been determined primarily from
    A)   radio-isotope analysis of rocks brought back from Venus by space probes.
    B)   the number of impact craters per unit area of surface.
    C)   the amount of weathering of lava flows imaged by the *Magellan* radar mapper.
    D)   soil analysis by Russian landers.
    Ans: B   Section: 12-6

96. The reason Venus has very few impact craters compared to the Moon is believed to be that
    A)   lava flows have covered all but the most recent craters.
    B)   Venus formed closer to the Sun than did the Moon, where the cratering rate was much lower.
    C)   the surface of Venus is subducted back down into the mantle over periods of several hundred million years.
    D)   erosion due to wind and rainfall has eroded away all but the most recent craters.
    Ans: A   Section: 12-6

97. There are very few impact craters on the surface of Venus compared to the surfaces of Mercury and Mars because
    A)   ancient oceans washed away all the craters formed during the early bombardment phase.
    B)   immense lava flows have obliterated all but the younger craters.
    C)   plate tectonic motions have recycled the surface several times since the early bombardment period.
    D)   wind erosion from its dense atmosphere and chemical action from its corrosive clouds have destroyed most craters.
    Ans: B   Section: 12-6

98. Which of the following properties of Venus are very similar to those of Earth?
    A)   mass and radius, hence average density and surface gravity
    B)   temperatures of surface and atmosphere
    C)   rotation rate around its axis and length of solar day
    D)   magnetic field and magnetosphere
    Ans: A   Section: 12-6

99. Venus and Earth are about the same size, yet they have only one of the following characteristics in common. Which one?
    A)   evidence of plate tectonics
    B)   volcanic activity
    C)   a planet-wide magnetic field
    D)   an atmosphere made up predominantly of greenhouse gases
    Ans: B   Section: 12-6

100. If we characterize the age of a surface by the age of the oldest feature we have dated there, then the ages of the following surfaces are, from youngest to oldest,
    A) Venus, Earth, Moon.
    C) Earth, Moon, Venus.
    B) Earth, Venus, Moon.
    D) Venus, Moon, Earth.
    Ans: A Section: 12-6

Chapter 13: Red Planet Mars

1. Which of the planets fits the following description: "A planet with a very hot, solid, cratered surface with no atmosphere"?
   A) Venus   B) Mars   C) Jupiter   D) Mercury
   Ans: D   Section: Chapter 13

2. Which planet in our solar system fits the following description: "A planet with a large iron core, heavily cratered surface, and no (or almost no) atmosphere"?
   A) Earth   B) Mars   C) Mercury   D) Neptune
   Ans: C   Section: Chapter 13

3. Which of the planets fits the following description: "a solid, cool surface, with occasional dust clouds and a thin CO_2 atmosphere"?
   A) Venus   B) Jupiter   C) Mars   D) Mercury
   Ans: C   Section: Chapter 13

4. The only planet whose solid surface features can easily be seen through a telescope from Earth is
   A) Mars.   B) Venus.   C) Mercury.   D) Jupiter.
   Ans: A   Section: 13-1

5. There are several reasons the surface of Mars is more easily seen from Earth than any other planet's surface. Which of the following is NOT one of those reasons?
   A)   relative proximity to Earth
   B)   high mountain ranges casting strong shadows and providing high-contrast images
   C)   visible high in the sky at midnight when at opposition
   D)   a thin, almost cloudless atmosphere
   Ans: B   Section: 13-1

6. During favorable oppositions of Mars, when the planet comes relatively close to Earth, where would Mars be seen in the sky by an observer in the Earth's northern hemisphere?
   A)   high in the south at midnight   C)   on the western horizon at midnight
   B)   high in the north at midnight   D)   high in the south at sunset
   Ans: A   Section: 13-1 and 4-2

7. Mars is best viewed from Earth when it is at opposition. What will be the time interval between two such favorable viewing times?
   A)   2 synodic periods of Mars, because after every alternate synodic period, Mars will be on the other side of the Sun from Earth.
   B)   1 sidereal period
   C)   1 Earth year, the interval between two times when Earth is at a particular position in its orbit.
   D)   1 synodic period
   Ans: D   Section: 13-1

8. Mars is best viewed from Earth when it is at opposition, but some occasions are more favorable than others. Why is this?
   A) Mars has an elliptical orbit, and favorable oppositions occur when Mars is at perihelion in its orbit and hence closest to Earth.
   B) Mars has an elliptical orbit, and favorable oppositions occur when Mars is at aphelion in its orbit and hence closest to Earth.
   C) Mars's orbit is inclined at a significant angle to the ecliptic, so favorable oppositions occur when it is crossing the ecliptic plane while at opposition.
   D) Even though Mars moves in a circular orbit, the orbit of Earth is elliptical and so favorable oppositions occur when Earth is at perihelion.
   Ans: A   Section: 13-1

9. Assume Earth has a circular orbit with a radius of 1 AU. At its most favorable opposition Mars is 0.37 AU from earth, and at its least favorable opposition it is 0.68 AU from Earth. From these data, what do you calculate as the sidereal period of Mars (in years)?
   A) 1.0   B) 1.52   C) 1.88   D) 3.55
   Ans: C   Section: 13-1

10. When we view Mars at its most favorable opposition, a Martian would view Earth at
    A)   most favorable opposition.   C)   superior conjunction.
    B)   least favorable opposition.   D)   inferior conjunction.
    Ans: D   Section: 13-1

11. Earth and Mars are very similar planets. Which of the following pairs of physical characteristics are most alike for these planets?
    A)   overall mass and diameter
    B)   length of solar day and inclination of spin axis to the ecliptic
    C)   length of solar day and diameter
    D)   planet diameter and inclination of spin axis to the ecliptic plane
    Ans: B   Section: 13-2

12. Earth and Mars possess two properties in which they are very similar. Which are they?
    A)   length of solar day and diameter
    B)   orbital period and length of solar day
    C)   length of solar day and inclination of equator to the ecliptic
    D)   planet diameter and inclination of equator to the ecliptic plane
    Ans: C   Section: 13-2

13. Prominent but variable ice caps were detected by early observers on which planet?
    A) Venus   B) Mars   C) Jupiter   D) Mercury
    Ans: B   Section: 13-2

14. The period and direction of rotation of Mars are
    A)   about twice as long as Earth's period, about 48 hours, in the same direction as Earth.
    B)   a little longer than 1 Earth day, in the opposite direction to Earth.
    C)   about 240 days, in the opposite direction to Earth.
    D)   a little longer than 24 hours, in the same direction as the Earth.
    Ans: D   Section: 13-2

15. The tilt of the spin axis of Mars to the perpendicular to its orbital plane
    A)   varies rapidly through the Martian year.
    B)   is 90°.
    C)   is 0°.
    D)   is very similar to that of Earth.
    Ans: D   Section: 13-2

16. Mars, with its spin axis tilted with respect to the perpendicular to its orbital plane,
    A)   shows no seasonal variation whatsoever.
    B)   occasionally shows some seasonal variation.
    C)   shows similar seasons to those on Earth, in both intensity and duration.
    D)   shows similar seasons to Earth, but with each season lasting about twice as long as a season on Earth.
    Ans: D   Section: 13-2

17. Mars experiences similar seasonal changes to those on Earth because
    A)   it has about the same shape of elliptical orbit as that of the Earth, producing similar changes in solar radiation intensity as the planet orbits the Sun.
    B)   its spin axis is tilted at about the same angle to its orbital plane as is the Earth's axis.
    C)   the length of its day is very close to an Earth day.
    D)   the length of its year is very close to that of Earth.
    Ans: B   Section: 13-2

18. The equator of Mars is tilted with respect to its orbital plane and therefore Mars
    A)   shows similar seasons to those on Earth, each season lasting about three months.
    B)   experiences very long (20 years) seasonal variations.
    C)   shows no seasonal variation at all.
    D)   shows similar seasons to Earth, each season lasting about twice the length of seasons on Earth.
    Ans: D   Section: 13-2

19. In view of Mars's tilted angle of rotation at 25° to the ecliptic, its very similar rotation period to that of Earth (24 hours, 37 minutes), and its orbital period of nearly 2 years, what will be the seasonal variations on Mars, compared to those upon Earth?
    A) very similar seasonal variations, but each season lasting about half as long as those upon Earth because of the different orbital periods
    B) very similar seasonal variations, including seasons lasting about as long as those upon Earth because of the similar rotation rates of the two planets
    C) very similar seasonal variations, but with each season lasting twice as long as the Earth's seasons
    D) much smaller seasonal variations than Earth's because of Mars's distance from the Sun, each season lasting about twice as long as those upon Earth
    Ans: C   Section: 13-2

20. How did optical illusion mislead early visual observers of Mars?
    A) Apparent movement of surface features because of fluctuations in images when viewed through the Earth's atmosphere, were interpreted as evidence for moving life-forms or Martians.
    B) Volcano and rock structures were seen as eye-shaped and face-like and were interpreted as having been made by intelligent beings to indicate their presence.
    C) Moving areas of obscured detail on the planet were interpreted as massive flash floods rather than dust storms.
    D) Chance alignments of faint, dark features looked like canals whereas darker areas, when viewed against the orange-red surface, were interpreted as vegetation.
    Ans: D   Section: 13-2

21. Observers in the nineteenth century reported seeing many straight-line features criss-crossing the surface of Mars, and these were interpreted as canals constructed by intelligent beings. What is the most likely present-day explanation for these observations?
    A) stationary linear cloud formations (mountain lee wave clouds) and weather fronts, rotating with the planet
    B) optical illusions caused by vague shadings on the planet surface
    C) rifts at the boundaries of geological tectonic plates
    D) lines of volcanoes similar to those of the Hawaiian Islands on Earth
    Ans: B   Section: 13-2

22. What observations of the Martian surface led Lowell to the conclusion that intelligent life forms existed upon Mars?
    A) lakes and rivers of water flowing from polar icecaps, detected by strong specular reflection of sunlight
    B) melting icecaps, a network of linear features that look like canals, and varying dark surface markings, assumed to be vegetation
    C) sculpted mountains in the shape of humanoid heads, obviously (to him) carved to indicate the presence of intelligent life to distant observers
    D) geometrical structures and patterns, which he interpreted as the remains of buildings and cities
    Ans: B   Section: 13-2

23. The so-called "canals" that Schiaparelli reported seeing upon the surface of Mars were actually
    A) an optical illusion.
    B) river valleys, caused by massive floods early in Mars's history.
    C) the remnants of the walls of ancient craters that have been eroded by winds and dust over Mars's history.
    D) lines of volcanoes along faults in the Martian surface.
    Ans: A   Section: 13-2

24. On Mars, which of the following features have NOT been confirmed by space probe observations?
    A) polar ice caps   B) extinct volcanoes   C) craters   D) straight canals
    Ans: D   Section: 13-2

25. One 19th-century observation, which convinced many of the existence of at least plant life on Mars, was the behavior of the polar caps and the dark areas. This is that
    A) the northern polar cap grows during the northern winter while the dark patches in the northern hemisphere turn white, suggesting that they become ice covered.
    B) the northern polar cap grows during the northern winter while the dark areas in the northern hemisphere begin to radiate in the ultraviolet and infrared.
    C) the polar caps are connected to the dark areas by a network of canals.
    D) the dark areas in the northern hemisphere grow during the northern summer as the northern polar cap recedes.
    Ans: D   Section: 13-2

26. The central regions of craters on Mars are flatter and their rims are more worn than the craters on either the Earth's Moon or Mercury. Why is this?
    A) erosion and infilling by dust storms
    B) erosion by rainfall, at present and in the past
    C) breakdown of the rocks by the extreme temperature variations between day and night
    D) erosion by seasonal carbon dioxide snowfall and melting
    Ans: A   Section: 13-3

27. The overall geography of Mars can be best summarized as
    A) major volcanoes in the northern hemisphere, extensively cratered plains in the southern hemisphere, the hemispheres separated by one major valley system.
    B) moving lithospheric plates whose motions have produced long, folded mountain chains, deep subduction trenches, and several large rift valleys.
    C) smooth plains where continuous resurfacing by ongoing volcanic activity has hidden older impact craters and other details.
    D) mostly rolling plains, with several volcanoes on two continent-sized uplands.
    Ans: A   Section: 13-3

28. One of the striking features of the overall surface of Mars is
    A) the two very distinct hemispheres, one of them lower and smoother than its counterpart and almost free of craters.
    B) the presence of active volcanoes and lava flows over the whole surface, including near to the poles, where these flows melt the icecaps regularly.
    C) the remarkable similarity of surface features across the whole of the planet, including uniform distribution of craters and ancient river valleys.
    D) the uniform distribution of water-ice frost over the whole surface, hidden in the shade of rocks, both winter and summer.
    Ans: A   Section: 13-3

29. The thickness of the crust of Mars has been measured to be different under two different hemispheres. How was this measurement made?
    A) by radar measurements from an orbiting spacecraft, detecting radar waves reflecting back from the interface between crust and mantle on Mars
    B) by drilling from Mars lander spacecraft into the crust of the planet, down to the mantle
    C) by measuring the effect of slight differences in gravitational field upon the motion of a spacecraft orbiting Mars
    D) by a seismology from the Mars landers, detecting the waves generated by Martian "earthquakes" as they passed through Mars
    Ans: C   Section: 13-3

30. The massive extinct supervolcano Olympus Mons is on which planet or moon?
    A) Io   B) Earth   C) Venus   D) Mars
    Ans: D   Section: 13-3

31. Olympus Mons is
    A) a long-lived anticyclone on Jupiter.   C) a mountain on Venus.
    B) a valley on the Moon.   D) a volcano on Mars.
    Ans: D   Section: 13-3

32. Where is Olympus Mons, the huge extinct volcano, located?
    A) Venus   B) the Moon   C) Mars   D) Antarctica
    Ans: C   Section: 13-3

33. On Mars, where are most of the extinct volcanoes located?
    A)   in the northern hemisphere
    B)   around the southern polar cap
    C)   along the bottom of the deep valley, Valles Marineris, which was originally
         formed by enormous geological stresses
    D)   in a line along the equator, the line of maximum tidal stress on the planet
    Ans: A   Section: 13-3

34. The major volcanoes on Mars have formed
    A)   in regions of ridges where the crust is being compressed and buckled without
         being subducted.
    B)   directly above stationary hot-spots in the mantle.
    C)   on long, interconnecting ridges and rifts, where magma rising from the mantle is
         pushing the crust apart.
    D)   in mountain belts, where the crust is being subducted back into the mantle.
    Ans: B   Section: 13-3

35. Which of the following statements appears to be TRUE for Mars?
    A)   The oppressive heat on Mars has kept the lithosphere thin and prevented the onset
         of plate tectonics.
    B)   Plate tectonics has not been important because Mars, being small, cooled more
         rapidly than the Earth, thereby solidifying to form a thicker crust.
    C)   Plate tectonics is the dominant process creating large-scale surface features.
    D)   Plate tectonics is only just beginning and will be important in the distant future,
         because geologic processes happen more slowly on a small planet.
    Ans: B   Section: 13-3

36. The huge volcano Olympus Mons on Mars and those that make up the Hawaiian Islands
    on Earth appear to be very similar, but they differ in one important respect. What is this
    difference?
    A)   Olympus Mons is very close to the Martian north pole where tidal stress from the
         Sun is small whereas the Hawaiian Islands are close to the equator where tidal
         stresses from Moon and Sun have formed the fault along which they lie.
    B)   Olympus Mons is formed almost solely of sulfur, whereas the Hawaiian Islands
         are formed of rock from the solidification of lava.
    C)   Olympus Mons is a very steep-sided volcano, whereas the volcanoes of Hawaii
         are rather flat, with gentle slopes right up to their calderas.
    D)   In the Hawaiian Islands, plate tectonic motion has moved the Pacific Ocean floor
         over a hot spot, forming a line of volcanoes. No such motion occurred for
         Olympus Mons over an equivalent hot spot on Mars.
    Ans: D   Section: 13-3

37. Evidence of hot-spot volcanoes caused by hot, rising plumes under the planet's surface is present on Venus and Mars, as well as on Earth. What distinguishes those on Earth from those on the other planets?
    A)   Those on the other planets occurred on tectonic plate boundaries and they are therefore distorted and have spread over the planet surface.
    B)   Plate tectonics on all three planets has formed chains of small volcano cones but those on Earth have all occurred under the sea and are hidden.
    C)   This type of volcano occurred only at the spin axes or poles of the other planets where tidal stress was greatest, whereas on the Earth they occurred near the equator.
    D)   Plate tectonics on Earth has moved the hot-spot volcanic site continuously over recent geological time, whereas no such movement has occurred on Venus or Mars.
    Ans: D   Section: 13-3 and Chapters 9 and 12

38. What feature of the Hawaiian Islands is similar to many geological features on Mars and Venus?
    A)   They, like the major mountains on Venus and Mars, were formed by upthrust from collisions of two tectonic plates.
    B)   They were produced by impacts of massive asteroid-like bodies on the ancient Earth and are now being eroded by the ocean.
    C)   They were produced by slow build-up of coral reefs in ancient oceans.
    D)   They, like mountains on Venus and Mars, were produced by hot-spot volcanism and upflow of heat from below.
    Ans: D   Section: 13-3 and Chapters 9 and 12

39. The most important mechanism that transports heat outward from the interiors of Venus and Mars is
    A)   asteroid impact, which splits the crust and allows the heat to escape.
    B)   rifting and subduction, where rigid plates are pushed around by magma rising up from the mantle.
    C)   thermal conduction, where heat is conducted outward through the crust with relatively little flow of lava.
    D)   hot-spot volcanism, where molten lava flows upward to the surface above hot-spots in the mantle.
    Ans: D   Section: 13-3 and Chapter 12

40. Hot-spot volcanism is a process that
    A)   produces dome-shaped rises on Venus and Mars and mid-ocean ridges on Earth.
    B)   does not operate on Venus or Mars but produces subduction zones on Earth.
    C)   produces large rift valleys on Mars, Venus, and the Earth.
    D)   produces gigantic volcanoes on Venus and Mars but produces chains of smaller volcanoes on the Earth.
    Ans: D   Section: 13-3

41. The Tharsis rise on Mars, a region that is higher than the surrounding plain by about 5 km (over 16,000 ft), was caused by
    A)   the collision of two tectonic plates.
    B)   the focusing of seismic waves from the impact of a massive asteroid at the diametrically opposite point on Mars.
    C)   an upwelling magma plume in Mars's interior, which has raised this whole region.
    D)   erosion of the surrounding plain by massive floods.
    Ans: C   Section: 13-3

42. Two observed features on Mars appear to lead to contrary geological conclusions—the appearance of massive solitary volcanoes apparently caused by "hot spots" under the planet's surface and the discovery of a long, deep rift valley across the planet. What is this apparent contradiction?
    A)   Volcanoes suggest a molten inner planet, while a rift valley suggests the presence of a solid core.
    B)   Massive volcanoes should have covered the planet's surface with dust and ash and filled in the valley, but the valley remains as a major feature.
    C)   Single massive volcanoes indicate no plate tectonic motion, while a rift valley suggests otherwise.
    D)   Noneroded ancient volcanoes indicate no significant erosion by water, whereas the valley suggests prolonged rainfall and erosion.
    Ans: C   Section: 13-3 and 9-3

43. On which planet does the great valley system, Valles Marineris, exist?
    A) Mercury   B) Mars   C) on the far side of the Moon   D) Venus
    Ans: B   Section: 13-3

44. What is the Valles Marineris?
    A)   a large rift valley system associated with the great volcanoes on Mars
    B)   a long scarp-and-trough system in the lava plains of Mercury
    C)   a system of tectonic faults on the Jovian satellite Ganymede
    D)   a system of deep trenches bordering Aphrodite Terra on Venus
    Ans: A   Section: 13-3

45. The Martian valley Valles Marineris has a length equivalent to which Earth-bound distance? (See Fig. 13-7, Freedman and Kaufmann, *Universe,* 7th ed.)
    A)   the width of the North American continent at mid-latitudes, a few thousand kilometers
    B)   half the length of the Earth's equator, about 20,000 km
    C)   only about 100 km, but still a significant distance on Mars
    D)   a few hundred kilometers; New York to Washington, D.C.
    Ans: A   Section: 13-3

46. The magnetic field of Mars, compared to that of Earth, is
    A)   nonexistent anywhere on the planet.
    B)   very similar in strength and orientation, its north-south axis being almost along the planet's spin axis.
    C)   localized and very weak.
    D)   much stronger, but with its north-south axis lying in the equatorial plane, the north pole coinciding with the large volcano, Olympus Mons.
    Ans: C   Section: 13-3

47. The Martian magnetic field is
    A)   much stronger and more extensive than the Earth's magnetic field.
    B)   comparable to Earth's magnetic field.
    C)   nonexistent—no spacecraft has ever detected a magnetic field on Mars.
    D)   weak and localized, not at all like the global magnetic field of Earth.
    Ans: D   Section: 13-3

48. The Martian magnetic field is apparently created by
    A)   the interaction of the solar wind with the Martian ionosphere.
    B)   electric currents in the molten, metallic core.
    C)   remnant magnetism from earlier times, retained by the localized regions of the crust.
    D)   a permanent magnet in the solidified core.
    Ans: C   Section: 13-3

49. The origin of the Martian magnetic field appears to be
    A)   convection of molten, iron-rich lava in the Martian mantle.
    B)   electric currents flowing in the high atmosphere, caused by the motion of the solar wind.
    C)   magnetism retained by the surface rocks, from a global magnetic field that Mars possessed when it was young.
    D)   magnetic material deposited by impacts of iron meteorites.
    Ans: C   Section: 13-3

50. Of the three planets Mercury, Earth, and Mars, which ones have global magnetic fields?
    A)   the Earth   C)   the Earth and Mars
    B)   Mercury, the Earth, and Mars   D)   Mercury and the Earth
    Ans: D   Section: 13-3 and Chapters 9 and 11

51. A magnetosphere that deflects the incoming solar wind is found around which terrestrial planet or planets?
    A)   Mercury, Earth, and Mars   C)   Mercury, Venus, Earth, and Mars
    B)   Mercury and Earth   D)   only Earth
    Ans: B   Section: 13-3

52. Regions of high-energy trapped particles (like the Van Allen belts) occur around which terrestrial planet or planets?
   A) Earth only
   B) Mercury, Earth, and Mars
   C) Mercury, Venus, Earth, and Mars
   D) Mercury and Earth
   Ans: A   Section: 13-3

53. Which of the following are youngest?
   A) the oldest craters on Mercury
   B) the oldest craters on Venus
   C) the oldest craters on the Moon
   D) the oldest craters on Mars
   Ans: B   Section: 13-3

54. All of the following are characteristics usually associated with a planet-wide magnetic field. Which one does Mars lack?
   A) some liquid in the core
   B) some solid in the core
   C) some electrically conducting material in the core
   D) a relatively rapid rotation rate
   Ans: C   Section: 13-3

55. On the basis of the surface and atmospheric conditions existing on Mars today, why could there be no liquid water on its surface?
   A) The water would boil and evaporate rapidly under the low atmospheric pressure or freeze to ice at the low surface temperatures.
   B) It would have reacted chemically with the surface rocks.
   C) The UV radiation from the Sun would have dissociated the water molecules into hydrogen (which would leave the planet) and oxygen, which is still present.
   D) It would have soaked into the porous surface of Mars.
   Ans: A   Section: 13-4

56. Why can liquid water NOT exist on Mars today?
   A) Both atmospheric pressure and surface temperature are too low, and any water would be in the form of ice or vapor.
   B) The surface of Mars is too porous to allow water to remain on the surface.
   C) Water would react with the CO_2 in the atmosphere to form carbonic acid, which would react quickly with the rocks on Mars to destroy the water.
   D) Surface temperatures are too high, since at the low Martian atmospheric pressure, water would just boil away at the present Martian temperatures.
   Ans: A   Section: 13-4

57. Water exists on Mars. Where and in what state does it NOT exist on this planet?
   A) as liquid, flowing in river valleys
   B) in permafrost, below the surface
   C) in polar icecaps
   D) as water vapor in the atmosphere and as clouds
   Ans: A   Section: 13-4

58. Water has been discovered on Mars. In what state is it likely to be?
    A) only as atmospheric water vapor, never condensing out as liquid water or solid ice
    B) as a liquid flowing along the numerous flood valleys and meandering stream beds
    C) in permafrost, polar icecaps, and atmospheric vapor
    D) as a liquid in lakes and rivers
    Ans: C   Section: 13-4

59. Which of the following statements is true for Mars?
    A) Mars has canals, apparently built to carry water for irrigation.
    B) Mars has dry riverbeds but no liquid water on its surface.
    C) Mars has some liquid water flowing on its surface now.
    D) Mars shows no sign of ever having had liquid water on its surface.
    Ans: B   Section: 13-4

60. Distinct evidence of the flow of water at an earlier time is seen on photographs of which planetary body?
    A) Mars   B) Mercury   C) Venus   D) the Earth's Moon
    Ans: A   Section: 13-4

61. Recent observations of Mars have revealed strong evidence that water once existed in substantial amounts on Mars. Which of the following is NOT one of these observations?
    A) teardrop-shaped islands in smooth valleys
    B) evidence of mud flows around relatively young volcanoes.
    C) deep meandering gullies
    D) a network of linear features resembling canals
    Ans: D   Section: 13-4

62. What significant evidence exists for the idea that large quantities of water once flowed on the planet Mars?
    A) clouds and frost forming above and around the *Viking* spacecraft, released by the heat of the descent rockets
    B) frozen but dust-covered lakes inside ancient craters
    C) a network of relatively straight canals linking polar and equatorial regions
    D) deep, winding canyons and flood plains
    Ans: D   Section: 13-4

63. Which of the following signs of water is NOT seen on Mars?
    A) evidence of permafrost under the Martian surface
    B) water ice (as opposed to CO_2 ice) in the polar caps
    C) occasional clouds of ice crystals
    D) melting pools at the edges of the polar caps
    Ans: D   Section: 13-4

64. The polar caps on Mars are most likely made up of
    A)   water and CO_2 ices.
    B)   light-colored dust blown there by intense dust storms and large dust devils.
    C)   volcanic outflow of light-colored lava and dust similar to that produced by Earth-based volcanoes.
    D)   sulfur dioxide and sulfur compounds.
    Ans: A   Section: 13-4

65. The polar caps on Mars are now known to consist of
    A)   only H_2O ice, which does not melt easily and survives the summer heat.
    B)   methane (CH_4), ammonia (NH_3), and water (H_2O) ices, whose relative abundances vary with the seasons.
    C)   only CO_2 ice, which is very volatile and melts easily.
    D) CO_2 ice overlying thicker H_2O ice.
    Ans: D   Section: 13-4

66. The initial and very rapid recession of the edge of the white polar cap region toward the poles in springtime is caused by
    A)   the melting and evaporation of CO_2 ice.
    B)   the increased growth of vegetation toward the poles from mid-latitudes.
    C)   the change in color of the rocks by photochemical action, similar to bleaching.
    D)   the melting of H_2O ice and subsequent runoff of water.
    Ans: A   Section: 13-4

67. Evidence for recent water flow on Mars comes from
    A)   images of gullies carved into the walls of pits or craters.
    B)   changes in the shapes of some meandering valleys between images taken in the 1970's and those taken in the 1990's.
    C)   observation of momentary flashes of sunlight, reflected to orbiting spacecraft from the bottoms of deep canyons.
    D)   observation of vegetation near the ends of some deep canyons.
    Ans: A   Section: 13-4

68. *Mars Odyssey* was unsuccessful in detecting evidence of large bodies of frozen water well below the Martian surface. This is not surprising because
    A)   the neutrons it was detecting can only escape from the top meter or so of the ground.
    B)   volcanic activity suggests it is too hot below the surface for frozen water to exist.
    C)   the lack of tectonic activity suggests that the crust of Mars is very solid with no possibility of water penetration in the past.
    D)   the spectral signature of H_2O, which *Mars Odyssey* was detecting, can only escape from the top few centimeters of the soil.
    Ans: A   Section: 13-4

69. A major feature of the atmosphere of Mars is
    A)   occasional strong winds and dust storms.
    B)   very dense clouds shrouding most of the planet.
    C)   a chemical mixture very similar to that of Earth.
    D)   very high temperatures and pressures.
    Ans: A   Section: 13-5 and 13-7

70. Which of the following is NOT a possible weather report from Mars given the present atmospheric conditions on that planet?
    A)   clear and cold   C)   dry and windy with blowing dust
    B)   rain tapering off by noon   D)   dry-ice snow
    Ans: B   Section: 13-5

71. Tomorrow's weather forecast for Mars is
    A)   cloudy, oppressively hot, with sulfuric acid rain.
    B)   frost overnight, then clear and sunny.
    C)   overcast, possible light rain.
    D)   sunny and cold; Mars has no atmosphere to retain heat.
    Ans: B   Section: 13-5

72. Tomorrow's (and most days') weather forecast for Mars is likely to be
    A)   continuous rain, possible flooding in low-lying areas.
    B)   sunny, clear and warm; Mars has no atmosphere in which clouds can form.
    C)   heavy overcast, possible light acid rain and mist.
    D)   sunny and cold, possible thin high clouds, windy.
    Ans: D   Section: 13-5

73. Carbonate rocks result from
    A)   compression of frozen CO_2 (dry ice).
    B)   atmospheric carbon dioxide combining chemically with minerals in the soil or the planetary regolith.
    C)   cooling and solidification of magma in a CO_2-rich atmosphere.
    D)   carbon dioxide dissolved in water reacting with rocks, the residue being deposited in solid form.
    Ans: D   Section: 13-5

74. Carbonate rocks might be expected to be found on
    A)   all rocky, planet-sized bodies: Mercury, Venus, Earth, Mars, and the Moon.
    B)   only the Earth.
    C)   the Earth and Mars.
    D)   the three largest terrestrial planets: Earth, Venus, and Mars.
    Ans: C   Section: 13-5 and Chapters 10, 11, and 12

75. In which of the following ways are Venus and Mars alike, yet are both markedly different from the Earth?
    A)   Their surface temperatures are both much higher than that of the Earth.
    B)   They are both perpetually shrouded in clouds.
    C)   They both have either active or extinct volcanoes on their surfaces.
    D)   Their atmospheres are made up primarily of carbon dioxide.
    Ans: D   Section: 13-5 and Chapters 9 and 12

76. The greenhouse effect, which heats a planet's surface above the predicted equilibrium surface temperature for the planet without an atmosphere, is far less effective on Mars than on the Earth. Why is this?
    A)   The Martian surface temperature is very low, and this reduces the effectiveness of the greenhouse effect.
    B)   There is less energy being conducted upward from the Martian interior to the surface of Mars because of the thickness of its crust compared to that of Earth.
    C)   The Martian atmosphere contains no gases that can absorb solar radiation.
    D)   The Martian atmosphere is very thin and traps less infrared radiation from the surface.
    Ans: D   Section: 13-5

77. The carbon dioxide atmosphere of Mars was much denser in Mars's early history than it is now. What process is now believed to have begun this atmospheric thinning?
    A)   The solar wind stripped the outer atmosphere from the planet.
    B)   The light CO_2 molecules escaped directly into space because of the weak gravity of Mars.
    C)   The CO_2 molecules were broken down by solar UV photons, creating the lighter molecules, CO and O_2, which then escaped into space.
    D)   The CO_2 was washed out of the atmosphere by rain.
    Ans: D   Section: 13-5

78. On Earth (and in the past, on Mars), volcanoes have been vital for keeping the planet warm. This is because
    A)   heat conducted from the molten mantle to the surface near volcanoes, where the crust is thin, is a major heat source for the atmosphere.
    B)   heat released along the major rift zones is the biggest source of heating for the atmosphere.
    C)   direct heat input by underwater volcanoes keeps the oceans from freezing.
    D)   they have replenished the CO_2 (a greenhouse gas) that is washed out of the atmosphere by rain.
    Ans: D   Section: 13-5

79. The time period(s) over which major water flows created the meandering channels on Mars is (are) believed
    A)   to have begun about a billion years after Mars formed as the atmosphere thickened and ended about a billion years later as the atmosphere slowly escaped into space.
    B)   to have been only the first half billion years of Mars's history.
    C)   to have been only the first 2 to 3 billion years of Mars's history, ending about 2 billion years ago.
    D)   to have been intermittent over all of Mars's history as the climate changed, with Mars now being in a dry phase.
    Ans: B   Section: 13-5

80. What is the major constituent of the atmosphere of Mars?
    A) CO_2 (carbon dioxide)   C) H_2 (hydrogen)
    B) CH_4 (methane)   D) H_2O (water vapor)
    Ans: A   Section: 13-5

81. The pressure of the atmosphere of Mars—primarily carbon dioxide (CO_2)—compared to the atmospheric pressure at the Earth's surface, is
    A)   extremely small (less than 1 millionth).
    B)   about 90 times greater.
    C)   less than 1/100.
    D)   about the same.
    Ans: C   Section: 13-5

82. There are many reasons a multiday hiking trip on foot through the Valles Marineris on Mars would not be advisable, at least not without suitable protection. Which of the following is NOT one of the reasons?
    A)   possibility of dust storms
    B)   oppressively high atmospheric pressure
    C)   high levels of ultraviolet radiation
    D)   predominantly carbon dioxide atmosphere
    Ans: B   Section: 13-5

83. The noticeable red color of Mars when viewed from Earth is probably caused by
    A)   interplanetary reddening of sunlight as it traverses the space between the Sun and Mars and then Mars and the Earth.
    B)   the scattering of blue sunlight out of the optical beam by dust in the atmosphere.
    C)   red dust, which is suspended high above the surface by winds and filters the light.
    D)   iron oxides or rust in the soil.
    Ans: D   Section: 13-5

84. The dominant component of the soil on Mars is probably
    A)   sedimentary rocks laid down by massive floods early in Mars's history.
    B)   basaltic lava pulverized by meteoritic bombardment.
    C)   iron oxides.
    D)   volcanic ash from eruptions in recent geological times.
    Ans: C   Section: 13-5

85. The reddish color of Mars is probably due to
    A)   the very high temperature on the sunlit parts of Mars.
    B)   vegetation turning red in the Martian autumn.
    C)   sulfur compounds thrown out by active volcanoes.
    D)   iron oxides such as rust.
    Ans: D   Section: 13-5

86. What material produces the distinct red color of Mars?
    A)   reddish vegetation which seems to fluctuate seasonally, particularly near the
         equator
    B)   scattered sunlight from very fine dust, similar to sunset effects upon Earth
    C)   atmospheric CO_2, because it absorbs blue and green light preferentially
    D)   rust or iron oxides
    Ans: D   Section: 13-5

87. The early Martian atmosphere probably contained as much nitrogen as the Earth's
    atmosphere. But the present Martian atmosphere is less than 5% nitrogen gas. Where
    did the original nitrogen gas go?
    A)   It was locked up in the rocks and minerals of the Martian surface.
    B)   At the elevated temperatures of the early Martian atmosphere, nitrogen's average
         velocity was high enough to cause it to escape.
    C)   As UV-absorbing H_2O and CO_2 were depleted, UV radiation penetrated the
         Martian atmosphere. This was absorbed by N_2, which received enough energy to
         escape.
    D)   It is still present in nitric acid droplets and vapors in the Martian clouds.
    Ans: C   Section: 13-5

88. What is the status of the greenhouse effect on Mars at the present time?
    A)   It no longer exists at all.
    B)   It is very weak and raises the planet's temperature only a few degrees above the
         temperature it would have with no atmosphere at all.
    C)   It is weak but becoming stronger as Martian volcanoes continue to dump large
         amounts of CO_2 into the atmosphere.
    D)   It is very strong and has caused the temperature to be at least 100 degrees above
         the temperature it would have been with no atmosphere at all.
    Ans: B   Section: 13-5

89. The *Viking* spacecraft landed on which planet or Moon?
    A) Venus   B) Europa, a moon of Jupiter.   C) Mars   D) the Earth's Moon
    Ans: C   Section: 13-6

90. *Viking,* the planet-exploring spacecraft, was sent to which planet?
    A) Mercury   B) Venus   C) Mars   D) Jupiter
    Ans: C   Section: 13-6

91. On the surface of which planet have experiments been carried out to search for life-forms or evidence of life?
    A) Jupiter   B) Mars   C) Venus   D) Mercury
    Ans: B   Section: 13-6

92. The dominant component of the regolith on Mars is probably
    A)   basaltic lava pulverized by meteoritic bombardment.
    B)   concrete from ancient canals, pulverized by meteoritic bombardment.
    C)   volcanic ash from geologically recent eruptions.
    D)   iron-rich clay.
    Ans: D   Section: 13-6

93. The exploratory life-sciences experiments on board the *Viking* spacecraft landers found evidence
    A)   that life-forms had existed on Mars in its early history but that they had not survived.
    B)   of a very sterile environment in which life could not have existed and a very chemically inert soil, reacting with almost no reagents.
    C)   of very reactive chemistry in the Martian surface rocks but no evidence of life or remnants of life-forms.
    D)   of primitive life-forms such as elementary bacteria, which should not be a hazard when humans explore Mars.
    Ans: C   Section: 13-6

94. Several components of the atmosphere and the environment on Mars render it sterile and antiseptic, and would destroy life on the planet. Which of the follow is NOT one of these factors?
    A)   solar UV radiation, not absorbed by the thin atmosphere
    B)   ozone in the atmosphere, produced by solar UV light
    C)   hydrogen peroxide in the soil
    D)   sulfuric acid in a mist in the atmosphere
    Ans: D   Section: 13-6

95. There appear to be several chemical agents in the regolith of Mars that would impede the growth of life, if not prevent it altogether, by sterilizing the soil. Which of the following does NOT appear to play this role on Mars?
A) hydrogen peroxide   B) sulfuric acid   C) solar UV radiation   D) ozone
Ans: B   Section: 13-6

96. What method was used to land the *Mars Pathfinder* spacecraft successfully on the Martian surface?
A)   It was surrounded by balloons, similar to the airbags in automobiles, and allowed to bounce and roll to a stop, after impact on the planet.
B)   It was suspended beneath a large gas-filled balloon heated by sunlight allowing it to float in the atmosphere like a hot-air balloon until sunset, when it descended gently to the surface.
C)   Retro rockets were fired automatically to slow it to a safe landing speed as it neared the surface.
D)   It was flown down on a parachute similar to a hang glider to a smooth, if rather fast, landing.
Ans: A   Section: 13-6

97. At what speed did the Mars Pathfinder spacecraft touch down on Mars?
A)   9 km/h (jogging speed), while suspended under a parachute
B)   essentially zero speed, while under thrust by descent rockets
C)   100 km/h (typical highway speed), landing as an unpowered glider
D)   50 km/h (typical speed limit in a school zone), using airbags to cushion the fall
Ans: D   Section: 13-6

98. Compared to those of ten or twenty years ago, what is different about the spacecraft being sent to other planets today?
A)   Today's spacecraft are all sample return missions.
B)   Today's spacecraft cost less and are almost as good.
C)   Today's spacecraft are cheaper and better.
D)   Today's spacecraft are bigger, cleaner, and more efficient.
Ans: C   Section: 13-6

99. Which of the following has apparently had the least influence on the evolution of the surface and geology of Mars?
A)   water flow   C)   erosion by winds
B)   an internal magnetic field   D)   impacts by meteoroids
Ans: B   Section: 13-6

100. Where did the *Mars Pathfinder* carrying the wheeled robot *Sojourner* land?
    A)   very close to one of the large shield volcanoes
    B)   near to the northern water and CO_2 icecap
    C)   on a flat, moderately cratered plain
    D)   in an ancient flood channel
    Ans: D   Section: 13-6

101. One surprising discovery from the exploration of rocks near the landing site of the *Mars Pathfinder*, by the *Sojourner* robot was that
    A)   the igneous rocks apparently produced by volcanic action were not basalts but andesites, rich in silicon.
    B)   there was a high proportion of gold in the rocks, sufficient to warrant farther exploration and mining.
    C)   the majority of the rocks were igneous and composed of basalt, apparently produced by volcanic action.
    D)   the rocks were all sedimentary, evidence of production under an ancient ocean.
    Ans: A   Section: 13-6

102. What evidence did *Sojourner*, the robotic rover of the *Mars Pathfinder* mission, find to indicate that Mars may have undergone chemical differentiation earlier in its history?
    A)   silicon-rich rocks, indicating differentiation to form a crust
    B)   a deficiency of iron at the surface, indicating that iron had settled toward the Martian core
    C)   basaltic dykes, indicating ancient upwelling of subsurface magma
    D)   a global magnetic field, indicating differentiation to form a molten iron core
    Ans: A   Section: 13-6

103. The unstable chemicals dissolved in the Martian regolith suggest that the amount of ultraviolet radiation reaching the surface of Mars is much greater than that reaching the surface of Earth. This is because the Martian atmosphere lacks what constituent in sufficient quantities to absorb incoming ultraviolet radiation?
    A) O_2 B) ozone   C) CO_2 D) N_2
    Ans: B   Section: 13-6

104. The dark markings near the equator of Mars show seasonal variations because of
    A)   changes in coverage of rocks by CO_2 ice as the temperature varies from above to below the freezing point of CO_2.
    B)   changes in the growth of vegetation.
    C)   changes in the flow of water released from permafrost by sunlight.
    D)   variations in the dust coverage of the surface.
    Ans: D   Section: 13-7

105. What effect causes the seasonal variation in color and shading of parts of the Martian surface?
    A) changes in dust covering in response to wind storms
    B) changes in the fluorescent glow caused by the varying intensity of solar UV radiation
    C) growth and decay of vegetation
    D) moisture falling as light rain, dampening the surface
    Ans: A   Section: 13-7

106. The dark, seasonal markings on Mars that grow in the spring and fade in the autumn are believed to result from
    A) microbial activity in the soil (or regolith).
    B) lighting effects that vary as the angle of the Sun changes with the seasons.
    C) dust being blown by winds, alternately covering and uncovering dark rocks.
    D) plant life.
    Ans: C   Section: 13-7

107. The "snow" that occasionally falls upon Mars and covers the bottoms of craters is most probably made of
    A) very fine white dust, disturbed occasionally by fierce wind storms.
    B) carbon dioxide ice.
    C) water ice.
    D) frozen sulfuric acid droplets.
    Ans: B   Section: 13-7

108. On Mars, which of the following features have NOT been seen or detected?
    A) dust storms and dust devils
    B) advancing and receding polar icecaps
    C) thin, wispy clouds
    D) active volcanoes
    Ans: D   Section: 13-7

109. On Mars, the air pressure varies much more from one season to another than it does on Earth. Why is this?
    A) Seasonal dust storms on Mars blanket the entire planet, increasing the weight of the atmosphere.
    B) Because the atmosphere of Mars is so thin, water vapor condensing on the polar ice caps in winter removes a much larger fraction of the atmosphere than on Earth.
    C) Because of the low density of the atmosphere, solar heating has a much larger effect on Mars than on Earth.
    D) On Mars, much of the CO_2, the major constituent of the atmosphere, condenses out to the surface as snow. This gas is only a minor constituent in the Earth's atmosphere.
    Ans: D   Section: 13-7

110. The reason for the surprising result measured by the *Viking* landers on Mars, that the pressure readings of the atmosphere seemed to go down continuously after the spacecraft landed, is that
    A) the sensors were measuring outgassing of the spacecraft as it adjusted to the very low atmospheric pressure on Mars.
    B) the sensors were slowly deteriorating in the intense solar UV radiation, making them progressively less sensitive.
    C) the major constituent of the atmosphere, CO_2, was freezing out into dry ice flakes as winter approached.
    D) the wake caused by the landing of the spacecraft acted like a hole in the atmosphere to allow the surface gases to escape.
    Ans: C   Section: 13-7

111. The atmospheric pressure in the CO_2 atmosphere on Mars is observed to drop rapidly at certain times, for example during winter periods in the northern hemisphere. Why is this?
    A) because the CO_2 has become warm enough during the preceding summer to escape from the planet
    B) because the CO_2 dissociates into carbon and oxygen under solar UV radiation
    C) because the CO_2 migrates to the summer hemisphere
    D) because the CO_2 freezes out on the cold Martian surface at this time
    Ans: D   Section: 13-7

112. The *Viking Lander* spacecraft measured a steadily decreasing atmospheric pressure soon after landing on Mars. What was found to be the cause of this observation?
    A) The spacecraft was slowly outgassing contaminant gases it had carried from Earth.
    B) The spacecraft had melted a significant region of permafrost with its descent rockets and the resulting vapor was slowly dissipating.
    C) The planet's atmosphere was slowly returning to normal after a massive influx of gas from a recent volcanic eruption.
    D) Atmospheric CO_2 was freezing out into "dry ice" as colder temperatures signaled the onset of the Martian winter.
    Ans: D   Section: 13-7

113. Temperatures fluctuate in response to the seasons on both Mars and the Earth. What other atmospheric effect happens ONLY on Mars and not on Earth?
    A) CO_2 absorbs infrared radiation from the planet's surface, preventing this heat from escaping to outer space.
    B) Atmospheric components condense, freeze out, and fall to the surface.
    C) The angle of sunlight at a particular site varies throughout the planetary year.
    D) The overall atmospheric pressure varies in response to the seasons.
    Ans: D   Section: 13-7

114. In view of the observed freezing of the major atmospheric constituent CO_2 in the Martian atmosphere during winter times on that planet, how much time would elapse between minima in the atmospheric CO_2 pressure at any site?
    A)   24 hours 37 minutes, 1 Martian day   C)   0.94 years, ½ sidereal Martian year
    B)   0.475 years, ¼ sidereal Martian year   D)   1.88 years, 1 sidereal Martian year
    Ans: C   Section: 13-7

115. If a significant amount of the CO_2 in the atmosphere of Mars freezes out at the poles under winter conditions, what would be the nature of the cycle of overall Martian atmospheric pressure per Martian year?
    A)   pressure varying between two maxima and two minima per year
    B)   pressure varying between one maximum and one minimum per year
    C)   no major variation in atmospheric pressure, since CO_2 is only a minor atmospheric constituent
    D)   pressure varying from a maximum one year to a minimum the next year (and back to maximum the third year, etc.)
    Ans: A   Section: 13-7

116. How do summer temperatures compare at the Martian north and south pole?
    A)   Mars is closer to the Sun during the southern summer than it is during the northern summer, so the south pole is warmer.
    B)   Mars is farther from the Sun during the northern summer, but the north pole experiences summer under a relatively clear sky, so the north pole is warmer.
    C)   The south pole has a cooler summer because it is surrounded by mountains while the north pole is on a relatively flat plain.
    D)   Because of the tilt of its axis, Mars does not experience seasons. So there is no summer or winter.
    Ans: B   Section: 13-7

117. Phobos and Deimos are moons of which planet?
    A) Venus   B) Mars   C) Jupiter   D) Uranus
    Ans: B   Section: 13-8

118. Phobos and Deimos, the two moons of Mars, were discovered in which year?
    A) 1846   B) 1930   C) 1610   D) 1877
    Ans: D   Section: 13-8

119. The moons of Mars are
    A)   ice-covered; spherical but flattened by rapid rotation.
    B)   irregularly shaped, cratered, and grooved.
    C)   spherical and smooth-surfaced (no visible craters or volcanoes).
    D)   spherical, with active volcanoes.
    Ans: B   Section: 13-8

120. The moons of Mars are
    A)   spherical and quite large, compared to the planet; about 1000 km in diameter, similar to the largest asteroid.
    B)   irregular but quite large, compared to the planet, between 500 and 1500 km across.
    C)   irregular in shape and very small, only several tens of kilometers across.
    D)   almost spherical but very small, between 10 and 30 km in diameter.
    Ans: C   Section: 13-8

121. The inner Martian moon, Phobos, is 28 km in diameter and 6000 km above the Martian surface. Our own Moon is about 3500 km in diameter and 400,000 km from the Earth. How big in apparent diameter (angular size) would Phobos be in the Martian sky when seen directly overhead compared to our own Moon as seen from Earth?
    A)   less than 1/100 the size of our Moon   C)   about 1/12 the size of our Moon
    B)   almost twice the size of our Moon   D)   about half the size of our Moon
    Ans: D   Section: 13-8

122. The rotation of Mars and the orbital motion of its inner moon, Phobos, are in the same direction and Phobos orbits near the equatorial plane of Mars in just over 7.5 hours. As a result, what is the motion of Phobos across the Martian sky as seen from the surface of the planet?
    A)   It rises in the east, moves rapidly to set in the west, and appears several times per Martian day.
    B)   It rises in the west, moves rapidly to set in the east, and appears only once per Martian day.
    C)   It rises in the west, moves rapidly to set in the east, and appears several times per Martian day.
    D)   It stays almost stationary in the sky in almost synchronous orbit, since its period is close to Mars's rotation period.
    Ans: C   Section: 13-8

123. Phobos, the innermost moon of Mars, has an orbital period that is less than one Martian day. This means that, as seen from Mars, Phobos appears to
    A)   hover over one position all the time in a synchronous orbit.
    B)   rise in the west, moving eastward.
    C)   oscillate back and forth in the sky, never rising or setting from a given location.
    D)   rise in the east, traveling westward.
    Ans: B   Section: 13-8

124. Phobos and Deimos, the two moons of Mars, rotate on their axes
    A)   so that they always have the same sides facing each other as they orbit Mars.
    B)   with no particular relationship to their revolutionary periods, that is, non-synchronously.
    C)   to maintain the same face toward the Sun at all times, because of tidal forces.
    D)   synchronously, keeping one face toward Mars at all times.
    Ans: D   Section: 13-8

125. One consequence of the combination of rapid orbital motion and synchronous rotation of Phobos as it orbits Mars is that
    A)   its orbital plane is slowly moving toward a polar orbit around Mars.
    B)   it is slowly spiraling into the planet.
    C)   it is slowly spiraling outward from the planet.
    D)   one side of the moon never receives sunlight.
    Ans: B   Section: 13-8

126. Phobos, the inner satellite of Mars, has a diameter of about 28 km and circles about 6000 km above the Martian surface. Approximately what is the angular diameter of Phobos when viewed from Mars (in degrees)?
    A) 1/100   B) ¼   C) 1   D) 5½
    Ans: B   Section: 13-8 and Box 1-1

127. Mars rotates toward the east and takes about 24½ hours for one rotation. Phobos, the inner satellite of Mars, revolves around Mars toward the east and requires about 7½ hours to circle the planet once. Viewed from the surface of Mars, how long does it take Phobos to traverse the 180° across the sky from rising to setting (in hours)?
    A) 17   B) 8½   C) 7½   D) 5½
    Ans: D   Section: 13-8

Chapter 14: Jupiter and Saturn: Lords of the Planets

1. The mass of Jupiter is 11.25 times that of Earth. What would be the force of gravity exerted by Jupiter on a spacecraft at a distance of 1 AU from Jupiter compared to that exerted on the same spacecraft by Earth at 1 AU from Earth?
    A) $(11.25)^2$ or 126.25 times as large   C)   11.25 times as large
    B) 1/11.25 as large   D)   the same magnitude of force
    Ans: C   Section: 14-1 and 4-7

2. The fraction of the mass of the planetary system (excluding the Sun) that is concentrated in the planet Jupiter is about (See Section 14-1, Freedman and Kaufmann, *Universe*, 7th ed.)
    A) 70%.   B) 10%.   C) 98%.   D) 50%.
    Ans: A   Section: 14-1

3. Compared to that of Earth, the mass of Jupiter is
    A) several thousand times larger.
    B) about 11 times as large.
    C) about 300 times larger.
    D) about 1/300, because of Jupiter's low density.
    Ans: C   Section: 14-1

4. The low average density of Jupiter (about 1300 kg/m^3 compared with that of water, 1000 kg/m^3) indicates that this planet is composed mainly of
    A) hydrogen, in liquid or gaseous form.
    B) helium as gas and liquid only, because low temperatures and great pressures are needed to form solid helium.
    C) water, compressed somewhat by gravity, maybe in the form of ice.
    D) methane, ammonia, and water, from spectroscopic observation of its atmosphere.
    Ans: A   Section: 14-1

5. When viewed from Earth, the apparent angular diameter of Jupiter varies with time because
    A) the distance between Jupiter and Earth varies.
    B) of tidal influence of the four massive moons of Jupiter.
    C) the fluid planet pulsates with a long natural oscillation period.
    D) Jupiter's gaseous atmosphere expands and contracts as the strength of sunlight varies because of the planet's elliptical orbit.
    Ans: A   Section: 14-1

6. The best time to observe Jupiter from Earth is when it is
    A) at conjunction—when it appears closest to the Sun and is at its brightest.
    B) at maximum eastern or western elongation and is farthest away from the Sun in our sky at sunrise or sunset.
    C) high above our southern horizon at sunrise or sunset.
    D) at opposition—hence closest to Earth.
    Ans: D   Section: 14-1 and Chapter 4

7. At what point in its orbit does Jupiter appear to be brightest when viewed from Earth?
    A) opposition
    B) Its brightness does not vary with orbital position because of its almost circular orbit.
    C) conjunction
    D) when the Earth-Jupiter line is at a right angle to the Sun-Jupiter line
    Ans: A   Section: 14-1

8. At what point in its orbit would Jupiter appear to be faintest when viewed from Earth?
    A) conjunction
    B) when the line from Earth to Jupiter is at a right angle to the line from Jupiter to the Sun
    C) Its apparent brightness does not vary with orbital position, because it has an almost circular orbit.
    D) opposition
    Ans: A   Section: 14-1 and Chapter 4

9. What is the physical appearance of Jupiter as seen from Earth or a spacecraft?
    A) a series of dark belts and light zones parallel to the equator
    B) a uniform bluish color with a high-level haze
    C) v-shaped cloud forms around the equator, indicative of rapid winds
    D) uniform red-colored dust clouds over cratered surface
    Ans: A   Section: 14-1

10. The lighter-colored bands that encircle the high atmosphere of Jupiter and are visible through telescopes from Earth are known as
    A) belts.   B) white spots.   C) rings.   D) zones.
    Ans: D   Section: 14-1

11. The darker-colored bands that encircle the high atmosphere of Jupiter and are visible through telescopes from Earth are known as
    A) rings.   B) white spots.   C) belts.   D) zones.
    Ans: C   Section: 14-1

12. One distinctive feature that is visible on the "surface" of Jupiter through a telescope from Earth is
    A)   the Cassini Division.   C)   Olympus Mons.
    B)   Maxwell Montes.   D)   the Great Red Spot.
    Ans: D   Section: 14-1

13. The existence of the Great Red Spot of Jupiter has been known since
    A)   the 1600s.
    B)   the first fly-by of a spacecraft, *Pioneer 10,* in December, 1973.
    C)   the arrival at Jupiter of *Voyager 1* with its imaging cameras in 1979.
    D)   first light at the 200-inch telescope on Mt. Palomar in 1948.
    Ans: A   Section: 14-1

14. The lifetime of the Great Red Spot appears to be
    A)   similar to that of a sunspot that it resembles—about 2 to 4 weeks between successive appearances.
    B)   one Jupiter orbital period—about 12 years between successive appearances, because the spot is produced by tidal effects from interaction with other planets.
    C)   at least 300 years, from visual records.
    D)   well over 2000 years, from ancient Greek records.
    Ans: C   Section: 14-1

15. The Great Red Spot is
    A)   a large, long-lived, high-pressure storm in Jupiter's atmosphere.
    B)   the colored polar cap of Jupiter.
    C)   clouds of dust-laden gas upwelling above the top of a massive mountain or a volcano on the planet's surface.
    D)   a type of storm in Jupiter's atmosphere that can last for a few months at a time before disappearing.
    Ans: A   Section: 14-1

16. The Great Red Spot is
    A)   a rapidly rotating large region at the north pole of Saturn.
    B)   a hot-spot on Venus detected by Russian landers and the U.S. *Magellan* orbiter.
    C)   a large, stable, circulating storm system in the atmosphere of Jupiter.
    D)   a large red crater on Mars.
    Ans: C   Section: 14-1

17. The dark, reddish bands across the surface of Jupiter are known as
    A) great circles.   B) brown ovals.   C) zones.   D) belts.
    Ans: D   Section: 14-1

18. Suppose a planet is discovered in a prograde circular orbit with an orbital radius of 100 AU. The time from opposition to opposition, viewed from Earth, will be longer than one Earth year. How much longer?
    A) only a few seconds   B) about 9 hours   C) 3.65 years   D) about 5 weeks
    Ans: B   Section: 14-1 and Box 4-2

19. What is the mass of Saturn compared to the mass of Jupiter?
    A)   about 1.5 times the mass of Jupiter   C)   about 1/3 the mass of Jupiter
    B)   about 1/10 the mass of Jupiter   D)   almost the same mass
    Ans: C   Section: 14-1

20. For someone standing on the surface of Jupiter, tomorrow's weather forecast is
    A)   sunny, possible thin, high clouds.
    B)   sunny and clear, because Jupiter has no atmosphere in which clouds can form.
    C)   overcast, possible rain with snow at higher elevations.
    D)   The question is meaningless, because there is no solid surface on which to stand.
    Ans: D   Section: 14-2

21. Evidence of volcanism (lava outflow, etc.), either active or ancient, is NOT found on
    A) Venus.   B) Mars.   C) Earth.   D) Jupiter.
    Ans: D   Section: 14-2

22. Which of the following objects in the solar system rotates the quickest around its own axis?
    A) the Earth   B) the Sun   C) a Jovian planet   D) the Earth's moon
    Ans: C   Section: 14-2 and Appendix 2

23. The rotation periods of Jupiter and Saturn are
    A)   very short—on the order of 1 hour.
    B)   very long—several weeks because of their great size and mass.
    C)   long—on the order of several days.
    D)   relatively short—on the order of 10 hours.
    Ans: D   Section: 14-2

24. The rotation periods for the Jovian planets—Jupiter, Saturn, Uranus, and Neptune—are
    A)   very short—between 1 and 2 hours.
    B)   very long—on the order of years because of the sizes.
    C)   very short—about 10 to 20 hours.
    D)   reasonably long—on the order of several Earth days.
    Ans: C   Section: 14-2

25. Detailed observations of Jupiter's rotation suggest that
    A) it is not a rigid object, because equatorial regions rotate faster than polar regions.
    B) it rotates in two separate parts, equatorial regions rotating in a direction opposite to polar regions.
    C) it is slowing down noticeably at the present time.
    D) it rotates like a solid body, with equatorial and polar regions having the same rotational period.
    Ans: A   Section: 14-2

26. The interesting feature of Jupiter's rotation is that
    A) it rotates in a direction opposite to that of most of the planets and opposite to its direction of revolution around the Sun.
    B) its rotation rate has slowed down significantly since it was first observed through telescopes in the 1600s.
    C) regions at different latitudes appear to rotate at different rates.
    D) its axis of rotation lies almost in the plane of its orbit.
    Ans: C   Section: 14-2

27. The presence of helium in the atmosphere of Jupiter was first established by
    A) careful observation of the spectrum of hydrogen by spacecraft.
    B) precise spectrophotometry of infrared emission lines of helium from Earth.
    C) detection of weak absorption bands of molecular helium by the *Ulysses* spacecraft.
    D) direct sampling of Jupiter's atmosphere by the *Galileo Probe*.
    Ans: A   Section: 14-2

28. The brown ovals seen in Jupiter's atmosphere are
    A) upwelling ammonia and methane gas which condenses to form clouds in the cold upper atmosphere.
    B) vortices of a similar nature to the Great Red Spot, but smaller and with shorter lifetimes.
    C) ammonia ice crystals over high-pressure systems.
    D) holes in Jupiter's cloud cover, through which we can see deeper layers of the atmosphere.
    Ans: D   Section: 14-2

29. What are the fractional proportions of the components that make up the mass of Jupiter?
    A) almost pure hydrogen, with at most about 1% rock in the core
    B) 50% hydrogen, 49% helium, 1% rocky core
    C) 71% hydrogen and helium, 25% rocky core, 4% everything else
    D) 95% hydrogen and helium, 2½% rocky core, 2½% everything else
    Ans: D   Section: 14-2

30. Hydrogen and helium are the major constituents of Jupiter, but they proved hard to detect. Which one of the following was *not* a reason for this difficulty?
    A) The spectral signatures of these molecules contain few prominent *visible* lines.
    B) Ultraviolet radiation is absorbed in Earth's atmosphere.
    C) Jupiter is always very far away from Earth and from the Sun.
    D) The hydrogen and helium on Jupiter exist only in solid form deep under the atmosphere, and they emit very little radiation.
    Ans: D   Section: 14-2

31. How does Saturn's size (e.g., diameter) compare to that of Jupiter?
    A) slightly larger—because Saturn is rotating much faster then Jupiter
    B) significantly larger—because Saturn contains a greater proportion of hydrogen than Jupiter
    C) about the same—because Saturn is less massive and less compressed
    D) significantly smaller—because Saturn has only about one tenth the mass of Jupiter
    Ans: C   Section: 14-2

32. Saturn is less massive than Jupiter but has almost the same size. Why is this?
    A) Saturn's interior is hotter than that of Jupiter.
    B) Saturn is composed of lighter material than is Jupiter.
    C) Saturn is rotating faster than Jupiter, and the increased centrifugal force results in a larger size.
    D) The smaller mass exerts less gravitational force and is unable to compress the mass as much as in Jupiter.
    Ans: D   Section: 14-2

33. How does the composition of Saturn's atmosphere compare to that of Jupiter, which is the same as that of the Sun?
    A) Saturn's atmosphere contains less helium than does that of either Jupiter or the Sun.
    B) They are almost equivalent, with the same proportions of hydrogen, helium, and heavier elements.
    C) Saturn's atmosphere contains far more heavy elements than does that of either Jupiter or the Sun.
    D) Saturn's atmosphere has far less hydrogen than does that of either Jupiter or the Sun.
    Ans: A   Section: 14-2

34. Which is the least dense planet in the solar system?
    A) Uranus   B) Pluto   C) Saturn   D) Jupiter
    Ans: C   Section: 14-2 and Appendix 2

35. The major constituent of Saturn is
    A) rock.   B) carbon dioxide.   C) hydrogen.   D) nitrogen.
    Ans: C   Section: 14-2

36. What is the Great Red Spot on Jupiter?
    A)   a large, long-lived, counterclockwise rotating storm maintained by high-speed wind and circulation in Jupiter's atmosphere
    B)   the point where charged particles from the satellite Io collide with Jupiter's cloud tops
    C)   a region over the south pole of Jupiter where ammonia compounds have condensed in the colder atmosphere
    D)   clouds above the summit of a large volcanic mountain
    Ans: A   Section: 14-3

37. The circulation pattern in and around the Great Red Spot on Jupiter is
    A)   clockwise between two sets of winds flowing in the same direction but with different speeds.
    B)   from west to east, rising and falling like air flowing over a mountain.
    C)   outward (away from Jupiter's center) inside the Great Red Spot and back down (into Jupiter's interior) outside it, like a convection cell.
    D)   counterclockwise between two sets of winds flowing in opposite directions.
    Ans: D   Section: 14-3

38. The white ovals seen on Jupiter appear to be
    A)   vortices (whirlpools) created between regions of oppositely directed winds.
    B)   upwelling gas that then descends in the brown ovals.
    C)   descending masses of gas within the dark belts.
    D)   clouds of ammonia ice crystals that condense when Jupiter's atmosphere flows over fixed obstacles such as mountains.
    Ans: A   Section: 14-3

39. Which of the following spacecraft did NOT visit Jupiter?
    A) *Galileo*   B) *Pioneer 10*   C) *Viking*   D) *Voyager 1*
    Ans: C   Section: 14-3

40. Jupiter's Great Red Spot
    A)   has remained virtually unchanged during the three and a half centuries it has been observed.
    B)   has disappeared (for decades at a time) and then re-emerged several times in the past three and a half centuries.
    C)   has changed color dramatically more than once, becoming white or brown.
    D)   has changed its size significantly during the past three and a half centuries.
    Ans: D   Section: 14-3

41. What causes the banded structure on Jupiter's visible "surface"?
    A)   an underlying rising and falling convection pattern, stretched into bands by
         Jupiter's rapid rotation
    B)   an underlying north-south flow pattern, stretched into bands by Jupiter's rapid
         rotation
    C)   the "sweeping" of Jupiter's clouds through magnetic field lines from Jupiter's
         magnetosphere
    D)   the breakup of strong eastward flows, due to Jupiter's rapid rotation by underlying
         mountain ranges
    Ans: A   Section: 14-4

42. The *Cassini* observations of Jupiter suggest that the light-colored zones on Jupiter are
    A)   volcanic plumes that have been stretched around the planet by Jupiter's high speed
         of rotation.
    B)   holes in the atmosphere through which lighter, deeper layers can be seen.
    C)   regions in which the gas is falling.
    D)   regions in which the gas is rising.
    Ans: D   Section: 14-4

43. The *Cassini* observations of Jupiter suggest that the dark belts on Jupiter are
    A)   holes in the cloud bank through which the dark planet surface can be seen.
    B)   regions in which the gas is falling.
    C)   dust clouds from volcanoes that have been spread around the planet by very
         strong winds.
    D)   regions in which the gas is rising.
    Ans: D   Section: 14-4

44. When viewed in the infrared light emitted by the clouds, the brightest parts of Jupiter
    are
    A)   in the belts, which correspond to deeper and hotter regions.
    B)   directly along the equator, where sunlight is most direct and effective in heating
         the gas.
    C)   in the zones, corresponding as expected to brighter regions in visible light.
    D)   over the north and south magnetic poles, where magnetospheric interaction heats
         the atmosphere.
    Ans: A   Section: 14-4

45. The dark-colored belts on Jupiter are brighter than the surrounding regions when viewed in infrared or heat radiation because
    A) chemical reactions causing the dark, visible colors also release energy and heat these regions.
    B) these regions are composed of hot dust and gases released from volcanoes and distributed around the planet by high winds.
    C) these regions are higher in Jupiter atmosphere, receive more sunlight, and hence are hotter in IR radiation.
    D) these regions are deeper and therefore hotter layers of gas in Jupiter's atmosphere.
    Ans: D   Section: 14-4

46. The composition of the clouds that we see on Jupiter is
    A) very different from Earth clouds—composed almost entirely of ammonia and ammonium hydrosulfide crystals with almost no water.
    B) similar to Earth clouds through the whole atmosphere—water droplets and crystals of frozen water.
    C) similar to Earth clouds (water droplets and crystals of frozen water) in the higher levels but very different (e.g., ammonia crystals) in the lower levels.
    D) similar to those of Earth (water droplets and crystals of frozen water) in the lower levels but very different (e.g., ammonia crystals and other chemicals) in the higher levels.
    Ans: D   Section: 14-4

47. Which of the following chemicals is the least abundant in the atmosphere of Jupiter?
    A) NH_3—ammonia   C) CH_4—methane
    B) H_2O—water vapor   D) CO_2—carbon dioxide
    Ans: D   Section: 14-4

48. Other than hydrogen and helium, the major components of the atmospheres of Jupiter and Saturn have been found to be
    A) H_2O (water) and CO_2 (carbon dioxide).
    B) N_2 (nitrogen), O_2 (oxygen), and CO_2 (carbon dioxide).
    C) dust and iron oxides.
    D) CH_4 (methane), NH_3 (ammonia), and H_2O (water).
    Ans: D   Section: 14-4

49. The composition of Jupiter's clouds is
    A) liquid droplets of water and ammonia.
    B) ice crystals of water, ammonium hydrosulfide, and carbon dioxide.
    C) water-ice crystals.
    D) ice crystals of ammonia, ammonium hydrosulfide, and water.
    Ans: D   Section: 14-4

50. An astronomer detects a new feature in Jupiter's atmosphere. Subsequent observation shows that this feature is brighter than its surroundings when observed in infrared light. We can conclude that this feature is a
    A) localized storm feature.
    B) region of higher density in the ammonium hydrosulfide layer.
    C) region of high-altitude clouds created by upwardly moving winds.
    D) deeper layer observed through a hole in Jupiter's clouds.
    Ans: D   Section: 14-4

51. The high-speed winds observed on Jupiter occur mainly
    A) in a north-south direction from the dark belts toward the light zones.
    B) near the centers of the dark belts.
    C) at the boundaries between the dark belts and the light zones.
    D) near the centers of the light zones.
    Ans: C   Section: 14-4

52. What are zonal winds on Jupiter?
    A) winds blowing horizontally northward and southward above the cloud layer
    B) winds blowing vertically upward and downward in regions of strong convection
    C) winds blowing horizontally in a circular pattern, such as around the Great Red Spot
    D) winds blowing horizontally eastward and westward in the cloud layer
    Ans: D   Section: 14-4

53. The large-scale atmospheric circulation pattern on Jupiter is characterized predominantly by
    A) strong winds blowing parallel to the equator but in opposite directions at different latitudes.
    B) strong winds blowing eastward at all latitudes so that the entire atmosphere rotates faster than the planet.
    C) isolated cyclones (low-pressure areas) and anticyclones (high-pressure areas), as on Earth.
    D) strong winds blowing westward at all latitudes so that the entire atmosphere rotates more slowly.
    Ans: A   Section: 14-4

54. What is the dominant circulation pattern in Jupiter's atmosphere (i.e., at the visible "surface")?
    A) uniform eastward flow of the entire atmosphere, with occasional dark storms and turbulent swirls
    B) isolated storms and turbulent swirls, with little overall flow pattern in any particular direction
    C) alternating bands of eastward and westward flow parallel to the equator, with light and dark ovals between these flows
    D) air rising at the equator, flowing north and south toward the poles, then sinking and returning to the equator at a lower level
    Ans: C   Section: 14-4

55. The source of excess heat emitted by Jupiter, above that which is absorbed as sunlight and reemitted, is thought to be
    A) heat generated in the interior by the same electrical currents that generate the planet's magnetic field.
    B) heat caused by friction between oppositely directed winds at mid-latitudes.
    C) gravitational potential energy released as heat during its formation stages, still being released.
    D) chemical reactions between methane, ammonia, and water in the planet's atmosphere and clouds.
    Ans: C   Section: 14-4

56. Because its interior is so hot, Jupiter radiates about twice as much heat as it receives from the Sun. How does this fraction compare with the excess energy radiated by the Earth as a fraction of the energy Earth receives from the Sun?
    A) The fraction is about 10 times larger for Jupiter.
    B) The fraction is about 1000 times larger for Jupiter.
    C) The fraction is about 10,000 times larger for Jupiter.
    D) The fraction is about 10^8 times larger for Jupiter.
    Ans: D   Section: 14-4

57. How thick are the cloud layers on Jupiter's visible "surface"?
    A) very thin—only about 10 km
    B) greater than 10,000 km, as seen through the dark ovals, holes in the cloud layers
    C) about 100 km
    D) about 1000 km
    Ans: C   Section: 14-4

58. One unsolved question about Jupiter and Saturn is
    A) why Jupiter radiates more energy than it receives from the sun.
    B) why Saturn is more effective than Jupiter in terms of radiating excess energy.
    C) why wind speeds on Saturn are greater than those on Jupiter.
    D) why Saturn's cloud layers are more spread out than Jupiter's.
    Ans: C   Section: 14-4

59. "Markings" on the surface of Saturn are
    A)   of a completely different pattern from those on Jupiter and more distinct.
    B)   nonexistent, because Saturn shows completely uniform cloud tops.
    C)   similar in appearance to those on Jupiter but much less distinct.
    D)   similar to those on Jupiter but much more pronounced.
    Ans: C   Section: 14-4

60. Other than the rings, how does the appearance of Saturn differ from that of Jupiter?
    A)   There are belts and zones on Saturn, but they are very faint and hazy compared to Jupiter's.
    B)   Saturn's visible surface is basically featureless, with no hint of the belts and zones of Jupiter.
    C)   Saturn shows an ever-changing system of dark storms and light eddies, without the belts and zones of Jupiter.
    D)   Saturn has many more belts and zones than Jupiter, with large storms distorting their shapes.
    Ans: A   Section: 14-4

61. Saturn's atmosphere does not show the same colorful contrast that we see in Jupiter's atmosphere. This is because
    A)   Saturn's clouds and circulation pattern resemble those of Earth (individual cyclones and anticyclones) rather than those of Jupiter.
    B)   Saturn's features are obscured by an upper cloud deck of methane ice crystals, whereas Jupiter has too high a temperature for methane ice.
    C)   Saturn has a similar circulation pattern to Jupiter, but it is obscured by a much deeper atmosphere.
    D)   Saturn has counterflowing eastward and westward winds like Jupiter but lacks the three differently colored cloud levels.
    Ans: C   Section: 14-4

62. Spectroscopy of Jupiter and Saturn has revealed atmospheres containing large quantities of which of the following gases, in addition to hydrogen and helium?
    A)   nitrogen (N_2), oxygen (O_2), and water vapor (H_2O)
    B)   methane (CH_4), ammonia (NH_3), and water vapor (H_2O)
    C)   clouds of sulfuric acid droplets (H_2SO_4)
    D)   carbon dioxide (CO_2) and traces of water vapor (H_2O)
    Ans: B   Section: 14-4

63. One observational fact that is common to both Jupiter and Saturn is that
   A)   both planets appear cooler than is expected on the basis of received solar energy and emit less radiant energy than expected.
   B)   the temperature appears to fall continuously as depth into these planets increases, leading to the conclusion that the interiors of these planets are probably extremely cold.
   C) CO_2 in their atmospheres appears to produce an intense greenhouse effect with very enhanced atmospheric temperatures of greater than 200°C in the outer layers.
   D)   both planets emit more energy (in the form of infrared radiation) than they receive from the Sun.
   Ans: D   Section: 14-4

64. Saturn appears to emit heat as infrared radiation in excess of the energy absorbed from sunlight. The most likely major cause of this heating is
   A)   condensation of helium into droplets that fall into the planet, releasing gravitational energy as heat.
   B)   the radioactive decay of naturally occurring isotopes in the atmosphere and interior of Saturn.
   C)   energy released from the continuous shrinking and condensation of this fluid planet.
   D)   remnant heat from the original formation of the planet.
   Ans: A   Section: 14-4

65. What was the most surprising discovery of the *Galileo Probe* when it penetrated the atmosphere of Jupiter?
   A)   It measured only traces of the NH_3, NH_4SH, and water vapor cloud layers that are easily measured spectroscopically from Earth.
   B)   It found no evidence of hydrogen at all in the atmosphere of Jupiter.
   C)   It hit a hard surface just under the cloud layers, contrary to our understanding of Jupiter's atmospheric structure.
   D)   It measured vast quantities of invisible water vapor above the cloud layers.
   Ans: A   Section: 14-5

66. The relative proportions of hydrogen and helium that the *Galileo Probe* found in the atmosphere of Jupiter were almost exactly the same as in the Sun (as was expected), but the abundances of carbon, nitrogen, and sulfur were proportionally higher than in the Sun. What is believed to be the reason for this?
   A)   The probe probed an anomalous region where abundances were abnormal compared to the rest of Jupiter.
   B)   Jupiter formed farther out from the Sun than it is now, where temperatures are colder.
   C)   Comets and asteroids plunging into Jupiter brought heavier elements with them.
   D)   The lighter elements collect preferentially in the core, leaving an excess of heavier elements in the atmosphere.
   Ans: C   Section: 14-5

67. The relative proportions of hydrogen and helium that the *Galileo Probe* found in the atmosphere of Jupiter were almost exactly the same as in the Sun (as was expected), but the noble gases argon, krypton, and xenon were three times as abundant in Jupiter's atmosphere than in the Sun's. Which of the following ideas is considered to be a possible reason for this?
    A) Jupiter formed farther out from the Sun than it is now, where temperatures are colder.
    B) Jupiter formed closer to the Sun than it is now, where temperatures were warmer.
    C) The noble gases do not combine with any other elements and floated to the "surface" (atmosphere) of Jupiter.
    D) The probe probed an anomalous region where abundances were abnormal compared to the rest of Jupiter.
    Ans: A   Section: 14-5

68. The *Galileo Probe* found that the wind speed was an almost constant 650 km/h over the entire 200 km of its descent below Jupiter's cloud tops. What does this result imply for Jupiter?
    A) Jupiter must have a solid surface within about 500 km below the clouds.
    B) Jupiter cannot have a solid surface.
    C) Solar heating of Jupiter's atmosphere is much more efficient than was previously thought.
    D) Jupiter's atmospheric circulation is driven primarily by the escape of internal heat.
    Ans: D   Section: 14-5

69. The *Galileo Probe* made all of the following measurements, most of which gave unexpected results. Which result was *expected*?
    A) The amounts of carbon, nitrogen, and sulfur are greater than solar abundances.
    B) The amounts of argon, krypton, and xenon are greater than solar abundances.
    C) No water clouds were encountered in the atmosphere.
    D) Only traces of ammonia and ammonium hydrosulfide clouds were found.
    Ans: A   Section: 14-5

70. Oblateness is a measure of the
    A) nonspherical shape of a planet, with the polar diameter being shorter than the equatorial diameter.
    B) nonspherical shape of a planet, with the polar diameter being longer than the equatorial diameter.
    C) inclination of the orbit of a planet or a moon to the ecliptic plane.
    D) noncircular shape of a planet's orbit.
    Ans: A   Section: 14-6

71. The reason for the slightly flattened or oblate shape of Jupiter is
    A)   its rapid rotation rate.
    B)   its cloud cover, more clouds forming over the equator on average.
    C)   that it was formed that way in the beginning and has maintained this shape.
    D)   the gravitational pull of the Sun and the other planets in the ecliptic.
    Ans: A   Section: 14-6

72. Jupiter appears as a flattened, oblate spheroid in the sky because
    A)   it is spinning rapidly, and is composed mostly of fluid matter.
    B)   it was formed in this way at the time of planetary formation, and has solidified to
         this shape.
    C)   tidal distortion from its moons and from the Sun have distorted its shape.
    D)   it is moving rapidly around its orbit, flattening its shape.
    Ans: A   Section: 14-6

73. The three-dimensional shape of Jupiter is
    A)   a sphere but with extended radius near the belts and zones, within +/−10° of the
         planet's equator.
    B)   an oblate spheroid with its spin axis shorter than its equatorial diameter because of
         its rapid spin.
    C)   almost a perfect sphere because of its fluid physical structure.
    D)   a prolate spheroid with its spin axis longer than its equatorial diameter because of
         its rapid spin.
    Ans: B   Section: 14-6

74. The oblateness of Jupiter, which is a measure of the amount by which its equatorial
    diameter exceeds its polar diameter and is a consequence of its fluid structure and rapid
    rotation, is
    A)   zero, or perfectly spherical, because the planet is fluid.
    B)   6.5%.
    C)   10%.
    D)   32%.
    Ans: B   Section: 14-6

75. The deepest central cores of the interiors of Jupiter and Saturn are thought to be
    composed of
    A)   methane, ammonia, and water vapor.   C)   magnetized iron.
    B)   liquid metallic hydrogen.   D)   rock.
    Ans: D   Section: 14-6

76. The overall interior structure of Jupiter and Saturn is expected to be
    A)   three-layered—a large, solid, inner core of rock, a liquid outer core of "ices," and an extensive gaseous, hydrogen-rich atmosphere.
    B)   four-layered—a solid iron inner core, a liquid iron outer core, a partially molten mantle of rock, and a solid crust.
    C)   a ball of hydrogen and helium of gradually increasing density inward from gas to liquid to solid.
    D)   four-layered—a rocky inner core, a liquid outer core of "ices," a mantle of liquid hydrogen and helium, and an extensive gaseous atmosphere.
    Ans: D   Section: 14-6

77. The internal structure of the two largest Jovian planets (from center outward) is
    A)   rocky core with an outer layer of liquid "ices," liquid methane mantle, gaseous methane atmosphere.
    B)   iron-nickel core, rocky mantle, solid crust, ocean of liquid "ices."
    C)   rocky core with an outer layer of liquid "ices," liquid molecular hydrogen layer, liquid metallic hydrogen layer.
    D)   rocky core with an outer layer of liquid "ices," liquid metallic hydrogen layer, liquid molecular hydrogen layer.
    Ans: D   Section: 14-6

78. Where in the solar system would you look for liquid hydrogen?
    A)   nowhere, because it is not cold enough anywhere in the solar system to liquefy hydrogen.
    B)   at the polar regions of the Moon.
    C)   in the deep interiors of Jupiter and Saturn.
    D)   on the polar caps of Mars.
    Ans: C   Section: 14-6

79. The outer cores of Jupiter and Saturn are made of "ices," which are actually in the liquid state. Why are they not solid?
    A)   The pressure here is too great.
    B)   The temperature here is too high.
    C)   These ices consist of hydrogen and helium, which cannot exist in a solid form.
    D)   The constant agitation caused by the planets' rotation prevents the formation of a solid.
    Ans: B   Section: 14-6

80. What is the interior structure of Saturn?
    A)   a thick mantle of liquid hydrogen with a rocky core and a relatively thin, gaseous atmosphere
    B)   a thick, gaseous atmosphere over a thin mantle of liquid hydrogen and a rocky core
    C)   a large, rocky core with a very thin mantle of liquid hydrogen and a thin, gaseous atmosphere
    D)   a large liquid hydrogen core overlain by a thin, gaseous atmosphere
    Ans: A   Section: 14-6

81. The planet Saturn appears to be
    A)   a "sphere," flattened along its polar diameter, significantly more so than for the planet Jupiter.
    B)   a "sphere," flattened along its polar diameter, considerably less than for Jupiter.
    C)   a "sphere" in which the equatorial diameter is significantly less than the polar diameter because of the planet's rapid rotation.
    D)   almost a perfect sphere, with equal polar and equatorial diameters.
    Ans: A   Section: 14-6

82. The distribution of mass inside the planet Saturn is believed to be concentrated more centrally than it is in Jupiter. The most important observation supporting this conclusion is that
    A)   Saturn is more massive than Jupiter and is more gravitationally compressed at its center.
    B)   Saturn has a significantly lower density than has Jupiter.
    C)   Saturn is less oblate (flattened) than Jupiter, even though it rotates at approximately the same speed.
    D)   Saturn is more oblate (flattened) then Jupiter, even though it rotates more slowly.
    Ans: D   Section: 14-6

83. The material in the interiors of Jupiter and Saturn thought to be responsible for their powerful magnetic fields is
    A)   molten iron and nickel.
    B)   liquid metallic hydrogen.
    C)   gases of NH_3 (ammonia), CH_4 (methane), H_2O (water vapor).
    D)   solid magnetic iron.
    Ans: B   Section: 14-7

84. The requirements for the generation of a powerful magnetic field in a Jovian planet (e.g., Jupiter, Saturn) appear to be
    A)   liquid "metal" interior and relatively rapid rotation.
    B)   solid iron core forming a permanent magnet.
    C)   liquid "metal" core and interior and slow rotation.
    D)   solid interior throughout the planet and slow rotation.
    Ans: A   Section: 14-7

85. What conditions are considered necessary for a planet to be able to generate an intense magnetic field?
    A) ionized and electrically conducting layer in its atmosphere
    B) solid iron core into which a magnetic field was induced early in the planet's history
    C) electrically conducting material in its interior and slow rotation, because rapid rotation will destroy a magnetic field
    D) relatively rapid rotation and electrically conducting material in its interior
    Ans: D   Section: 14-7

86. Jupiter has a magnetic field that is
    A) much stronger than that of Earth and greatly extended in space.
    B) about the same strength and extent as that of Earth.
    C) variable, often nonexistent, sometimes existing only at the Great Red Spot, which behaves like a sunspot.
    D) very strong and localized close to the planet.
    Ans: A   Section: 14-7 and 14-8

87. The strength of the magnetic field at Jupiter's equator exceeds that at Earth's equator by a factor of
    A) about 1,000,000.   B) about 2.   C) about 15.   D) about 1500.
    Ans: C   Section: 14-7

88. The source of Jupiter's intense magnetic field is
    A) electric currents in ionized layers of Jupiter's atmosphere.
    B) remnant magnetism in Jupiter's rock and iron core.
    C) electric currents in Jupiter's liquid hydrogen mantle.
    D) electric currents in Jupiter's molten rocky core.
    Ans: C   Section: 14-7

89. What is believed to be the source of Jupiter's decametric radiation (radio waves of wavelength around 10 meters)?
    A) synchrotron radiation from electrons spiraling in Jupiter's immense magnetosphere
    B) lightning in regions of strong upwelling in Jupiter's atmosphere
    C) electric currents in the high-velocity boundaries between Jupiter's belts and zones
    D) electrical discharges in Jupiter's ionosphere, caused by the large satellite, Io
    Ans: D   Section: 14-7

90. What is believed to be the source of Jupiter's decimetric radiation (radio waves of wavelength around 1/10 meter or 100 cm)?
    A)   electric currents in the high-velocity boundaries between Jupiter's belts and zones
    B)   synchrotron radiation from electrons spiraling in Jupiter's immense magnetosphere
    C)   lightning in regions of strong upwelling in Jupiter's atmosphere
    D)   electrical discharges in Jupiter's ionosphere, caused by the large satellite, Io
    Ans: B   Section: 14-7

91. The basic mechanism that causes the short-wavelength (less than 1 meter) radio outbursts from Jupiter is
    A)   lightning strikes in the atmosphere of Jupiter.
    B)   deceleration of solar protons and electrons, as they plunge into the planet's atmosphere.
    C)   synchrotron radiation from electrons being forced to move in spiral patterns by Jupiter's magnetic field.
    D)   synchrotron radiation from solar protons diverted around the planet and accelerated by its magnetic field.
    Ans: C   Section: 14-7

92. Radio waves less than 1 meter in wavelength detected from Jupiter are produced by
    A)   the long-wavelength tail of its black body "thermal" radiation.
    B)   energetic electrons spiraling rapidly in the magnetic field of Jupiter, producing synchrotron radiation.
    C)   lightning strikes in its atmosphere.
    D)   electrons falling into atoms of hydrogen and cascading down the quantum energy levels.
    Ans: B   Section: 14-7

93. Synchrotron radiation is energy produced whenever
    A)   electrons jump from higher levels of atoms to lower levels, emitting specific wavelengths of radiation.
    B)   high-speed electrons are forced by magnetic fields to follow spiral patterns, thereby producing mainly radio waves.
    C)   electrons meet antielectrons, called positrons, and are annihilated to produce electromagnetic energy.
    D)   charged particles are decelerated rapidly by being stopped in a planet's atmosphere.
    Ans: B   Section: 14-7

94. Where might you find liquid helium on Jupiter?
    A) in the outer core   B) in the mantle   C) in the lower atmosphere   D) nowhere
    Ans: D   Section: 14-7

95. The magnetosphere of Jupiter is
    A) a narrow layer in which intense electric currents flow, just above the cloud tops in the planet's atmosphere, generating the planet's magnetic field.
    B) the inner regions of Jupiter just outside the solid core that contain liquid metallic hydrogen, in which electric currents flow to produce the planet's magnetic field.
    C) a doughnut-shaped region similar to the Van Allen belts around Earth containing high-speed protons and electrons whose motions produce the planet's magnetic field.
    D) a large cavity created and maintained within the solar wind stream by the planet's magnetic field and filled with extremely hot ionized plasma.
    Ans: D   Section: 14-8

96. The magnetosphere of Jupiter is
    A) a large region outside Jupiter occupied by its magnetic field and filled with high-energy charged particles.
    B) the magnetized hydrogen in the inner regions of Jupiter just outside the solid core, where the planet's magnetic field is produced.
    C) a region of charged particles extending along the orbit of the satellite Io, forming a ring around Jupiter.
    D) a dark belt around the planet's equator where intense electric currents flow, generating the planet's magnetic field.
    Ans: A   Section: 14-8

97. If we could see the full extent of the magnetosphere of Jupiter from Earth, how big would it appear in our sky?
    A) 16 times larger than the full Moon
    B) about as large as the full Moon
    C) about 16 times larger than Jupiter itself
    D) about twice as large as Jupiter itself
    Ans: A   Section: 14-8

98. If we could see Jupiter's magnetosphere with our eyes, how big would it appear?
    A) It would be easily visible—several times larger than the Full Moon.
    B) It would be about 1 arcminute in diameter—just big enough to see but at the limit of unaided-eye visibility.
    C) It would be too small to be visible without a telescope.
    D) It would cover essentially our entire sky whenever Jupiter was above the horizon.
    Ans: A   Section: 14-8

99. Jupiter's current sheet is
    A)   a large set of overlapping rings of current in Jupiter's liquid metallic hydrogen mantle, near the plane of the rotational equator.
    B)   the outer edge of Jupiter's magnetosphere facing the Sun, where solar wind particles are deflected by Jupiter's magnetic field.
    C)   a wide region of charged particles in Jupiter's magnetosphere, near the plane of the magnetic equator.
    D)   a long tube of current extending in both directions from the satellite Io to the north and south magnetic poles of Jupiter.
    Ans: C   Section: 14-8

100. What causes Jupiter's current sheet?
    A)   Positively and negatively charged solar wind particles move in opposite directions as they flow along Jupiter's magnetospheric tail.
    B)   Jupiter's magnetosphere forces charged particles to spiral northward and southward in a thin sheet like Earth's Van Allen belts.
    C)   Charged solar wind particles are pushed aside in a thin, sheet-like layer on the sunward side of Jupiter's magnetosphere.
    D)   Charged particles in Jupiter's magnetosphere are thrown outward into a thin sheet by Jupiter's rapid rotation.
    Ans: D   Section: 14-8

101. How have astronomers been able to measure Jupiter's internal rotation period (i.e., the rotation period of the bulk of Jupiter's great mass)?
    A)   by measuring subtle changes in the shape of Jupiter as the interior rotates underneath the clouds
    B)   by measuring variations in radio emission from Jupiter's magnetosphere
    C)   by measuring periodic variations in wind speeds in the belts and zones
    D)   by measuring periodic variations in the intensity of infrared emission from deeper layers below the clouds
    Ans: B   Section: 14-8

102. The plasma that exists within Jupiter's magnetosphere is composed of
    A)   neutral hydrogen gas.
    B)   a mixture of neutral atoms with the same constituents as the Sun—hydrogen, helium, and some heavy elements such as sulfur.
    C)   energetic electrons moving in spiral patterns around magnetic field lines.
    D)   electrically charged particles such as electrons and ionized atoms—mostly hydrogen but some heavier elements.
    Ans: D   Section: 14-8

103. The shape and dimensions of the magnetosphere surrounding Jupiter are controlled by
    A)   the outward motion of the atoms of Jupiter's outer atmosphere, as it rotates rapidly within the planet's powerful gravitational field.
    B)   solar radiation pressure pushing against the planet's outer atmosphere.
    C)   the pressure of the solar wind against the outer atmosphere of Jupiter.
    D)   the pressure of the ionized gas of the solar wind against the planet's magnetic field.
    Ans: D   Section: 14-8

104. Compared to the stability of the size and shape of Earth's magnetosphere against varying solar wind pressure, that of Jupiter
    A)   is very weak, varying wildly in size and shape.
    B)   is about as stable, varying a little under strong solar wind changes.
    C)   is extremely weak, the magnetosphere disappearing whenever the solar wind pressure increases beyond a certain limit.
    D)   is much more stable, because of Jupiter's much stronger magnetic field and its greater distance from the Sun, and hence weaker solar wind pressure.
    Ans: A   Section: 14-8

105. On what planet would you *not* expect to find an aurora?
    A) Venus   B) Earth   C) Jupiter   D) Saturn
    Ans: A   Section: 14-8

106. Saturn's magnetosphere contains many fewer charged particles than does Jupiter's magnetosphere. Which one of the following is *not* part of the reason for this difference?
    A)   Saturn has a smaller magnetic field than does Jupiter.
    B)   Saturn has a much slower rotation rate than Jupiter.
    C)   Saturn's rings absorb charged particles.
    D)   Saturn does not have a geologically active satellite within its magnetosphere.
    Ans: B   Section: 14-8

107. The orbital period of Saturn is about 30 years. What is the time between our "top view" of its rings at maximum tilt and our next observation of this "top view"?
    A)   15 years
    B)   30 years
    C)   60 years
    D)   The time depends on the difference in directions between the Earth's rotation axis and Saturn's rotation axis.
    Ans: B   Section: 14-9

108. Which planet has wide, bright rings that are easily visible from Earth?
    A) Venus   B) Jupiter   C) Neptune   D) Saturn
    Ans: D   Section: 14-9

109. Who was the first person to see the rings of Saturn although he did not realize that they were rings?
    A) We do not know—the rings have been known since ancient times.
    B) Galileo Galilei
    C) Christiaan Huygens
    D) Johannes Kepler
    Ans: B   Section: 14-9

110. What observing technique was being used when Saturn's rings were originally discovered?
    A) momentary occultation of starlight as the planet moved in front of a star
    B) spacecraft photography
    C) ground-based photography
    D) visual observations through a telescope
    Ans: D   Section: 14-9

111. Who first understood that the "ears" that Galileo saw on Saturn were in fact a wide, thin ring surrounding the planet?
    A) Christiaan Huygens   C) Isaac Newton
    B) Gian Domenico Cassini   D) Johannes Kepler
    Ans: A   Section: 14-9

112. What was the nationality of the first person to correctly interpret Galileo's observations of "ears" on Saturn?
    A) English   B) American   C) German   D) Dutch
    Ans: D   Section: 14-9

113. The rings of Saturn are in which plane with respect to the planetary system?
    A) a plane inclined at an angle to both the orbital and equatorial planes of the planet, and to the ecliptic plane, which is why we can easily see the rings face-on from Earth
    B) the orbital plane of Saturn around the Sun
    C) the equatorial plane of Saturn
    D) the ecliptic plane
    Ans: C   Section: 14-9

114. Why do the rings of Saturn alternately appear very distinct and then almost disappear when viewed from Earth over periods of a few years?
    A) Earth is very much closer to Saturn at opposition than at conjunction; hence the rings are more easily seen at this time.
    B) The solar wind occasionally blows away the ring particles when the Sun is particularly active.
    C) The ice crystals from which they are made melt and refreeze as the planet approaches and recedes from the Sun.
    D) The plane of the rings is tilted with respect to the ecliptic plane and thus appear edge-on at times.
    Ans: D   Section: 14-9

115. Where is the Cassini division found in our solar system?
    A) between two band systems on the visible "surface" of Jupiter
    B) between two major groups of asteroids in the asteroid belt
    C) between two major ring systems around Saturn
    D) between the terrestrial and the Jovian planets
    Ans: C   Section: 14-9

116. The Cassini division is
    A) a major division in the rings of Saturn that is visible from Earth.
    B) a gap between two mountain ranges on the Moon.
    C) the division between terrestrial and Jovian planets.
    D) a gap between two groups of asteroids in the asteroid belt.
    Ans: A   Section: 14-9

117. The mean thickness of Saturn's rings is now thought to be
    A) a few tens of meters.   C) a few thousand meters.
    B) a few kilometers.   D) about 10,000 meters.
    Ans: A   Section: 14-9

118. The outer radius of the Saturnian ring system is about 274,000 km, whereas the outer radius of Jupiter's ring system is about 222,000 km. How does the period of the outermost particles in Jupiter's rings compare with the period of the outermost particles in Saturn's rings?
    A) For Jupiter the period is about 39% of the period for Saturn.
    B) For Jupiter the period is about 73% of the period for Saturn.
    C) For Jupiter the period is about 81% of the period for Saturn.
    D) For Jupiter the period is about 123% of the period for Saturn.
    Ans: A   Section: 14-10 and Box 4-4

119. Jupiter's ring was discovered by
    A) direct, ground-based photography.
    B) momentary occultation of starlight as the planet and the rings moved in front of a star.
    C) visual observations by Galileo.
    D) spacecraft photography.
    Ans: D   Section: 14-10

120. Rings of dust and icy particles are found around which planets?
    A) all planets that have moons associated with them
    B) all four of the Jovian planets
    C) all four of the terrestrial planets
    D) only Saturn
    Ans: B   Section: 14-10

121. What kind of ring or rings does Jupiter have?
    A) several thin, dark rings made up of dust particles about 1/1000 in size
    B) three wide, bright, rings, composed of icy particles about 1 cm to 1 m in size
    C) one narrow, dark ring composed of icy particles less than 1 mm in size
    D) only a ring of glowing ions at Io's orbital distance, no rings of solid particles
    Ans: A   Section: 14-10

122. The ring of material that surrounds Jupiter appears to be made up of
    A) pure ice crystals, similar to those in high cirrus clouds on Earth.
    B) extremely fine dust particles, about the size of smoke particles, of average diameter 1/1000 mm.
    C) gas vapor of individual molecules of hydrogen sulfide and sulfur dioxide from Io's volcanoes.
    D) icy, reflective rocks, averaging about 1 cm in diameter but with wide variation in size.
    Ans: B   Section: 14-10

123. A manned space mission to Saturn some time in the future places an observer in a spacecraft within the its ring system. What motions would this observer see between the ring particles and the spacecraft?
    A)   Particles orbiting farther from the planet would be traveling faster and would overtake the spacecraft, while particles closer to the planet would be moving slower and would be overtaken by the spacecraft.
    B)   All particles would be moving with the same orbital speed and would travel around the planet together with the spacecraft, because the motions of particles and spacecraft are all governed by gravity.
    C)   The particles would move in ellipses and would therefore sometimes move ahead of and at other times fall behind the spacecraft.
    D)   Particles closer to the planet would overtake the spacecraft, while particles farther from the planet would be overtaken by the spacecraft following Kepler's laws.
    Ans: D   Section: 14-10

124. The particles in Saturn's rings
    A)   move in circular orbits, with the outer particles moving fastest because they are farthest from the planet.
    B)   all move as if they are one solid disk.
    C)   revolve in different directions depending on the distance from the planet.
    D)   move in circular Keplerian orbits, the inner particles moving fastest.
    Ans: D   Section: 14-10

125. How does the orbital period P of particles moving around the rings of Saturn depend on their distance R from the center of the planet?
    A) P^2 is proportional to R^3.
    B) P is proportional to $1/R^2$.
    C) P is constant for all R, because the rings move as a solid disk.
    D) P increases directly with R.
    Ans: A   Section: 14-10 and Box 4-4

126. Which of the following describes the motions of the particles in the rings of Saturn?
    A)   Each moves in almost circular Keplerian orbit around the planet.
    B)   They move in zigzag patterns within the ring system because of interaction with the major moons.
    C)   They move in randomly oriented elliptical orbits and collide frequently with each other.
    D)   They all move in concert as if they were a solid sheet because of electrostatic interaction.
    Ans: A   Section: 14-10

127. There are two main rings of Saturn, the outer A ring and the inner B ring. How are the particles in these rings seen to move when examined (by Doppler effect of reflected sunlight) from Earth?
    A)   The speeds of the particles vary because of attraction by the Sun, such that A particles sometimes move faster, while at other times B particles move faster.
    B)   Particles in the A ring move faster than those in the B ring, because they are farther from the planet.
    C)   Particles in the A ring move more slowly than those in the B ring.
    D)   The speeds of the particles in all rings are the same, because mutual gravitational forces between them ensure that they move as a solid disk.
    Ans: C   Section: 14-10

128. How and by whom was it FIRST determined that the rings of Saturn must be made up of a myriad of small particles, all separately orbiting Saturn in a wide, flat plane?
    A)   Astronomers at JPL and NASA found from photographs by the *Voyager 1* spacecraft that the rings were composed of thousands of tiny ringlets, with particles orbiting even in the Cassini division.
    B)   Sir George Airy observed that wave-like brightenings propagated through the rings in the direction of rotation, as could be true only if the rings were composed of interacting particles.
    C)   James Keeler observed that the Doppler shift in reflected sunlight increased inward across the rings, whereas if the rings rotated as a solid body the Doppler shift should increase outward.
    D)   James Clerk Maxwell calculated that no material could be strong enough to withstand the differential gravitational forces of Saturn on the rings if they were solid.
    Ans: D   Section: 14-10

129. The size distribution of particles in the rings of the Jovian planets is
    A)   from pebble-sized fragments to objects a few meters in diameter with significant amounts of fine dust particles in some rings.
    B)   a mixture of gas (mostly hydrogen) and dust grains, none larger than about 1 mm across.
    C)   individual bodies varying in size from 10 m to 1 km across, with no smaller components.
    D)   only dust and smoke-like particles.
    Ans: A   Section: 14-10

130. The particles in Saturn's rings are composed of
    A)   a mixture of iron and nickel.
    B)   water ice or rock coated with water ice.
    C)   ammonia and methane ice, possibly with rocky centers.
    D)   rocks with the reflectivity of dark asphalt.
    Ans: B   Section: 14-10

131. The composition of Saturn's rings is
    A)   particles of methane and ammonia ice.
    B)   small grains of rock.
    C)   sodium and sulfur ions.
    D)   water ice or ice-coated rock.
    Ans: D   Section: 14-10

132. The Roche limit around a planet is defined as
    A)   the distance beyond which the orbital velocity of a body in a Keplerian orbit is
          greater than the escape velocity and matter is no longer captured by the planet.
    B)   the distance inside which a solid satellite (e.g., a fragment of rock) will be pulled
          apart by tidal forces.
    C)   the outer extent of the magnetic field of the planet, or the magnetospheric
          boundary.
    D)   the distance inside which relative tidal forces will overcome the mutual
          gravitational forces of a group of particles.
    Ans: D   Section: 14-10

133. The reason why the individual particles within Saturn's rings have not combined
     together by mutual gravitational attraction to form one or two moons is that
    A)   the gravitational force from the Sun is sufficient to prevent coalescence.
    B)   tidal distortion forces from the planet are greater than the mutual gravity between
          the particles.
    C)   the excess heating from Saturn has melted the ice on the rocks so that the rocks
          will no longer stick together.
    D)   they are moving too fast to stick together even if they bump into one another.
    Ans: B   Section: 14-10

134. The rings of Saturn are composed of very many small particles because
    A)   they are made up of ice and ice-coated rocks, which break up easily in sunlight.
    B)   they are inside the Roche limit of Saturn, where tidal forces are stronger than the
          mutual gravitational forces between particles.
    C)   they were formed by the impact of a fast-moving asteroid on a large moon, which
          broke up into very many pieces.
    D)   they were spun out of the planet under its rapid rotation over a long period of
          time.
    Ans: B   Section: 14-10

135. The reason why boulder-sized moonlets are able to orbit within the Roche limit in Saturn's rings without being destroyed is that
    A) billions of years of alternate freezing and thawing as they pass from sunlight into Saturn's shadow and out again has given them an iron-hard crust of ice.
    B) the gravitational forces between the different parts of the moonlet are greater than the tidal forces pulling them apart.
    C) they are too small for tidal forces to operate on them effectively.
    D) the chemical bonds between their atoms and molecules are greater than the tidal forces pulling them apart.
    Ans: D   Section: 14-10

136. The physical structure of Saturn's rings is
    A) a thin, solid ring of rock and ice that is partly transparent.
    B) hot, ionized gas in a current sheet within the planet's magnetosphere.
    C) a thin but extensive gas cloud over the equator.
    D) a sequence of many hundreds of separate rings made of ice and rock particles.
    Ans: D   Section: 14-11

137. The rings of Saturn are seen by
    A) fluorescence, a glow produced by photochemistry when material is illuminated by solar UV light and/or high-speed cosmic particles.
    B) emitted light from the molecules of the material of the rings, such as methane, ammonia, and so on.
    C) reflected and scattered sunlight.
    D) reflected light from Saturn, since we can see them at night.
    Ans: C   Section: 14-11

138. What basic optical process makes the rings of Saturn visible to observers upon Earth?
    A) refraction of sunlight by ice crystals
    B) scattering of sunlight
    C) absorption of sunlight, making the rings appear dark against the bright sunlit planet
    D) self-emission of light from atoms of the ring material under UV excitation
    Ans: B   Section: 14-11

139. Mimas, the inner large moon of Saturn, orbits the planet at what distance compared to the rings of Saturn? (See Fig. 14-21, Freedman and Kaufmann, *Universe*, 7th ed.)
    A) outside the main ring system
    B) just on the inner edge of the main ring system
    C) in the Cassini division, between the A and B rings
    D) just above the planet's surface, well inside the ring system
    Ans: A   Section: 14-11

140. Some astronomers suspect that Saturn's satellite Enceladus could be heated enough by tidal flexing to produce active geysers of water on its surface, in a mechanism similar to that operating on Jupiter's satellite Io. Which one of the following statements is a correct observational fact supporting this conjecture?
    A)   A strong electric current flows from Enceladus to Saturn along Saturn's magnetic lines of force.
    B)   Enceladus is a "shepherd satellite" for the braided F ring, which could be made up of ice particles from the geysers.
    C)   Active volcanoes were photographed on Enceladus by the *Voyager* spacecraft.
    D)   Enceladus orbits inside the faint E ring, which may be made up of ice particles from the geysers.
    Ans: D   Section: 14-11

141. Which one of the following is *not* a suspected source of at least some of the particles that make up Saturn's rings?
    A)   ancient material that failed to accrete into satellites
    B)   material ejected from volcanic eruptions
    C)   debris from collisions between satellites and asteroids or comets
    D)   water from geysers on the Saturnian moon Enceladus
    Ans: B   Section: 14-11

142. The *Pioneer 2* and *Voyager 1* and *2* spacecrafts discovered four new rings of Saturn—the D, F, G, and E rings. How do these four rings compare to each other?
    A)   The F and G rings are narrow, the D and E rings are broad and diffuse.
    B)   The D, F, and G rings are narrow, the E ring is broad and diffuse.
    C)   All four rings are very faint, broad, and diffuse.
    D)   All four rings are very narrow.
    Ans: A   Section: 14-12 and Figure 14-21

143. The Saturnian satellite Pan moves along the Encke gap. Suppose a rock is orbiting within the gap at an orbital radius slightly smaller than that of Pan. Which one of the following is a correct description of the interaction between Pan and the electrical system?
    A)   Pan catches up to and passes the rock. As it does so it pulls back on the rock, slowing it and causing it to move in an orbit with a larger radius.
    B)   Pan catches up to and passes the rock. As it does so it pulls back on the rock, slowing it and causing it to move in an orbit with a smaller radius.
    C)   The rock catches up to and passes Pan. As it does so Pan pulls itself forward, making it move faster and causing it to move into an orbit with a larger radius.
    D)   The rock catches up to and passes Pan. As it does so Pan pulls itself forward, making it move faster and causing it to move into an orbit with a smaller radius.
    Ans: D   Section: 14-12

144. The main gravitational effect that organizes the particles in the rings of Saturn into specific orbits is
    A)   the complex gravitational tidal effects of the planet and the Sun on the ring particles.
    B)   collisions between the major moons of the planets and the ring particles at the same orbital distance, clearing gaps in the rings.
    C)   the perturbing effects of neighboring planets, such as Jupiter and Neptune.
    D)   the perturbing effects of major and minor moons or satellites whose orbital periods are related to those of the ring particles by simple ratios (e.g., 2:1, 3:2).
    Ans: D   Section: 14-12

145. The major gaps in the rings of Saturn are most likely caused by
    A)   mutual gravitational interactions between the multitude of particles in the rings.
    B)   the major moons of Saturn, which move in these gaps and sweep out the ring material.
    C)   the intervention of a massive body, which moved through the rings in their early history, leaving the gaps.
    D)   the combined gravitational forces of Saturn and its major moons, which deflect the paths of particles which stray into the gaps.
    Ans: D   Section: 14-12

146. What is the Cassini division?
    A)   the layer of relatively clear air separating Saturn's upper cloud deck from the middle cloud deck.
    B)   the boundary between the bright B ring and the faint C ring in Saturn's rings.
    C)   a wide, dark gap in Saturn's rings.
    D)   a major gap in the asteroid belt.
    Ans: C   Section: 14-12

147. How was the Cassini division created in Saturn's rings?
    A)   A small moon orbited within the division, clearing particles from the gap.
    B)   One of Saturn's satellites exerted a resonant pull on particles in the division, clearing a gap.
    C)   An intense region of high-energy electrons in Saturn's magnetosphere at that distance eroded the particles from the gap.
    D)   The rings simply formed that way in the ancient past.
    Ans: B   Section: 14-12

148. The relationship between the Saturnian moon Mimas and the Cassini division in the rings of Saturn is that
    A)   Mimas's circular orbital distance is twice the radius of the Cassini division.
    B)   Mimas passes through the rings of Saturn at the position of the Cassini division on its elliptical orbit, thereby disrupting the rings at this position.
    C)   Mimas's orbital period is exactly the same as particles that exist inside the Cassini division, thereby perturbing their orbits.
    D)   Mimas's orbital period is a factor of 2 greater than that of particles inside the Cassini division, thereby perturbing their orbits.
    Ans: D   Section: 14-12

149. Cassini's division in the rings of Saturn is thought to be due to gravitational forces from the moon Mimas. If the revolution period of Mimas is 22.6 hours, what would be the orbital period of any particles that exist within Cassini's division?
    A)   22.6 hours—Mimas moves within Cassini's division.
    B)   7.5 hours—1/3 of Mimas's period
    C)   45.2 hours—2 × Mimas's period
    D)   11.3 hours—1/2 of Mimas's period
    Ans: D   Section: 14-12

150. The gravitational effect that confines the particles of the F ring of Saturn to a narrow orbit is
    A)   the gravitational influence of two small shepherding satellites in orbits adjacent to the ring.
    B)   major gravitational distortion caused by Jupiter.
    C)   the pressure of the solar wind on these particles.
    D)   the gravitational effects of the major moons of Saturn, such as Mimas and Enceladus.
    Ans: A   Section: 14-12

151. The physical mechanism that is thought to control the motion and position of material in the narrow F ring around Saturn is the
    A)   complex gravitational interactions between the major moons of Saturn and the F ring material.
    B)   effect of sunlight focused on this material by the planet's atmosphere.
    C)   confining gravitational interactions between this material and two shepherd satellites.
    D)   effect of the planet's intense magnetic field on the material.
    Ans: C   Section: 14-12

152. Why is the F ring much narrower than the main rings?
    A)   The ring is constrained by Saturn's strong magnetic field.
    B)   There are not enough particles available to make a wider ring.
    C)   Two "shepherd" satellites focus the particles into a narrow ring.
    D)   The ring is in a stronger part of Saturn's gravitational field and cannot spread out any farther.
    Ans: C   Section: 14-12

153. Two tiny but significant satellites that follow nearly identical orbits around Saturn are called shepherd moons because they
    A)   appear to trigger volcanoes or geysers on the surfaces of larger moons by gravitational interaction.
    B)   clear particles from the Cassini division in Saturn's rings.
    C)   seem to trail streams of gases behind them, like comet tails.
    D)   appear to concentrate particles in the narrow but twisted F ring of Saturn.
    Ans: D   Section: 14-12

154. What process maintains the Encke gap in Saturn's rings?
    A)   The gap is simply the space between the A ring and an outer ring that formed from the breakup of a small satellite.
    B)   One of Saturn's satellites orbits Saturn twice for every three times that a particle in the gap would orbit, and exerts a resonant pull that clears the gap of particles.
    C)   A gravitational disturbance by Titan, Saturn's largest satellite, creates waves in the A ring, which sweep the region immediately outside the A ring clear of particles.
    D)   A small moon orbits within the gap and shepherds particles outward and inward away from the middle of the gap.
    Ans: D   Section: 14-12

Chapter 15: Jupiter and Saturn: Satellites of Fire and Ice

1. What conclusions were reached about the nature of the four Galilean moons in orbit around Jupiter when images were first sent back from exploring spacecraft?
   A) The moons were very different from our Moon in nature but very similar to each other.
   B) The moons all seemed to have surfaces of water ice, maybe with underlying oceans of water.
   C) The moons were fundamentally different from anything seen before and radically different from each other.
   D) The moons were all found to be similar to our Moon in surface color and details.
   Ans: C   Section: Introductory Section, Chapter 15

2. The outer three Galilean moons of Jupiter differ from Io, the innermost such moon, by having surfaces of
   A) water ice.   B) smoothly polished rock.   C) carbon dioxide.   D) sulfur.
   Ans: A   Section: Introductory Section, Chapter 15

3. The four giant moons of Jupiter were discovered by
   A) the *Pioneer* spacecraft.   B) Galileo.   C) Ptolemy.   D) Newton.
   Ans: B   Section: 15-1

4. The four major moons of Jupiter are collectively named after which early astronomer?
   A) Copernicus   B) Newton   C) Ptolemy   D) Galileo
   Ans: D   Section: 15-1

5. How many moons of Jupiter were seen by Galileo?
   A) 12   B) None—he was unable to see them with the naked eye.   C) 4   D) 1
   Ans: C   Section: 15-1

6. It has been known that Jupiter has moons since
   A) the time of the ancient Greeks.
   B) the *Voyager* flybys in 1979.
   C) Galileo turned his telescope to the sky in 1610.
   D) Isaac Newton predicted their existence in 1708.
   Ans: C   Section: 15-1

7. How many large, spherical moons are in orbit around Jupiter?
   A) none   B) 16   C) 11   D) 4
   Ans: D   Section: 15-1

8. Which spacecraft reached Jupiter most recently?
   A) *Ulysses*   B) *Magellan*   C) *Voyager 2*   D) *Galileo*
   Ans: D   Section: 15-1

9. Which of the following early telescope observations convinced Galileo that the Copernican heliocentric model provided a better explanation for the solar system than did the Greek geocentric model?
   A)   sunspots on the Sun and apparent solar rotation
   B)   the Moon changing in angular size as it orbits Earth
   C)   Venus changing in angular size and apparent shape with time
   D)   Moons seen to be orbiting another planet, Jupiter, rather than Earth
   Ans: D   Section: 15-1

10. Which of the following motions is seen to be characteristic of the four Galilean moons of Jupiter?
   A)   They orbit the planet in a plane carrying them over both the north and south poles of Jupiter.
   B)   They orbit the planet in the opposite direction to the planet's rotation.
   C)   They each keep the same face toward the Sun at all times.
   D)   They each keep the same face toward the planet at all times.
   Ans: D   Section: 15-1

11. How many of the large Galilean satellites are in synchronous rotation around Jupiter (always turning the same face toward Jupiter)?
   A) all 4   B) only Io   C) the inner 3   D) the inner 2
   Ans: A   Section: 15-1

12. What is significant about the rotational and revolutional motions of the Galilean moons of Jupiter?
   A)   synchronous rotation with one face always pointed toward the planet
   B)   nonsynchronous rotation with independent periods of rotation and revolution, and spin axes perpendicular to their orbit
   C)   nonsynchronous rotation with axes of rotation in any direction with respect to their orbital plane
   D)   synchronous rotation with one face always pointed toward the Sun
   Ans: A   Section: 15-1

13. Brightness variations of Jupiter's moons as they orbit the planet indicate that the relation between the spin around their axes and their orbital motions is that the
   A)   moons do not rotate at all while orbiting the planet.
   B)   moons' rotation is controlled by the gravitational influence of the Sun, and they always keep one face toward it, producing the observed brightness variations.
   C)   moons rotate on their axes independently of their orbital motion.
   D)   moons rotate exactly once per orbital period.
   Ans: D   Section: 15-1

14. Because of mutual gravitational forces between the moons and the planet, the orbital periods of the three inner Galilean moons of Jupiter are in the ratio
    A) 1:2:3.   B) 1:10:100.   C) 1:1:1—equal orbital periods.   D) 1:2:4.
    Ans: D   Section: 15-1

15. If the orbital period of Io, the innermost Galilean moon of Jupiter, is 1.77 days, what is the rotation period around its own axis?
    A)   3.54 days—twice the orbital period
    B)   1.77 days
    C)   1.18 days—2/3 of the orbital period
    D)   5.31 days—three times the orbital period
    Ans: B   Section: 15-1

16. What is the relationship between the orbital periods of the four Galilean satellites of Jupiter?
    A)   1:2:4:8—Europa takes twice as long to orbit Jupiter as Io, Ganymede takes twice as long as Europa, and Callisto takes twice as long as Ganymede.
    B)   1:2—Europa takes twice as long to orbit Jupiter as Io, but there is no simple integer relationship between Callisto, Ganymede, and Europa.
    C)   The periods appear to be random, with no simple relationship between them.
    D)   1:2:4—Europa takes twice as long to orbit Jupiter as Io, and Ganymede takes twice as long as Europa, but there is no simple integer relationship between Callisto and Ganymede.
    Ans: D   Section: 15-1

17. If the orbital period of Jupiter's moon Ganymede is 7.15 days, what would be the view from a point on its surface at the equator?
    A)   Jupiter and the Sun would rise and set with a period of about 7.15 days.
    B)   Jupiter, if visible, would always remain at the same point in the sky, but the Sun would rise and set with a period of about 7.15 days.
    C)   The Sun, if visible, would always be at the same point in the sky, but Jupiter would rise and set with a period of about 7.15 days.
    D)   The Sun and Jupiter would remain fixed in the sky above Ganymede.
    Ans: B   Section: 15-1

18. In terms of the relationship between the period P and radius a of their orbits around the planet, how do the moons of Jupiter behave?
    A) The moons do not obey the Keplerian relation $P^2 = ka^3$, because they orbit Jupiter and not the Sun.
    B) They obey the Keplerian relation, $P^2 = ka^3$, in which k is the same for planetary motion around the Sun, because it is a universal constant.
    C) They follow a Keplerian relationship, $P^2 = ka^3$, where k is a constant that is different from the relation governing planetary motion around the Sun.
    D) The moons do not obey the Keplerian relation $P^2 = ka^3$, because their motion about Jupiter is affected by Jupiter's motion about the Sun.
    Ans: C   Section: 15-1

19. In describing the observations of the movements of the moons of Jupiter, what is the difference between an occultation and an eclipse?
    A) An occultation is the passage of the moon into Jupiter's shadow, whereas an eclipse is the disappearance of the moon behind the planet.
    B) There is no difference—these terms both describe the disappearance of the moon behind the planet.
    C) An occultation is the passage of the moon in front of the planet, whereas an eclipse is the disappearance of the moon behind the planet.
    D) An occultation is the disappearance of the moon behind the planet, whereas an eclipse is the passage of the moon into Jupiter's shadow.
    Ans: D   Section: 15-1

20. The following planets and satellites of planets are, in increasing order of size (with Europa being one of the major moons of Jupiter),
    A) Moon, Europa, Mars, Mercury.   C) Europa, Mercury, Moon, Mars.
    B) Mercury, Moon, Europa, Mars.   D) Europa, Moon, Mercury, Mars.
    Ans: D   Section: 15-1

21. It is rare to see Jupiter's Galilean moons occult one another. Why is such an event seen only rarely?
    A) The moons are very small and move very rapidly, so the occultation happens very quickly and it is easy to miss.
    B) The orbits of these moons are in different planes, so the moons themselves are rarely along our line of sight at the same time.
    C) The orbits of these moons all lie very nearly in the same plane, but the Earth only occasionally crosses this plane.
    D) The occultations occur most often when the moons are on the far side of Jupiter, not visible from Earth.
    Ans: C   Section: 15-1

22. Of the three types of spacecraft—*Pioneer*, *Voyager*, and *Galileo*—that have visited Jupiter, which was placed in orbit around the planet?
    A)   none of them; they all provided fly-by views as they traveled to other planets
    B)   *Pioneer*
    C)   *Voyager*
    D)   *Galileo*
    Ans: D   Section: 15-2

23. The following planets and satellites of planets are, IN ORDER OF DECREASING DENSITY (Io and Europa are two of the major moons of Jupiter),
    A)   Mercury, Io, Moon, Europa.   C)   Moon, Mercury, Io, Europa.
    B)   Mercury, Moon, Io, Europa.   D)   Europa, Mercury, Moon, Io.
    Ans: A   Section: 15-2 and Table 15-1

24. What has proven to be the best method for measuring the mass of a Galilean moon of Jupiter?
    A)   observing its orbital motion around Jupiter and applying Kepler's Laws
    B)   measuring the density of material using a lunar lander vehicle and multiplying this density value by the moon's volume
    C)   measuring the mutual gravitational disturbances of the orbits of neighboring moons by the moon
    D)   observing the slight changes in the motion of a spacecraft caused by gravitational force, as the spacecraft passed near the moon
    Ans: D   Section: 15-2

25. The densities of the four Galilean satellites of Jupiter are
    A)   all low, typical of rock and ice, because they formed in the outer solar system.
    B)   very low because, as with Jupiter, they are composed mostly of hydrogen.
    C)   high (rocky) for the two inner satellites because they formed close to Jupiter, low (rock and ice) for the two outer satellites because they formed farther away from Jupiter.
    D)   all high, typical of rock, because they are planetary satellites (similar to our Moon).
    Ans: C   Section: 15-2

26. The average densities of the Galilean moons of Jupiter follow which pattern with increasing distance from the planet?
    A)   Average density is the same for all moons, because they were made from the same material.
    B)   Average increases with distance from the planet.
    C)   Averge density shows NO pattern with distance, the highest-density moon being Ganymede, the largest moon.
    D)   Average density decreases with distance from the planet.
    Ans: D   Section: 15-2

27. The inner two Galilean satellites of Jupiter differ from the outer two by having
    A)   much higher average densities.
    B)   almost the same average density, but much older, more heavily cratered surfaces.
    C)   much lower average densities.
    D)   almost the same average density, but much younger, less-cratered surfaces.
    Ans: A   Section: 15-2

28. What observation leads to the conclusion that the two outer Galilean moons of Jupiter
    are composed of roughly equal parts of rock and water ice?
    A)   Their densities are very low compared to other objects of comparable size such as
          our Moon or Mercury.
    B)   Their highly variable and localized magnetic fields closely resemble that of a
          mixture of iron rocks and water ice.
    C)   Their rotations show variations which are thought to be due to changes in shape,
          and this could only happen if they were composed of a loose mixture of rocks
          embedded in the flexible ice.
    D)   Images of their surfaces show equal parts of rock and ice.
    Ans: A   Section: 15-2

29. The three outer Galilean satellites of Jupiter—Europa, Ganymede, and Callisto—all
    appear to have cores of rock. In addition to rocky material, the major constituent of
    these satellites seems to be ices of
    A) H_2O B) CO_2 C) NH_3 D) CH_4
    Ans: A   Section: 15-2

30. The four Galilean moons of Jupiter do not all have the same mean density because
    A)   heat from Jupiter prevented ice from forming at the locations of the inner moons.
    B)   heat from the Sun prevented ice from forming in the outer part of the "Jovian
          Nebula," from which the moons formed.
    C)   the larger moons are more gravitationally compressed.
    D)   the moons formed at different distances from the Sun and were later captured by
          Jupiter.
    Ans: A   Section: 15-3

31. In what important way does the Jupiter-moon system resemble a miniature solar system, perhaps providing a hint to the initial formation of both systems?
    A)   The reflectivity of their surfaces decreases, the farther away they are from the central object, because the nearer objects have thicker clouds around them.
    B)   Average density of objects decreases as distance increases from the central object, because the heat from this object would have melted and evaporated the volatile low-density ices from the closer objects.
    C)   Average density of objects increases the farther away they are from the central object, because this central object can attract high-density material over a greater range of distances than for low-density material.
    D)   The masses of objects increase as distance increases from the central object, because the probability of accretion of small objects into larger objects increases with distance.
    Ans: B   Section: 15-3

32. In composition and density
    A)   Io and Europa are more like Mars, whereas Ganymede and Callisto are more like Jupiter.
    B)   Io and Europa are more like Jupiter, whereas Ganymede and Callisto are more like Mars.
    C)   Io and Callisto are more like Mars, whereas Europa and Ganymede are more like Jupiter.
    D)   Io and Callisto are more like Jupiter, whereas Europa and Ganymede are more like Mars.
    Ans: A   Section: 15-3

33. Our solar system might have become a double star system if Jupiter had been formed with enough mass to undergo nuclear fusion. Approximately what percent of the Sun's mass would Jupiter have needed for this to happen? The mass of the Sun is 2.0×10^{30} kg.
    A) 0.08   B) 0.8   C) 8   D) 80
    Ans: C   Section: 15-3

34. Which satellite of Jupiter is volcanically active?
    A) Europa   B) Ganymede   C) Callisto   D) Io
    Ans: D   Section: 15-4

35. The most geologically active object in the planetary system at the present time is
    A) Io, a moon of Jupiter.   B) the Earth's Moon.   C) the Earth.   D) Mars.
    Ans: A   Section: 15-4

36. The most active volcanic object in the solar system is
    A)   Earth, with many continuously active volcanoes and numerous earthquakes.
    B)   Io, the inner Galilean moon of Jupiter.
    C)   Venus, its high surface temperature indicating molten lava while its cloud cover is made up of volcanic gases.
    D)   The Moon, where volcanism is causing many new craters per year.
    Ans: B   Section: 15-4

37. What characteristic of Jupiter's moon Io makes it different from any other known satellite in the solar system?
    A)   It has geyser-like plumes of nitrogen gas.
    B)   It is volcanically active.
    C)   It has a permanent, dense atmosphere which totally obscures the solid surface.
    D)   Its surface shows uncratered, flooded regions (now frozen) and other signs of geologically recent activity involving water.
    Ans: B   Section: 15-4

38. How would "Interplanetary Travel" advertise a holiday on Jupiter's satellite Io?
    A)   Glaciers galore for your hiking pleasure under star-studded skies!
    B)   Hot and dry—never rains—beautiful sulfurous skies!
    C)   Exquisite ethane lakes, hydrocarbons beyond your wildest dreams!
    D)   Largest number of volcanoes for your travel dollar anywhere in the Solar System!
    Ans: D   Section: 15-4

39. One of the most important sources of heat in the interiors of moons that orbit close to giant planets is
    A)   reflection of sunlight from the planet's surface onto the moons.
    B)   continuous tidal distortion from other moons and the planet.
    C)   absorption of thermal radiation from the planet.
    D)   decay of radioactive elements within the moons.
    Ans: B   Section: 15-4

40. The heating of the interior of the large Galilean moon Io of Jupiter, in order to produce volcanic activity, is probably caused by
    A)   its original heat of formation.
    B)   radioactive elements in its surface.
    C)   nuclear fission within its interior.
    D)   tidal distortion by Jupiter and its other moons.
    Ans: D   Section: 15-4

41. The heating of the interior of Io, the innermost Galilean moon of Jupiter, is caused by
    A)   continual bombardment by meteoroids attracted by Jupiter's enormous gravitational pull.
    B)   thermal heating from Jupiter, because Jupiter emits more radiation than it receives from the Sun.
    C)   the fact that Io moves inside Jupiter's magnetosphere, where the temperature is as high as anywhere in the solar system.
    D)   continuous tidal distortion by Jupiter and the other moons.
    Ans: D   Section: 15-4

42. The source of intense heating in the interior of Jupiter's moon Io, causing continuous and intense volcanic activity, is
    A)   tidal flexing and distortion, caused by Jupiter and the other large moons.
    B)   frictional heating as the solar wind impacts on the moon surface.
    C)   solar UV and visible radiation.
    D)   heat released by continuous shrinkage after creation, transforming potential gravitational energy to heat.
    Ans: A   Section: 15-4

43. Io, one of the major Jupiter moons, is undergoing extensive volcanic activity associated with interior heating that is caused by
    A)   original heat, caused by gravitational condensation at the moon's formation.
    B)   solar radiation and heat falling on the surface.
    C)   the impact of Jupiter's Van Allen particles on Io's surface.
    D)   tidal distortion, and internal friction because of flexing.
    Ans: D   Section: 15-4

44. Extensive volcanic activity observed on Jupiter's satellite Io is caused by
    A)   tidal stresses from Jupiter and the other Galilean moons.
    B)   "primordial" heat remaining from the release of gravitational energy during Io's formation.
    C)   frictional heating between the moon's mantle and crust during plate movement, driven by convection.
    D)   heat released by radioactivity in Io's core and mantle.
    Ans: A   Section: 15-4

45. The eruptions observed on Io are thought to most closely resemble
    A)   terrestrial midocean ridges, where upwelling molten rock pushes the crust apart.
    B)   geysers, where material is shot upward by the pressure of gas produced below the surface.
    C)   volcanoes, producing lava flows and columns of erupting silicate ash.
    D)   explosions, where material is thrown upward by a single burst and then falls back to the surface.
    Ans: B   Section: 15-4

46. Which of the following Earth-bound phenomena do "volcanoes" on Io, the innermost Galilean moon of Jupiter, most resemble in behavior?
    A)   undersea volcanoes, where hot lava produces explosive boiling of the water
    B)   mountain volcanoes such as Mount St. Helens, exhibiting rare but devastating explosions throwing material high into the atmosphere
    C)   lava-flow volcanoes occurring on the tops of mountains, such as those on Hawaii
    D)   regularly spouting geysers in relatively flat hotsprings areas
    Ans: D   Section: 15-4

47. The numerous small black spots on Jupiter's satellite Io appear to be
    A) impact craters.   B) rocky outcrops.   C) volcanic vents.   D) sulfur deposits.
    Ans: C   Section: 15-4

48. The major chemical constituent of the layers of material continuously being deposited on the surface of Io, a moon of Jupiter, by "volcanic" action is
    A) sulfur.   B) silicate dust and rock.   C) hydrogen.   D) water.
    Ans: A   Section: 15-4

49. Which chemical or chemicals appear to play a prominent role in the volcanoes of Io?
    A)   methane and ammonia   C)   sulfur and sulfur dioxide
    B)   molten lava   D)   water and steam
    Ans: C   Section: 15-4

50. What chemical substances are believed to be the source of the many colors seen on the surface of Io, the inner large satellite of Jupiter?
    A)   iron and iron oxides or rust
    B)   sulfur and sulfur compounds
    C)   organic (carbon) compounds discolored by solar ultraviolet light
    D)   impurities in a water-ice crust
    Ans: B   Section: 15-4

51. The "snow" that falls continuously on the surface of Io, the innermost Galilean moon of Jupiter, is composed of
    A)   water crystals.   C)   sulfur and sulfur dioxide.
    B)   ammonia crystals.   D)   methane crystals.
    Ans: C   Section: 15-4

52. Which gas is thought to provide the propulsive force that is responsible for the tremendous eruptions of material from Jupiter's innermost Galilean moon, Io?
    A)   steam, or heated water vapor   C)   sulfur in vapor form
    B)   carbon dioxide—CO_2 D)   sulfur dioxide—SO_2
    Ans: D   Section: 15-4

53. What is estimated to be the annual thickness of the layer of sulfur-laden material laid down by the "volcanoes" on Jupiter's Galilean moon Io?
    A) 1 meter   B) 1 centimeter   C) 10 meters   D) about 1 millimeter
    Ans: B   Section: 15-4

54. Which of the following are NOT seen on Jupiter's satellite Io?
    A) sulfur dioxide frost   B) volcanic plumes   C) lava flows   D) impact craters
    Ans: D   Section: 15-4

55. Why does the innermost Galilean moon of Jupiter, Io, not show a cratered surface, as expected from the appearance of equivalent-sized objects like our Moon, Mercury, and Mars?
    A)   The large gravitational force generated by Jupiter has diverted most objects away from Io.
    B)   The surface is completely covered by an ocean of water, partly frozen into ice, which will obviously not show craters.
    C)   Volcanic action recoats the surface regularly and continuously.
    D)   Dust storms triggered by heating from Jupiter have quickly filled in any craters.
    Ans: C   Section: 15-4

56. Why would you expect to see no craters, such as those on the Moon or Mars, on Io, the innermost Galilean moon of Jupiter?
    A)   because the surface is always reentering the planet's interior by subduction in rapid plate tectonic motion, similar to but faster than that on Earth
    B)   because continuous rainfall quickly erodes and washes away all trace of craters
    C)   because its liquid surface cannot maintain a crater, just as Earth's oceans cannot do
    D)   because volcanoes are continuously depositing new material on the surface
    Ans: D   Section: 15-4

57. Suppose you could stand on Io's surface on the end of its long axis. When Io is at that point in its orbit closest to Jupiter, you would see Jupiter along your meridian. Half an orbital period later you would again see Jupiter along your meridian. Where would Jupiter appear in your view *one quarter* of an orbital period after that? (Io's orbital and rotational motions are prograde.)
    A)   west of the meridian
    B)   east of the meridian
    C)   still on the meridian
    D)   on the opposite side of Io (and thus not visible)
    Ans: A   Section: 15-4

58. What peculiar feature accompanies Io in its orbit around Jupiter?
    A)   a torus or ring of ionized sulfur, oxygen, atoms, and electrons
    B)   an auroral storm in the magnetosphere that always keeps pace with Io
    C)   a comet-like tail of rocks and dust, shining by reflected sunlight
    D)   a narrow ring of rocks and dust, Jupiter's ring, at about Io's orbital distance
    Ans: A   Section: 15-5

59. How is the Io plasma torus formed?
    A)   Io's motion through Jupiter's magnetosphere creates currents of electrons and
          charged particles in a loop between Io and Jupiter's north and south magnetic
          poles.
    B)   Io disturbs Jupiter's magnetosphere, causing magnetospheric charged particles to
          collect in a ring around Io's orbit.
    C)   Charged particles from Jupiter's magnetosphere ionize and eject atoms from Io's
          surface and from its volcanic plumes.
    D)   Io's volcanic plumes propel neutral atoms into orbit around Jupiter, where they are
          then ionized by high-energy charged particles in Jupiter's magnetosphere.
    Ans: C   Section: 15-5

60. What is the connection between Io and the intense outbursts of radio energy that
    emanate from the Jupiter system occasionally?
    A)   Material sprayed out of volcanoes on Io falls back to the moon's surface with
          sufficient energy to generate electromagnetic waves, most of which are radio
          emissions.
    B)   Ionized atoms and electrons from Io's volcanoes form an electrical circuit between
          Jupiter's magnetosphere and Io, and these electrons generate radio waves as they
          spiral in the magnetic field of Jupiter.
    C)   Volcanic material becomes ionized and forms a ring or torus along Io's orbit, and
          electric currents around this ring generate radio energy.
    D)   Lightning storms in clouds above volcanoes on Io cause the radio outbursts.
    Ans: B   Section: 15-5

61. What is the relationship between Io and the aurorae in Jupiter's atmosphere?
    A)   Io blocks the motion of charged particles in Jupiter's magnetosphere, creating a
          shadow, or dark spot, in Jupiter's aurorae.
    B)   Io's gravitational pull raises tides in Jupiter's atmosphere, and the atmosphere
          emits light (aurorae) as it rises and falls through Jupiter's strong magnetic field.
    C)   The motion of Jupiter's magnetic field past Io generates electric currents between
          Io and Jupiter, which create aurorae at specific locations near Jupiter's magnetic
          poles.
    D)   Sulfurous solid particles ejected from Io's volcanoes fall into Jupiter's atmosphere,
          where they are ionized and emit light.
    Ans: C   Section: 15-5

62. As a result of measurements by the *Galileo* spacecraft, what is now believed to be the internal structure of Io?
    A)   a thick mantle of rock over a core of iron and iron sulfide
    B)   a thick mantle of ice over a core of rock
    C)   entirely or almost entirely rock, with no evidence of ice or a differentiated metallic core
    D)   a thick crust of ice over a rocky mantle and a small, possibly molten, iron core
    Ans: A   Section: 15-5

63. Which of the Galilean moons of Jupiter are within Jupiter's magnetosphere?
    A)   only Io; the others are well outside the magnetosphere
    B)   only Io and Europa; the others are well outside the magnetosphere
    C)   all except Callisto, which is well outside the magnetosphere
    D)   all four of them
    Ans: D   Section: 15-5, Table 15-1, and Figure 14-11

64. Which of Jupiter's satellites is characterized by an exceptionally smooth, icy surface, few craters, and many streaks and cracks?
    A) Ganymede   B) Callisto   C) Io   D) Europa
    Ans: D   Section: 15-6

65. Jupiter's satellite Europa is believed to be made up of
    A)   ice, with possibly a small, rocky core.
    B)   rock only.
    C)   ice and rock mixed throughout in roughly equal proportions.
    D)   a metallic inner core and a rocky outer core covered by an "ocean" of ice.
    Ans: D   Section: 15-6

66. Which of the following objects in the solar system has the smoothest surface relative to its radius?
    A)   Io, the volcanic moon of Jupiter, whose surface is continuously coated with volcanic material
    B)   Earth, with its oceans and molten interior that both allow readjustment of the surface
    C)   Mercury, in view of the intense solar radiation that has melted and smoothed the surface
    D)   Europa, a moon of Jupiter coated with water ice
    Ans: D   Section: 15-6

67. Based on its average density of 3020 kg per cubic meter and its smooth surface, what is thought to be the internal structure of Jupiter's moon Europa?
    A) metallic core, rocky mantle, and a 100–200-km-thick ocean of ice and water
    B) almost entirely ice, with only a small, rocky core
    C) entirely rock except for a metallic core about 300 km in diameter
    D) half rock and half ice, with the rock forming the core and the ice forming the mantle
    Ans: A   Section: 15-6

68. The surface of Europa, one of the Galilean moons of Jupiter, appears to be covered with
    A) dark areas of older crust separated by lighter, grooved terrain.
    B) many ancient craters and maria.
    C) rugged mountain ranges and ancient volcanoes.
    D) a smooth layer of ice, crossed by many cracks.
    Ans: D   Section: 15-6

69. Europa, one of the Galilean satellites of Jupiter, has a surface consisting of
    A) rock, heavily cratered like the highlands of our Moon.
    B) an ancient, icy crust covered with numerous craters; no surface cracks or groove belts that would indicate internal activity.
    C) a relatively young, icy crust covered with a network of streaks and cracks, and only a few impact craters.
    D) an icy crust showing two interlocking types of terrain, one ancient and heavily cratered, the other younger with systems of parallel grooves.
    Ans: C   Section: 15-6

70. What does the surface of Europa, a moon of Jupiter, look like?
    A) entirely ice, with fractures and ridges going in every direction and no features more than about 100 m high
    B) entirely ice, with light and dark areas containing many impact craters and parallel ridges up to about 1 km high
    C) rocky and densely cratered, except for a few large, dark, relatively uncratered plains
    D) We don't know; the surface is hidden below a dense layer of clouds.
    Ans: A   Section: 15-6

71. What property is shared by the Earth and Europa, one of Jupiter's large moons?
    A) They have both been shown to harbor intelligent life in their oceans.
    B) They both have thick atmospheres of nitrogen and oxygen.
    C) Both have warm oceans of water.
    D) They are about the same physical size.
    Ans: C   Section: 15-6

72. On which other world in the solar system do we find evidence of ice rafts (now apparently frozen) similar in many respects to ice rafts in the Arctic Ocean?
    A) in the tropical regions of Saturn's satellite Titan
    B) on Pluto, in the equatorial region facing most directly toward the Sun
    C) on Mars, at the edges of the polar caps
    D) in the icy surface of Jupiter's satellite Europa
    Ans: D   Section: 15-6

73. What appears to have caused the extensive cracking and streaking of the surface of Europa?
    A) tidal flexing by Jupiter
    B) shrinking of the satellite as it cooled
    C) impacts by cometary debris
    D) expansion of the surface as the ice froze
    Ans: A   Section: 15-6

74. What physical mechanisms most probably caused the very long cracks and streaks that crisscross the surface of Europa, a moon of Jupiter?
    A) They are the tops of gigantic greenhouses built by inhabitants of Europa to protect their cucumber crops.
    B) They are frozen rivers which, in warmer times, flowed across the moon's surface.
    C) Volcanic eruptions caused lava flows which then froze in place.
    D) tidal flexing and cracking of the surface, with subsurface fluids gushing upward and freezing
    Ans: D   Section: 15-6

75. The origin of the very thin oxygen atmosphere around Europa is
    A) from electrolysis of water into O_2 and H_2 in the ocean under the ice, as a result of intense electrical currents induced by Europa's motion through Jupiter's magnetic field.
    B) from photosynthesis in primitive plant life living in the deep oceans beneath the ice surface.
    C) the dissociation of water molecules by solar UV radiation.
    D) the breakup of water molecules by the impact of ionized material from Jupiter's magnetosphere.
    Ans: D   Section: 15-6

76. The weak and variable magnetic field measured by the *Galileo* spacecraft on Europa is generated by
    A)   its magnetized solid iron core.
    B)   electrical currents between the moon and Jupiter, through the conducting magnetosphere.
    C)   the motion of molten iron in Europa's core.
    D)   electrical currents in the ocean water, induced by Europa's motion through Jupiter's intense magnetic field.
    Ans: D   Section: 15-6

77. Which of the following features have NOT been found on Europa, one of the Galilean satellites of Jupiter?
    A) mountains   B) craters   C) ice   D) cracks running along the surface
    Ans: A   Section: 15-6

78. Europa does not generate a satellite-wide magnetic field of its own. Which is not a factor in Europa's lack of a magnetic field?
    A)   Europa is very small in comparison to most bodies that produce their own magnetic fields.
    B)   Europa rotates slowly on its axis.
    C)   Europa does not have a large, molten iron core.
    D)   Europa has no electrically conducting liquid within it.
    Ans: D   Section: 15-6

79. Where in the universe would you look for Ganymede?
    A)   near Jupiter, because it is one of Jupiter's moons
    B)   around the planet Mars, because it is one of the moons of Mars
    C)   on the Moon, because it is one of the largest craters
    D)   in the asteroid belt
    Ans: A   Section: 15-7

80. The largest satellite (moon) in our planetary system is
    A)   the Earth's Moon.   C)   Phobos, one of the moons of Mars.
    B)   Titan, a moon of Saturn.   D)   Ganymede, a moon of Jupiter.
    Ans: D   Section: 15-7

81. The most massive planetary satellite in the solar system is
    A)   the Earth's Moon.   C)   Jupiter's satellite Europa.
    B)   Jupiter's satellite, Ganymede.   D)   Saturn's satellite Titan.
    Ans: B   Section: 15-7

82. How are the relative ages of the different types of terrain on Ganymede estimated?
    A)   The lighter the coloration, the older the terrain.
    B)   The colder the surface, the older the terrain.
    C)   The denser the cratering, the older the terrain.
    D)   The smoother the surface, the older the terrain.
    Ans: C   Section: 15-7

83. Ganymede, one of the large Galilean satellites of Jupiter, is very different from the Earth, but in which one of the following ways does Ganymede RESEMBLE Earth?
    A)   Like Earth, but unlike all other moons in the solar system, Ganymede has a dense atmosphere.
    B)   Based on its density, Ganymede appears to have a large iron core surrounded by a thick rocky mantle directly beneath its icy crust.
    C)   Ganymede has active volcanoes.
    D)   Ganymede appears to have had tectonic activity at some time in its past.
    Ans: D   Section: 15-7

84. Ganymede, one of the Galilean satellites of Jupiter, has a surface consisting of
    A)   rock, heavily cratered like the highlands of our Moon.
    B)   an icy crust showing two interlocking types of terrain, one ancient and heavily cratered, the other younger with systems of parallel grooves.
    C)   an ancient, icy crust covered with numerous craters; no surface cracks or groove belts that would indicate internal activity.
    D)   a relatively young, icy crust covered with a network of streaks and cracks and only a few impact craters.
    Ans: B   Section: 15-7

85. The surfaces of Ganymede and Callisto appear to consist of
    A)   sulfur.
    B)   ices of methane, ammonia, and water.
    C)   rocks and lava.
    D)   water ice.
    Ans: D   Section: 15-7

86. The surface of Ganymede, a Galilean satellite of Jupiter, is characterized by
    A)   dark areas of ancient terrain and bright, younger, but still very old areas with many folded ridges indicating tectonic activity on Ganymede in the distant past.
    B)   multicolored deposits of sulfur and sulfur compounds, with several lava lakes and active volcanic plumes.
    C)   dark areas of ancient terrain, and bright areas with almost no craters and many signs of recent tectonic activity such as fracturing, creation of ice rafts and eruptions of icy lava.
    D)   bright, eroded and ancient terrain broken by darker and younger areas which show signs of tectonic activity in the past, such as water or slush volcanoes and faulting along subduction zones.
    Ans: A   Section: 15-7

87. What appears to be the origin of the light, grooved terrain on the surface of Ganymede?
    A)   cracking of the surface due to shrinkage of the satellite as it cooled
    B)   impacts by cometary debris
    C)   tidal flexing by Jupiter
    D)   expansion and cracking of the surface as the ice froze
    Ans: D   Section: 15-7

88. The structure of Ganymede, a Galilean satellite of Jupiter, is thought to be
    A)   a thick crust of ice, a rocky mantle, and metallic core.
    B)   about half rock and half ice, with the rock at the center and the ice outside.
    C)   a large rocky core with a thin layer (100 km thick) of ice and water over it.
    D)   mostly or entirely rock with no firm evidence of an iron core, but with active volcanoes on its surface.
    Ans: A   Section: 15-7

89. Which of the Galilean moons of Jupiter appears to have a significant and permanent magnetic field?
    A) Europa   B) Ganymede   C) Callisto   D) Io
    Ans: B   Section: 15-7

90. The permanent and stable magnetic field detected on Ganymede by the *Galileo* spacecraft indicates that this moon must have a source of internal heat to provide for the movement of electrically charged material. What is thought to be the source of this heat?
    A)   heat from the decay of radioactive materials
    B)   heat from the release of gravitational potential energy at the moon's original formation
    C)   remnant heat from tidal flexure caused when this moon moved in an elliptical orbit, earlier in its history
    D)   tidal heating by flexure at the present time from neighboring moons and Jupiter
    Ans: C   Section: 15-7

91. Which of the following statements describes the surface of Callisto, the outer Galilean moon of Jupiter?
    A)   dark, rocky surface with a thin ice frost which occasionally disappears by evaporation in sunlight
    B)   ammonia and methane ice surface, with methane clouds above it, making the moon appear very bright
    C)   sulfur-coated surface, with molten sulfur lakes and active volcanoes
    D)   ice-covered surface with dark coating, maybe of meteoritic dust or hydrocarbon material, making the moon appear dark
    Ans: D   Section: 15-7

92. The structure of Callisto, the outer Galilean satellite of Jupiter, is thought to be
    A)   a thick ice crust and a slushy mantle of ice and water over a core of rock.
    B)   mostly or entirely rock with no firm evidence of an iron core, and active volcanoes on its surface.
    C)   a large rocky core with a thin layer (100 km thick) of ice and water over it.
    D)   a jumbled mixture of about half rock and half ice.
    Ans: A   Section: 15-7

93. The surface of Callisto, the outer Galilean moon of Jupiter, can best be described as
    A)   relatively smooth, with a great many small impact craters and one large basin created by an asteroid impact.
    B)   very smooth, with a network of streaks and cracks and very few craters.
    C)   rough and mountainous, with evidence of volcanic or geyser-like activity.
    D)   relatively smooth, with many small craters but no evidence of large impacts.
    Ans: A   Section: 15-7

94. What features dominate the surface of Callisto, one of Jupiter's satellites?
    A)   volcanoes, lava lakes, and sulfur dioxide frost
    B)   cracks, streaks, and very few craters in an otherwise smooth, icy surface
    C)   craters, densely spread over the entire surface
    D)   old, dark and highly cratered polygons separated by younger, lighter, grooved terrain
    Ans: C   Section: 15-7

95. Callisto, the outer Galilean moon of Jupiter, has a surface consisting of
    A)   an icy crust showing two interlocking types of terrain, one ancient and heavily cratered, the other younger with systems of parallel grooves.
    B)   an ancient, icy crust covered with numerous craters and no surface cracks or groove belts that would indicate internal activity.
    C)   rock, heavily cratered like the highlands of our Moon.
    D)   a relatively young, icy crust covered with a network of streaks and cracks, and only a few impact craters.
    Ans: B   Section: 15-7

96. What have we learned about the atmospheres of the Galilean satellites of Jupiter?
    A)   None of these satellites has a permanent atmosphere.
    B)   Only Ganymede, the largest, has a permanent atmosphere of CO_2.
    C)   Ganymede has a thin atmosphere of CO_2, whereas Callisto has a thin atmosphere of O_2 and O_3.
    D)   Ganymede and Callisto have thin atmospheres, whereas Io has a thick atmosphere of sulfur compounds.
    Ans: C   Section: 15-7

97. Why do we suspect the existence of some liquid beneath the surface of Callisto?
    A)   The interior appears to be highly differentiated, suggesting the existence of residual heat from the moon's formation.
    B)   The moon is close enough to Jupiter (which emits more energy than it receives from the Sun) so that its interior should be warm enough to keep pure water liquid.
    C)   The tidal churning caused by the pull of Jupiter should keep the interior warm enough to keep pure water liquid.
    D)   There is evidence of an induced magnetic field caused by Callisto's passage through Jupiter's magnetosphere.
    Ans: D   Section: 15-7

98. The spacecraft Galileo and its predecessors left many questions about Callisto unanswered. Which of these is *not* an unanswered question?
    A)   Why does Callisto have few small (< 1 km) craters?
    B)   What is the origin of the blanket of dark, dusty material on Callisto's surface?
    C)   Is Callisto's interior warm or cold?
    D)   Does Callisto have an atmosphere?
    Ans: D   Section: 15-7

99. All of the following exist on Titan except:
    A) clouds.   B) volcanoes.   C) rain.   D) nitrogen in vapor form.
    Ans: B   Section: 15-8

100. Which of the following satellites of planets in our solar system has a significant, dense atmosphere?
    A)   Titan, a moon of Saturn   C)   Triton, a moon of Neptune
    B)   the Moon, of Earth   D)   Io, a moon of Jupiter
    Ans: A   Section: 15-8

101. Which of the moons of the giant planets is known to have a significant atmosphere?
    A)   Titan, a moon of Saturn   C)   Triton, a moon of Neptune
    B)   Callisto, a moon of Jupiter   D)   Europa, a moon of Jupiter
    Ans: A   Section: 15-8

102. Saturn's moon Titan is different from all other moons of planets because
    A)   lakes of water with floating icebergs are seen upon its surface.
    B)   it possesses a thick atmosphere.
    C)   its orbit carries it directly over both poles of the planet.
    D)   continuously erupting volcanoes are observed upon it.
    Ans: B   Section: 15-8

103. What characteristic of Saturn's satellite Titan makes it different from any other known satellite in the solar system?
    A)   Its surface is broken into heavily cratered and lightly cratered regions in a pattern similar to plate tectonics.
    B)   It has geyser-like plumes of nitrogen gas.
    C)   It is volcanically active.
    D)   It has a permanent, dense atmosphere.
    Ans: D   Section: 15-8

104. The major constituent of the atmosphere of Titan (the largest moon of Saturn) is
    A)   water vapor—H_2O.   C)   methane—CH_4.
    B)   carbon dioxide—CO_2.   D)   nitrogen—N_2.
    Ans: D   Section: 15-8

105. The composition of the atmosphere of Titan, a satellite of Saturn, is mostly
    A)   methane with small quantities of other gases.
    B)   nitrogen, methane, and other hydrocarbons.
    C)   carbon dioxide with small quantities of other gases.
    D)   methane, ammonia, and water vapor.
    Ans: B   Section: 15-8

106. How is nitrogen thought to have become the dominant gas in the atmosphere of the moon Titan?
    A)   from the breakup of ammonia into nitrogen and hydrogen, with the hydrogen being lost to space
    B)   from the collision of comets with the surface of Titan
    C)   It has been present from primordial times, when Titan first formed.
    D)   from outgassing through volcanic vents
    Ans: A   Section: 15-8

107. In what way was methane, CH_4, first discovered on Titan, the giant moon of Saturn?
    A)   by chemical "sniffers" carried by *Voyager 2* when it passed very close to Titan
    B)   spectroscopically, by noting specific absorptions in reflected sunlight
    C)   by detecting the light of burning methane spectroscopically, similar to that seen from oil or gas-well flares
    D)   by noting the formation on its surface of colored "ice," characteristic of methane ice
    Ans: B   Section: 15-8

108. Which chemical in the atmosphere of Titan (a moon of Saturn) appears to play the same role that water plays upon Earth in producing "rain" and forming lakes and streams at the temperature encountered on the moon?
A) ammonia—NH_3 B) ethane—C_2H_6 C) nitrogen—N_2 D) oxygen—O_2
Ans: B   Section: 15-8

109. What would be a typical weather forecast on Titan, Saturn's largest moon?
A)   dust storms and high winds in a thin CO_2 atmosphere
B)   turbulent winds in an ammonia, methane, and water vapor atmosphere, with dense clouds of ammonia compounds and water ice
C)   hydrocarbon fog and ethane rain in a nitrogen atmosphere
D)   occasional sulfur clouds and sulfur dioxide fog from volcanic eruptions
Ans: C   Section: 15-8

110. How would "Interplanetary Travel" advertise a holiday on Titan, one of the satellites of Saturn?
A)   The largest number of volcanoes for your travel dollar anywhere in the solar system!
B)   Exquisite ethane lakes, hydrocarbons beyond your wildest dreams!
C)   Glaciers galore for your hiking pleasure under star-studded skies!
D)   Hot and dry—never rains—beautiful sulfurous skies!
Ans: B   Section: 15-8

111. The surface temperature of Titan, the largest moon of Saturn, is
A)   368 K (+95°C).   C)   178 K (195°C).
B)   273 K (0°C).   D)   95 K (−178°C).
Ans: D   Section: 15-8

112. What is the atmospheric pressure at the surface of Titan, Saturn's largest satellite? (one atmosphere = air pressure at sea level on Earth)
A)   82 atmospheres, almost as much as on Venus
B)   1½ atmospheres, just a bit more than on Earth
C) 2.4×10^{-5} atmospheres, about half again that on Triton, Neptune's large moon
D)   0.023 atmospheres, about 1/3 of that on Mars
Ans: B   Section: 15-8

113. The atmospheric pressure at the surface of Titan, Saturn's largest satellite, is 1½ atmospheres (i.e., 1½ times the air pressure at sea level on Earth). How much mass is contained in the atmosphere above a square meter of Titan's surface compared to the mass above a square meter of Earth's surface?
    A)   2/3 as much as on Earth, because Titan has a smaller diameter and therefore a stronger gravitational pull than does Earth
    B)   0.92 times that on Earth, because Titan rotates faster than Earth, reducing the gravitational pull at the equator
    C)   1½ times that on Earth, because the atmospheric pressure is directly proportional to the mass of the atmosphere
    D)   ten times that on Earth, because Titan has less mass and therefore less gravity than does Earth
    Ans: D   Section: 15-8

114. What are the physical characteristics of the "other" (non-Galilean) satellites of Jupiter?
    A)   500 to 1000 km in diameter and irregular in shape
    B)   less than about 200 km in diameter and irregular in shape
    C)   all sizes up to 1500 km in diameter, the smaller ones irregular in shape and the larger ones spherical
    D)   100 to 500 km in diameter and spherical in shape
    Ans: B   Section: 15-9

115. Most of the satellites of Jupiter beyond the innermost eight appear to be
    A)   loose collections of small rocks, held together by self-gravity.
    B)   rocky or icy debris left over from the formation of the Jovian satellite system.
    C)   asteroids captured by Jupiter.
    D)   about the same size as our Moon or Mercury.
    Ans: C   Section: 15-9

116. For which of the following objects is the ORBITAL motion (direction of motion around the orbit) retrograde?
    A)   most of the satellites of Jupiter beyond the innermost eight
    B)   the Martian satellite Phobos
    C)   the four Galilean satellites of Jupiter
    D)   the planet Venus
    Ans: A   Section: 15-9

117. What observational facts lead to the conclusion that the small outer moons of Jupiter were captured by its gravitational field rather than being formed at the same time as the planet?
    A) They move in circular orbits in the planet's equatorial plane in the same direction as Jupiter's rotation.
    B) They move within the dust ring around Jupiter, above the planet's equator.
    C) They move in circular orbits above the planet's equator in a retrograde direction, opposite to that of Jupiter's rotation.
    D) They move in orbits that are steeply inclined to Jupiter's equator, many of them in a retrograde direction, opposite to Jupiter's rotation.
    Ans: D   Section: 15-9

118. Amalthea, the largest of the four innermost moons of Jupiter, has a distinct reddish color. What is the origin of this?
    A) material from volcanic plumes on Io
    B) iron oxide (rust) in the rocks on the surface (like Mars)
    C) colors produced in the aurora created when Amalthea passes through the intense magnetic field from Jupiter
    D) particles carried to Amalthea from Jupiter across the intense magnetic field tube connecting the two bodies
    Ans: A   Section: 15-9

119. Saturn's moon Titan has a size
    A) about the size of the moons of Mars.
    B) intermediate between Mercury and Mars.
    C) intermediate between Mercury and the Earth's moon.
    D) intermediate between Mars and Earth.
    Ans: B   Section: 15-10

120. Based on their average densities, the six moderate-sized satellites of Saturn are believed to be composed
    A) mostly of ice, with perhaps a small, rocky core.
    B) of about half rock and half ice.
    C) mostly of rock, with only a thin mantle of ice.
    D) mostly of liquid hydrogen.
    Ans: A   Section: 15-10

121. Some of Saturn's moderate-sized satellites (smaller than Titan) have peculiar surfaces in which their leading hemispheres (pointing ahead in the satellite's orbit) are distinctly different from their trailing hemispheres. Which of the following does not show this distinct patterning?
    A) Iapetus   B) Rhea   C) Enceladus   D) Dione
    Ans: C   Section: 15-10

122. The most striking characteristic observed on the surface of Iapetus, one of the outer satellites of Saturn, is
    A)   a brightness variation, its leading hemisphere being as dark as asphalt whereas its trailing hemisphere appears as bright as ice.
    B)   plumes of nitrogen gas rising from cracks in the icy surface, apparently as a result of geyser activity.
    C)   a crater so large that the impact that created it must have come close to shattering the satellite.
    D)   an interconnecting network of parallel grooves, indicating tectonic activity in geologically recent times.
    Ans: A   Section: 15-10

123. What feature of the Saturnian moon Enceladus makes it a unique object in our solar system?
    A)   It rotates about its axis about every 2 minutes.
    B)   It passes through the planet's ring system every orbit on its highly elliptical path.
    C)   It has the most reflective surface of all objects in the solar system.
    D)   It orbits its planet in a retrograde direction.
    Ans: C   Section: 15-10

124. Saturn's moon Tethys shows evidence of at least one large lava flow on its surface. Based on other characteristics of Saturn's satellites, what is the most probable composition of this lava?
    A)   a dense mixture of liquid ethane and several kinds of hydrocarbon polymers
    B)   liquid nitrogen with dissolved sulfur dioxide
    C)   molten silicate rock
    D)   a viscous fluid of water and ammonia
    Ans: D   Section: 15-10

125. What characteristics do Dione and Rhea, two of Saturn's satellites, share?
    A)   two distinctly different hemispheres, one heavily cratered and the other having a network of wispy markings
    B)   sparse crater over all regions photographed by *Voyager 2*, indicating relatively young surfaces
    C)   long, steep-sided troughs indicating expansion of the surface due to freezing of the satellites
    D)   two distinctly different hemispheres, one almost black and the other white like ice
    Ans: A   Section: 15-10

126. Where are Saturn's six moderately sized satellites in relation to the rings?
    A)   All are closer to Saturn than the main ring system.
    B)   Mimas is between the G ring and the E ring; the other five are within the boundaries of the E ring.
    C)   Enceladus and Tethys are within the boundaries of the E ring; Mimas is closer to Saturn than this, and the other three are outside the boundary of the E ring.
    D)   All are well outside the ring system.
    Ans: C   Section: 15-10 and Figure 14-21

Chapter 16: The Outer Worlds

1. The discoverer of the planet Uranus was
   A) Clyde Tombaugh.
   B) William Herschel.
   C) Galileo Galilei.
   D) Edmund Halley.
   Ans: B   Section: 16-1

2. How was Uranus discovered?
   A) by a careful search in the 1930s by an astronomer who was convinced it must be there
   B) by accident, by an astronomer conducting a sky survey
   C) by an astronomer studying old photographs of the sky, several years after they were taken
   D) by careful application of Newton's laws to the motion of other planets
   Ans: B   Section: 16-1

3. Which of the following planets was discovered by accident by an astronomer who was surveying the sky with his telescope but had no idea that he would discover a planet?
   A) Uranus   B) Neptune   C) Saturn   D) Pluto
   Ans: A   Section: 16-1

4. If Uranus has an orbital period of about 84 years, how far does it appear to move across our sky in one year?
   A) $0.23°$
   B) a very small angle because Uranus is a very long way away from Earth
   C) $43°$
   D) $4.3°$
   Ans: D   Section: 16-1

5. Using the best telescopes under the best observing conditions, the smallest angle in the sky that can be resolved from Earth's surface is approximately 0.1 arcsec. (You may wish to review the small-angle formula in Box 1-1 of Freedman and Kaufmann, *Universe,* 7th ed.) Consequently, the smallest feature that can be resolved at the distance of Uranus is about
   A) 1/400 of the diameter of Uranus.
   B) 1/4 of the diameter of Uranus.
   C) 4 times the diameter of Uranus.
   D) 1/40 of the diameter of Uranus.
   Ans: D   Section: 16-1 and Box 1-1

6. Which is the eighth planet from the Sun in order of increasing semimajor axis?
   A) Pluto   B) Saturn   C) Uranus   D) Neptune
   Ans: D   Section: 16-1 and Appendix 1

7. Neptune was discovered by
   A) the careful application of Newton's laws to the motion of other planets.
   B) an astronomer who was conducting a sky survey.
   C) a more precise theoretical prediction.
   D) a careful search by an astronomer in the 1930s who was convinced that one extra planet must be out there.
   Ans: A   Section: 16-1

8. When Couch Adams, the English student, and Le Verrier, the French astronomer, independently predicted the existence of Neptune on the basis of measured deviation of Uranus's motion by gravitational interaction, what factor ultimately led to Neptune's discovery by Galle at Berlin Observatory rather than by Challis at Cambridge, England, even though Challis was told of the prediction much earlier than Galle?
   A) better eyesight
   B) Galle used photography, while Challis had to rely on eye observation.
   C) better star charts
   D) better telescope
   Ans: C   Section: 16-1

9. How did the discovery of Neptune differ from the discoveries of Uranus and Pluto?
   A) Neptune's presence was first predicted using Newton's gravitational law to interpret deviations in the motion of another planet, whereas Uranus and Pluto were discovered during sky searches.
   B) Neptune was discovered by accident by an amateur astronomer, whereas Uranus and Pluto were both found by professional astronomers doing specific searches for a new planet.
   C) Neptune was found during a survey of the sky, whereas Uranus and Pluto were found after being predicted on the basis of their gravitational influence on the motions of neighboring planets, Saturn and Neptune, respectively.
   D) Neptune was discovered by photographic surveys of the sky, whereas Uranus and Pluto were found by visual searches.
   Ans: A   Section: 16-1 and 16-9

10. Which planet was discovered as a result of the detailed prediction of its position using Newton's gravitational theory to explain deviations in the motions of other planets?
    A) Pluto   B) Neptune   C) Mercury   D) Saturn
    Ans: B   Section: 16-1

11. The planet whose discovery was prefaced by accurate prediction using the measured deviations of other planets from regular orbits and the application of Newton's laws of mechanics, is
    A) Uranus.   B) Neptune.   C) Pluto.   D) Mercury.
    Ans: B   Section: 16-1

12. The shape and alignment of the orbit of Neptune is
    A) almost circular (eccentricity = 0.009), larger than the orbit of Uranus, and close to the ecliptic plane.
    B) almost circular (eccentricity = 0.009), smaller than the orbit of Uranus, and close to the ecliptic plane.
    C) almost circular (eccentricity = 0.009), but steeply inclined to the ecliptic plane (17°).
    D) very elliptical, such that its orbit occasionally carries it beyond Pluto's circular orbit, but in the ecliptic plane.
    Ans: A   Section: 16-1 and Table 16-1

13. The smallest angle in the sky that can be resolved from Earth's surface, using the best telescopes under the best observing conditions, is approximately 0.1 arcsec. (You may wish to review the small-angle formula in Box 1-1 of Freedman and Kaufmann, *Universe,* 7th ed.) The smallest feature that can be resolved at the distance of Neptune is therefore approximately
    A) 1/2 of the diameter of Neptune.   C) 20 times the diameter of Neptune.
    B) 1/200 of the diameter of Neptune.   D) 1/20 of the diameter of Neptune.
    Ans: D   Section: 16-1 and Box 1-1

14. Uranus is just visible as a naked eye object when seeing conditions are very good and when it is at
    A) superior conjunction.   C) opposition.
    B) inferior conjunction.   D) greatest elongation.
    Ans: C   Section: 16-1

15. The spacecraft that successfully photographed Uranus on a 1986 flyby mission was
    A) *Viking.*   B) *Voyager.*   C) *Magellan.*   D) *Galileo.*
    Ans: B   Section: 16-2

16. In its flyby of Uranus, *Voyager* spent many days imaging the planet, but it was able to photograph only the southern hemisphere of Uranus. Why was this?
    A) Uranus's rotation period was such that it kept the same face, the southern hemisphere, facing *Voyager* for the whole encounter.
    B) Because of Uranus's extreme axis tilt and the planet's position in its orbit, the northern hemisphere was pointed away from the Sun during the *Voyager* passage and was therefore in darkness for the whole time.
    C) The very long rotation period of Uranus meant that *Voyager* was not able to observe the planet for more than part of a rotation.
    D) *Voyager* passed by the side of the planet that contained the southern hemisphere, and Uranus's extreme axis tilt meant that planet rotation would never bring the other hemisphere into view.
    Ans: B   Section: 16-2

17. The major planet whose spin axis lies almost in its orbital plane is
    A) Neptune.   B) Mercury.   C) Uranus.   D) Mars.
    Ans: C   Section: 16-2

18. Which planet has its spin axis tilted 98° from the perpendicular to its orbital plane?
    A) Mercury   B) Neptune   C) Venus   D) Uranus
    Ans: D   Section: 16-2

19. One of the major planets has its spin axis lying almost in its orbital plane. Which planet is this?
    A) Saturn   B) Uranus   C) Neptune   D) Mars
    Ans: B   Section: 16-2

20. By what angle is the rotation axis of Uranus tilted from the vertical to its orbit?
    A)   less than 2°
    B)   almost 180°
    C)   24° (almost the same as the tilt of Earth)
    D)   98°
    Ans: D   Section: 16-2

21. The tilt of Uranus's axis was first deduced from observed orbital motions of its moons. For the deduction of this tilt to be correct, it was necessary to assume that
    A)   the moons moved in the ecliptic plane, or at least in the plane of the orbit of Uranus.
    B)   the moons passed over both north and south poles of the planet, thereby indicating the planet's spin axis.
    C)   the moons were not affected by the gravitational field of the Sun, which would force their orbits to deviate from the planet's equatorial plane.
    D)   the moons were orbiting in the equatorial plane of Uranus.
    Ans: D   Section: 16-2

22. The expected seasonal changes on Uranus because of its orbital and spin-axis alignments, compared to those on Earth, will be
    A)   the same, because the tilt of the spin axis is the same as that of Earth.
    B)   much less, because its orbit is circular.
    C)   absent, because the spin axis is perpendicular to the orbital plane.
    D)   very much exaggerated, because the spin axis is almost in the orbital plane.
    Ans: D   Section: 16-2

23. Seasonal variations at a particular point on Uranus during a Uranian year would be
    A)   almost nonexistent, because Uranus moves in an almost perfectly circular orbit, therefore maintaining a constant distance from the Sun.
    B)   not present at any point on the planet, because dense clouds shield it from climate changes.
    C)   nonexistent, because such variations at any point on the planet would be smoothed out during its long "year" by the planet's rapid rotation.
    D)   extreme, because its spin axis is nearly in its orbital plane.
    Ans: D   Section: 16-2

24. Where would the Sun be located in midsummer in the northern hemisphere on Uranus as seen by an observer floating above the clouds?
    A)   almost directly over the south pole
    B)   directly over latitude 45°, to the north of the equator
    C)   almost directly above the north pole
    D)   almost directly above the equator, because it is midsummer
    Ans: C   Section: 16-2

25. If the orbital period of Uranus is 84 years and its rotational period is about 17 hours, how often will the Sun shine vertically on the north pole ?
    A)   never, because of the extreme tilt of the spin axis to the ecliptic plane
    B)   once every 42 years
    C)   once every 17 hours
    D)   once every 84 years
    Ans: D   Section: 16-2

26. If the south pole of Uranus (orbital period = 84 years) was pointing toward the Sun in 1986, when will the Sun next be over the equator of this planet?
    A)   2070
    B)   It will NEVER happen because of the large tilt of Uranus's axis to the perpendicular to its orbital plane.
    C)   2028
    D)   2007
    Ans: D   Section: 16-2

27. Which planets rotate about their axes in a retrograde direction, opposite to their orbital directions?
    A)   Mercury, Venus, and Neptune   C)   Venus, Uranus, and Pluto
    B)   Venus, Uranus, and Neptune   D)   Mercury, Mars, and Uranus
    Ans: C   Section: 16-2

28. What does Uranus look like from space?
    A)   perpetually covered with yellowish, sulfur-rich clouds
    B)   blue-green and featureless
    C)   blue-green with white, high-altitude clouds, and dark storms
    D)   reddish belts and light zones, parallel to the equator
    Ans: B   Section: 16-2

29. What gives Uranus its blue-green coloration?
    A)   absorption of blue and green sunlight by ammonia gas
    B)   emission of spectral lines in the blue and green by ethane and propane, excited by
          solar UV radiation
    C)   continuous emissions from auroras in the upper planetary atmosphere
    D)   absorption of the red sunlight by methane gas
    Ans: D   Section: 16-2

30. The blue-green appearance of Uranus is caused by
    A)   the atmosphere of methane gas, which preferentially absorbs the red parts of the
          solar spectrum.
    B)   the reflection of blue light by the ice crystals on the planet's surface and in its
          atmosphere.
    C)   the color of the surface of the planet.
    D)   scattering of light from the dust in the thick atmosphere.
    Ans: A   Section: 16-2

31. As photographed by *Voyager 2*, the atmosphere of Uranus shows
    A)   a pinkish haze due to scattering from silicate dust particles.
    B)   some extremely faint cloud markings but is otherwise featureless.
    C)   dark, whirlpool-like features and high, white clouds of methane ice crystals.
    D)   light zones and dark belts circling the planet parallel to the equator.
    Ans: B   Section: 16-2

32. The atmosphere of Uranus appears to be similar to those of Jupiter and Saturn except
    that it shows far less structure and patterns than they. Why is this?
    A)   Dust storms continually hide the features and patterns in the Uranus atmosphere.
    B)   Substances that make up the clouds and patterns on Jupiter and Saturn, such as
          NH_3 and H_2O, have frozen and fallen out of Uranus's colder atmosphere.
    C)   The glow of atomic auroral emissions from the polar regions of Uranus, caused by
          the magnetosphere, outshines the dim reflected light from the Sun, particularly
          because methane absorbs most the sunlight.
    D)   A very high and featureless haze layer hides the clouds and patterns expected to
          occur on Uranus.
    Ans: B   Section: 16-2

33. What are the most abundant gases in the atmosphere of Uranus?
    A)   hydrogen and helium
    B)   carbon dioxide and nitrogen
    C)   nitrogen and ammonia
    D)   methane and water
    Ans: A   Section: 16-2

34. In the sunlit southern hemisphere of Uranus, the observed variation of temperature with latitude is
    A)   unknown, because Uranus is too far away for us to measure temperatures at different latitudes.
    B)   much cooler at the equator than at the south pole because the south pole is tilted almost directly toward the Sun.
    C)   much cooler at the south pole than at the equator because the Sun is always close to (or below) the horizon, as seen from the pole of any planet.
    D)   almost nonexistent between the equator and the south pole, implying an efficient equator-to-pole circulation pattern.
    Ans: D   Section: 16-2

35. The pattern of winds observed on Uranus by *Voyager 2* is
    A)   in bands parallel to the equator, as on Jupiter and Saturn.
    B)   unknown, because Uranus is too featureless for us to detect wind patterns.
    C)   primarily in bands perpendicular to the equator, with winds alternating between north-south and south-north directions.
    D)   dominated by individual cyclones and anticyclones linked by an overall west-to-east flow, similar to the pattern in the mid-latitudes on Earth.
    Ans: A   Section: 16-2

36. Which of the following effects is now thought to be the most likely cause for the inclinations of the spin axes of several of the planets, such as Uranus (and even Earth), to the perpendicular of their orbital planes?
    A)   an out-of-balance force on the irregular mass distributions of planets from their moons, some of which have significant masses
    B)   a small but steady force on one hemisphere of the planet from the highly directional solar wind
    C)   a major collision with another planet-like body
    D)   tidal distortion and deflection caused by neighboring planets
    Ans: C   Section: 16-2

37. The interior rotational period of a Jovian planet is determined by
    A)   measuring the precession of the spin axis of the planet, which is related directly to the planet's interior.
    B)   observing the effects of gravitational field variations on the orbital periods of the planet's moons.
    C)   observing cloud-tops, because the clouds rotate with the overall planet on all the Jovian planets.
    D)   observing radio emission variations that are associated with the magnetic field, the origin of which is deep in the planet's interior.
    Ans: D   Section: 16-2

38. How has the rotational period of the interior of Uranus been determined?
    A)   by using measurements of Uranus's magnetic field taken by *Voyager 2* during its flyby.
    B)   by photographing Uranus's surface through occasional holes in the clouds.
    C)   from measurements taken by the lander vehicle from *Voyager 2* that penetrated to Uranus's surface through the clouds.
    D)   by measuring the speeds of clouds moving around the planet.
    Ans: A   Section: 16-2

39. Why do scientists use magnetic field measurements and observations of radio emission to determine the rotation rates of the interiors of the outer planets such as Uranus?
    A)   The radio emission comes primarily from the moons, and their motion is governed to some extent by the magnetic field generated in the planet's interior.
    B)   The magnetic field originates deep inside the planet and radio emission originates in the magnetosphere, the structure and motion of which is linked to this internal magnetic field.
    C)   Radio energy is produced when cosmic rays pass through magnetic fields in the deep interiors of the planets and variations in this output reflect internal motions.
    D)   Magnetic field changes produce radio emission in the deep interiors of the planets.
    Ans: B   Section: 16-2

40. If you could "stand" on the equator of Uranus, what would the Sun's apparent motion look like? Three of the following statements are correct; which is *incorrect*?
    A)   When the northern hemisphere experiences spring, the Sun would rise in the east and set in the west, one full day lasting about 17 hours.
    B)   When the northern hemisphere experiences summer, the Sun would rise and set very close to the north polar direction.
    C)   When the northern hemisphere experiences autumn, the Sun would rise in the east and set in the west, one full day lasting about 17 hours.
    D)   When the northern hemisphere experiences winter, the Sun would not be visible.
    Ans: D   Section: 16-2

41. The spacecraft that successfully photographed Neptune on a 1989 flyby mission was
    A) *Pioneer.*   B) *Viking.*   C) *Voyager.*   D) *Magellan.*
    Ans: C   Section: 16-3

42. The tilts of the equators of Uranus and Neptune to their respective orbital planes are
    A)   almost zero for both planets.
    B)   very similar—each about 45°.
    C)   very similar—at a large angle, near 90°.
    D)   very different.
    Ans: D   Section: 16-3

43. Which planet is characterized by a blue-green appearance, with dark storms and white, high-altitude methane clouds?
    A) Saturn   B) Pluto   C) Neptune   D) Uranus
    Ans: C   Section: 16-3

44. What does Neptune look like from space?
    A)   blue-green with white, high-altitude clouds and dark storms
    B)   perpetually covered with yellowish, sulfur-rich clouds
    C)   blue-green and featureless
    D)   reddish belts and light zones parallel to the equator
    Ans: A   Section: 16-3

45. Neptune's predominantly blue appearance is caused by
    A)   the fact that solar light has lost much of its red light by scattering in the interplanetary medium by the time it reaches Neptune.
    B)   auroral emissions caused by solar wind particles exciting the atoms and molecules in Neptune's high atmosphere.
    C)   preferential scattering of the blue end of the solar spectrum by Neptune's atmosphere, similar to the process that causes the blue sky on Earth.
    D)   the absorption of reflected sunlight at the red end of the spectrum by methane in its atmosphere.
    Ans: D   Section: 16-3

46. The Great Dark Spot (which is not the same as the Great Red Spot) was found on which planet or moon?
    A) Mars   B) Jupiter   C) Miranda, a moon of Uranus   D) Neptune
    Ans: D   Section: 16-3

47. The Great Dark Spot on Neptune, photographed by *Voyager 2* during its flyby of the planet, was
    A)   a cyclonic system with clockwise winds, opposite to those in Jupiter's Great Red Spot.
    B)   a cyclonic system with counterclockwise winds, the same direction as those in Jupiter's Great Red Spot.
    C)   a volcanic caldera.
    D)   a region of upwelling gas in Neptune's atmosphere, above a hot-spot on its surface.
    Ans: B   Section: 16-3

48. The Great Dark Spot on Neptune
    A)   has been visible through telescopes since at least as far back as 1665.
    B)   disappeared sometime between the *Voyager 2* flyby and when the Hubble Space Telescope photographed Neptune in 1994.
    C)   was the short-lived result of a comet crash in 1995.
    D)   came into existence sometime between the *Voyager 2* flyby and when the Hubble Space Telescope photographed Neptune in 1994.
    Ans: B   Section: 16-3

49. Neptune's high cirrus clouds consist of
    A)   crystals of water ice.   C)   ammonia ice crystals.
    B)   droplets of sulfuric acid.   D)   methane ice crystals.
    Ans: D   Section: 16-3

50. The views of Neptune provided by the *Voyager* spacecraft show that the patterns and motions of Neptune's atmosphere most closely resemble those of which other planet?
    A)   Uranus, with no very distinct features
    B)   Venus, with rapidly moving clouds of sulfuric acid droplets, and a thick CO_2 atmosphere
    C)   Jupiter, with clouds and rotating spots
    D)   Saturn, with indistinct cloud bands
    Ans: C   Section: 16-3

51. Which of the following statements describes CORRECTLY how the atmosphere of Neptune DIFFERS from that of Uranus?
    A) Neptune's atmosphere is almost featureless, whereas the atmosphere of Uranus shows wispy clouds and whirlpool-like vortices.
    B) Methane clouds form in Neptune's atmosphere, but not in that of Uranus, because of Neptune's much greater distance from the Sun.
    C) All parts of Neptune's visible atmosphere rotate at the same speed, whereas different parts of the atmosphere of Uranus rotate differently.
    D) Neptune's atmosphere shows considerable vertical convective motion in addition to east-west circulation, whereas Uranus' atmosphere has very little up-and-down motion.
    Ans: D   Section: 16-2 and 16-3

52. Which of the following statements is NOT true of the planet Neptune?
    A) Like Jupiter and Saturn, Neptune has a number of whirlpool-like vortices in its atmosphere.
    B) UNLIKE Jupiter and Saturn, Neptune has a distinct bluish-green color.
    C) Like Jupiter and Saturn, Neptune gives off more heat than it receives from the Sun.
    D) Like Jupiter and Saturn, Neptune's atmosphere is divided into prominent, differently colored belts, and zones of alternating eastward and westward circulation.
    Ans: D   Section: 16-3

53. The atmospheres of Uranus and Neptune consist mostly of
    A) methane, with small quantities of hydrogen and helium.
    B) hydrogen and helium, with significant amounts of methane, ammonia, and water vapor.
    C) carbon dioxide, with a small amount of nitrogen.
    D) hydrogen and helium, with significant amounts of methane and water vapor but very little ammonia.
    Ans: D   Section: 16-2 and 16-3

54. Uranus and Neptune are similar in size and have similar atmospheres, but Neptune is significantly farther away from the Sun than is Uranus, by a ratio of about 30/19. What conclusion can be reached, therefore, from the fact that Neptune's temperature is about the same as Uranus's?
    A) Neptune's atmosphere must contain a more effective greenhouse gas to maintain more solar energy.
    B) Neptune must have a significant source of internal energy or heat.
    C) The solar wind is able to penetrate to Neptune's cloud-tops and deposit energy there, while Uranus's magnetic field deflects the solar wind.
    D) Neptune is being distorted, therefore heating more than Uranus by tidal effects from Jupiter and Saturn.
    Ans: B   Section: 16-3

55. Several of the Jovian planets appear to be emitting more energy than they absorb from solar radiation. What is the reason for this?
    A)   Rapid rotation is generating excess energy by friction between the planetary atmospheres and the interplanetary medium.
    B)   Excess energy comes from impact energy of meteoroids hitting the planetary atmospheres.
    C)   The solar wind deposits energy into the planetary atmospheres, and this energy is reradiated.
    D)   They are still cooling and contracting from their original formation.
    Ans: D   Section: 16-3

56. Which of the giant Jovian planets is NOT generating energy internally (or whose internal energy source is weak enough that it is masked by the energy received from the Sun), from evidence of excess infrared emission?
    A) Saturn   B) Jupiter   C) Neptune   D) Uranus
    Ans: D   Section: 16-3

57. The most likely reason why Neptune shows significant cloud-forms and associated activity in its atmosphere, compared to the quiet atmosphere of Uranus, is that
    A)   Neptune does not have the deep, high-altitude layer of haze that blankets Uranus.
    B)   Neptune is rotating much faster, thereby stirring the atmosphere into rotating storms like hurricanes on Earth.
    C)   Neptune is closer to the Sun at the present time and receives more energy to cause more convection and turbulence.
    D)   Neptune has a significant source of internal heat that causes convection and turbulence.
    Ans: D   Section: 16-3

58. Uranus lacks an internal source of heat. One consequence of this is that
    A)   Uranus lacks dynamic atmospheric activity.
    B)   it is much colder than Neptune, even though it is closer to the Sun.
    C)   the atmosphere is very thin because most of the atmospheric materials lie frozen on the surface.
    D)   frozen material on the surface results in a much higher albedo than, say, Neptune.
    Ans: A   Section: 16-3

59. What is believed to be the basic structure of the interior of Uranus?
    A)   rocky core, thick layer of water, thin gaseous atmosphere
    B)   iron core, thick layer of rock, thin gaseous atmosphere
    C)   rocky core, thick layer of water, thick layer of liquid hydrogen, thin gaseous atmosphere
    D)   rocky core, thick layer of liquid hydrogen, thin gaseous atmosphere
    Ans: C   Section: 16-4

60. Which planets are believed to have a thick layer of ammonia- and methane-laden water in their interiors?
    A)   Saturn and Uranus   C)   Uranus and Neptune
    B)   Saturn and Neptune   D)   Saturn, Uranus, and Neptune
    Ans: C   Section: 16-4

61. Which ONE of the following four statements applies to ALL FOUR of the Jovian planets?
    A)   Liquid metallic hydrogen makes up a large part of their interiors.
    B)   Their spin axes are approximately perpendicular to their orbital planes.
    C)   They are almost entirely hydrogen and helium—only about 1% of the planet's mass is made up of heavier elements.
    D)   They are all thought to have a substantial rocky core.
    Ans: D   Section: 16-4

62. Uranus and Neptune appear to be smaller versions of Jupiter and Saturn, but they differ significantly from these planets, in that
    A)   they show much more structure and activity on their "surfaces."
    B)   their masses are larger that those of Jupiter and Saturn, even though they are smaller planets.
    C)   their average densities are greater, and hence their internal structure and constituents must be different.
    D)   their rotation periods are much shorter, a few hours compared to Jupiter and Saturn's periods of a few days.
    Ans: C   Section: 16-4

63. One theory of the origin of Uranus and Neptune is that
    A)   they condensed directly out of the gases of the solar nebula at their present orbital radii.
    B)   they condensed directly out of the gases of the solar nebula, but in the inner part of the solar system.
    C)   they formed from planetesimals at their present orbital radii.
    D)   they formed from planetesimals, but much further out in the solar system.
    Ans: B   Section: 16-4

64. The idea that Uranus and Neptune formed at their present orbital radii by the accretion of planetesimals has some serious difficulties. One of these is that
    A)   these planets contain abnormally large amounts of hydrogen and helium, suggesting they were formed further out in the solar system.
    B)   we do not expect planetisimals to exist that far out in the early solar system.
    C)   evidence from other stars suggests that solar nebulae do not last long enough to form a massive planet at that distance by the accretion of planetesimals.
    D)   Planetesimals at this distance would be expected to have far more iron than we have postulated for the composition of Uranus and Neptune.
    Ans: C   Section: 16-4

65. In what way do Uranus and Neptune differ from Jupiter and Saturn?
    A)   Uranus and Neptune do not have observable magnetic fields.
    B)   Uranus and Neptune apparently do not have rocky cores.
    C)   The atmospheric winds of Uranus and Neptune are not parallel to the equator.
    D)   Hydrogen and helium make up a smaller fraction of the total mass of Uranus and Neptune.
    Ans: D   Section: 16-5

66. The surprising fact about the magnetic field of Uranus, compared to that of the Earth or Jupiter, is that
    A)   its axis is precisely aligned with the spin axis of the planet.
    B)   it is much more intense than that of any other planet.
    C)   it is extremely small or absent.
    D)   its axis lies at a larger angle (59°) to the planet's spin axis than that of other planets.
    Ans: D   Section: 16-5

67. What are the characteristics of the magnetic field of Uranus?
    A)   It is aligned almost exactly along the planet's axis of rotation, through the center of the planet.
    B)   It passes through the center of Uranus but is tilted almost 60° from the axis of rotation.
    C)   It is tilted almost 60° to the axis of planetary rotation and offset from the planet's center.
    D)   It is almost parallel to the axis of planetary rotation but is offset from the planet's center.
    Ans: C   Section: 16-5

68. Compared to Earth, Jupiter, and Saturn, the magnetic fields of Uranus and Neptune
    A)   are much more powerful, dominating the motions of clouds on these planets.
    B)   have axes that are aligned almost exactly along the planet's spin axis.
    C)   are nonexistent—Uranus and Neptune have no magnetic fields.
    D)   have axes tilted a long way from the spin axis of the planets.
    Ans: D   Section: 16-5

69. The magnetic fields of Uranus and Neptune are generated by
    A)   the flow of atmospheric (gaseous) methane which has been ionized by solar UV.
    B)   the flow of electrically conducting molten iron in the core.
    C)   the bulk flow of liquid metallic hydrogen.
    D)   electrical currents in water, rendered electrically conducting by ionized molecules such as ammonia.
    Ans: D   Section: 16-5

70. The source of the magnetic fields in Uranus and Neptune is probably
    A)   the flow of ionized solar wind particles around the planets in their
          magnetospheres.
    B)   the flow of impure water in deep layers of these planets.
    C)   the flow of liquid metallic hydrogen in the planet's interiors.
    D)   permanently magnetized solid iron cores.
    Ans: B   Section: 16-5

71. One distinct difference between the two otherwise similar planets, Uranus and Neptune,
    is
    A)   the almost featureless visible image of the solid surface of Uranus, occasionally
          glimpsed through clouds, compared to the totally cloud-enshrouded Neptune.
    B)   the absence of an internal magnetic field and surrounding magnetosphere at
          Neptune.
    C)   the large tilt of the equator of Uranus to its orbital plane compared to the much
          smaller tilt of Neptune's.
    D)   the absence of moons around Neptune.
    Ans: C   Section: 16-5

72. The north pole of a bar magnet would be attracted to which pole of Uranus?
    A)   the magnetic pole above the ecliptic   C)   the spin axis pole above the ecliptic
    B)   the magnetic pole below the ecliptic   D)   the spin axis pole below the ecliptic
    Ans: A   Section: 16-5 and Figure 16-8

73. Uranus and Neptune resemble each other in many ways. In this context, which of the
    following statements is INCORRECT?
    A)   Both planets have a system of rings circling the planet.
    B)   Both planets appear basically featureless in photographs from *Voyager 2*.
    C)   Both planets appear to have three layers: rocky core, watery mantle, and thick
          hydrogen-helium atmosphere.
    D)   Both planets have much stronger magnetic fields than Earth's.
    Ans: B   Section: 16-6

74. Which of the following statements CORRECTLY describes how Neptune differs from
    Uranus?
    A)   Neptune's magnetic axis is closely aligned with its rotation axis, whereas for
          Uranus, these two axes are at a large angle to each other.
    B)   Neptune rotates quite rapidly (16 hours), whereas Uranus rotates very slowly (243
          days).
    C)   Neptune is encircled by a system of narrow, dark rings, whereas those of Uranus
          are wide like of Saturn's.
    D)   Neptune has a number of vortices and ice clouds visible in its atmosphere,
          whereas Uranus's atmosphere appears almost featureless.
    Ans: D   Section: 16-6

75. In which of the following planets was a ring system discovered by the occultation or blocking of light from a distant star, as the planet and rings moved in front of it?
    A) Saturn   B) Uranus   C) Mercury   D) Jupiter
    Ans: B   Section: 16-6

76. The ring system around Uranus was originally discovered by what observation technique?
    A)   infrared observations from the *IRAS* spacecraft in Earth's orbit
    B)   occultation of light from a star as Uranus (and the rings) passed in front of it
    C)   radar reflection from the particles in the rings
    D)   observation by the cameras on board the *Voyager 1* spacecraft
    Ans: B   Section: 16-6

77. How were the rings of Uranus discovered?
    A)   by the *Ulysses* spacecraft, when observing from above the Sun's north pole
    B)   by the Hubble Space Telescope, observing in infrared light
    C)   by *Voyager 2*, during its pass through the Uranian system
    D)   from an airborne telescope, when each ring momentarily blocked off light from a background star
    Ans: D   Section: 16-6

78. Which scientific method was used to discover the rings around Uranus?
    A)   spacecraft exploration of the planet
    B)   direct photography from Earth
    C)   X-ray photography from space
    D)   occultation of a star as the planet and rings moved in front of it
    Ans: D   Section: 16-6

79. The rings of Uranus are
    A)   wide, dense, ice-covered, and hence very bright (70% reflectivity).
    B)   narrow and very dark (1% reflectivity).
    C)   intrinsically very bright (70% reflectivity) but hard to detect because they are very narrow.
    D)   broad, diffuse (almost transparent) bands, made up of fine dust particles.
    Ans: B   Section: 16-6

80. The material in the Uranus ring system differs from that in the Saturn ring system in what important way?
    A)   The individual particles move as a solid ring for some reason, not in Keplerian orbits as do the Saturnian ring particles.
    B)   The particle sizes are larger, those of the Saturnian system being only snowflake or dust grain sizes.
    C)   It reflects much more sunlight than that of the Saturn ring material.
    D)   It reflects much less sunlight than does the material of Saturn's rings.
    Ans: D   Section: 16-6

81. Does Neptune have rings orbiting the planet?
    A)   no
    B)   yes—one almost transparent ring composed entirely of fine dust particles
    C)   yes—three very wide, bright rings and several faint, thin ones
    D)   yes—a system of thin, dark rings of particles of methane ice
    Ans: D   Section: 16-6

82. Why are the rings of Neptune dark?
    A)   The small, icy grains of which they are made are very transparent and reflect little light back toward Earth.
    B)   There are so few of them, making the rings dark even though the individual icy ring particles have high reflectivities.
    C)   The ice from which they are made is coated with dark space dust.
    D)   The ring material, methane ice, has been darkened by impact by electrons from the magnetosphere.
    Ans: D   Section: 16-6

83. The particles in the rings of Uranus and Neptune are very dark. This is thought to be because they are composed partly of
    A)   iron.
    B)   ice particles coated with dark dust, probably carbon.
    C)   methane ice, damaged by impact by electrons from the magnetosphere: radiation darkening.
    D)   very dark rock.
    Ans: C   Section: 16-6

84. What mechanism appears to have made the surfaces of many moons and the particles in the ring material of the outer planets very dark?
    A)   collection of large amounts of fine dust, perhaps carbon dust or soot, from interplanetary space
    B)   long-term bombardment by electrons and ions in the magnetosphere: radiation darkening
    C)   burning and charring of the surfaces by successive passages through the planet's atmosphere, similar to the formation of dark fusion crusts on meteorites that have hit Earth
    D)   chemical changes that are caused by long-term exposure to solar ultraviolet radiation
    Ans: B   Section: 16-6

85. How were the rings of Neptune discovered?
    A)   direct photography from Earth
    B)   direct photography by a flyby mission
    C)   occultation of a star as the rings moved in front of it
    D)   ultraviolet emissions picked up by the Hubble Space Telescope
    Ans: C   Section: 16-6

86. In which of the following characteristics is Uranus significantly different from the rest of the Jovian planets?
    A)   It has an atmosphere composed primarily of hydrogen and helium.
    B)   It has a planet-wide magnetic field.
    C)   It does not have an internal source of heat.
    D)   It has a system of rings.
    Ans: C   Section: 16-6

87. Where are the five moderate-sized satellites of Uranus in relation to the rings?
    A)   All five are closer to Uranus than the rings.
    B)   Miranda is closer to Uranus than the rings; Ariel and Umbriel are shepherd satellites for the rings; Titania and Oberon are beyond the rings.
    C)   Only Miranda is within the ring system; the rest are beyond.
    D)   All five are well outside the ring system.
    Ans: D   Section: 16-6, 16-7, Appendix 3

88. The densities of the five largest moons of Uranus—about 1500 kg/m^3, compared with the value of 3340 kg/m^3 for our Moon and 1000 kg/m^3 for water ice, suggest a composition of
    A)   primarily hydrogen and helium, with a slushy core of ice-forming compounds such as water, methane, and ammonia.
    B)   30% rock and 70% ice-forming compounds such as water, methane, and ammonia.
    C)   30% rock and 70% pure water ice.
    D)   almost entirely water ice, with small amounts of other ice-forming compounds such as methane and ammonia.
    Ans: B   Section: 16-7

89. Evidence of flooding by a thick, viscous fluid is seen on which Uranian moon?
    A) Ariel   B) Umbriel   C) Oberon   D) Miranda
    Ans: A   Section: 16-7

90. Miranda is a satellite of
    A) Neptune.   B) Uranus.   C) Pluto.   D) Jupiter.
    Ans: B   Section: 16-7

91. Miranda, a satellite of Uranus,
    A)   shows a rough surface, indicating that it has either been shattered by one or more large impacts or has undergone partial chemical differentiation.
    B)   is almost completely smooth and featureless.
    C)   is smooth, with networks of cracks that were apparently created during the formation of its icy crust.
    D)   has an ancient surface covered with impact craters like the highland areas of our Moon.
    Ans: A   Section: 16-7

92. Which one of the following statements correctly describes Miranda, one of the satellites of Uranus?
    A) icy surface with chaotically varied terrain
    B) rocky surface with lava lakes and several active volcanoes
    C) smooth and very dark (1% reflectivity), showing only a network of fine cracks
    D) icy, frost-covered surface with vents of rising gas visible in the northern hemisphere
    Ans: A   Section: 16-7

93. Miranda, a satellite of Uranus,
    A) is almost spherical and has a very smooth uncratered surface, suggesting that it consists almost completely of ice.
    B) appears to have undergone a period of partial chemical differentiation during internal tidal heating.
    C) shows an ancient surface covered with impact craters.
    D) shows active geysers and resurfacing due to water flows.
    Ans: B   Section: 16-7

94. Which planetary satellite shows strong evidence of having undergone partial chemical differentiation as a result of tidal heating some time in its past?
    A) Io   B) Callisto   C) Triton   D) Miranda
    Ans: D   Section: 16-7

95. Triton, the giant moon of Neptune, differs from all other major moons of planets in that
    A) its orbit is very elliptical.
    B) its orbit lies inside the rings of Neptune.
    C) it orbits in a retrograde way, opposite to the planet's rotation.
    D) its orbit takes it over the planet's poles.
    Ans: C   Section: 16-8

96. Which property of Triton, a moon of Neptune, makes it significantly different from all other major moons in the solar system?
    A) Its orbit is at right angles to the equator of its mother planet.
    B) It has an extremely dark, smooth surface and consequently was not discovered until very recently.
    C) It orbits in a direction opposite to most other moons and opposite to the normal direction of planetary rotation and revolution.
    D) It has an atmosphere of nitrogen and oxygen, with H_2O clouds.
    Ans: C   Section: 16-8

97. Which planet has among its satellites one large moon, which orbits in a retrograde direction, and one moderate-sized moon with a highly elliptical orbit?
    A) Uranus   B) Saturn   C) Neptune   D) Jupiter
    Ans: C   Section: 16-8

98. Triton, the largest satellite of Neptune, has
    A)   a surface of ice with frozen lakes, plumes of escaping gas, and few craters.
    B)   a densely cratered surface of ice, with at least one ringed structure indicating an ancient asteroid impact.
    C)   a surface of ice in which ancient, densely cratered regions are surrounded by interconnecting systems of parallel ridges.
    D)   a thick atmosphere that hides the surface from view.
    Ans: A   Section: 16-8

99. What features characterize the visible surface of Triton, Neptune's largest moon?
    A)   lava flows, volcanoes, and sulfur dioxide frost
    B)   ice, heavily cratered by ancient impacts
    C)   relatively smooth areas surrounding "islands" of chaotic terrain
    D)   wrinkled surface, frozen lakes, and plumes of nitrogen gas
    Ans: D   Section: 16-8

100. Which of the following does NOT describe Triton, the strange moon of Neptune?
    A)   size almost as big as the Earth's Moon
    B)   orbit inclined at 23° to Neptune's equator
    C)   retrograde orbital motion
    D)   rocky, cratered surface
    Ans: D   Section: 16-8

101. Triton, the largest satellite of Neptune, has
    A)   no measurable atmosphere.
    B)   a very thin atmosphere of nitrogen gas.
    C)   a dense atmosphere of methane and ammonia.
    D)   a dense atmosphere of nitrogen with methane clouds.
    Ans: B   Section: 16-8

102. The plumes that were seen to rise from the surface of Triton, Neptune's largest satellite, are believed to be
    A)   sulfur dioxide from geysers heated by tidal stresses.
    B)   volcanic ash from eruptions similar to, but much smaller than, an Earth-bound eruption.
    C)   water, methane, and ammonia ice crystals above volcanic vents.
    D)   dark material projected upward by nitrogen gas released from sunlight or by undersurface heating.
    Ans: D   Section: 16-8

103. A striking characteristic on Triton, the largest satellite of Neptune, is
    A) a crater so large that the impact that created it must have come close to shattering the satellite.
    B) plumes of dark material driven upward from fissures by nitrogen gas, as a result of either solar or internal heating.
    C) a brightness variation, with one hemisphere being as bright as ice and the other hemisphere as dark as asphalt.
    D) an interconnecting network of parallel grooves, indicating tectonic activity in geologically recent times.
    Ans: B   Section: 16-8

104. How would "Interplanetary Travel" advertise a holiday to Neptune's satellite Triton?
    A) The largest number of volcanoes for your travel dollar anywhere in the solar system!
    B) Hot and dry—never rains—beautiful sulfurous skies!
    C) Skate on frozen nitrogen lakes all morning—bask beside nitrogen geysers in the afternoon!
    D) Exquisite ethane lakes—hydrocarbons beyond your wildest dreams!
    Ans: C   Section: 16-8

105. Which planetary satellites are known to have plumes of gas escaping through their surfaces?
    A) Europa and Miranda   C) Io and Triton
    B) Ganymede and Charon   D) Io and Titan
    Ans: C   Section: 16-8

106. What future awaits Triton, the largest satellite of Neptune?
    A) eventual escape from Neptune as it gradually spirals outward
    B) tidal breakup as it slowly spirals closer to Neptune
    C) probable destruction on impact onto Pluto
    D) gravitational capture by Pluto
    Ans: B   Section: 16-8

107. We expect that a massive planet will eventually pull its satellites into circular orbits. What is the situation with the moons of Neptune?
    A) All are in circular orbits.
    B) Triton is in a highly elliptical retrograde orbit—probably the result of its capture by Neptune.
    C) Nerid is in a highly elliptical orbit—probably the result of the violent interaction that caused the capture of Triton.
    D) All Neptune's satellites are in non-circular orbits.
    Ans: C   Section: 16-8

108. Which planet was discovered in the twentieth century?
    A) Ceres   B) Uranus   C) Pluto   D) Neptune
    Ans: C   Section: 16-9

109. The planet Pluto was discovered in
    A) 1846.   B) 1930.   C) 1781.   D) 1609.
    Ans: B   Section: 16-9

110. The planet Pluto discovered by
    A)   the infrared cameras on the *IRAS* spacecraft, searching for very cold objects.
    B)   prediction, using Newton's laws to account for the deviations from uniform orbits of Uranus and Neptune.
    C)   searching for an object that moved day by day on successive photographs of the sky.
    D)   *Voyager* spacecraft cameras, which were used between planetary encounters to survey the planetary system.
    Ans: C   Section: 16-9

111. Of the nine major planets in our solar system, which one has an orbit with the greatest inclination to the orbit of Earth, i.e., to the ecliptic?
    A) Earth   B) Mars   C) Mercury   D) Pluto
    Ans: D   Section: Appendix 1, Table 1

112. Of the nine major planets in our solar system, which one has the most elliptical orbit?
    A) Earth   B) Mars   C) Mercury   D) Pluto
    Ans: D   Section: Appendix 1, Table 1

113. Which was the eighth planet from the Sun in 1990?
    A) Charon   B) Uranus   C) Neptune   D) Pluto
    Ans: D   Section: 16-9

114. How much closer than Neptune was Pluto to the Sun during Pluto's 1989 perihelion passage?
    A)   1.82 AU
    B)   Pluto NEVER gets closer to the Sun than Neptune.
    C)   0.23 AU
    D)   0.67 AU
    Ans: D   Section: 16-9

115. The smallest angle in the sky that can be resolved from Earth's surface, using the best telescopes under the best observing conditions, is approximately 0.1 arcsec. (You may wish to review the small-angle formula in Box 1-1 of Freedman and Kaufmann, *Universe*, 7th ed.) Consequently, no feature can be resolved at the distance of Pluto if it is smaller than
    A) 7 times the diameter of Pluto. C) 1/15 of the diameter of Pluto.
    B) 2/3 of the diameter of Pluto.   D) 1.2 times the diameter of Pluto.
    Ans: D   Section: 16-9 and Box 1-1

116. What is the moon of the planet Pluto called?
    A) Charon   B) Chiron   C) Callisto   D) Triton
    Ans: A   Section: 16-9

117. For which planet in our solar system is the ratio of moon's diameter to planet's diameter the highest?
    A) Saturn   B) Pluto   C) Earth   D) Neptune
    Ans: B   Section: 16-9

118. The probable composition of Pluto and its satellite, Charon, based on their average densities and location in the solar system (which determined their temperature when they formed), is
    A) almost entirely ice of one type or another.
    B) about half rock and half ice.
    C) mostly rock, with a relatively thin layer of water ice over it.
    D) rock, with possibly a small, iron-rich core.
    Ans: B   Section: 16-9

119. What method was recently used to determine the diameters of Pluto and its moon, Charon?
    A) observation of the sequential disappearance of the planet and the moon behind our Moon in an occultation
    B) photography from a visiting spacecraft
    C) radio interferometry, with arrays of telescopes producing extremely high resolution images
    D) observation of the mutual eclipses of planet and moon
    Ans: D   Section: 16-9

120. How do the sizes of Pluto and its moon, Charon, compare to that of our Moon?
    A) Pluto is larger than our Moon, but Charon is smaller than our Moon.
    B) Pluto is almost the same size as our Moon, but Charon is much smaller than our Moon.
    C) Both Pluto and Charon are larger than our Moon.
    D) They are both smaller than our Moon.
    Ans: D   Section: 16-9

121. What significant surface features have been detected on Pluto?
    A)   surface cracks produced by tidal stresses
    B)   large impact craters
    C)   linear ridge belts produced by tectonic activity
    D)   bright polar caps
    Ans: D   Section: 16-9

122. Pluto and its satellite, Charon, differ from each other in that
    A)   Charon always turns the same side toward Pluto, while Pluto rotates relatively quickly, a situation similar to that of our Earth and its Moon.
    B)   Pluto contains a larger fraction of rock compared to ice than does Charon, as indicated by Pluto's higher density.
    C)   Pluto has a methane atmosphere, whereas Charon has a nitrogen atmosphere.
    D)   Pluto has a surface of methane, nitrogen, and carbon monoxide ice, whereas Charon has a surface of water ice.
    Ans: D   Section: 16-9

123. What is unique about the Pluto-Charon system compared to all other planets in the solar system?
    A)   Charon is an icy moon but is in orbit around a giant planet made mostly of liquid hydrogen.
    B)   Both Pluto and Charon are in synchronous rotation, so each one always has the same face turned toward the other.
    C)   Both Pluto and Charon are volcanically active with lava flows and vents of sulfur-dioxide gas.
    D)   Pluto has only one satellite.
    Ans: B   Section: 16-9

124. If you were standing on Pluto, how often would you see the satellite Charon rise above your horizon each day?
    A)   once every two days, because Charon orbits in the same direction as Pluto's rotation but more slowly
    B)   twice in each 6-hour day, because Charon is in a retrograde orbit
    C)   once in each 6-hour day as Pluto rotates on its axis
    D)   Never—Charon is a synchronous satellite like the communications satellites that are in orbit around Earth.
    Ans: D   Section: 16-9

125. The Pluto-Charon system moves in which way in its mutual motion?
    A)   Charon orbits Pluto with exactly Pluto's rotation period.
    B)   Charon orbits Pluto twice, while Pluto rotates once.
    C)   There is no relationship between rotation period of Pluto and orbital period of Charon.
    D)   Charon orbits Pluto once, while Pluto rotates twice.
    Ans: A   Section: 16-9

126. Some astronomers feel that there may be many large, icy bodies beyond the orbit of Pluto. Which of the following is not used as a major argument in favor of this hypothesis?
    A)   large tilt of Uranus's rotation axis
    B)   binary nature of the Pluto system
    C)   retrograde orbit of Neptune's satellite, Triton
    D)   abundance of craters observed on planets and moons in the outer solar system
    Ans: D   Section: 16-9

127. If there were once a large number of Pluto-sized objects and several Earth-sized objects in the outskirts of the present planetary system, what happened to them?
    A)   They were shattered by mutual collisions, and the fragments are visible today as comets such as Halley's Comet.
    B)   Most of them were flung out of the solar system by the gravitational pull of Uranus and Neptune.
    C)   With the exception of Pluto and Triton, they all collided with (and became part of) Uranus and Neptune.
    D)   They are still there, and we are only now beginning to discover them.
    Ans: B   Section: 16-9

128. What technique will probably be most successful in a search for cold Pluto-like objects beyond the orbit of Neptune?
    A)   Hubble Space Telescope surveys in the ecliptic plane
    B)   observations at ultraviolet wavelengths, because this radiation can penetrate the dust and gas in the outer planetary system
    C)   radar observations, sending powerful pulses outward and searching for reflected radio pulses
    D)   dedicated spacecraft like *New Horizons*
    Ans: D   Section: 16-9

129. Charon is about 1200 km in diameter and is about 18,490 km away from the surface of Pluto. How large an angle does it subtend when viewed from Pluto?
    A) 37 arcsec   B) 0.5°   C) 3.7°   D) 57°
    Ans: C   Section: 16-9 and Box 1-1

130. Use Newton's form of Kepler's Third Law to calculate a rough estimate for the mass of Charon, Pluto's moon. Take the semimajor axis of Charon's orbit to be 19,640 km and the period to be 6.39 days. This gives the mass of Charon to be about
    A) 10^{10} kg   B) 10^{17} kg   C) 10^{21} kg   D) 10^{23} kg
    Ans: C   Section: 16-9 and Box 4-4

Chapter 17: Vagabonds of the Solar System

1. Which solar system object was found on January 1, 1801, located between the orbits of Mars and Jupiter?
   A) the Kuiper belt object 1993 SC   C)   Halley's Comet
   B) the asteroid Ceres   D)   the asteroid Gaspra
   Ans: B   Section: 17-1

2. A chunk of rock and metal 10 km in diameter orbiting the Sun would be called
   A) an asteroid.   B) a meteoroid.   C) a moon.   D) a comet.
   Ans: A   Section: 17-1

3. An asteroid is
   A)   another name for the nucleus of a comet, a volatile object that moves around the Sun in a long, elliptical orbit.
   B)   an object smaller than a planet, moving around the Sun in an orbit close to the plane of the ecliptic.
   C)   a meteorite before it enters the atmosphere and plunges to Earth.
   D)   a small, easily recognizable group of stars within a constellation.
   Ans: B   Section: 17-1

4. Who was the first person to discover an asteroid?
   A)   the German mathematician, Karl Friedrich Gauss
   B)   the German astronomer, Johann Bode
   C)   the English astronomer, Sir William Herschel
   D)   the Italian astronomer, Guiseppe Piazzi
   Ans: D   Section: 17-1

5. What major contribution did the German mathematician Karl Friedrich Gauss make to astronomy?
   A)   He discovered a regular progression of planetary distances from the Sun, so that each planet's orbit could be calculated knowing the distance of any one planet from the Sun.
   B)   He developed a method for computing an object's temperature from measurements of the intensity of emitted light at only two wavelengths.
   C)   He derived the Stefan-Boltzmann law, emitted flux = σT^4, mathematically, from basic physical principles.
   D)   He developed a method for computing an object's orbit from only three observations.
   Ans: D   Section: 17-1

6. The object found about 2.8 AU from the Sun when astronomers were looking for a "missing" planet between the orbital distances of Mars and Jupiter was
   A) the asteroid Ceres.   B) Pluto.   C) Halley's Comet.   D) Mercury.
   Ans: A   Section: 17-1

7. The asteroid belt exists between the orbits of which planets?
   A)   Mars and Jupiter   C)   Jupiter and Saturn
   B)   Earth and Mars   D)   Venus and Earth
   Ans: A   Section: 17-1

8. Most of the asteroids of our solar system move around the Sun between the orbits of the planets
   A)   Earth and Mars.   C)   Jupiter and Saturn.
   B)   Mars and Jupiter.   D)   Venus and Earth.
   Ans: B   Section: 17-1

9. On a time-exposure photograph of the sky as it orbited the Sun, how would a typical asteroid appear if the camera were tracking the background stars?
   A)   It would look like a small, diffuse patch against the sharp images of stars because of the dust and gas surrounding it.
   B)   It would produce a flash of light as it crossed the field of view of the camera.
   C)   It would look like any other star, a small extra dot not shown on star charts of this area of the sky.
   D)   It would produce a short trail as it moved slowly against the background stars.
   Ans: D   Section: 17-1

10. How would we be able to detect a large asteroid if it were heading straight for Earth?
   A)   It would appear as a slowly brightening and growing diffuse sphere of light where no star was charted because of light scattered from the dust and gas surrounding it, and it would show a blueshifted spectrum.
   B)   It would appear as a slowly brightening star-like object where no star was previously charted, with a redshifted solar spectrum of reflected light.
   C)   It would appear as a slowly brightening point of light where no star had previously been charted, and the spectrum of sunlight reflected from it would be blueshifted by the Doppler effect.
   D)   It would appear as a short trail against the background stars on a sky-tracked, long-exposure photograph, and its spectrum would show no Doppler shift.
   Ans: C   Section: 17-1

11. Most asteroids
   A)   are dark and spherical in shape, with many craters on their surfaces.
   B)   are spherical and ice-coated and hence light-colored and shiny.
   C)   are irregularly shaped, and are covered with very light-colored dust that reflects sunlight well.
   D)   are dark, irregular in shape, and heavily cratered.
   Ans: D   Section: 17-1

12. The largest known asteroid in our solar system is
   A) Gaspra.   B) Titan.   C) Pallas.   D) Ceres.
   Ans: D   Section: 17-1

13. How big is the largest asteroid, Ceres, in comparison with the largest mare or impact basin on the Moon, Mare Imbrium?
    A) Ceres is much larger than Mare Imbrium.
    B) much smaller—because asteroids are very small objects (1 km diameter), whereas maria are large (100–1000 km diameter)
    C) The Mare Imbrium is much larger than Ceres.
    D) very similar—about 1000 km across
    Ans: D Section: 17-1

14. How do the biggest asteroids compare in size with the Moon?
    A) They are very much smaller (less than 1/10).
    B) They are between 1/10 and 1/2 as large.
    C) They are about the same size.
    D) They are very much larger (greater than 5×).
    Ans: B Section: 17-1

15. Which of the following statements is NOT true for asteroids?
    A) The total mass of all asteroids is much smaller than the mass of a planet like Earth.
    B) Some asteroids occupy the same orbit as Jupiter.
    C) Some asteroids pass closer to the Sun than Earth's orbital distance.
    D) A minority of all asteroids are in the asteroid belt.
    Ans: D Section: 17-1

16. The total number of asteroids bright enough to be visible on Earth-based photographs, is estimated to be about
    A) 1 million.   B) 100,000.   C) 33.   D) 3000.
    Ans: B Section: 17-1

17. The combined matter in the asteroid belt would produce an object of what approximate size?
    A) about 1500 km in diameter—significantly smaller than the Moon
    B) about the size of Earth
    C) only a few kilometers in diameter—similar to an average mountain on Earth
    D) about the size of Mercury
    Ans: A Section: 17-1

18. According to Kepler's law, the average sidereal period around the Sun for an asteroid moving in the asteroid belt is
    A) 4.68 years.   B) 2.8 years.   C) 46.8 years.   D) 1.99 years.
    Ans: A Section: 17-1

19. If an asteroid orbits the Sun in a circular orbit with an orbital period of 1/5 of that of Jupiter, what will be its orbital radius?
    A) 1.78 AU   B) 15.2 AU   C) 1.04 AU   D) 3.65 AU
    Ans: A   Section: 17-1

20. The name 1987 FD refers to the
    A)   fourth asteroid to be discovered in the month of February, 1987.
    B)   sixth asteroid to be discovered in the month of April, 1987.
    C)   1987th asteroid ever to be discovered, named after Frances Draibre.
    D)   fourth asteroid to be discovered during the second half of March, 1987.
    Ans: D   Section: 17-1

21. How are space probes to the outer planets, such as Jupiter, protected from being obliterated by collisions with asteroids in the asteroid belt?
    A)   They aren't—we lose only one out of every four spacecraft to collisions with asteroids, so it is cheaper to take our chances.
    B)   The spacecraft are equipped with cameras to detect asteroids, so they can be directed safely around them.
    C)   They aren't—asteroids are so far apart that the spacecraft just sail safely on through.
    D)   The spacecraft are sent in an inclined orbit that arcs above or below the asteroid belt, crossing the ecliptic again near Jupiter.
    Ans: C   Section: 17-1

22. How well does Ceres fit the Titus-Bode rule?
    A)   Neither the Ceres/Mars ratio nor the Jupiter/Ceres ratio falls into the range suggested by the Titus-Bode rule.
    B)   The Ceres/Mars ratio fits the Titus-Bode rule but the Jupiter/Ceres ratio does not.
    C)   The Ceres/Mars ratio does not fit the Titus-Bode rule but the Jupiter/Ceres ratio does.
    D)   Both the Ceres/Mars ratio and the Jupiter/Ceres ratio fall into the range suggested by the Titus-Bode rule.
    Ans: D   Section: 17-1

23. The asteroid belt is believed by most astronomers to be composed of
    A)   icy fragments similar to the nuclei of comets.
    B)   genuine leather.
    C)   rocky debris left over from the formation of the solar system.
    D)   the remnants of a gaseous planet disrupted by an impact.
    Ans: C   Section: 17-2

24. Computer simulations of the formation of the solar system show that the material in the vicinity of the asteroid belt did not form into a much larger planet because
    A) of a violent collision between two protoplanets, the debris from which became the asteroid belt.
    B) Jupiter's gravitational pull flung most of the material in this region out of the solar system and prevented coalescence of the rest.
    C) this region is where the gravitational field of the Sun is often balanced by that of Jupiter, and this prevented coalescence of matter into a planet.
    D) this material was inside the Roche limit for the gravitational field of Jupiter.
    Ans: B   Section: 17-2

25. Why does no major planet orbit the Sun at the location of the asteroid belt?
    A) In the early solar nebula, the temperature that close to the Sun was too high for rock or iron to condense into solid form.
    B) One such object did form there but was destroyed by a collision with an early comet; the asteroid belt is the debris from the collision.
    C) Jupiter's gravitational pull stirred up the planetesimals, preventing them from coalescing into a single large object.
    D) Three earth-sized planets did form there, but they destroyed each other by mutual collisions; the asteroid belt is the debris from these collisions.
    Ans: C   Section: 17-2

26. The orbits of asteroids have a surprisingly large variety of semimajor axes, eccentricities, and inclinations to the ecliptic compared to most of the major planets. What is believed to be the cause of this?
    A) Asteroids are "small" objects, and they formed with the kinds of orbits they now have.
    B) The orbits were stirred up when the Sun passed within the Oort cloud of another star.
    C) Jupiter's gravitational pull has stirred up the asteroid orbits.
    D) One or more Mars-sized planets formed in the asteroid belt, and their gravitational influence stirred up the orbits of the rest of the asteroids.
    Ans: D   Section: 17-2

27. The Kirkwood Gaps (see Fig. 17-4, Freedman and Kaufmann, *Universe*, 7th ed.) are found in the
    A) equatorial region of the Sun.   C) spectrum of hydrogen gas.
    B) rings of Saturn.   D) asteroid belt.
    Ans: D   Section: 17-2

28. The Kirkwood Gaps are primarily caused by
    A)   the gravitational tug of Jupiter nudging asteroids into new orbits.
    B)   shepherd satellites controlling the orbits of ring particles.
    C)   orbits of material being disturbed because Jupiter's gravitational field balances the Sun at this distance, and objects can escape from the solar system.
    D)   large asteroids sweeping parts of the asteroid belt clear of smaller asteroids.
    Ans: A   Section: 17-2

29. What is the relationship between the Kirkwood Gaps in the asteroid belt and the Cassini and Enke divisions in the rings of Saturn?
    A)   Both are caused by large objects passing through swarms of smaller objects, sweeping out gaps in the swarms.
    B)   Both were discovered by observers from the same group—Kirkwood and Enke worked at the Cassini Observatory.
    C)   Both are caused by selective melting of material at these specific locations from the central radiating body, the Sun and Saturn respectively.
    D)   Both are caused by disruptions of orbits of small objects by a larger object whose orbital period is a simple ratio of that of the small objects.
    Ans: D   Section: 17-2 and 14-12

30. What effect does Jupiter have on asteroids in the asteroid belt?
    A)   It will disturb only the orbits of those asteroids whose orbital distances (or semimajor axes) are a simple fraction (e.g., 1/2, 1/3, 2/3, 2/7) of the radius of Jupiter's orbit.
    B)   It perturbs only the orbits of asteroids whose orbital periods are a simple fraction (e.g., 1/2, 1/3, 2/3, 2/7) of its own orbital period.
    C)   It has no effect whatsoever on such small objects because they are a long way away from Jupiter, and Jupiter's gravitational influence varies as the inverse square of distance by Newton's law.
    D)   It disturbs only the orbits of all the asteroids in the belt, slowing them down and causing them to spiral slowly toward the Sun.
    Ans: B   Section: 17-2

31. If objects in the asteroid belt are prevented from occupying an orbit for which their period would be one-third of that of Jupiter because of repeated gravitational disturbances, at what distance would you expect a gap in the asteroid belt?
    A) 1.0 AU   B) 7.86 AU   C) 3.28 AU   D) 2.5 AU
    Ans: D   Section: 17-2

32. What happened to the Mars-sized planets believed to be a part of the asteroid belt early in the solar system's history? Three of these answers are reasonable fates for these planets and one is not. Which one is *not* a reasonable final scenario for these planets?
    A)   Gravitational interaction with Jupiter eventually kicked them out of the solar system.
    B)   Gravitational interaction with Jupiter caused them to fall into the Sun.
    C)   They collided with other large bodies and shattered.
    D)   They are still present in the asteroid belt, although not yet detected.
    Ans: D   Section: 17-2

33. A technique that is proving very useful for determining the shapes of a large number of asteroids is
    A)   radar signals reflected from the asteroid's surface.
    B)   direct photography from spacecraft.
    C)   optical and infrared Doppler shift measurements as the asteroid rotates.
    D)   CCD photography using large, Earth-based telescopes.
    Ans: A   Section: 17-3

34. The general shape of most asteroids is thought to be
    A)   double, two asteroids orbiting the Sun together.
    B)   perfectly spherical.
    C)   loose collections of very small particles, held together by gravity.
    D)   irregular.
    Ans: D   Section: 17-3

35. Only the few largest asteroids are found to be spherical. Why is this?
    A)   Repeated collisions with other asteroids have worn them down to spheres.
    B)   Self-gravity for the most massive asteroids was sufficient to pull them to this shape during their early history.
    C)   Their visible outer atmospheres assume a spherical shape even though their surfaces are irregular.
    D)   They solidified from spherical gas clouds in their early history and retained this shape.
    Ans: B   Section: 17-3

36. The first asteroid to be photographed in detail by a spacecraft was
    A) Ceres.   B) Icarus.   C) Gaspra.   D) Vesta.
    Ans: C   Section: 17-3

37. What is unusual about the asteroid Mathilde, which was studied and photographed by the *NEAR* spacecraft (Fig. 17-7, Freedman and Kaufmann, *Universe,* 7th ed.)?
    A) It has almost no craters visible anywhere on its surface.
    B) It has a much higher mass for its volume than any other known asteroid.
    C) It is not much denser than water.
    D) It has a very bright surface, possibly caused by fresh material thrown out by impacts.
    Ans: C   Section: 17-3

38. The asteroid Mathilde has a mean density of only 1300 kg/m^3, which is about half the density of rock. What is believed to be the reason for Mathilde's low density?
    A) Mathilde is a "rubble pile," having been shattered by collisions with other asteroids.
    B) Mathilde is a binary asteroid that is too far away for us to see the individual components, and the low density is an illusion created by the space between the two rocky components.
    C) Mathilde is composed of about 1/4 rock and 3/4 ice.
    D) Mathilde is a primitive asteroid, composed of loosely aggregated dust grains from the early solar nebula.
    Ans: A   Section: 17-3

39. The surfaces of the asteroids Ida and Mathilde, photographed by the *Galileo* and NEAR Shoemaker spacecraft (Fig. 17-7 and the figure accompanying Chapter 17, Advanced Question 32, Freedman and Kaufmann, *Universe*, 7th ed.) show
    A) icy surfaces criss-crossed with cracks and systems of parallel grooves.
    B) young, sharp, jagged surfaces, due to fragmentation by collision with other asteroids, and few craters.
    C) irregular, somewhat rounded, and moderately cratered surfaces.
    D) ancient surfaces densely covered with large and small overlapping craters, like the surface of the highland areas of the Moon.
    Ans: C   Section: 17-3

40. A Hirayama family of asteroids is
    A) a group of asteroids that have identical spectra, and therefore identical compositions.
    B) either of two groups of asteroids that orbit at Jupiter's distance from the Sun.
    C) a group of asteroids that have orbits that cross Earth's but remain outside Venus's orbit.
    D) a group of asteroids that have nearly identical orbits.
    Ans: D   Section: 17-3

41. Often an asteroid viewed from Earth will appear to change its brightness periodically. We believe this happens because
    A) the albedo is significantly different on one side compared to the other.
    B) like Iapetus, a satellite of Saturn, the leading side is very dark and the trailing side is very bright.
    C) the asteroid is elongated, so that it may present a larger or a smaller cross section to us as it rotates.
    D) the asteroid is simply passing through the shadow of another asteroid.
    Ans: C   Section: 17-3

42. Asteroids that orbit the Sun at the same distance as Jupiter are known as the
    A) Adenoids.   B) Apollo asteroids.   C) Trojan asteroids.   D) Jupitoids.
    Ans: C   Section: 17-4

43. The Trojan asteroids orbit the Sun in circular orbits at the same distance as
    A) the main asteroid belt.   B) Jupiter.   C) Mars.   D) Earth.
    Ans: B   Section: 17-4

44. What kind of orbits do the Trojan asteroids follow?
    A) circular orbits at the same distance from the Sun as Jupiter
    B) circular orbits at about 2.8 AU from the Sun
    C) long, elliptical orbits that cross that of Earth
    D) long, elliptical orbits ranging from Neptune's orbital distance to Jupiter's orbital distance
    Ans: A   Section: 17-4

45. Two of the Lagrangian points in the Jupiter-Sun planetary system are
    A) points at high latitudes on Jupiter where auroras (called Lagrangian auroras on Jupiter) occur most frequently.
    B) positions in space at Jupiter's orbital distance from the Sun, where the combined gravitational forces from the Sun and Jupiter trap asteroids.
    C) areas in the asteroid belt where gravitational interaction of Jupiter with asteroids disturbs their orbits and causes a Kirkwood Gap.
    D) an area between the Sun and Jupiter where their gravitational forces on an object are equal and opposite.
    Ans: B   Section: 17-4

46. If an asteroid is found to be orbiting in a circular path around the Sun at the same distance as Jupiter (5.2 AU), what will be its orbital period compared to that of Jupiter, which is 11.86 years?
    A) the same as that of Jupiter, 11.86 years
    B) exactly 1/2 or 5.93 years, because it will be in a synchronous orbit with Jupiter
    C) about 10 times as long, or 118.6 years, because the Sun's gravitational force is much smaller on such a small object
    D) about 1/10 of Jupiter's period, because it is a much smaller object
    Ans: A   Section: 17-4

47. What is the orbital sidereal period of a Trojan asteroid? (See Fig. 17-8 and Appendix 1, Freedman and Kaufmann, *Universe,* 7th ed.)
    A) 1.88 years
    B) It is difficult to be specific because they all have different orbital periods, depending on their masses.
    C) 5.9 years, the same as most asteroids in the asteroid belt
    D) 11.86 years
    Ans: D   Section: 17-4

48. Asteroids should be able to remain stably trapped at the stable Lagrangian points of the Earth-Sun system (see Section: 17-4 and Fig. 17-8, Freedman and Kaufmann, *Universe*, 7th ed.), provided that they are NOT subjected to other, stronger, gravitational influences. As a test of this stability, calculate how strong Jupiter's gravity is at Earth's stable Lagrangian points (when Jupiter is closest to them) compared to the strength of Earth's gravity at the same points. (You will need to use Newton's law of gravitation; it will also help to draw a diagram.) Compared to Earth's gravitational force at these points, Jupiter's gravity is
    A) 1/18 as strong.   C) 12 times stronger.
    B) 18 times stronger.   D) 76 times stronger.
    Ans: B   Section: 17-4

49. Asteroids whose elliptical orbits have perihelion distances shorter than the orbital distance of Mars are known as
    A) Kirkwood objects, or KOs.   C) Hirayama family asteroids, or HFAs.
    B) near-Earth objects, or NEOs.   D) Mars-crossing asteroids, or MCAs.
    Ans: B   Section: 17-4

50. One example of a near-Earth object, or NEO, is the
    A) asteroid Eros.   B) Moon.   C) asteroid Ceres.   D) Trojan asteroid Hector.
    Ans: A   Section: 17-4

51. The Barringer meteorite crater is located in
    A) Iceland.   B) Australia.   C) Siberia.   D) Arizona.
    Ans: D   Section: 17-4

52. The estimated energy of impact of the large object that produced the Barringer Crater in Arizona in terms of explosive power (tons of TNT equivalent, a somewhat dubious scale) is
    A)   less than 10 kilotons, similar to the first nuclear weapons.
    B)   about 20 megatons.
    C)   greater than 1000 megatons.
    D)   about 1 megaton.
    Ans: B   Section: 17-4

53. A metal that is relatively abundant in meteorites but generally rare on Earth has been found in specific layers of clay throughout the world, and its study is helping to evaluate the effect of meteor impacts on Earth's climate and its inhabitants in recent geological time (e.g., dinosaurs). This metal is
    A) nickel.   B) cobalt.   C) iridium.   D) iron.
    Ans: C   Section: 17-4

54. The astronomical event that is now thought to have occurred some 65 million years ago to produce a layer of iridium in the geological record in rocks and to have resulted in the deaths of a great fraction of all living species was
    A)   a very large volcanic eruption on Earth.
    B)   the impact of an asteroid on Earth.
    C)   a supernova that exploded relatively near the solar system.
    D)   an extraordinary solar eruption or flare.
    Ans: B   Section: 17-4

55. The impact of a 10-km-diameter asteroid on the surface of Earth would very likely
    A)   shatter Earth into fragments.
    B)   create havoc near the impact site but have relatively little lasting effect elsewhere.
    C)   shatter the global ecology and cause the extinction of a large percentage of all species living on Earth.
    D)   completely destroy all life on Earth.
    Ans: C   Section: 17-4

56. The impact that took place at about the time of the extinction of the dinosaurs (and may in fact have caused their extinction) is believed to have created
    A)   the Barringer Crater in Arizona.
    B)   the Chicxulub Crater in the Yucatan Peninsula, Mexico.
    C)   Hudson Bay in northern Canada.
    D)   the Manicouagan Crater in Quebec.
    Ans: B   Section: 17-4

57. What is the likely connection between the metal iridium and the demise of the Earth's dinosaur population?
    A)   Iridium, which is found in abundance on Earth's surface, is poisonous to reptiles.
    B)   Iridium is found beneath Earth's crust. Meteor impacts during the dinosaur age probably exposed and uncovered enough of it to poison the dinosaurs.
    C)   Iridium is found in meteorites but is rare on the Earth. The existence of a world-wide layer of it suggests a large meteor impact during the dinosaur age. This probably raised enough dust to block out sunlight and kill the dinosaurs.
    D)   Iridium is highly radioactive. Its presence in a geologic layer dating to the dinosaur age suggests that natural radioactivity reached dangerous levels at that time, and the dinosaurs died from overexposure.
    Ans: C   Section: 17-4

58. The luminous trails of small dust particles that are completely vaporized in the Earth's atmosphere and are commonly known as shooting stars are
    A) meteoroids.   B) meteors.   C) auroral flashes.   D) meteorites.
    Ans: B   Section: 17-5

59. A shooting star is
    A)   a violently erupting star, ejecting matter rapidly away from it into interstellar space.
    B)   a small particle of interplanetary dust, burning up and glowing as it enters the Earth's atmosphere.
    C)   the leading scorer on a basketball team.
    D)   a near-neighbor star, moving rapidly across our field of view.
    Ans: B   Section: 17-5

60. A piece of rock from outer space that reaches the Earth's surface after surviving a fiery passage through the Earth's atmosphere is known as
    A) a meteoroid.   B) a meteor.   C) a meteorite.   D) an asteroid.
    Ans: C   Section: 17-5

61. A small piece of rock orbiting the Sun would be called
    A) a meteor.   B) a meteorite.   C) a micrometer.   D) a meteoroid.
    Ans: D   Section: 17-5

62. A meteoroid is the name for a solid particle that
    A)   has burned up in Earth's atmosphere.
    B)   originated on the Moon and has landed on Earth.
    C)   has impacted on Earth's surface.
    D)   is drifting around in space.
    Ans: D   Section: 17-5

63. Stony meteorites
    A)   are composed of rocks similar to terrestrial rocks.
    B)   contain large quantities of carbon and H_2O, and even hydrocarbons and amino acids.
    C)   have solid iron cores and rocky silicate shells.
    D)   are made of solid iron and nickel.
    Ans: A   Section: 17-5

64. Stony-iron meteorites are believed to
    A)   have been ejected by volcanoes on Mars.
    B)   originate from undifferentiated asteroids (same composition throughout).
    C)   be pieces of primordial solar system material, unaltered since the solar system formed.
    D)   originate from differentiated asteroids (in which iron sank to the center).
    Ans: D   Section: 17-5

65. Iron meteorites
    A)   are normally composed almost entirely of iron and nickel.
    B)   are normally composed almost entirely of iron.
    C)   normally contain between three and five times as much iron as terrestrial rocks, in the form of pure grains embedded a rocky matrix.
    D)   are normally composed almost entirely of iron, nickel, and carbon.
    Ans: A   Section: 17-5

66. A few meteorites on Earth are believed to have come from another planet. Which planet is this?
    A) Mars   B) Jupiter   C) Venus   D) Mercury
    Ans: A   Section: 17-5

67. The estimated total infall of meteoritic and extraterrestrial material from space per day on Earth is
    A)   about 1 million tons.   C)   about 300 tons.
    B)   about 30 tons.   D)   less than 1 ton.
    Ans: C   Section: 17-5

68. Interplanetary material
    A)   falls on Earth at the rate of several hundred tons per day, mostly as small meteorites.
    B)   hits Earth at specific times of the year in the form of small particles that produce meteor showers, but does not fall on Earth at other times.
    C)   falls on Earth only very rarely in the form of single large objects, but these individual impacts can devastate parts of Earth and threaten life.
    D)   occasionally hits Earth in the form of fairly large objects that form craters, but there is no continuous stream of incoming matter.
    Ans: A   Section: 17-5

69. What fraction of the material arriving on Earth from outer space is in the form of iron meteorites?
A) 95%   B) 50%   C) 75%   D) 4%
Ans: D   Section: 17-5

70. What fraction of the material arriving on Earth from outer space is in the form of stony meteorites?
A) 50%   B) 4%   C) 75%   D) 95%
Ans: D   Section: 17-5

71. Which of the following descriptions would allow you tentatively to identify a rock as a fallen meteorite?
A)   layered rock, consisting of limestone
B)   solid iron, with a distinctive crystal structure throughout its interior
C)   rough-surfaced rock with small inclusions of coal
D)   large transparent crystals of common salt embedded in sandstone
Ans: B   Section: 17-5

72. The Widmanstätten pattern uncovered by acid etching of the surfaces of many iron meteorites consists of
A)   fracture lines, created by the impact that knocked the meteoroid off the parent asteroid.
B)   large crystals, formed as the iron cooled slowly over many millions of years.
C)   small holes and bubbles, created by partial melting of the meteorite as it entered the Earth's atmosphere.
D)   minute crystals, formed when the iron cooled quickly in the vacuum of space.
Ans: B   Section: 17-5

73. An iron meteorite, when cut open and etched with acid, often shows a peculiar pattern of nickel-iron crystals called a Widmanstätten pattern. What does the presence of this pattern tell us about the meteorite?
A)   It was blasted from the surface of the planet Mars by an impact.
B)   It is a fragment of a shattered asteroid that was at least 200 km in diameter.
C)   It is a primitive (unaltered) piece of the early solar nebula.
D)   It is a fragment of a shattered asteroid that was no more than about 25 km in diameter.
Ans: B   Section: 17-5

74. An iron meteorite, when cut open and etched with acid, often shows a peculiar pattern of nickel-iron crystals called a Widmanstätten pattern. Through what process was this pattern created?
    A) partial melting during the impact that ejected the meteorite from its parent asteroid, with subsequent rapid cooling in space
    B) rapid crystal growth as molten iron cooled and solidified in the interior of a small asteroid
    C) slow crystal growth as iron condensed from gas directly to solid form in the early solar nebula
    D) slow crystal growth as molten iron cooled and solidified in the interior of a large asteroid
    Ans: D   Section: 17-5

75. The fact that there are several distinct and different types of meteorites (stony, stony-iron, and iron) is probably indicative of
    A) preferential accretion of iron particles to other iron particles because of their magnetic properties, leaving stony particles to accrete separately.
    B) fragmentation of asteroids that had become differentiated in a similar fashion to Earth (with the heavier iron sinking to the center).
    C) different amounts of heating and "erosion" of the outer layers of meteorites as they pass through Earth's atmosphere.
    D) formation in different parts of the early solar nebula, with stones condensing closer to the Sun and irons farther out.
    Ans: B   Section: 17-5

76. Widmanstätten patterns uniquely identify samples as iron meteorites. Why is this?
    A) These patterns require iridium, which is common in iron meteorites but is rare on Earth.
    B) Widmanstätten patterns are radioactive.
    C) These patterns involve crystals, which only form after millions of years of slow cooling.
    D) These patterns are actually cracks in the structure of the meteorite that form only when an iron meteorite becomes heated during its passage through the Earth's atmosphere.
    Ans: C   Section: 17-5

77. A meteorite is a solid object reaching the Earth's surface after plunging through our atmosphere. A meteorite might have originally been a part of any of the following *except*
    A) a meteoroid or asteroid.   C) the Van Allen Radiation Belt.
    B) a comet.   D) Mars or the Moon.
    Ans: C   Section: 17-5 and 9-4

78. Which of the following types of meteoroids is expected to be most common out in the solar system?
    A) carbonaceous chondrites   B) stony-irons   C) irons   D) stones
    Ans: D   Section: 17-6

79. The most common meteorites to hit Earth are
    A)   the stony meteorites.
    B)   the carbonaceous chondrites.
    C)   the iron meteorites.
    D)   the stony-iron meteorites.
    Ans: A   Section: 17-6

80. Which meteorites are believed to be samples of primordial solar nebula material?
    A)   stony-iron meteorites
    B)   iron meteorites
    C)   meteorites showing Widmanstätten patterns when etched with acid
    D)   carbonaceous chondrites
    Ans: D   Section: 17-6

81. Of the following characteristics of carbonaceous chondrites, which one is unusual compared to other meteorites?
    A)   They show a fusion crust—a sure sign of short-lived, rapid heating.
    B)   They contain water—a sure sign that they have never been melted.
    C)   They contain rocky material—a sure sign that they come from a differentiated asteroid.
    D)   They never show Widmanstätten patterns.
    Ans: B   Section: 17-6

82. Why are carbonaceous chondrites thought to be original material that formed in the early solar nebula?
    A)   They show a Widmanstätten pattern, which indicates slow condensation from gaseous material.
    B)   They consist mostly of carbon, which was the dominant substance condensing in the outer solar nebula.
    C)   They consist almost entirely of ice, which would have sublimed away by now if this were not the first time that the chondrite was passing close to the Sun.
    D)   They contain up to 10% water, which would have evaporated if the chondrite had been strongly heated.
    Ans: D   Section: 17-6

83. Which of the following biochemical materials has been found and identified in rocks recovered from outer space (e.g., meteorites)?
    A) viruses   B) living cells   C) lichens and mosses   D) amino acids
    Ans: D   Section: 17-6

84. Perhaps the most interesting material to be found inside rocks that have come to us from outer space is
    A) radioactive material.   C) carbon.
    B) amino acids or proteins.   D) pure iron.
    Ans: B   Section: 17-6

85. A meteorite is seen to impact upon the Earth and is found to contain significant amounts of ^{26}Mg, the stable decay product of radioactive ^{26}Al.. What conclusion can be drawn from this observation?
    A) Radioactivity occurs naturally in normal matter and so this finding is not surprising.
    B) An energetic nuclear event, possibly a supernova, occurred near the Sun and produced ^{26}Al at about the time that this meteorite was formed.
    C) The meteorite became so hot on its descent through Earth's atmosphere, that it became radioactive.
    D) The meteorite had probably passed through radioactive clouds in space before hitting Earth.
    Ans: B   Section: 17-6

86. What evidence do we have from meteorite studies that suggest that the formation of our Sun and solar system might have been triggered by a supernova explosion?
    A) the detection of pure iron in many meteorites
    B) the measurement of a fusion crust around most meteorites, indicating intense heating at some time
    C) the discovery of amino acids in some meteorites
    D) the discovery of the decay products of short-lived radioactive elements within some meteorites
    Ans: D   Section: 17-6

87. The Allende meteorite contained a large abundance of ^{26}Mg, an isotope of magnesium. What is the significance of this?
    A) Magnesium has a high melting point, so the asteroid of which Allende was originally a part must have formed in the inner part of the solar system.
    B) ^{26}Mg is radioactive, and the sample was probably produced in a nearby supernova explosion about the time the solar system was formed.
    C) ^{26}Mg is the stable product of the decay of radioactive ^{26}Al. The ^{26}Al from which the ^{26}Mg formed was probably produced in a nearby supernova explosion about the time the solar system was formed.
    D) This discovery suggests that heavy elements such as magnesium were more abundant in the early Kuiper Belt than we had originally thought.
    Ans: C   Section: 17-6

88. Widmanstätten patterns are a test for which kind of meteorite?
    A) stones   B) stony irons   C) irons   D) carbonaceous chondrites
    Ans: C   Section: 17-6

89. Most meteorites show evidence of having been melted or of being fragments of asteroids that were once differentiated by heat. Carbonaceous chondrites, however, are believed to have never been melted. Which one of the following is *not* a reason to believe carbonaceous chondrites have never been melted?
    A)   Carbonaceous chondrites contain complex carbon compounds, which would have been broken down into simpler compounds by high heat.
    B)   The minerals in carbonaceous chondrites contain as much as 20% water. This would have been driven out if these minerals had been heated.
    C)   Amino acids are occasionally found in carbonaceous chondrites. They would have been destroyed by melting.
    D)   Carbonaceous chondrites do not show fusion crusts after passage through Earth's atmosphere.
    Ans: D   Section: 17-6

90. Most comet nuclei are believed to be
    A)   chuncks of rock or iron chipped from asteroids by impacts.
    B)   large carbon chondrite meteoroids that have been set on fire by the Sun and are trailing long smoke trails.
    C)   chunks of water and methane ice ejected from the surface of the icy satellites of the outer planets by asteroid impacts.
    D)   chunks of dirty ice left over from the formation of the solar system.
    Ans: D   Section: 17-7

91. The major difference between the orbital paths of most asteroids and those of comets is that
    A)   comet orbits are mostly circular and in the ecliptic plane, whereas asteroids have elliptical orbits inclined at random to the ecliptic plane.
    B)   comets never approach closer to the Sun than approximately Jupiter's orbit, whereas some asteroids approach very close to the Sun.
    C)   asteroids orbit the Sun continuously, whereas all comets approach the Sun's vicinity only once before leaving the solar system.
    D)   comet orbits are highly elliptical and at random inclinations to the ecliptic plane, whereas asteroids have circular orbits in the ecliptic plane.
    Ans: D   Section: 17-7

92. The nucleus of Comet Halley, photographed close-up by the *Giotto* spacecraft, is
    A)   oblong, with a bright ice surface.
    B)   roughly spherical, moderately cratered, and covered with dark dust.
    C)   roughly spherical, icy, and covered with many cracks and grooves.
    D)   potato-shaped and darker than coal.
    Ans: D   Section: 17-7

93. The expected (and now measured, at least for Halley's Comet) size of the nucleus of a typical comet is about
    A) 10^6 km.   B) 10^7 km.   C) 10 km.   D) 100 m.
    Ans: C   Section: 17-7

94. The typical size of the coma or gas cloud surrounding the comet nucleus as it reaches its closest point to the Sun is about
    A) 10^8 km.   B) 10^7 km.   C) 10^6 km.   D) 10 km.
    Ans: C   Section: 17-7

95. What experimental technique was used to discover the huge hydrogen cloud that surrounds the nucleus and the coma of a comet?
    A)   Hubble Space Telescope IR photography
    B)   ground-based photography, at the hydrogen Balmer α wavelength
    C)   radio measurements at 21 cm wavelength
    D)   rocket-borne ultraviolet photography
    Ans: D   Section: 17-7

96. The huge hydrogen cloud that surrounds the nucleus of a comet has a typical diameter of about
    A) 1/2 AU.   B) 2 AU.   C) 1 million km.   D) 10 million km.
    Ans: D   Section: 17-7

97. Comet tails are the result of
    A)   sunlight glinting on and reflecting from the icy nucleus of the comet.
    B)   dust collected by the comet as it moves in its orbit.
    C)   solar wind particles being guided and excited to emit light by the comet's magnetic field.
    D)   melting and evaporation of ices from the comet's nucleus.
    Ans: D   Section: 17-7

98. The tail of a comet
    A)   is longest when the comet is farthest from the Sun, because then it is unaffected by sunlight.
    B)   is longest when the comet is closest to the Sun.
    C)   remains constant throughout its complete orbital path.
    D)   is longest when the comet is within the powerful gravitational field of Jupiter.
    Ans: B   Section: 17-7 and Figure 17-24

99. A comet's tail points
    A)   toward the Sun because it is caused by jets of gases evaporated off the comet's nucleus by the heat of the Sun.
    B)   back along the comet's orbit, and points away from the Sun while only the comet is approaching the Sun.
    C)   toward Jupiter because of the its gravitational pull.
    D)   away from the Sun regardless of the comet's motion.
    Ans: D   Section: 17-7 and Figure 17-24

100. A comet's gas and ion tail
    A)   always lies in the ecliptic plane, because a comet is a part of the solar system.
    B)   lies between the comet and the Sun, because of gravitational attraction.
    C)   always trails along the orbital path, because of the comet's motion.
    D)   is always blown away from the comet in the anti-Sun direction by the solar wind.
    Ans: D   Section: 17-7

101. The ionized gas tail of a comet is always aligned with
    A)   the celestial equator.
    B)   the comet's direction of motion.
    C)   the line between the comet and the nearest planet as it moves in its orbit.
    D)   the comet-Sun line.
    Ans: D   Section: 17-7

102. A comet's tail is always aligned from the comet head in a direction
    A)   away from the Sun.
    B)   toward the nearest planet, because of mutual gravitational attraction.
    C)   in a direction along its orbital path, always behind the comet.
    D)   toward the Sun, because of gravitational attraction.
    Ans: A   Section: 17-7

103. The particular feature of a comet that exhibits the most structure and always points away from the Sun is
    A)   the ion or gas tail.   C)   the dust tail.
    B)   the coma.   D)   the hydrogen envelope.
    Ans: A   Section: 17-7

104. Which of the following governs the direction in which a comet's ion tail is aligned in space?
    A)   its direction of motion, because the tail simply trails behind it in its orbit
    B)   the gravitational attraction of the Sun for the tail material
    C)   the gravitational attraction of Earth for the tail material
    D)   the flow of solar wind past the comet's nucleus
    Ans: D   Section: 17-7

105. The dust tail of a comet has which of the following characteristics?
    A) curved, wide, without structure, and transparent to starlight
    B) spherical, very large, and of low brightness, centered on the comet nucleus, showing up on only UV photographs
    C) narrow, straight, and pointed directly at the Sun at all times
    D) long, straight, structured, and pointed directly away from the Sun
    Ans: A   Section: 17-7

106. Dust grains released by the melting of ice in a comet nucleus
    A) drift away from the Sun along magnetic field lines, outlining the structure of this field.
    B) become a uniform, curved tail, moving away from the comet under radiation pressure from sunlight.
    C) become a cloud around the nucleus, the coma, scattering sunlight very efficiently at blue wavelengths.
    D) become a straight, highly structured, and very variable tail, blown away from the comet by the solar wind.
    Ans: B   Section: 17-7

107. The orbits of comets are
    A) randomly oriented in the solar system and can extend far beyond the orbit of Pluto.
    B) randomly oriented in the solar system and confined to distances closer to the Sun than approximately the orbit of Pluto.
    C) primarily in the plane of the ecliptic and confined to distances closer to the Sun than approximately the orbit of Pluto.
    D) primarily in the plane of the ecliptic and can extend far out beyond the orbit of Pluto.
    Ans: A   Section: 17-7

108. If the sidereal period of Halley's Comet is about 76 years, how far will this comet be from the Sun when it reaches its farthest point from the Sun, or aphelion? (Caution: This calculation needs Kepler's law and a little care. Assume that the comet's perihelion distance from the Sun is negligible.)
    A) about 36 AU—between the orbits of Neptune and Pluto
    B) about 18 AU—between the orbits of Saturn and Uranus
    C) about 9 AU—between the orbits of Jupiter and Saturn
    D) about 1324 AU—well beyond the orbit of Pluto
    Ans: A   Section: 17-7

109. Which one of the following parts of a comet is not visible to the naked eye?
    A) dust tail   B) ion tail   C) coma   D) hydrogen envelope
    Ans: D   Section: 17-7

110. The aphelion (farthest distance from the Sun) of a comet's orbit
    A)   are all located far beyond the orbit of Pluto.
    B)   are all closer to the Sun than the orbit of Pluto.
    C)   are mostly confined to the region between Mars and Jupiter, although some have orbits reaching well beyond Pluto.
    D)   can be located anywhere from inside the orbit of Pluto to as far as 100,000 AU from the Sun.
    Ans: D   Section: 17-8

111. What is the Kuiper belt?
    A)   a band of dust in the plane of the ecliptic, extending from near the orbit of Mars to beyond the orbit of Pluto
    B)   the broadest band of asteroids in the asteroid belt, separated from other bands by Kirkwood Gaps
    C)   a relatively flat distribution of comets in the plane of the ecliptic, extending from around the orbit of Pluto out to about 500 AU from the Sun
    D)   an approximate spherical distribution of comets centered on the Sun, and extending out to about 50,000 AU
    Ans: C   Section: 17-8

112. Where are the comets that we find in the Kuiper belt believed to have formed?
    A)   in the inner solar system. Sunlight, and the solar wind acting over billions of years, have pushed them out past the orbit of Pluto
    B)   in elliptical orbits extending out to tens of thousands of AU, and gravitational interactions with the giant planets have circularized their orbits into a band beyond Pluto
    C)   exactly where we see them now, in a band beyond the orbit of Pluto
    D)   between the orbits of Jupiter and Neptune. They were flung out beyond Pluto by gravitational interactions with the giant planets.
    Ans: C   Section: 17-8

113. The Oort cloud is
    A)   a band of dust in the plane of the ecliptic, extending from the orbit of Mars to beyond the orbit of Pluto.
    B)   an approximate spherical distribution of comets centered on the Sun, extending out to about 50,000 AU.
    C)   another name for the early solar nebula.
    D)   a relatively flat distribution of comets in the plane of the ecliptic, extending from around the orbit of Pluto out to about 500 AU from the Sun.
    Ans: B   Section: 17-8

114. The most likely origin of the "dirty snowballs" that become long-period comets when deflected into orbits bringing them closer to the Sun, is
   A) the Oort cloud surrounding the solar system.
   B) the surfaces of the moons of Jupiter and Saturn.
   C) the gas clouds in the Milky Way.
   D) the asteroid belt.
   Ans: A   Section: 17-8

115. The Oort cloud of comets, which surrounds the solar system at a distance of about 50,000 AU, is believed to be
   A) material flung out of the inner solar system by the gravity of the newly formed giant planets early in the solar system history.
   B) an interstellar cloud through which the Sun and planets happen to be passing, but which is not otherwise connected to the solar system.
   C) debris left behind at that distance by the collapse of the interstellar cloud that formed the Sun and planets.
   D) material captured from interstellar space by the Sun's gravity.
   Ans: A   Section: 17-8

116. Why do most comets have very elliptical orbits, often extending far out beyond the orbit of Pluto?
   A) They originally formed in circular orbits far from the Sun (> 500 AU), and passing stars have perturbed them into long, elliptical orbits.
   B) They are interstellar objects that have been captured in orbit by the Sun.
   C) They formed so far from the Sun (e.g., 10,000 AU) that their orbits naturally drop deeply into the inner solar system.
   D) They originally formed inside the orbit of Pluto and were flung into highly elongated orbits by the giant planets.
   Ans: D   Section: 17-8

117. What is the approximate orbital period of a comet nucleus that is moving in a circular orbit around the Sun in the Oort cloud?
   A) 1000 years   B) 100,000 years   C) 10,000 years   D) 10 million years
   Ans: D   Section: 17-8

118. The nearest star beyond the Sun is Proxima Centauri, which is approximately 4.22 light years away. Suppose Proxima Centauri is surrounded by an Oort cloud the same size as our own. What would be the distance between these Oort clouds as a fraction of the distance between these two stars?
   A) 0.27   B) 0.63   C) 0.87   D) 0.99
   Ans: B   Section: 17-8

119. A typical comet loses what fraction of its mass each time it passes close to the Sun (i.e., at each perihelion passage)?
    A) less than 0.001%   B) 10%   C) 0.1%   D) 0.5% to 1%
    Ans: D   Section: 17-9

120. The number of times that a typical comet can pass close to the Sun (i.e., the number of orbits that the comet can complete) before it completely vaporizes is between
    A) 10,000 and 50,000.   B) 1 and 5.   C) 10 and 25.   D) 100 and 200.
    Ans: D   Section: 17-9

121. Showers of shooting stars or meteors are seen at regular times each year on Earth because
    A)   Earth passes through the fringes of the asteroid belt at these times.
    B)   Earth is bombarded by material, including dust grains, ejected from the Sun during regular sunspot activity.
    C)   Earth runs into material within the spiral arm structure of the Milky Way at these times.
    D)   Earth passes through a cloud of remnant dust and rock fragments from an old comet that is circling the Sun in the comet's old orbit.
    Ans: D   Section: 17-9

122. A meteor shower occurs when
    A)   the Earth passes through the asteroid belt.
    B)   the head of a comet hits the Earth's atmosphere.
    C)   a meteor is about to get married.
    D)   the Earth passes through a swarm of dust particles in space.
    Ans: D   Section: 17-9

123. A meteor shower results from
    A)   material re-entering the Earth's atmosphere after being ejected into space by violent volcanic eruptions on Earth.
    B)   a small piece of rock or asteroid fragmenting as it passes through the Earth's atmosphere.
    C)   a meteor passing through a rain cloud on the Earth.
    D)   the Earth passing through debris strewn along a comet's orbit.
    Ans: D   Section: 17-9

124. A meteor shower, the appearance of greater than average numbers of "shooting stars" at a particular time in the year from a specific direction in the sky, is related to which astronomical phenomenon?
    A) the Earth's passage through different parts of the spiral arms of the galaxy
    B) the passage of Earth through the remnants of an old comet
    C) the passage of Earth through intense streams of solar material, including dust particles, during regular solar activity
    D) the Earth's passage through part of the asteroid belt
    Ans: B   Section: 17-9

125. Why do the meteors that are seen in the sky in a particular meteor shower appear to come from one specific direction in the sky?
    A) Meteors appear only to come from a specific direction because of the Earth's orbital motion.
    B) This specific direction is always along the ecliptic plane because meteor showers occur when Earth catches up with a bunch of particles moving in the Earth's orbit.
    C) This is the direction of the orbit of the comet that disintegrated to produce the shower.
    D) This direction is that along which objects being attracted to the Sun by its gravity will pass.
    Ans: C   Section: 17-9

126. Recent calculations show that the Tunguska explosion in Siberia in 1908, which had an explosive power of several hundred kilotons of TNT, was probably caused by
    A) a small comet nucleus about 150 m across suddenly vaporizing in the atmosphere.
    B) the impact and annihilation of a very small amount of antimatter from somewhere else in the universe.
    C) a small natural nuclear explosion in uranium deposits.
    D) a small stony asteroid about 80 m across disintegrating explosively in the atmosphere before hitting the ground.
    Ans: D   Section: 17-9

127. Suppose an intense meteor shower occurs on a certain date this year, but there was no shower last year on that date, and it turns out that there is no shower next year on that date. A likely explanation is that
    A) this year the Earth passed through the orbit of a recently disintegrated comet, one for which the debris is not yet distributed along the entire orbit.
    B) a small comet has passed through the Earth's atmosphere.
    C) the meteor shower is the remnant of a comet that had a semimajor axis larger than one AU and a period longer than one year.
    D) the debris along the orbit was mostly fine dust, which has been blown away by the solar wind.
    Ans: A   Section: 17-9

Chapter 18: Our Star, the Sun

1. The Sun's source of energy at the present time is thought to be
   A) thermonuclear fusion (combining) of hydrogen atoms.
   B) thermonuclear fission (splitting) of heavy elements into hydrogen.
   C) chemical burning of hydrogen gas with oxygen.
   D) gravitational contraction.
   Ans: A   Section: 18-1

2. At the present time, the energy of the Sun is generated
   A) in its central core only, by fission of heavy nuclei.
   B) by the release of gravitational energy as the Sun slowly shrinks.
   C) in the central core by fusion of helium nuclei and in an outer shell by fusion of hydrogen nuclei.
   D) in its central core only, by fusion of hydrogen nuclei.
   Ans: D   Section: 18-1

3. What is the Sun's energy source?
   A) primordial heat left over from the release of gravitational energy when the Sun first formed
   B) radioactivity
   C) thermonuclear fusion in the core
   D) heat released by gravitational contraction
   Ans: C   Section: 18-1

4. What process provides the power for the Sun?
   A) fusion of helium into carbon   C) emission of neutrinos
   B) fission of uranium to form lead   D) fusion of hydrogen into helium
   Ans: D   Section: 18-1

5. In the thermonuclear process that heats the Sun, the nuclei of which chemical elements are converted to other nuclei to produce the requisite energy?
   A) hydrogen to helium
   B) uranium to lead
   C) helium to hydrogen
   D) spitting of the very abundant iron to lighter elements in a chain reaction, eventually leading to hydrogen
   Ans: A   Section: 18-1

6. Nuclear fusion is
   A) the combining of electrons with nuclei to produce atoms and release energy.
   B) the combining of hydrogen atoms to produce hydrogen molecules, H_2, and energy.
   C) the process of fusing together light nuclei (e.g., hydrogen) to produce heavier nuclei (e.g., helium) and energy.
   D) the splitting of heavier nuclei to produce lighter nuclei and energy.
   Ans: C   Section: 18-1 and Box 18-1

7. What is nuclear fusion?
   A) a heavy nucleus splitting apart to form two lighter nuclei
   B) the attachment of electrons to nuclei to form atoms
   C) two nuclei sticking together to form a new, heavier nucleus
   D) a nucleus changing to become the nucleus of a different element by emitting an electron and a neutrino
   Ans: C   Section: 18-1

8. The nuclei of which chemical elements are converted to other nuclei to produce the requisite energy in the thermonuclear process that heats the Sun?
   A) Helium is split into hydrogen.
   B) The abundant iron is successively split into lighter elements in a chain reaction to produce helium and hydrogen.
   C) Hydrogen is converted to helium.
   D) Carbon, nitrogen, and oxygen are used as catalysts in a chain reaction to combine hydrogen to produce helium.
   Ans: C   Section: 18-1

9. At the present time, the dominant energy source that powers the Sun is
   A) release of gravitational energy as the Sun slowly contracts.
   B) thermonuclear fusion of helium into heavier elements in the core.
   C) release of energy trapped in strong magnetic fields.
   D) thermonuclear fusion of hydrogen into helium in the core.
   Ans: D   Section: 18-1

10. Thermonuclear fusion reactions in the core of the Sun convert four hydrogen nuclei into one helium nucleus. The helium nucleus has
    A) less mass than the four hydrogen nuclei, the lost mass becoming energy in an amount given by $E = mc^2$.
    B) the same mass as the four hydrogen nuclei, because the mass of any product has to equal the mass of the sum of its parts by the law of conservation of matter.
    C) an undetermined amount of mass that depends on the temperature at which the reaction occurs.
    D) more mass than the four hydrogen nuclei, because energy is produced in the reaction, and this energy adds the extra mass, $m = E/c^2$.
    Ans: A   Section: 18-1

11. Who first postulated that hydrogen fusion reactions might be responsible for generating the energy produced by the Sun?
    A) Roger Atkinson and Arthur Eddington
    B) Lord Kelvin and Hermann von Helmholtz
    C) Stephen Hawking
    D) Albert Einstein
    Ans: A   Section: 18-1 and Box 18-1

12. When four protons collide to form helium, what fraction of the original mass of the protons is converted to energy?
    A) 1/20 of a percent   B) 0.7%   C) 100%   D) 4%
    Ans: B   Section: 18-1 and Box 18-1

13. By how much does the mass of the Sun decrease each second because of the energy it radiates (its luminosity)? (See the discussion in Box 18-1 of Freedman and Kaufmann, *Universe*, 7th ed.)
    A) 4.2×10^9 kg   B) 3.9×10^{26} kg   C) 2.0×10^7 kg   D) 6.0×10^{11} kg
    Ans: A   Section: 18-1 and Box 18-1

14. How much hydrogen is converted into helium and energy in the Sun each second?
    A) 600 million tons   B) 6 billion tons   C) 600 tons   D) 6 tons
    Ans: A   Section: 18-1 and Box 18-1

15. Hydrogen "burning" by fusion reactions occurs only in the deep interior of the Sun (and other stars), because this is the only place in the Sun where
    A) there is sufficient hydrogen.
    B) the density is sufficiently low for the high temperature atoms to build up enough energy to collide and undergo fusion.
    C) the temperature is low enough and the density is high enough to allow hydrogen atoms to collide with each other often enough for fusion to occur.
    D) the requisite conditions of high temperature and high density occur.
    Ans: D   Section: 18-1

16. How much longer can the Sun continue to generate energy by nuclear reactions in its core?
    A) about 500,000 years   C) about 5 billion years
    B) about 50 billion years   D) about 5 million years
    Ans: C   Section: 18-1

17. Approximately where is the Sun in terms of its total lifetime?
    A) It is about halfway through its life.
    B) It is only 1/10 of the way through its life.
    C) It is about 3/4 of the way through its life.
    D) It is about 1/4 of the way through its life.
    Ans: A   Section: 18-1 and Box 18-1

18. The total time that the Sun will spend converting hydrogen to helium in its core is
    A) less than 1 million years.
    B) at least 200 billion years (2×10^{11}) years.
    C) about 4.5 million years.
    D) about 10 billion years (10^{10} years).
    Ans: D   Section: 18-1

19. The contraction of a star (or other object) due to its own gravity generates heat. If this process, known as the Kelvin-Helmholtz mechanism, were to be the source of heat energy from the Sun, then the Sun's age
    A) would be about 10,000 years.
    B) would be about 1 billion years.
    C) would be about 25 million years.
    D) could easily be its present age of 4.5 billion years.
    Ans: C   Section: 18-1

20. A positron is
    A) an antielectron, similar to a normal electron but with inverse properties, including a positive electrical charge.
    B) another name for a proton, or a positively charged hydrogen nucleus.
    C) a charged neutron.
    D) a positively charged neutrino, having positive charge and very small or zero mass.
    Ans: A   Section: 18-1, Box 18-1

21. What is a positron?
    A) the nucleus of a helium atom   C) the nucleus of a hydrogen atom
    B) a positive electron   D) a chargeless, massless particle
    Ans: B   Section: 18-1 and Box 18-1

22. A positron is
    A) a positively charged neutrino.
    B) a positively charged electron.
    C) a charged neutron.
    D) a positively charged particle with intermediate mass between a proton and an electron.
    Ans: B   Section: 18-1 and Box 18-1

23. What happens to the positrons produced by the nuclear reactions in the core of the Sun?
    A) They collide with electrons, producing energy.
    B) They collide and stick together to form helium.
    C) They combine with neutrons to form protons.
    D) They escape from the Sun into space.
    Ans: A   Section: 18-1 and Box 18-1

24. How does the average density of the Sun compare to that of Jupiter?
    A) The Sun is considerably less dense than Jupiter.
    B) It is not possible to specify an average density for an object as large as the Sun.
    C) The Sun is many times denser than Jupiter.
    D) The Sun has approximately the same average density as Jupiter.
    Ans: D   Section: 18-1, Table 18-1 and Appendix 2

25. The Sun is about a thousand times more massive than the planet Jupiter. Why, then, does it have about the same average density as Jupiter?
    A) The Sun has a much weaker gravitational field than Jupiter.
    B) The Sun is rotating much faster than Jupiter and is supported by the resulting centrifugal force.
    C) The Sun is composed of lighter elements than Jupiter.
    D) The Sun is much hotter than Jupiter and is supported by the resulting high pressure.
    Ans: D   Section: 18-1, Table 18-1 and Appendix 2

26. How much matter is converted into energy in the Sun each second?
    A) 2×10^7 kg   B) 4.2×10^9 kg   C) 6.0×10^{11} kg   D) 3.9×10^{26} kg
    Ans: C   Section: 18-1 and Box 18-1

27. The phrase "hydrostatic equilibrium" in the Sun refers to
    A) the balance of gas pressure outward and magnetic forces inward.
    B) the creation of one helium nucleus for the "destruction" of every four hydrogen nuclei.
    C) the balance of gas pressure inward and heat outward.
    D) the balance of gravity inward and gas pressure outward.
    Ans: D   Section: 18-2

28. The Sun has existed for a very long time without change in its size, appearance, or behavior. This means that it must be in hydrostatic equilibrium. Under these conditions, which two parameters must be in exact balance within the Sun?
    A) numbers of hydrogen and helium nuclei
    B) hydrogen gas pressure and helium gas pressure
    C) inward force of gravity and outward gas pressure
    D) magnetic field and force of gravity
    Ans: C   Section: 18-2

29. Any massive object will collapse under its own weight unless something stops it. In an ordinary star like the Sun, this collapse is prevented by
    A) the rotation of the star.
    B) the star's solid core.
    C) gas pressure pushing outward.
    D) turbulence and upwelling in the atmosphere of the star.
    Ans: C   Section: 18-2

30. What stops the Sun from collapsing under the force of its own gravity?
    A) Ions and electrons are pushed apart by the electric forces between their charges.
    B) The interior of the Sun is under such high pressure that it is a liquid, and liquids are incompressible.
    C) It is held up by the pressure of the very high temperature gas within it.
    D) The very large number of neutrinos within the core collide with gas atoms and prevent them from falling inward.
    Ans: C   Section: 18-2

31. Which of the three ways by which heat energy can be transmitted from one place to another—radiation, conduction, convection—is important in the solar interior below the surface of the Sun?
    A) radiation and convection   C) conduction and convection
    B) conduction and radiation   D) radiation alone, by photons of energy
    Ans: A   Section: 18-2

32. Of the three ways in which energy is transported in nature (radiation, conduction, convection), which two are important in the Sun?
    A) The statement is wrong—all three are equally important in the Sun.
    B) radiation and convection
    C) convection and conduction
    D) radiation and conduction
    Ans: B   Section: 18-2

33. The energy transfer process that operates in the Sun via mass motion is known as
    A) thermonuclear fusion.   B) conduction.   C) radiation.   D) convection.
    Ans: D   Section: 18-2

34. The mechanism at work when energy is transmitted by convection is
    A) the successive exchange of radiant energy between atoms.
    B) the passage of radiation through a gas.
    C) the fusion of hydrogen nuclei into helium nuclei.
    D) the mass motion of hot gases.
    Ans: D   Section: 18-2

35. The average time taken for energy generated by thermonuclear fusion in the center of the Sun to reach the surface layers and escape is calculated to be
    A) just a few seconds, because this energy travels at the speed of light.
    B) about 10 million years.
    C) about 1 year.
    D) 170,000 years.
    Ans: D   Section: 18-2

36. Energy is transported from the center of the Sun to the surface
    A)   by radiation in the central thermonuclear core and convection through the rest of the interior.
    B)   mostly by convection but with radiation in the outer layers.
    C)   by convection in the central thermonuclear core and radiation through the rest of the interior.
    D)   mostly by radiation but with convection in the outer layers.
    Ans: D   Section: 18-2

37. What is the dominant mechanism by which energy is transported through the core of the Sun?
    A)   by photons (radiative transport of energy)
    B)   by collisions of faster-moving particles with slower-moving particles (conductive transport of energy)
    C)   by neutrinos streaming outward through the Sun's material (particle transport of energy)
    D)   by hotter gas rising and cooler gas falling (convective transport of energy)
    Ans: A   Section: 18-2

38. What is the dominant mechanism by which energy is transported through the outer regions of the solar interior?
    A)   by photons (radiative transport of energy)
    B)   by neutrinos streaming outward through the Sun's material (particle transport of energy)
    C)   by collisions of faster-moving particles with slower-moving particles (conductive transport of energy)
    D)   by hotter gas rising and cooler gas falling (convective transport of energy)
    Ans: D   Section: 18-2

39. Represented as a fraction of the solar radius, convection currents in the Sun's interior occupy what fraction of the Sun?
    A)   only about 1% of the radius
    B)   the outer 29% of the radius
    C)   only the inner 9% of the radius, at the core
    D)   100%, the whole radius
    Ans: B   Section: 18-2

40. From the center outward, the order of the layers or parts of the Sun is
    A)   radiative zone, convection zone, corona, chromosphere, photosphere.
    B)   radiative zone, convection zone, chromosphere, photosphere, corona.
    C)   corona, chromosphere, convection zone, photosphere, radiative zone.
    D)   radiative zone, convection zone, photosphere, chromosphere, corona.
    Ans: D   Section: 18-2, 18-5, 18-6 and 18-7

41. The temperature at the center of the Sun, where thermonuclear processes take place, is approximately
    A)   about 4500 K, as shown by holes in the Sun.
    B)   1.5 million K.
    C)   6000 K.
    D) 1.5×10^7 K.
    Ans: D   Section: 18-2

42. The temperature of the Sun throughout its radius and including its atmosphere
    A)   is almost constant from the center to the surface but falls abruptly just above the visible surface.
    B)   decreases outward from the center, but increases several times at certain specific radial distances from the center, before decreasing to match the temperature of interplanetary space.
    C)   decreases outward from the center, but then increases again.
    D)   decreases continuously outward from the center, gradually merging into the cold of the interplanetary medium.
    Ans: C   Section: 18-2, 18-6 and 18-7

43. According to the theoretical model of the Sun tabulated in Table 18-2 and shown graphically in Fig. 18- 4 of Freedman and Kaufmann, *Universe*, 6th ed., within what radial distance of the solar center is the vast majority of solar energy generated?
    A)   0.8 or 80%
    B)   0.25 or 25%
    C)   100%—because energy is generated throughout the whole Sun
    D)   0.60 or 60%
    Ans: B   Section: 18-2

44. The core of the Sun, in which all the Sun's thermonuclear energy is produced, takes up about
    A)   1/10 of the Sun's radius.   C)   less than 1/100 of the Sun's radius.
    B)   ½ the Sun's radius.   D)   ¼ of the Sun's radius.
    Ans: D   Section: 18-2

45. Where is most of the mass of the Sun concentrated?
    A)   It is spread uniformly through the Sun.
    B)   in the inner core
    C)   in the photosphere
    D)   in the convective zone
    Ans: B   Section: 18-2

46. Virtually all of the Sun's mass is concentrated within what fraction of its radius?
    A)   the innermost 10%   C)   the innermost 60%
    B)   the innermost 30%   D)   the outer 70%
    Ans: C   Section: 18-2 and Table 18-2

47. Half of the Sun's mass is concentrated in what fraction of its *volume*? (The volume of a sphere is proportional to the cube of its radius.)
    A) the innermost 2%   B) the innermost 10%   C) the innermost 25%   D) 50%
    Ans: A   Section: 18-2 and Box 18-2

48. What is the nature and extent of the oscillations and waves in the Sun?
    A)   There are many millions of pure "tones" or frequencies.
    B)   They have one very specific frequency, the resonant frequency of the Sun, whose period is close to 5 minutes.
    C)   There are several billion known frequencies or "tones."
    D)   There are now 10 known harmonics of the resonant frequency of the Sun, all at very specific frequencies.
    Ans: A   Section: 18-3

49. How do the low-frequency sound waves associated with the 5-minute oscillations traverse the interior of the Sun?
    A)   They move in straight lines from point to point but lose energy when they reach the solar surface.
    B)   They move in straight lines from point to point and reflect from the underside of the surface, bouncing back and forth across the Sun.
    C)   They follow curved paths through the interior and reflect from the underside of the solar surface.
    D)   They follow curved paths through the interior but lose energy in raising the solar surface, disappearing when they reach the underside of the surface.
    Ans: C   Section: 18-3

50. What measurements first showed the 5-minute oscillations of the Sun's surface?
    A)   high-resolution positional observations of the edge of the solar disk
    B)   high precision Doppler shifts of spectral lines
    C)   measurement of the modulation of radio emissions from the solar surface, similar to the modulation used to transmit sound signals by radio on Earth
    D)   Zeeman effect measurements of magnetically sensitive lines
    Ans: B   Section: 18-3

51. In recent times, one method that has been used successfully to investigate the deep interior of the Sun has been to observe
    A)   the spectrum and behavior of a sunspot, whose roots are deep inside the Sun.
    B)   the deep atmospheric conditions, as encountered by a spacecraft as it entered the solar atmosphere.
    C)   regular 5-minute oscillations and fluctuations of the surface.
    D)   the progress of a solar-impacting comet.
    Ans: C   Section: 18-3

52. Which of the following lines of research is NOT used in the study of the solar interior?
    A)   cosmic ray interactions with the Earth's atmosphere
    B)   neutrino astronomy
    C)   observations of surface oscillations on the Sun
    D)   magnetic field and sunspot studies
    Ans: A   Section: 18-3 and 18-9

53. The study of solar oscillations has provided information about each of the following topics *except one*. Which one is the exception?
    A)   the amount of helium in the Sun's core
    B)   the explanation for the solar neutrino problem
    C)   the thickness of the transition region between the radiation zone and the convection zone
    D)   the thickness of the convective zone
    Ans: B   Section: 18-3

54. The neutrino is
    A)   an uncharged nuclear particle with mass intermediate between those of the electron and the proton, like a low-mass neutron, capable of penetrating large thicknesses of matter.
    B)   another name for an electron that carries a positive charge instead of a negative charge.
    C)   a heavy, uncharged nuclear particle, easily detected.
    D)   an elusive, subatomic particle having little or no mass, and very difficult to detect.
    Ans: D   Section: 18-4

55. The neutrino is
    A)   a tiny particle that interacts very weakly with matter, with extremely low or zero mass and no charge.
    B)   another name for the neutron, a component of almost all atomic nuclei, with a mass close to the proton and no charge.
    C)   another name for a photon of very high energy, i.e., short wavelength electromagnetic radiation, with great penetrating power.
    D)   a massive but very elusive nuclear particle that carries most of the energy generated in the core of the Sun to the surface, but that then decays to release electromagnetic radiation (i.e., light).
    Ans: A   Section: 18-4

56. Which of the following physical products is NOT produced by the Sun during the thermonuclear process, in which hydrogen nuclei are combined together in its core?
    A)   neutrinos
    B)   heavy nuclei such as uranium
    C)   helium nuclei
    D)   electrons (with positive charge, known as positrons)
    Ans: B   Section: 18-1, 18-4

57. Apart from the helium nuclei and energy that are produced in thermonuclear reactions between protons in the center of the Sun, what are the other byproducts?
    A) γ rays, negative electrons, and neutrinos
    B) positive electrons (positrons), γ rays and neutrinos
    C) γ rays and neutrinos
    D) protons, neutrinos, and negative electrons
    Ans: B   Section: 18-1 and 18-4

58. What happens to the neutrinos produced by the nuclear reactions in the core of the Sun?
    A) They collide and stick together with protons to form helium nuclei.
    B) They escape from the Sun into space.
    C) They combine with protons to form neutrons.
    D) They collide with electrons, producing energy.
    Ans: B   Section: 18-4

59. How many neutrinos pass through your outstretched hand (10 × 10 cm) from the Sun every second, day and night?
    A) 1 trillion or 10^{12}
    B) 1 trillion or 10^{12} in daytime—almost none during the night because they are stopped by the Earth
    C) 10 billion or 10^{10}
    D) only a few hundred, otherwise we would notice them
    Ans: A   Section: 18-4

60. A neutrino produced in the nuclear furnace in the core of the Sun
    A) can penetrate easily through both the gas of the Sun's interior and the solid Earth.
    B) can penetrate easily through both the gaseous Sun's interior and the solid Earth but will be easily stopped by chemicals containing chlorine.
    C) can penetrate easily through the Sun's gaseous interior but will be stopped just below the surface of the solid Earth.
    D) can penetrate easily through the Sun's interior but will be deflected away from the Earth by its magnetic field.
    Ans: A   Section: 18-4

61. Which of the following particles or types of radiation will provide the most direct information on the processes of nuclear fusion that are occurring in the solar core?
    A) protons in the solar wind and from solar flares
    B) neutrinos
    C) highly penetrating X rays
    D) visible light from the photosphere
    Ans: B   Section: 18-4

62. The time taken for neutrinos generated in the thermonuclear reactions at the center of the Sun to escape from its surface is
    A)   about 170,000 years, just like the electromagnetic energy.
    B)   about 1 million years.
    C)   extremely short—a small fraction of a second—because they travel faster than the speed of light.
    D)   a few seconds.
    Ans: D   Section: 18-4

63. Which technique has been used for the past 25 years to attempt to measure solar neutrinos?
    A)   measuring the interaction of neutrinos with water molecules in huge underground tanks
    B)   production of radioactive argon nuclei by neutrino interaction with chlorine nuclei in deep underground tanks
    C)   measuring the proton-proton reaction in liquid hydrogen, where neutrinos play an intermediate role
    D)   measuring the interactions of neutrinos with radioactive argon nuclei producing chlorine nuclei that can be measured chemically
    Ans: B   Section: 18-4

64. The solar neutrino experiment designed by Raymond Davis has detected a rate of solar neutrinos arriving at the Earth that is
    A)   about 1/3 of the predicted rate.
    B)   almost exactly equal to the predicted rate.
    C)   less than 1% of the predicted rate.
    D)   almost double the predicted rate.
    Ans: A   Section: 18-4

65. The Chlorine-Argon neutrino detectors, like the one used by Davis, detect only neutrinos from a low-yield side branch of the main nuclear reaction in the Sun. Galium-Germanium neutrino detectors were developed to detect neutrinos from the main nuclear reaction itself. When these detectors were used it was found that
    A)   the measured neutrino flux was the originally predicted value—thus solving the solar neutrino problem.
    B)   the neutrino flux was still too low.
    C)   the neutrino flux was considerably higher than predicted, thus indicating a new solar neutrino problem.
    D)   the neutrinos being detected were not from the sun at all but from other sources.
    Ans: B   Section: 18-4

66. Which of the following seems to be the correct explanation for the low neutrino rates detected by Davis and others?
    A)   The neutrinos *oscillate* and change their nature *en route* from the Sun to the Earth.
    B)   The core of the Sun is actually about 10% cooler than had been originally predicted.
    C)   The Davis result was subjected to much uncertainty because it measured only a small yield side branch of the main nuclear reaction.
    D)   The neutrinos Davis detected were not coming from the Sun but instead of the Sun.
    Ans: A   Section: 18-4

67. Why should you NEVER look directly at the Sun?
    A)   It uses up valuable time.
    B)   Looking directly at the Sun causes blindness.
    C)   It can lead to baldness.
    D)   It is bad for the complexion.
    Ans: B   Section: 18-5

68. What is the photosphere of the Sun?
    A)   the core of the Sun, where nuclear energy is generated
    B)   the region of convecting gases below the visible surface of the Sun
    C)   the middle layer of the Sun's atmosphere
    D)   the visible "surface" of the Sun
    Ans: D   Section: 18-5

69. What is the Sun's photosphere?
    A)   the middle layer of the Sun's atmosphere
    B)   the lowest layer of the Sun's atmosphere
    C)   the envelope of convective mass motion in the outer interior of the Sun
    D)   the upper layer of the Sun's atmosphere
    Ans: B   Section: 18-5

70. What name is given to the visible "surface" of the Sun?
    A) corona   B) chromosphere   C) prominence   D) photosphere
    Ans: D   Section: 18-5

71. The thickness of the "photosphere," or the visible "surface" of the Sun, is about
    A) 1 km.   B) 300–400 km.   C) 3,000–4000 km.   D) 10,000 km.
    Ans: B   Section: 18-5

72. What causes the granular appearance of the surface of the Sun?
    A)   the regular impact of meteoroids and comets on the solar surface
    B)   differential rotation of the surface layers
    C)   thermonuclear fusion in its interior
    D)   convective motion under the solar surface
    Ans: D   Section: 18-5

73. Granulation, or the mottled appearance of the whole solar surface, is an indication of what physical process at work in the Sun?
    A)   convective motion of gases in the upper portion of the Sun's interior
    B)   thermonuclear fusion of hydrogen in the Sun's surface layers
    C)   the selective absorption by surface layers of neutrinos from the interior
    D)   magnetic field concentration under the solar surface
    Ans: A   Section: 18-5

74. Granulation on the surface of the Sun is caused by
    A)   magnetic field disturbances above the solar surface.
    B)   nuclear fusion processes occurring just beneath the surface.
    C)   differential rotation of the fluid surface.
    D)   convective currents carrying heat from beneath the surface.
    Ans: D   Section: 18-5

75. The granulation pattern seen on the surface of the Sun results from
    A)   heating of the photosphere by solar flares.
    B)   the differential rotation of the Sun.
    C)   strong magnetic fields cooling the gas in certain regions.
    D)   convection of gas in the region under the photosphere.
    Ans: D   Section: 18-5

76. A typical granule on the surface of the Sun
    A)   is about 1000 km across and lasts for a few minutes.
    B)   arches quietly for several days over a sunspot group.
    C)   is about 30,000 km across and lasts for several hours.
    D)   is a few thousand kilometers across and lasts for about two solar rotations.
    Ans: A   Section: 18-5

77. The surface of the Sun is divided into light-colored areas with dark boundaries in a cellular pattern. What are these cells called?
    A) granules   B) spicules   C) sunspots   D) filaments
    Ans: A   Section: 18-5

78. What is the cellular granulation pattern seen on the visible surface of the Sun?
    A)   The cells are regions of nuclear energy generation in the Sun's photosphere.
    B)   The cells are the bases of circulation patterns that extend from the photosphere to the outer corona.
    C)   Each cell is a region of stronger magnetic field that compresses and heats the gas within it.
    D)   The cells are the tops of rising blobs of hot gas in the Sun's convective interior.
    Ans: D   Section: 18-5

79. The granular appearance of the surface of the Sun is evidence of what phenomenon occurring in or on the Sun?
    A)   the regular impact of meteoroids and comets on the solar surface
    B)   thermonuclear fusion in its interior
    C)   rapid rotation of the surface layers
    D)   convective motion under the solar surface
    Ans: D   Section: 18-5

80. The centers of the granular cells on the surface of the Sun are brighter than the edges of the cells because
    A)   the centers are composed of different gases than the edges.
    B)   the centers are hotter than the edges.
    C)   the centers are denser than the edges.
    D)   the centers are cooler than the edges.
    Ans: B   Section: 18-5

81. Spectral lines observed in the granules on the Sun's surface near the center of the Sun's disk
    A)   are split by the Zeeman effect due to the strong magnetic fields in the granule.
    B)   are always redshifted, because granules are caused by gas descending into the Sun.
    C)   are redshifted near the center of the granule and blueshifted near the edge of the granule.
    D)   are blueshifted near the center of the granule and redshifted near the edge of the granule.
    Ans: D   Section: 18-5

82. If granulation on the Sun's surface is a result of convective motion below it, and material is upwelling at the centers of granular cells and returning in the regions between cells, what is the expected temperature distribution across a granular cell?
    A)   The center of a cell will be cooler than the edges.
    B)   Alternate cell centers will be hot and cold, with the edges at an intermediate temperature.
    C)   Temperature will be uniform across the cell.
    D)   The center of a cell will be hotter than the edges.
    Ans: D   Section: 18-5

83. If the temperature at the edge of a solar granular cell is 5500 K and the center of the cell is 300 K hotter, what will be the ratio of fluxes of energy out of these two regions of the Sun (i.e., brightness contrast)? (See Box 5-2, Freedman and Kaufmann, *Universe,* 7th ed.)
    A)   center brighter than edge by a factor of 1.11
    B)   center brighter than edge by a factor of 1.05
    C)   edge brighter than center by a factor of 1.24
    D)   center brighter than edge by a factor of 1.24
    Ans: D   Section: 18-5 and Box 5-2

84. At visible wavelengths, what type of intensity distribution does one see at the edge or limb of the Sun?
    A)   an image of uniform brightness right to the limb
    B)   an image with uniform distribution except where active regions occur
    C)   limb darkening
    D)   limb brightening
    Ans: C   Section: 18-5

85. The center of the disk of the visible Sun appears brighter than its edges because
    A)   at the center of the disk, we see a greater contribution from the corona of the Sun.
    B)   we see into deeper and hotter layers at the center of the disk.
    C)   we see into deeper and cooler layers at the center of the solar disk.
    D)   cooler sunspots are more visible at the Sun's edge than they are at the center of the disk.
    Ans: B   Section: 18-5

86. When we view the Sun's disk in visible light, we see less deeply into the Sun near the limb than at the center of the disk because of interaction of the light with atoms of the gas. What conclusion can be drawn from the observation that the Sun appears less bright near the limb than it does at the disk center?
    A)   The temperature of the gas falls with increasing height in the solar atmosphere.
    B)   The temperature of the gas increases with increasing height in the solar atmosphere.
    C)   The light has to travel through more of the solar corona from the limb, hence it is reduced in intensity and appears cooler.
    D)   The light from the solar limb is redshifted because of solar rotation, and this gives the appearance of redder and hence cooler gas at the limb.
    Ans: A   Section: 18-5

87. The chemical composition of the surface layers of the Sun is determined primarily by
    A)   examination of samples of meteorites that originated in the Sun.
    B)   satellite measurements of the solar wind.
    C)   theoretical modeling and computer calculation.
    D)   spectroscopy.
    Ans: D   Section: 18-5

88. The appearance of the visible spectrum of the Sun, when its light is separated in its component colors, is
    A) a uniform continuous spectrum with no structure.
    B) a spectrum containing many dark absorption and many bright emission lines on a continuous background.
    C) a continuous bright spectrum, crossed by thousands of dark absorption lines.
    D) a spectrum consisting only of a few bright emission lines.
    Ans: C   Section: 18-5 and 5-6

89. The temperature of the Sun's photosphere is
    A) about 10,000 K.   B) 4400 K.   C) 5800 K.   D) close to 1 million K.
    Ans: C   Section: 18-5

90. The approximate temperature of the visible surface of the Sun is
    A) 10,000 K.   B) 4400 K.   C) 2000 K.   D) 5800 K.
    Ans: D   Section: 18-5

91. If the temperature of the solar surface is 5800 K, and Wien's law for the peak wavelength of the spectrum of the Sun, assumed to be a blackbody, is given by $\lambda_{max} T = 2.9 \times 10^6$, with T in kelvins and λ in nanometers (nm), what is the expected peak wavelength of the continuum spectrum of the Sun?
    A) 600 nm   B) 500 nm   C) 300 nm   D) 50 nm
    Ans: B   Section: 18-5 and Box 5-2

92. In order from lowest to highest, what are the names of the three layers in the Sun's atmosphere?
    A) photosphere, chromosphere, corona   C) corona, chromosphere, photosphere
    B) chromosphere, photosphere, corona   D) photosphere, corona, chromosphere
    Ans: A   Section: 18-5

93. In order from highest to lowest, what are the names of the three layers in the Sun's atmosphere?
    A) photosphere, chromosphere, corona   C) chromosphere, photosphere, corona
    B) photosphere, corona, chromosphere   D) corona, chromosphere, photosphere
    Ans: D   Section: 18-5

94. A visible light spectrum of the Sun reveals many dark absorption lines. These lines are caused by photon absorption, which takes place in the
    A) corona.   C) lower part of the photosphere.
    B) upper part of the photosphere.   D) solar interior.
    Ans: B   Section: 18-5

95. Supergranules on the Sun are
    A) large and long-lived convecting gas cells, containing hundreds of ordinary granules.
    B) very large but otherwise ordinary granules.
    C) large areas in which the rapid convection of the gas destroys all granules that would otherwise form in that area.
    D) another name for large, long-lived sunspot groups.
    Ans: A   Section: 18-5

96. The word "chromosphere" refers to
    A) a light-emitting region just outside the event horizon of a black hole.
    B) a dense, spherical interstellar cloud of glowing gas.
    C) a layer in the Earth's atmosphere just below the ionosphere.
    D) a layer in the Sun's atmosphere.
    Ans: D   Section: 18-6

97. What is the name of the layer of the Sun's atmosphere that appears as a pinkish ring just outside the visible disk of the Sun during a total solar eclipse?
    A) the chromosphere   C) the photosphere
    B) the convective zone   D) the corona
    Ans: A   Section: 18-6

98. Where is the chromosphere on the Sun?
    A) It is the visible surface of the Sun.
    B) It is the layer above the visible surface of the Sun.
    C) It is the outermost part of the Sun's atmosphere.
    D) It is the layer below the visible surface of the Sun.
    Ans: B   Section: 18-6

99. The visible light coming from the solar chromosphere is dominated by light at what wavelength(s)?
    A) the red hydrogen Balmer Hα emission line
    B) a continuous spectrum over all wavelengths, crossed by numerous dark absorption lines
    C) a featureless and continuous spectrum over all wavelengths from blue to red, scattered by chromospheric material
    D) the green emission line from iron atoms that have lost 13 electrons, Fe XIV
    Ans: A   Section: 18-6

100. Spicules on the solar surface are
    A) streams of solar coronal material, usually seen only during a total solar eclipse.
    B) curtain-like structures hanging over sunspot regions.
    C) intense eruptions from sunspot groups and active regions, associated with solar flares.
    D) jets of gas surging out of the photosphere of the Sun into the chromosphere, usually at supergranule boundaries.
    Ans: D   Section: 18-6

101. Where would you expect to find spicules?
    A) in interstellar clouds heated by hot, massive stars
    B) in supernova remnants
    C) in the atmosphere of the Sun
    D) in the binary star systems in which one star is a neutron star attracting and collecting mass from the other.
    Ans: C   Section: 18-6

102. What is a spicule on the Sun?
    A) a jet of rising gas in the chromosphere
    B) a long, thin, curved line of bright gas in the corona
    C) a bright arc of gas suspended above the edge of the visible disk of the Sun
    D) a small, bright cell in the photosphere
    Ans: A   Section: 18-6

103. Where do spicules tend to occur on the Sun?
    A) at the boundaries of granules
    B) randomly over the surface of the Sun, with spacing equivalent to that of spicules
    C) in the vicinity of sunspot groups
    D) at the boundaries of supergranules
    Ans: D   Section: 18-6

104. What is the name of a jet of rising gas in the chromosphere of the Sun?
    A) a spicule   B) a granule   C) a flare   D) a prominence
    Ans: A   Section: 18-6

105. Material in solar spicules is ejected out of the Sun at typical speeds of 20 km/s. What would be the observed wavelength of the Balmer Hα hydrogen spectral line emitted by this gas, compared to that from stationary solar material? (See Box 5-6, Freedman and Kaufmann, *Universe,* 7th ed.)
    A) There will be no shift, because the light is emitted by hydrogen gas in both the spicule and the stationary solar material.
    B) 0.000067 nm shorter than the Hα from the stationary solar material
    C) 0.044 nm longer than the Hα from stationary solar material
    D) 0.044 nm shorter than the Hα from stationary solar material
    Ans: D   Section: 18-6 and Box 5-6

106. Where is the coolest region in the Sun?
    A) in the convective zone
    B) in the lower chromosphere
    C) in the photosphere
    D) in the lower corona
    Ans: B   Section: 18-6

107. Compared to the photosphere, the solar chromosphere is
    A) less dense but having a greater vertical extent.
    B) cooler and having a greater vertical extent.
    C) dense but having a narrower vertical extent.
    D) hotter and having a narrower vertical extent.
    Ans: A   Section: 18-6

108. The visible corona of the Sun is most effectively photographed
    A) during lunar eclipses, when the sky is darker.
    B) at solar maximum periods, over a period of a few years.
    C) during solar eclipses.
    D) in spring and fall seasons, because of the tilt of the spin axis of the Sun.
    Ans: C   Section: 18-7

109. What name is given to the outer atmosphere of the Sun?
    A) the corona
    B) the chromosphere
    C) the radiative zone
    D) the convective zone
    Ans: A   Section: 18-7

110. What is the corona on the Sun?
    A) the Sun's outer atmosphere
    B) the region above the Sun's north and south poles
    C) the large region beyond (outside of) the Sun's atmosphere, where the solar wind interacts with the interplanetary magnetic field
    D) the Sun's inner atmosphere, just above the photosphere
    Ans: A   Section: 18-7

111. The total light emitted by the solar corona, which is seen most effectively during a total solar eclipse, is equivalent in brightness to
    A) the brightness of the full moon—about one millionth as bright as the solar photosphere.
    B) about one thousandth of that of the solar photosphere.
    C) the photosphere, but its emissions are at wavelengths to which the eye and photographic film are insensitive.
    D) the average brightness of the Milky Way.
    Ans: A   Section: 18-7

112. The temperature of the corona of the Sun
    A)   is about the same as that of the photosphere, 5800 K.
    B)   is about twice as hot as the photosphere, 12,000 K.
    C)   is very cool, because it is farthest from the heat source.
    D)   is very hot—about 10^6 K.
    Ans: D   Section: 18-7

113. The corona of the Sun has a temperature
    A)   of about 10 K, because it merges with cold interstellar space.
    B)   about the same as the photosphere—about 6000 K.
    C)   noticeably less than the photosphere—about 1000 to 2000 K.
    D)   of 1 to 2 million K.
    Ans: D   Section: 18-7

114. One particular feature of the solar corona is
    A)   its variation with time over periods of a few minutes.
    B)   its very uniform density and structure.
    C)   its very high temperature.
    D)   its very cold temperature.
    Ans: C   Section: 18-7

115. How did astronomers first detect the high temperatures in the corona of the Sun?
    A)   by measuring the brightness of the corona in visible (white) light
    B)   by direct measurements using space probes
    C)   by observing emission lines of highly ionized elements like iron
    D)   by observing the effects the high temperature has on Mercury and Venus
    Ans: C   Section: 18-7

116. Which of the following features appear in the spectrum of the solar corona indicating very high gas temperatures?
    A)   bright emission from the hydrogen Balmer line, H_α, at the red end of the spectrum
    B)   intense, continuous emission in the infrared part of the spectrum
    C)   intense emission lines from highly ionized atoms, such as iron
    D)   dark absorption lines from H, Ca, and Fe on a continuous bright spectrum
    Ans: C   Section: 18-7

117. Why does the observation of spectral emission from a highly ionized atom such as iron, Fe XIV, with 13 electrons missing, indicate very high gas temperatures?
    A) The presence of iron means that nuclear fusion must be occurring, and this process needs very high temperatures.
    B) Highly ionized atoms must come from high-density regions that can only exist in high temperature gases.
    C) Collisions that remove this number of electrons must be very energetic between fast-moving atoms.
    D) Photons that will eject these electrons must be very energetic and come from high-temperature gas.
    Ans: C   Section: 18-7

118. Observations of the spectrum of the solar corona reveal emission lines that come from atoms from which many electrons have been stripped. What conclusion can be drawn from this result?
    A) The solar rotation speed at coronal height reduces the ability of atoms to retain electrons.
    B) The pressure of the gas is sufficient to squeeze the electrons from the atoms.
    C) The magnetic field intensity is high enough to drag electrons from the atoms.
    D) The atomic collision energies and hence the gas temperatures are extremely high.
    Ans: D   Section: 18-7

119. The extremely high gas temperatures in the solar corona mean that this region is best observed at wavelengths of
    A) Balmer Hα light from hydrogen gas.   C) X rays.
    B) infrared light.   D) visible light.
    Ans: C   Section: 18-7

120. What is the source of the X rays emitted by the solar corona?
    A) radioactivity in the coronal gases
    B) X rays from the solar photosphere scattered from ions in the corona
    C) the high temperature gas of the corona
    D) high-energy charged particles spiraling along the coronal magnetic fields
    Ans: C   Section: 18-7

121. The bright X-ray image that one obtains of the solar corona when the Sun is photographed at this wavelength indicates that the gas temperature at these heights is
    A) extremely high, above 10^6 K.
    B) about twice that of the photosphere.
    C) about the same temperature as the photosphere.
    D) extremely low, much cooler than the photosphere.
    Ans: A   Section: 18-7

122. A coronal hole shows up most prominently in photographs taken at what wavelengths?
   A) radio wavelengths
   B) visible light
   C) X ray
   D) the specific color of the first Balmer line of hydrogen, H_α, at 656.3 nm
   Ans: C   Section: 18-7

123. How do the physical conditions within a coronal hole compare with those of the rest of the solar corona?
   A) high temperature but very low density
   B) lower temperature but very high density
   C) higher temperature and higher density
   D) lower temperature and lower density
   Ans: D   Section: 18-7

124. What is the solar wind?
   A) the storm of waves and vortices on the Sun's surface generated by a solar flare
   B) the constant flux of photons from the Sun's visible surface
   C) the circulation of gases between the equator and the poles of the Sun
   D) the Sun's outer atmosphere streaming out into space
   Ans: D   Section: 18-7

125. Coronal holes are thought to be the source of
   A) the solar wind.
   B) powerful loops of magnetic field linked to active regions.
   C) influence on human behavior (e.g., astrology).
   D) dust released from the Sun.
   Ans: A   Section: 18-7

126. The solar wind appears to originate mainly from which regions of the Sun?
   A) sunspots
   B) all over the surface, with no preferred location
   C) granulation cells
   D) coronal holes
   Ans: D   Section: 18-7

127. What is the source of the solar wind?
   A) gas flung out from solar flares
   B) gas escaping from X-ray-bright regions of the solar corona
   C) gas flung out from the Sun's equatorial region by the centrifugal force due to the Sun's rotation
   D) gas escaping through coronal holes
   Ans: D   Section: 18-7

128. How much mass will the Sun lose to space during its lifetime, through the solar wind?
    A) up to 25% of its total mass   C) a few millionths of its total mass
    B) well over one-half of its total mass   D) a few thousandths of its total mass
    Ans: D   Section: 18-7

129. The continuous solar wind originates primarily
    A) in sunspots—magnetic "holes" in the Sun.
    B) in flare explosions.
    C) from the vicinity of the solar equator, where solar spin reduces the gravitational field.
    D) in coronal holes—cooler regions in the corona.
    Ans: D   Section: 18-7

130. The solar wind is ionized gas flowing outward
    A) more or less uniformly from the entire solar surface.
    B) primarily through coronal holes.
    C) only from solar flares or during coronal mass ejection events.
    D) from sunspots.
    Ans: B   Section: 18-7

131. The solar wind is
    A) a violent explosive expansion of specific regions of the Sun's atmosphere at certain times.
    B) another name for the electromagnetic radiation coming from the Sun.
    C) the inflow of matter onto the Sun under gravitational attraction.
    D) a gentle outflow of solar material, mostly protons and electrons, always moving outward from the Sun.
    Ans: D   Section: 18-7

132. The main components of the solar wind are
    A) about equal numbers of hydrogen nuclei and electrons and lower numbers of He nuclei.
    B) equal numbers of all light elements, up to oxygen, no electrons.
    C) electrons and He nuclei (the "ash" of nuclear fusion).
    D) hydrogen nuclei and a few helium nuclei, with very few electrons.
    Ans: A   Section: 18-7

133. The highest temperatures in the Sun are found in the
    A) corona. B) chromosphere. C) photosphere. D) solar interior.
    Ans: D   Section: 18-7 and 18-2

134. Sunspots are
   A)   cooler regions of the Sun's high corona.
   B)   the shadows of cool, dark curtains of matter, hanging above the solar surface.
   C)   cooler, darker regions on the Sun's surface.
   D)   hotter, deeper regions in the Sun's atmosphere.
   Ans: C   Section: 18-8

135. Which one of the following is NOT considered to be a feature of the quiet Sun?
   A) a sunspot   B) the solar wind   C) a granule   D) a spicule
   Ans: A   Section: 18-8

136. What is the lifetime of a typical sunspot?
   A)   from a few hours to a few months   C)   11 years
   B)   from a few years to a few decades   D)   Here today, gone tomorrow!
   Ans: A   Section: 18-8

137. What is the structure of a typical large sunspot?
   A)   an irregular dark area of uniform darkness
   B)   a dark center surrounded by a less dark area
   C)   a roughly circular, dark region with a lighter central area
   D)   usually round and of uniform darkness
   Ans: B   Section: 18-8

138. How does the temperature inside the umbra of a sunspot compare to that of the solar photosphere outside the sunspot?
   A)   The umbra is about 1500 K cooler.
   B)   The umbra is about 800 K hotter.
   C)   The umbra is about 4000 K cooler.
   D)   They are about the same temperature.
   Ans: A   Section: 18-8

139. Sunspots are cooler than the rest of the Sun's surface, sometimes by as much as 1500 K. What would be the peak wavelength of the radiation from the sunspot, when compared to that from the rest of the Sun?
   A)   It would be at a shorter wavelength.
   B)   It would be at a longer wavelength.
   C)   It could be at a shorter or longer wavelength, depending on the position of the spot.
   D)   It would be the same, because the light still originates from the hydrogen gas of the Sun.
   Ans: B   Section: 18-8 and Box 5-2

140. If sunspots are cooler than the photosphere (by at least 1000 K), what will be the peak wavelength in a sunspot spectrum compared with the peak wavelength of the photospheric spectrum?
    A)   the same, because the spectrum still originates on the Sun
    B)   either shorter or longer, depending upon the polarity (north or south) of the magnetic field of the spot
    C)   longer
    D)   shorter
    Ans: C   Section: 18-8 and Box 5-2

141. If the temperature near the center of a particular sunspot is 4350 K and the temperature of the surrounding photosphere is 5800 K, then the energy flux (energy passing through each square meter per second) from the center of the sunspot is what fraction of the energy flux from the surrounding photosphere?
    A) 75%   B) 87%   C) 56%   D) 32%
    Ans: D   Section: 18-8 and Box 5-2

142. Which of the following astronomers was first to detect the rotation of the Sun by watching sunspot motions?
    A) Ptolemy   B) Halley   C) Galileo   D) Copernicus
    Ans: C   Section: 18-8

143. Galileo observed the phenomenon of solar rotation in the early 1600s by
    A)   watching bright regions of hydrogen gas drift across the sun.
    B)   noting the periodic (monthly) variation of auroral disturbances or northern lights.
    C)   watching sunspots move across the solar surface with a telescope.
    D)   measuring the Doppler wavelength shift of hydrogen spectral lines from east and west limbs of the sun.
    Ans: C   Section: 18-8

144. The equatorial regions of the Sun are seen to rotate with an approximate period of
    A)   about 27½ days.   C)   about 33 days.
    B)   about 11 years.   D)   about 25 days.
    Ans: D   Section: 18-8

145. The rotation of the Sun is
    A)   fastest at the equator, slowest at mid-latitudes, rising to intermediate speeds near the poles.
    B)   fastest at mid-latitudes, slower at the equator, and slowest near the poles.
    C)   fastest at the equator, slower at mid-latitudes, and slowest near the poles.
    D)   slowest at the equator, faster at mid-latitudes, and fastest near the poles.
    Ans: C   Section: 18-8

146. How can we characterize the rotation of the Sun?
    A) differential rotation, with the equator rotating faster than the poles
    B) like a solid body (all parts rotating equally)
    C) in a banded pattern, with alternating bands of fast and slow rotation
    D) differential rotation, with the equator rotating more slowly than the poles
    Ans: A   Section: 18-8

147. What is the rotation period of the Sun?
    A) about four rotations per month   C) about one rotation per day
    B) about two rotations per year   D) about one rotation per month
    Ans: D   Section: 18-8

148. The average sunspot group on the solar surface will last for about
    A) one half-rotation of the Sun, or 14 days.
    B) 11 years.
    C) 1 day.
    D) two rotations of the Sun.
    Ans: D   Section: 18-8

149. How does the the number of sunspots on the Sun vary with time?
    A) They vary irregularly, with no periodicity.
    B) relatively regularly, with a period of about 11 years
    C) They increase and decrease regularly in number at exactly 11-year intervals.
    D) They increase and decrease every year as Earth revolves around the Sun.
    Ans: B   Section: 18-8

150. What is the average length of time from one maximum in the number of sunspots on the
    Sun to the next maximum?
    A) about 2 months   B) 7 years   C) 11 years   D) 22 years
    Ans: C   Section: 18-8

151. In the course of a sunspot cycle of about 11 years, the regions of sunspot occurrence on
    the Sun move
    A) from the northern to the southern hemisphere or vice-versa, across the equator,
        over a range of +/−30° latitude.
    B) equatorward—moving from the poles to the equator.
    C) poleward—moving from 10° to 30° latitude.
    D) equatorward—moving from 30° to 10° latitude.
    Ans: D   Section: 18-8

152. All of the following bodies exhibit differential rotation *except one*. Which is the
    exception?
    A) the Moon   B) the Sun   C) Jupiter   D) Saturn
    Ans: A   Section: 18-8

153. What is the character of the sunspot cycle?
    A) Sunspots increase and decrease in number over 11 years within a band of solar latitude between 10° and 30°, with no discernible dependence of sunspot latitude upon time.
    B) Starting at sunspot minimum, new spots appear uniformly over the Sun but gradually, new spots become concentrated at midlatitudes as they increase and then decrease in number.
    C) Starting at sunspot minimum, new spots appear close to the equator, followed by newer spots farther from the equator until, when numbers decrease, they grow and decay at high latitudes.
    D) Starting at sunspot minimum, spots first appear far from the equator, followed by new spots appearing successively closer to the equator as they increase in number and finally, spots form close to the equator as numbers begin to decrease.
    Ans: D   Section: 18-8

154. What is the Zeeman effect?
    A) When a light source is moving relative to an observer, the wavelengths of its spectral lines are shifted to longer or shorter wavelengths.
    B) When the temperature of a light source is increased, the wavelength of maximum emission decreases.
    C) When light shines on a metal surface, electrons are ejected from the metal only if the wavelength of the light is shorter than some critical wavelength.
    D) When a light source is located in a magnetic field, the spectral lines it emits are split into two or more components.
    Ans: D   Section: 18-9

155. In 1908, Hale noticed that the spectral lines from sunspots are split into closely spaced components, and concluded that the magnetic fields in the sunspots must be very strong. What is the name of the effect Hale was observing?
    A) the Doppler effect   C) Wien's Law
    B) the photoelectric effect   D) the Zeeman effect
    Ans: D   Section: 18-9

156. What specific physical effect was used to verify the existence of intense magnetic fields in sunspots?
    A) observation of ionized atoms in the region of the sunspots
    B) the Zeeman effect, the splitting of spectral absorption lines
    C) the measurement of relative strengths of spectral absorption lines from various atoms
    D) Doppler shift of light from sunspots
    Ans: B   Section: 18-9

157. The strength of the magnetic field in a sunspot is estimated from Earth by
    A)   measuring the shape of structures seen in the corona above sunspots during solar eclipses.
    B)   measuring the Doppler shift of spectral lines of light emitted from above the sunspot.
    C)   measuring the size and brightness of the sunspot.
    D)   observing the wavelength splitting of atomic spectral lines by the Zeeman effect.
    Ans: D   Section: 18-9

158. The Zeeman effect describes the shift in specific wavelengths of light caused by
    A)   magnetic fields acting on the radiating atoms.
    B)   relative motion of the source and observer.
    C)   the light passing through a transparent medium.
    D)   the extreme mass and the resulting gravitational field of the source.
    Ans: A   Section: 18-9

159. The Zeeman effect describes what change in spectral lines?
    A)   splitting of lines, because the atoms are within an intense magnetic field
    B)   the change in relative intensity of different lines from sources of different temperature
    C)   their shift because of the movement of the source
    D)   broadening associated with high temperatures
    Ans: A   Section: 18-9

160. The Zeeman effect refers to
    A)   the brightening of sunlight near sunspots.
    B)   the drift of sunspots across the solar disk.
    C)   the shift of spectral lines because of solar rotation.
    D)   the splitting of spectral lines when magnetic fields are applied to atoms.
    Ans: D   Section: 18-9

161. An astronomer observing certain regions of the Sun through a spectrograph notices that the spectral lines emitted from these regions are split into two or more components. What can the astronomer conclude about these regions from this observation?
    A)   They contain fast-moving gas, moving away from the observer.
    B)   They are very hot.
    C)   They contain strong gravitational fields.
    D)   They contain strong magnetic fields.
    Ans: D   Section: 18-9

162. What is a typical magnetic field strength inside a sunspot?
    A)   a million times stronger than the Earth's magnetic field
    B)   a few thousand times stronger than the Earth's magnetic field
    C)   1/100 of the strength of the Earth's magnetic field
    D)   a few times stronger than the Earth's magnetic field
    Ans: B   Section: 18-9 and Fig. 18-21

163. If the magnetic polarity of the north pole of the Sun at a particular time is north, what will be the polarity of the preceding or leading spot of a bipolar sunspot region rotating about the Sun in the northern hemisphere?
    A)   The polarity will depend upon the latitude of the spot and will be north if greater than 60° latitude and south if less than 60° latitude.
    B)   It is not possible to determine this from the information given.
    C)   south
    D)   north
    Ans: D   Section: 18-9

164. How does the Sun's overall magnetic field behave?
    A)   The northern and southern hemispheres have opposite magnetic polarity, and this polarity reverses every 11 years.
    B)   Magnetic polarity is randomly distributed over the Sun, while the strength of the magnetic field increases and decreases with an 11-year cycle.
    C)   The northern and southern hemispheres have the same magnetic polarity, and this polarity reverses every 11 years.
    D)   The poles of the Sun have the opposite magnetic polarity from the equator, and this polarity reverses every 11 years.
    Ans: A   Section: 18-9

165. At the present time, overall solar magnetic activity, including sunspots, seems to vary almost periodically with a timescale of
    A) 5 minutes.   B) 100 years.   C) 11 years.   D) 22 years.
    Ans: D   Section: 18-9

166. Most solar variations associated with the so-called solar cycle show a repetitive pattern of behavior with an approximate period of
    A)   about 1 year.
    B)   11 years.
    C)   22 years.
    D)   28 days—close to one solar rotation.
    Ans: C   Section: 18-9

167. Sunspots are caused by
    A) dark clouds hanging over the surface, above the magnetic field regions.
    B) the impact of meteoroids and comets on the solar surface.
    C) coronal holes darkening the surface.
    D) differential rotation and its effect on weak magnetic fields.
    Ans: D   Section: 18-9

168. What happened to the mean atmospheric temperatures in Europe in the period in history between 1645 and 1715, when virtually no sunspots were seen (now known as the Maunder minimum)?
    A) They were lower than average.
    B) They appeared to fluctuate more strongly above and below the average when compared to the period which followed, from 1715 to the present.
    C) They were higher than average.
    D) They appeared to remain unchanged, within statistical uncertainty.
    Ans: A   Section: 18-9

169. Which recently discovered fact about the Sun might have some bearing on climate changes and the overall weather on Earth?
    A) Solar wind seems to originate in cooler regions of the corona, the coronal holes.
    B) There are far fewer neutrinos emitted from the Sun than are predicted.
    C) The Sun's surface is oscillating up and down every 5 minutes.
    D) The Sun's overall energy output depends upon the 11-year sunspot cycle.
    Ans: D   Section: 18-9

170. Which of the following statements is NOT true for sunspots?
    A) They increase and decrease in number, relatively regularly.
    B) They often occur in pairs of opposite magnetic polarity.
    C) They are cooler than the surrounding photosphere of the Sun.
    D) They occur in regions of lower-than-average magnetic fields.
    Ans: D   Section: 18-9

171. The major feature that distinguishes a sunspot from other regions on the Sun is
    A) that it is much brighter than its surroundings.
    B) its very powerful magnetic field.
    C) faster rotation around the Sun's axis than neighboring regions.
    D) the coronal hole that exists above it.
    Ans: B   Section: 18-9

172. What causes sunspots?
   A)   Magnetic fields inhibit the emission of radiation from atoms in the solar surface.
   B)   Magnetic fields below the photosphere pull gas down, creating holes in the photosphere.
   C)   Differential rotation on the Sun creates vortices, or eddies, which are cooler and darker than the rest of the solar surface.
   D)   Magnetic fields breaking through the photosphere inhibit gas motion where the field is strong, lowering the amount of heat transferred to the surface.
   Ans: D   Section: 18-9

173. What is the cause of the sunspot cycle on the Sun?
   A)   Differential rotation on the Sun creates eddies, or vortices, which cool the photosphere and create sunspots, the eddies gradually canceling each other out, and the cycle starts over.
   B)   Comets crashing into the Sun cool the photosphere and create sunspots. The 11-year sunspot cycle is the result of an 11-year periodicity in the flux of comets.
   C)   Subsurface magnetic fields are concentrated by the Sun's differential rotation. These fields remain under the surface and prevent heat from reaching the photosphere, creating sunspots. The concentrated fields gradually cancel each other out, and the cycle starts over.
   D)   Subsurface magnetic fields are twisted by the Sun's differential rotation and break through the surface as sunspots, gradually canceling each other and returning below the surface.
   Ans: D   Section: 18-9

174. The umbra of a sunspot is about 1500 K cooler than the surrounding solar photosphere. How will the light from the umbra compare to the light from the rest of the photosphere?
   A)   The light from the umbra will be bluer.
   B)   The light from both will be the same color, but the umbra will emit less light per square meter.
   C)   The light will be of the same color and intensity from each region.
   D)   The light from the umbra will be redder.
   Ans: D   Section: 18-9

175. The 11-year sunspot cycle on the Sun is
   A)   the regular movement of a relatively constant number of sunspots from the poles to the equator of the Sun over an 11-year period.
   B)   an irregular, sometimes absent variation in the number of visible sunspots.
   C)   a perfectly regular buildup and decay of the number of sunspots, with a precise period of 11.1 years.
   D)   a somewhat irregular but always present cycle of buildup and decay of sunspot numbers.
   Ans: B   Section: 18-9

176. What is a plasma?
    A)   a region where the H_α line causes the Sun's surface to glow red, like blood
    B)   a region where the intense magnetic field has caused the Sun's atoms to line up in a rigid array
    C)   a gas-like mixture of ions and electrons
    D)   an unusual mixture of charged particles in which the positives and negatives do not occur in equal numbers
    Ans: C   Section: 18-9

177. What is a plage?
    A)   a bright area on the photosphere, seen in the light of helium and heavier atoms
    B)   a bright area in the chromosphere, seen in the light of hydrogen and other atoms
    C)   a sudden eruption on the photosphere in the vicinity of sunspot groups
    D)   a region in the corona that looks bright against the darkness of space but dark against the brighter photosphere
    Ans: B   Section: 18-10

178. What causes plages?
    A)   compression and heating of chromospheric gas by magnetic fields
    B)   blobs of convecting gas rising through the photosphere and depositing their energy in the chromosphere
    C)   matter descending along loops of magnetic field in the corona
    D)   sunspots preventing heat from reaching the chromospheric gases above them
    Ans: A   Section: 18-10

179. What name is given to a brighter region in the chromosphere, often in association with a sunspot?
    A) prominence   B) granule   C) plage   D) filament
    Ans: C   Section: 18-10

180. An arching column of gas suspended over a sunspot group is called
    A) a coronal hole.   B) a prominence.   C) a flare.   D) a spicule.
    Ans: B   Section: 18-10

181. What is the name of a large loop of bright gas extending outward from the edge of the Sun (often seen during total solar eclipses)?
    A) a prominence   B) a spicule   C) a plage   D) a filament
    Ans: A   Section: 18-10

182. What is a filament on the Sun?
    A)   a prominence seen in silhouette against the photosphere
    B)   a sunspot that has been stretched by solar differential rotation
    C)   a spicule seen in profile near the edge of the Sun's limb
    D)   a plage near the end of its life, when it is fading away
    Ans: A   Section: 18-10

183. What is a prominence on the Sun?
    A)   a loop of gas supported by magnetic fields
    B)   a jet of gas shot out of the center of a sunspot
    C)   a shock wave created by the eruption of a solar flare
    D)   another name for a plage
    Ans: A   Section: 18-10

184. What name is given to a dark line or streak often seen in hydrogen light photographs of the solar chromosphere, and often observed in association with sunspots?
    A) a plage   B) a granule   C) a spicule   D) a filament
    Ans: D   Section: 18-10

185. Which of the following phenomena on the Sun do NOT appear to be sources of particles traveling out into the solar system from the Sun?
    A) spicules   B) flares   C) coronal holes   D) eruptive prominences
    Ans: A   Section: 18-10

186. Solar flares occur at what positions on the solar disk?
    A)   only at the polar regions
    B)   only in a narrow band along the solar equator
    C)   only within sunspot groups
    D)   only in coronal holes
    Ans: C   Section: 18-10

187. Solar flares, the violent eruptive events on the Sun, occur most frequently
    A)   over single, isolated, but large sunspots.
    B)   in or above complex sunspot groups.
    C)   within solar coronal holes, from which the solar wind originates.
    D)   along the solar equator at positions aligned with Jupiter's position, caused by tidal disturbance on the Sun.
    Ans: B   Section: 18-10

188. What is the name of a sudden eruptive surge on the surface of the Sun?
    A) a sunspot   B) a plage   C) a flare   D) a prominence
    Ans: C   Section: 18-10

189. What are the most energetic eruptive events to occur on the Sun?
    A)   thermonuclear explosions   C)   coronal mass ejections
    B)   erupting prominences   D)   solar flares
    Ans: C   Section: 18-10

190. Which of the following is NOT a consequence of a coronal mass ejection event from the Sun, if the mass ejection is aimed toward the Earth?
    A) disruption to radio transmission and electrical power systems on Earth
    B) damage to and even destruction of satellite electronics and power systems
    C) major health hazard for astronauts in orbit around Earth and particularly on the Moon
    D) a major hurricane
    Ans: D   Section: 18-10

191. How are spicules formed in the Sun's chromosphere?
    A) They represent material on the tops of granules "tossed" to higher altitudes by the oscillations of the Sun's surface.
    B) They represent plasma carried upward along with the magnetic field lines at the edges of supergranules.
    C) They form where the Sun's twisted magnetic field lines break through the photosphere.
    D) They are the remnants or "stumps" of solar prominences, which have broken free of the magnetic fields that confine them and have erupted out into space.
    Ans: B   Section: 18-10 and 18-6

192. Why is the solar corona so much hotter than the photosphere?
    A) Energy is carried upward through the chromosphere by convective gas motion.
    B) The corona absorbs part of the light passing through it from the photosphere.
    C) The high-speed solar wind passes through it and some of it is stopped, depositing energy.
    D) Energy is carried upward through the chromosphere by magnetic fields.
    Ans: D   Section: 18-10

Chapter 19: The Nature of the Stars

1. The intensity of sunlight that reaches Jupiter is approximately what fraction of that at Earth's orbital distance? (See the discussion of the inverse square law in Chapter 19, Freedman and Kaufmann, *Universe*, 7th ed.)
   A) 1/25   B) the same   C) 1/100   D) 1/5
   Ans: A   Section: 19-1

2. Parallax is the
   A)   distance to an object, measured in parsecs.
   B)   angle subtended by an object, as seen by us.
   C)   apparent shift in position of a nearby object as we move.
   D)   shift in position of an object as it moves.
   Ans: C   Section: 19-1

3. Stellar parallax is the
   A)   elliptical motion of a star in a binary system, as the two stars orbit around each other.
   B)   difference between the apparent magnitude and the absolute magnitude of a star.
   C)   assumed change in the distance to a star when it dims, as it passes through an interstellar cloud.
   D)   apparent shift in the position of a nearby star because of the Earth's motion.
   Ans: D   Section: 19-1

4. As you drive along a road, trees in the middle distance seem to shift in position relative to faraway hills. What name is given to this phenomenon?
   A) Doppler effect   B) inverse-square law   C) perspective   D) parallax
   Ans: D   Section: 19-1

5. Stellar parallax exists because
   A)   the Earth moves in space.
   B)   stars move in space.
   C)   the Earth rotates about its own axis.
   D)   stars have size (they are not really just points of light).
   Ans: A   Section: 19-1

6. Parallax of a nearby star is used to estimate its
   A)   distance from Earth.   C)   physical size or diameter.
   B)   apparent magnitude.   D)   surface temperature.
   Ans: A   Section: 19-1

7. Stellar parallax is used to determine which of the following properties of a nearby star?
    A)   its spectral type and surface temperature
    B)   its rotation period
    C)   its apparent magnitude
    D)   its distance from the Sun
    Ans: D   Section: 19-1

8. The most straightforward way to measure the distance to a nearby star uses
    A)   a calculation involving apparent magnitude and luminosity.
    B)   trigonometric parallax.
    C)   its proper motion.
    D)   a comparison of apparent and absolute magnitudes.
    Ans: B   Section: 19-1

9. We can tell that some stars are relatively close to us in the sky because
    A)   they appear to move periodically back and forth against the background stars because of Earth's movement around the Sun.
    B)   they appear to be extremely bright.
    C)   they are occasionally occulted or eclipsed by our Moon.
    D)   the light from these stars shows only a very small redshift caused by the universal expansion of the universe.
    Ans: A   Section: 19-1

10. How many stars (other than the Sun) have a stellar parallax greater than one second of arc?
    A) over 100   B) 1   C) 0   D) 8
    Ans: C   Section: 19-1

11. Who was the first person to measure the parallax of a star successfully?
    A)   Henry Norris Russell, in the United States
    B)   Tycho Brahe, in Denmark
    C)   Friedrich Wilhelm Bessel, in Germany
    D)   Sir George Airy, in England
    Ans: C   Section: 19-1

12. What is the relationship between stellar parallax (p) measured in seconds of arc and distance (d) measured in parsecs?
    A) $d = 2p$ B) $d = p$ C) $1/d = 2p$ D) $p = 1/d$
    Ans: D   Section: 19-1

13. If stellar parallax can be measured to a precision of about 0.01 arcsec using telescopes on the Earth to observe stars, to what distance does this correspond in space?
    A) 500 pc   B) 200 pc   C) 100 pc   D) 0.01 pc
    Ans: C   Section: 19-1

14. If a nearby star shows a parallax of 0.5 arcseconds when the Earth moves through 1 AU, at what distance is it from Earth in light-years?
   A) 2 ly   B) 6.52 ly   C) 1.83 ly   D) 3.26 ly
   Ans: B   Section: 19-1

15. The triple star system α Centauri has the largest known stellar parallax of all stars in our sky: of 0.75 arcsecond. How far is this star system from the Sun in light-years? (Careful with units!)
   A) 0.41 ly   B) 0.75 ly   C) 4.33 ly   D) 1.33 ly
   Ans: C   Section: 19-1

16. If the Hipparchos satellite measures the parallax motion of a star against the background stars and concludes that the star has a parallax of 0.004 arcseconds, how far is that star from Earth?
   A)   250 pc or 800 ly   C)   25 pc or 81 ly
   B)   0.004 pc or 0.013 ly   D)   400 pc or 1300 ly
   Ans: A   Section: 19-1

17. The apparent motion against the background sky as a result of Earth's motion through 1 AU of a star whose distance from the Sun is 80 pc is
   A)   0.0125 radian or 0.72°.   C)   0.0125 arcsecond.
   B)   0.0125 arcminute.   D)   80 arcseconds.
   Ans: C   Section: 19-1

18. The apparent angular movement of a nearby star against the background stars as a consequence of its motion in space is known as
   A)   radial velocity.   C)   proper motion.
   B)   tangential velocity.   D)   retrograde motion.
   Ans: C   Section: 19-1 and Box 19-1

19. Proper motion of a star is defined as its
   A)   apparent motion toward or away from us, measured by the Doppler shift of its spectral lines.
   B)   apparent motion against the background stars as a consequence of Earth's orbital motion around the Sun.
   C)   real motion in three-dimensional space.
   D)   apparent motion across our sky against the background stars.
   Ans: D   Section: 19-1 and Box 19-1

20. The proper motion of a star is
    A)   the diameter of the circle through which the star appears to move in the sky each year, due to the motion of the Earth.
    B)   the angle through which the star moves across our sky against the background stars per year.
    C)   the speed of the star in km/s, measured in a direction perpendicular to the line of sight from the Earth to the star.
    D)   the speed of the star in km/s, measured along the line of sight from the Earth to the star.
    Ans: B   Section: 19-1 and Box 19-1

21. The speed of a star in km/s, measured in a direction perpendicular to the line of sight from the Earth to the star, is known as
    A)   tangential velocity.   C)   radial velocity.
    B)   proper motion.   D)   retrograde motion.
    Ans: A   Section: 19-1 and Box 19-1

22. What two quantities do we need to measure to calculate the tangential velocity of a star?
    A)   distance and radial velocity   C)   parallax and distance
    B)   distance and proper motion   D)   radial velocity and proper motion
    Ans: B   Section: 19-1 and Box 19-1

23. The star Procyon has a parallax of 0.287 arcsec and a proper motion of 1.25 arcsec per year. What is the tangential velocity of Procyon?
    A) 68 km/s   B) 21 km/s   C) 1.7 km/s   D) 16 km/s
    Ans: B   Section: 19-1 and Box 19-1

24. The star Ross 128 has a parallax of 0.301 arcsec, a radial velocity of 13 km/s, and a proper motion of 1.40 arcsec per year. At what total velocity does Ross 128 travel through space, relative to the Sun?
    A)   655 km/s or 2.36 million km/hr (1.47 million mph!)
    B)   22 km/s or 79,200 km/hr (49,500 mph!)
    C)   72 km/s or 259,200 km/hr (162,000 mph!)
    D)   26 km/s or 93,600 km/hr (58,500 mph!)
    Ans: D   Section: 19-1 and Box 19-1

25. We are about 8000 parsecs from the center of our Milky Way galaxy, and the smallest parallax angle we can measure from orbiting observatories is about 0.001 arcseconds. How far toward the galactic center can we see with this technique (ignoring galactic dust and other obstacles)?
    A)   all the way to the center
    B)   about half way to the center
    C)   about an eighth of the way to the center
    D)   only 0.008 = 1/125 of the way to the center
    Ans: C   Section: 19-1

26. The semimajor axis of Pluto's orbit is almost 40 AU. The smallest parallax angle we can measure from orbiting observatories is about 0.001 arcseconds. Suppose we use this technique to measure parallax from Pluto's orbit (over the course of half a Pluto "year"). What is the maximum distance we could measure?
    A) 40 pc   B) 1000 pc   C) 40,000 pc   D) 80,000 pc
    Ans: C   Section: 19-1

27. Light, leaving a point source, spreads out so that the apparent brightness, b, of light per unit area varies with distance d according to which law ($\propto$ means "proportional to")?
    A) $b \propto 1/d^2$.   B) $b =$ constant.   C) $b \propto 1/d$.   D) $b \propto d^2$.
    Ans: A   Section: 19-2

28. Suppose that, at night, the brightness of a light bulb is measured from a certain distance and then the light bulb is moved to a distance twice as far away. How bright will the light appear compared to the earlier measurement?
    A) 1/16 as bright   B) 1/2 as bright   C) 1/8 as bright   D) 1/4 as bright
    Ans: D   Section: 19-2

29. Suppose that two identical stars (having the same total light output or luminosity) are located such that star A is at a distance of 5 pc and star B is at a distance of 25 pc. How will star B appear, compared to star A?
    A) 1/2.2 as bright   B) 1/25 as bright   C) 1/20 as bright   D) 1/5 as bright
    Ans: B   Section: 19-2

30. The intensity of sunlight per square meter reaching Jupiter is approximately what fraction of the intensity at Earth's orbital distance? (See Fig. 19-4, Freedman and Kaufmann, *Universe*, 7th ed.)
    A) 1/5.2   B) about the same   C) 27 times   D) 1/27
    Ans: D   Section: 19-2

31. What is the intensity of sunlight per square meter reaching Saturn compared to the intensity at Earth's orbital distance? (See Fig. 19-4, Freedman and Kaufmann, *Universe*, 7th ed.)
    A) 1/91   B) 91 times brighter   C) 1/9.5   D) 1/3.1
    Ans: A   Section: 19-2

32. If Mercury is at 0.4 AU, the Moon is at 1.0 AU, and the inverse-square law holds, how much more light falls on a unit area of Mercury's surface than on an equivalent area of the Moon? (See Fig. 19-4, Freedman and Kaufmann, *Universe*, 7th ed.)
    A)   6.25 times more   C)   2.5 times more
    B)   0.4 times as much   D)   16 times more
    Ans: A   Section: 19-2

33. Which of the following statements is true of the population of stars in our neighborhood?
    A)   There are many more bright than faint stars.
    B)   There are about equal numbers of stars of various brightness.
    C)   There are more stars of intermediate brightness and less fainter or brighter stars.
    D)   There are many more faint than bright stars.
    Ans: D   Section: 19-2

34. The luminosity of a star is
    A)   another name for its color or surface temperature.
    B)   its brightness as seen by people on Earth.
    C)   its total energy output into all space over all wavelengths.
    D)   its brightness at a hypothetical distance of 10 parsecs (32.6 light-years) from Earth.
    Ans: C   Section: 19-2

35. The luminosity of a star is a unique measure of its
    A)   total energy output.   C)   velocity of recession away from us.
    B)   physical size.   D)   temperature.
    Ans: A   Section: 19-2

36. The luminosity of a star is
    A)   its apparent magnitude.
    B)   the total energy emitted at all wavelengths toward the Earth.
    C)   the total energy emitted at all wavelengths into all space from its whole surface.
    D)   the total energy emitted by the star within the sensitive range of the eye, in the so-called V filter band.
    Ans: C   Section: 19-2

37. The luminosity of a star is
    A)   the energy output of 1 m^2 of its surface space at all wavelengths.
    B)   its brightness when measured from Earth.
    C)   its total energy output emitted at all wavelengths into all space.
    D)   its brightness when measured from a distance of 10 parsecs, or 32.6 light-years.
    Ans: C   Section: 19-2

38. The absolute magnitude of the Sun is + 4.8 and its luminosity is 3.9×10^{26} watts. The luminosity of a star whose absolute magnitude is + 3.8 is
    A) 2.9×10^{26} watts.   C) 3.9×10^{27} watts.
    B) 9.8×10^{26} watts.   D) 1.6×10^{26} watts.
    Ans: B   Section: 19-2 and 19-3

39. The absolute magnitude of the Sun is +4.8 and its luminosity is 3.9×10^{26} watts. The absolute magnitude of the star ν (Nu) Hydrae is −0.2. What is the luminosity of ν Hydrae?
    A) 3.9×10^{24} watts   C) 3.9×10^{28} watts
    B) 2.0×10^{27} watts   D) 7.8×10^{25} watts
    Ans: C   Section: 19-2 and 19-3

40. Capella is 180 times more luminous than the Sun, whereas Aldebaran is 370 times more luminous than the Sun. Capella has an apparent brightness of 3.5×10^{-8} Watts/m^2. How far away is Aldebaran compared to Capella?
    A)   Aldebaran is 0.42 times as far away as Capella.
    B)   Aldebaran is 0.65 times as far away as Capella.
    C)   Aldebaran is 1.55 times as far away as Capella.
    D)   Aldebaran is 2.4 times as far away as Capella.
    Ans: C   Section: 19-2 and Box 19-2

41. Apparent magnitude is a measure of the
    A)   intrinsic brightness (actual light output) of a star.
    B)   brightness of a star, as seen from the Earth.
    C)   size (diameter) of a star.
    D)   temperature of a star.
    Ans: B   Section: 19-3

42. What does apparent magnitude tell us about a star?
    A)   its size compared to the Sun
    B)   the intrinsic brightness of a star (the total light actually emitted by the star)
    C)   the brightness of a star as it appears in our sky
    D)   the brightness the star would appear to have if it were exactly 10 pc from the Earth
    Ans: C   Section: 19-3

43. The relative brightnesses of stars as we see them in our sky are represented on star charts in terms of their
    A)   surface temperatures.   C)   apparent magnitudes.
    B)   absolute magnitudes.   D)   luminosities.
    Ans: C   Section: 19-3

44. The statement that the apparent magnitude of a variable star has increased indicates that its
    A)   surface temperature has decreased.   C)   brightness has decreased.
    B)   surface temperature has increased.   D)   brightness has increased.
    Ans: C   Section: 19-3

45. Two stars in our sky have the same apparent brightness. If neither of them is hidden behind gas or dust clouds, then we know that they
    A)   may be at different distances, in which case the nearest one must have the greater luminosity.
    B)   may be at different distances, in which case the farther one must have the greater luminosity.
    C)   must have the same temperature.
    D)   must be at the same distance away from us.
    Ans: B   Section: 19-3

46. How bright is a magnitude +3.0 star compared to a magnitude +4.0 star?
    A)   2.512 times brighter   C)   4/3 (1.333) times brighter
    B)   1/2.512 times as bright   D)   10 times brighter
    Ans: A   Section: 19-3

47. By approximately how many magnitudes is the star Sirius fainter than the full Moon in our sky? (See Fig. 19-6, Freedman and Kaufmann, *Universe*, 7th ed.)
    A) 2   B) 5   C) 15   D) 11
    Ans: D   Section: 19-3

48. What is the ratio of the brightness of two stars whose apparent magnitudes differ by one magnitude?
    A) 2.5   B) 10   C) 100   D) 2
    Ans: A   Section: 19-3

49. Two stars that differ from each other by five magnitudes have a ratio of brightness of
    A) 5.   B) 25.   C) 10.   D) 100.
    Ans: D   Section: 19-3

50. How many second-magnitude stars would be required to match the light intensity from a first-magnitude star?
    A) about 0.4, or 1/2.5   B) about 2.5   C) 2   D) about 10
    Ans: B   Section: 19-3

51. How many stars of sixth magnitude in a small cluster would it take for the cluster to appear as bright as a first-magnitude star?
    A) five   B) 2.5^7 or 610   C) 10^5 D) 100
    Ans: D   Section: 19-3

52. Sirius, visually the brightest star in our sky, has an apparent magnitude of about −1.5 (See Appendix 2, Freedman and Kaufmann, *Universe,* 7th ed.), whereas the Andromeda galaxy has an apparent magnitude of about +3.5. What is the ratio of their brightness, as seen by Earth bound observers?
    A) Andromeda is 2 times fainter than Sirius.
    B) Andromeda is 100 times fainter than Sirius.
    C) Andromeda is 100 times brighter than Sirius.
    D) Andromeda is 5 times brighter than Sirius.
    Ans: B   Section: 19-3

53. The absolute magnitude of a star is the brightness the star would appear to have if it were placed at what distance from Earth?
    A) 1 AU   B) 10 ly   C) the distance to the galactic center   D) 32.6 ly
    Ans: D   Section: 19-3

54. At what distance are stars assumed to be from the Earth when they are represented by their absolute (as opposed to their apparent) magnitude?
    A) 10 ly   B) 10 parsecs   C) 10 AU   D) 1 ly
    Ans: B   Section: 19-3

55. The Sun's absolute magnitude is about +5. The brightest stars in our sky have absolute magnitudes of about −10. What is the luminosity of these stars compared to the Sun, assuming that they have similar spectral light distributions?
    A)   1 million times larger   C)   1 million times smaller
    B)   5 times less   D)   15 times greater
    Ans: A   Section: 19-3

56. The star α Centauri C and the star Groombridge 34 B have the same apparent magnitude, but α Centauri C is 1.3 pc away from Earth, whereas Groombridge 34 B is 3.5 pc away. What is the luminosity of Groombridge 34 B compared to that of α Centauri C?
    A)   2.75 times fainter   C)   7.25 times fainter
    B)   2.75 times brighter   D)   7.25 times brighter
    Ans: D   Section: 19-3

57. A particular star is at a distance of 20 pc from the Earth. For this star, the apparent magnitude would be
    A)   either larger or smaller than the absolute magnitude, depending on the temperature and diameter of the star.
    B)   a smaller number than the absolute magnitude.
    C)   a larger number than the absolute magnitude.
    D)   the same as the absolute magnitude, because magnitude is independent of distance.
    Ans: C   Section: 19-3

58. A particular star is at a distance of 5 pc from the Earth. For this star, the apparent magnitude would be
    A)   a larger number than the absolute magnitude.
    B)   either larger or smaller than the absolute magnitude, depending on the temperature and diameter of the star.
    C)   a smaller number than the absolute magnitude.
    D)   the same as the absolute magnitude, because magnitude is independent of distance.
    Ans: C   Section: 19-3

59. The star Alphard has an apparent magnitude of 2.0, and the star Megrez has an apparent magnitude of 3.3. The only thing that can be said with certainty about Alphard is that it
    A)   is brighter than Megrez, as seen in our sky.
    B)   has a greater luminosity than Megrez.
    C)   is closer than Megrez.
    D)   is fainter than Megrez, as seen in our sky.
    Ans: A   Section: 19-3

60. The star Alderamin has an apparent magnitude of 2.4 and an absolute magnitude of 1.4. From this information (assuming that the starlight has not been dimmed by interstellar clouds), we can say for certain that Alderamin is
    A)   less than 10 AU away.   C)   less than 10 light-years away.
    B)   more than 10 parsecs away.   D)   less than 10 parsecs away.
    Ans: B   Section: 19-3

61. The star Fomalhaut has an apparent magnitude of 1.15 and an absolute magnitude of 2.0. From this information (assuming that the star has not been dimmed by interstellar clouds), we can say for sure that Fomalhaut is
    A)   more than 32.6 parsecs away.   C)   less than 10 parsecs away.
    B)   more than 10 parsecs away.   D)   less than 32.6 parsecs away.
    Ans: C   Section: 19-3

62. The star Alderamin has an apparent magnitude of 2.4 and an absolute magnitude of 1.4. The star Merak has an apparent magnitude of 2.4 and absolute magnitude of 0.5. Assuming that neither star has been dimmed by interstellar clouds, we can say for sure that
    A)   Merak and Alderamin are the same distance from us.
    B)   Merak is farther away from us than Alderamin.
    C)   Merak is an intrinsically fainter star than Alderamin.
    D)   Merak is closer to us than Alderamin.
    Ans: B   Section: 19-3

63. The star γ Phoenecis has an apparent magnitude of 3.4 and an absolute magnitude of −4.6. The North Star (Polaris) has an apparent magnitude of 2.0 and an absolute magnitude of −4.6. Assuming that no light has been absorbed or scattered by interstellar dust, we can say for sure that
    A)   both stars are the same distance away form us.
    B)   Polaris appears fainter in our sky than γ Phoenecis.
    C)   Polaris is closer to us than γ Phoenecis.
    D)   Polaris is farther away from us than γ Phoenecis.
    Ans: C   Section: 19-3

64. A star whose absolute magnitude M is + 2.2 is seen to have an apparent magnitude when viewed from Earth of m = + 5.2. How far away is the star? (See Section 19-3 and Box 19-3, Freedman and Kaufmann, *Universe*, 7th ed.)
    A) 40 pc   B) 130 pc   C) 10^3 or 1000 pc   D) 4 pc
    Ans: A   Section: 19-3 and Box 19-3

65. A star with an apparent magnitude of m = + 2.5 is at 100 pc from the Earth. What is its absolute magnitude, M?
    A) +7.5   B) −2.5   C) −7.5   D) −47.5
    Ans: B   Section: 19-3 and Box 19-3

66. The star β Arietis has an apparent magnitude of +2.7 and a distance of 52 light-years. What is its absolute magnitude, M? (See Box 19-3, Section 19-3, Freedman and Kaufmann, *Universe*, 7th ed.)
    A) +6.2   B) −0.9   C) +1.7   D) +3.7
    Ans: C   Section: 19-3

67. The ancient Greek astronomer Hipparchus introduced the magnitude scale on which he called the brightest stars *first magnitude*. Today, the brightest star in the night sky is Sirius, with a magnitude of −1.4. This is considerably brighter than first magnitude. Why the discrepancy?
    A)   Sirius was formed since the era in which Hipparchus lived.
    B)   Sirius existed during Hipparchus' lifetime, but it has obviously brightened considerably since then.
    C)   Hipparchus had poor eyesight and made many classification errors.
    D)   After using modern scientific instruments to measure the actual energy output of stars, astronomers modified the magnitude scale of Hipparchus.
    Ans: D   Section: 19-3

68. The Sun has an absolute magnitude of +4.8. How far away would we have to go in order for the Sun to be just barely visible to the naked eye (6th magnitude)?
    A) 1.2 pc   B) 6 pc   C) 17.4 pc   D) 22.4 pc
    Ans: C   Section: 19-3 and Box 19-3

69. The technique called photometry in stellar astronomy is the measurement of
    A)   the arrival times of photons from variable and pulsating stars, to determine
         accurately the pulsation or rotation periods of these stars.
    B)   the precise positions and relative motions of stars in the galaxy, from which
         galactic structure and overall rotation can be determined.
    C)   the intensity of light from stars through several limited-bandpass filters from
         which surface temperature, variability, luminosity, etc. of stars can be determined.
    D)   the relative absorption of light by different atoms and molecules in high resolution
         spectra of starlight, from which stellar temperatures can be estimated.
    Ans: C   Section: 19-4

70. Several optical glass filters are used to select specific portions of a star's light for
    photometry. Which of the following filters most closely matches the sensitivity of the
    eye, with peak wavelength sensitivity at about 550 nm?
    A) I   B) B   C) U   D) V
    Ans: D   Section: 19-4

71. Measurements of the brightness of a distant star through the three appropriate filters
    indicate that the star is brightest in U, less bright in B, and faintest in V. What
    conclusion can be drawn from this information, assuming no absorption of light
    between the star and Earth?
    A)   This information is insufficient to allow a conclusion to be drawn about star
         surface temperature.
    B)   The star has an intermediate temperature, close to the Sun.
    C)   The star has a very low surface temperature.
    D)   The star has a very high surface temperature.
    Ans: D   Section: 19-4

72. The ratio of the brightness of a star at two different colors, blue and visual—b_V/b_B—is a
    direct measure of what property of the star?
    A) distance from Earth   B) surface temperature   C) luminosity   D) radius
    Ans: B   Section: 19-4

73. A star with a ratio of brightness b_V/b_B of 1.00 has a surface temperature of (see Fig. 19-
    9, Freedman and Kaufmann, *Universe,* 7th ed.)
    A) 24,000 K.   B) 10,000 K.   C) 4500 K.   D) 7500 K.
    Ans: B   Section: 19-4

74. A star whose ratio of V and B magnitudes is $b_V/b_B = 5$ (see Figure 19-9, Section 19-4, Freedman and Kaufmann, *Universe*, 7th ed.) has a surface temperature of
    A)   12,000 K.
    B)   It is not possible to determine the star's temperature with this information alone, because the value of either b_V or b_B is also needed.
    C)   6000 K.
    D)   3000 K.
    Ans: D   Section: 19-4

75. What is the color of a star whose ratio of V and B brightnesses, b_V/b_B, is 1.8?
    A) blue-white   B) yellow-white, similar to that of the Sun   C) white   D) red
    Ans: B   Section: 19-4 and Figure 19-9

76. A particular star is brighter seen through a blue filter than through a yellow filter. Which of the following surface temperatures is possible for this star? (See Figure 19-9, Section 19-4, Freedman and Kaufmann, *Universe*, 7th ed.)
    A) 3000 K   B) 12,000 K   C) 4500 K   D) 6000 K
    Ans: B   Section: 19-4

77. A particular star is fainter seen through a blue filter than through a yellow filter. Which of the following surface temperatures is possible for this star? (See Figure 19-9, Section 19-4, Freedman and Kaufmann, *Universe*, 7th ed.)
    A) 38,000 K   B) 12,500 K   C) 3800 K   D) 9800 K
    Ans: C   Section: 19-4

78. A particular star is equally bright when viewed through a blue filter and a yellow filter. What is the approximate surface temperature of this star? (See Figure 19-9, Section 19-4, Freedman and Kaufmann, *Universe*, 7th ed.)
    A)   9000 K
    B)   15,000 K
    C)   3000 K
    D)   It is not possible for a star to be equally bright at two different wavelengths.
    Ans: A   Section: 19-4

79. The star Rigel, in the constellation Orion, appears brighter through a blue filter than it does through a yellow filter. Suppose a second star is found that has the same brightness as Rigel through the yellow filter but is brighter than Rigel through the blue filter. From this information, we can say conclusively that the second star has
    A)   a higher temperature.
    B)   the same temperature but a higher luminosity.
    C)   a lower temperature.
    D)   the same temperature but a lower luminosity.
    Ans: A   Section: 19-4

80. The star Regulus, in the constellation Leo, appears brighter through a blue filter than it does through a yellow filter. Suppose a second star is found that has the same brightness as Regulus through the blue filter but is brighter than Regulus through the yellow filter. From this information, we can say conclusively that the second star has
   A)   the same temperature but a lower luminosity.
   B)   the same temperature but a higher luminosity.
   C)   a higher temperature.
   D)   a lower temperature.
   Ans: D   Section: 19-4

81. What effect does interstellar dust have on the apparent color of a star seen through the dust?
   A)   The dust makes the star look brighter than it really is, but leaves the color of the star unchanged.
   B)   The dust makes the star look bluer than it really is.
   C)   The dust makes the star look fainter than it really is, but leaves the color of the star unchanged.
   D)   The dust makes the star look redder than it really is.
   Ans: D   Section: 19-4

82. A red filter passes light at the long wavelength end of the visible spectrum as shown (e.g., in Figure 19-7, Freedman and Kaufmann, *Universe*, 7th edition). Star 1 and Star 2 are viewed through identical red filters, and Star 1 appears brighter through the filter than does Star 2. What can be determined from this information?
   A)   Star 1 is hotter than Star 2.
   B)   Star 2 is hotter than Star 1.
   C)   Star 1 is more luminous than Star 2.
   D)   Nothing can be concluded from this fact alone.
   Ans: D   Section: 19-4

83. The chemical makeup of a star's surface is usually determined by
   A)   spectroscopy of the light emitted by the star.
   B)   examining the chemicals present in a meteorite.
   C)   theoretical methods, considering evolution of the star.
   D)   taking a sample of the star's surface with a probe.
   Ans: A   Section: 19-5

84. The spectrum of an ordinary main sequence star is a
    A)   continuum of colors crossed by dark absorption lines, caused by absorption of cooler atoms and molecules at the surface.
    B)   smooth continuum of color, peaking at a specific wavelength whose position is dependent on the surface temperature.
    C)   series of emission lines, mostly from hydrogen, the major constituent of stellar surfaces, that occasionally overlap to produce sections of continuous color.
    D)   continuum of colors crossed by brighter lines caused by emission of hot atoms and molecules on the surface.
    Ans: A   Section: 19-5

85. From which feature of light from a nearby star is the surface temperature determined most precisely?
    A)   relative distribution of the continuum light in the spectrum
    B)   relative strengths of emission lines in its spectrum
    C)   relative strengths of absorption lines from different atoms (e.g., H, Ca) and molecules (e.g., TiO)
    D)   Doppler shift of its spectral lines
    Ans: C   Section: 19-5

86. The spectral type of a star is most directly related to (and determines uniquely) its
    A)   size or radius.   C)   luminosity.
    B)   absolute magnitude.   D)   surface temperature.
    Ans: D   Section: 19-5

87. Spectral classification determines a nearby star's surface temperature by examining
    A)   the peak wavelength of the star spectrum.
    B)   the relative intensities of light measured through different wavelength band filters.
    C)   the pattern of spectral "absorption" lines from various atoms.
    D)   the overall shape of the star's spectrum compared to a black body.
    Ans: C   Section: 19-5

88. Spectral classification of a star into the lettered categories, O, B, A, F, G, K, M, is carried out by
    A)   finding the wavelength of peak emission in the continuum spectrum of the star.
    B)   determining the total energy emitted at all wavelengths by the star, taking account of the full spread of wavelengths and their distances, to place the star into its luminosity class.
    C)   determining the relative mass through the study of binary star motions to place the star into its proper mass classification.
    D)   examining the relative depths of absorption lines from various neutral and ionized atoms in a stellar spectrum.
    Ans: D   Section: 19-5

89. Which of the following spectral classifications of stars is in correct order of increasing temperature?
A) ABFGKMO   B) KMGFABO   C) MKGFABO   D) OBAFGKM
Ans: C   Section: 19-5

90. The spectral sequence of star surface temperature, as determined by relative spectral absorption line strengths, has been given which sequence of letters, in order of decreasing temperature?
A) MOFKGAB   B) OFMGABK   C) OBAFGKM   D) ABFGKMO
Ans: C   Section: 19-5

91. In the spectral sequence of star types, each category has been divided into ten intervals. The Sun is classified as
A) M9.   B) A1.   C) G2.   D) O1.
Ans: C   Section: 19-5

92. Which of the following four spectral classifications represents the hottest stellar surface temperature?
A) K   B) A   C) G   D) B
Ans: D   Section: 19-5

93. Which of the following four spectral classifications represents the coolest stellar surface temperature?
A) K   B) A   C) B   D) G
Ans: A   Section: 19-5

94. The spectral class of the Sun is G2 and the star Enif is K2. From this information, we know that Enif is
A)   intrinsically fainter than the Sun.   C)   intrinsically brighter than the Sun.
B)   cooler than the Sun.   D)   hotter than the Sun.
Ans: B   Section: 19-5

95. For Balmer series lines to show up strongly in stellar spectra, significant numbers of hydrogen atoms have to have electrons in the $n = 2$ energy level. What does the appearance of such lines in a stellar spectrum indicate about conditions on the star surface?
A)   The temperature must be high enough to excite the electrons to this level by collisions but not high enough to ionize the atoms.
B)   Hydrogen gas always shows significant Balmer absorption whatever the surface temperature, and these lines are not a sensitive indicator of temperature.
C)   To show absorption from this level, the temperature must be high enough to ionize the atoms by collisions.
D)   The temperature must be very low, in order that the majority of the atoms have electrons at this low energy level.
Ans: A   Section: 19-5

96. Why is there a limited range of stellar surface temperatures around 10,000 K, at which neutral hydrogen gas absorbs visible light in the Balmer series?
    A)   Electrons in hydrogen have to be at the $n = 2$ energy level to produce absorption in this series. If the gas is too cold, most atoms are in the $n = 1$ state, and if it is too hot, most atoms are ionized.
    B)   There must be sufficient continuum radiation from the stellar surface in the visible region to be absorbed by the hydrogen gas.
    C)   Electrons must be in the ground state $n = 1$ to undergo Balmer absorption. If the gas is too cold, electrons cannot be excited from this level, whereas if it is too hot, there are no electrons left in the $n = 1$ level.
    D)   There must be electrons at the $n = 3$ energy level for Balmer absorption to occur. If the gas is too cold, electrons are only in the $n = 1$ and 2 levels, whereas if the gas is too hot, the gas is ionized, and no electrons are left in the hydrogen atoms.
    Ans: A   Section: 19-5

97. Why is it that stars with low surface temperature, much cooler than 10,000 K, show very weak or no hydrogen Balmer lines in absorption?
    A)   To absorb at Balmer wavelengths, atoms need to have electrons in the $n = 2$ level, and electrons will not be excited to this level by collisions at these low temperatures.
    B)   The stellar gas is so cool that there is no radiation to be absorbed at the wavelength of Balmer lines.
    C)   Hydrogen atoms have to be hot enough to be ionized to show Balmer absorption.
    D)   Hydrogen atoms will have no electrons at any energy level at these low temperatures.
    Ans: A   Section: 19-5

98. For absorption lines in the Paschen series of hydrogen to be seen in the IR spectrum of a star, the temperature of its surface must be high enough to excite electrons by collision to the
    A) $n = 2$ energy level.   C) $n = 3$ energy level.
    B)   ionization level.   D) $n = 4$ energy level
    Ans: C   Section: 19-5 and 5-8

99. In the spectral classification of stars, strong absorption lines of which of the following atomic or molecular constituents would indicate very high surface temperature?
    A) H   B) Ca II   C) TiO   D) He II
    Ans: D   Section: 19-5 and Figure 19-12

100. In the spectral classification of stars, strong absorption lines of which of the following atomic or molecular constituents would indicate very low surface temperature?
    A) He II   B) Fe II   C) Mg II   D) TiO
    Ans: D   Section: 19-5 and Figure 19-12

101. Which molecule produces the spectral absorption bands that are prominent in the spectrum of the cool M-type star in Fig. 19-12, Freedman and Kaufmann, *Universe,* 7th ed.?
    A)   CH₄—methane
    B)   H₂O—water vapor
    C)   TiO—titanium oxide
    D)   HCl—hydrogen chloride
    Ans: C   Section: 19-5

102. What is "metal" to an astronomer?
    A)   any element heavier than hydrogen
    B)   any element heavier than hydrogen or helium
    C)   any element in solid or liquid form that can conduct electricity easily
    D)   any element
    Ans: B   Section: 19-5

103. The spectrum of a particular star shows absorption lines due to calcium, iron, carbon, and titanium oxide. Which of these substances is classified as a "metal" by astronomers?
    A)   only iron
    B)   only calcium, iron, and carbon
    C)   all four (calcium, iron, carbon, and titanium oxide)
    D)   only calcium and iron
    Ans: B   Section: 19-5

104. Which of the following atoms or ions will produce the strongest absorption lines in the spectra of stars with the highest surface temperatures?
    A)   Fe I, neutral iron
    B)   H I, neutral hydrogen
    C)   He II, ionized helium
    D)   Ca II, singly ionized calcium
    Ans: C   Section: 19-5 and Figure 19-12

105. Which of the following atoms or ions will produce strong absorption lines in the spectra of stars with relatively cool surface temperatures?
    A)   TiO, molecules of titanium oxide
    B)   He I, neutral helium
    C)   Mg II, ionized magnesium
    D)   Ca II, ionized calcium
    Ans: A   Section: 19-5 and Figure 19-12

106. On the basis of the graph of absorption line strengths in spectra of stars presented in Fig. 19-12, Section 19-5, Freedman and Kaufmann, *Universe,* 7th ed., what is the spectral type of a star with the following spectral pattern: very strong H, weaker Mg II and Si II, and no He I or Ca II lines?
    A) G   B) B   C) K   D) A
    Ans: D   Section: 19-5

107. On the basis of the graph of absorption line strengths (in Fig. 19-12, Section 19-5, Freedman and Kaufmann, *Universe*, 7th ed.), what is the spectral type of a star with the following spectral pattern: very strong He I lines, moderately strong H lines, weak Si III lines, and no Ca II, Fe II, or He II lines?
A) M   B) F   C) B   D) A
Ans: C   Section: 19-5

108. On the basis of the graph of absorption line strengths (in Fig. 19-12, Section 19-5, Freedman and Kaufmann, *Universe*, 7th ed.), what is the spectral type of a star with the following spectral pattern: very strong Ca II lines; weaker Fe I lines; equal strength but weaker Fe II and Ca I lines; and no He I, He II, or TiO lines?
A) A   B) F   C) K   D) O
Ans: C   Section: 19-5

109. In order of decreasing temperature, the complete spectral sequence for stars and brown dwarfs, as determined by relative spectral absorption line strengths, is
A)   OFMGABKLT.   C)   OBAFGKMLT.
B)   ABFGKLMOT.   D)   LMOFKGABT.
Ans: C   Section: 19-5

110. A star of spectral class L is
A)   a red star, intermediate between spectral classes K and M.
B)   not a star at all, but a white dwarf.
C)   a yellow star like the Sun.
D)   not a star at all, but a brown dwarf.
Ans: D   Section: 19-5

111. When the spectrum of a particular star is photographed and analyzed, it is found that the spectrum contains absorption bands of the metal hydrides methane (CH_4) and ammonia (NH_3). Based on this information, the star is
A)   an M-type star.
B)   actually a white dwarf.
C)   a true star, cooler than spectral class M.
D)   actually a brown dwarf.
Ans: D   Section: 19-5 and Table 19-2

112. A particular star is found to have a very faint companion. When the spectrum of the companion is photographed and analyzed, it is found to contain absorption bands of the metal hydrides methane (CH_4) and ammonia (NH_3), but no water (H_2O). Based on this information, the companion is a brown dwarf of spectral class
A) K.   B) T.   C) M.   D) L.
Ans: D   Section: 19-5

113. A particular star is found to have a very faint companion. When the spectrum of the companion is photographed and analyzed, it is found to contain absorption features of neutral potassium (K) and water (H_2O). Based on this information, the companion is a brown dwarf of spectral class
    A) T.   B) L.   C) K.   D) M.
    Ans: A   Section: 19-5

114. The Henry Draper Catalog of stellar classifications was developed beginning in the late nineteenth century. It originally classified stars according to the strengths of their hydrogen lines. By the 1920's, however, the sequence had been reorganized so that the stars were classified by surface temperature. What important scientific development made possible this reinterpretation?
    A)   the discovery of nuclear physics and how stars generate their energy
    B)   the discovery of blackbody radiation and the blackbody curve
    C)   the development of atomic physics and how atoms emit light
    D)   the development of radio astronomy and the detection of molecules in space
    Ans: C   Section: 19-5

115. The relationship between the luminosity of a star, L, its surface temperature, T, and its radius, R, is given (with σ = Stefan-Boltzmann constant) by
    A) $L = 4\pi \sigma R^4 T^2$.   B) $L = 4\pi \sigma R^2 T^2$.   C) $L = 4\pi \sigma R T^2$.   D) $L = 4\pi \sigma R^2 T^4$.
    Ans: D   Section: 19-6

116. A particular star has 12 times the radius of the Sun and only 60% of the Sun's surface temperature. What is the star's luminosity, in solar units ($L_\odot$)? (See Box 19-4, Freedman and Kaufmann, *Universe,* 7th ed.)
    A) 51.8 $L_\odot$.   B) 18.7 $L_\odot$.   C) 22.6 $L_\odot$.   D) 7.2 $L_\odot$.
    Ans: B   Section: 19-6

117. A particular star has a radius half that of the Sun and a luminosity equal to 60% of that of the Sun. What is the star's surface temperature? (See Box 19-4, Freedman and Kaufmann, *Universe*, 7th ed.) The surface temperature of the Sun is 5800 K.
    A) 7220 K   B) 6650 K   C) 4660 K   D) 3610 K
    Ans: A   Section: 19-6

118. If you compare two stars,
    A)   the one with the larger radius must have the greater luminosity.
    B)   the one with the higher surface temperature must have the greater luminosity.
    C)   the one with the smaller absolute magnitude must have the greater luminosity.
    D)   the one with the larger surface area has the greater energy flux from its surface.
    Ans: C   Section: 19-6

119. The Hertzsprung-Russell diagram is a statistical plot of which of the following two stellar parameters?
    A)   luminosity and surface temperature   C)   luminosity and mass
    B)   radius and mass   D)   mass and surface temperature
    Ans: A   Section: 19-7

120. The Hertzsprung-Russell diagram is a plot of
    A)   apparent brightness vs. intrinsic brightness or luminosity of a group of stars.
    B)   luminosity vs. period of variation for variable stars.
    C)   apparent brightness vs. distance for stars near the Sun.
    D)   intrinsic brightness or luminosity vs. temperature of a group of stars.
    Ans: D   Section: 19-7

121. Which two vital parameters are used to describe the systematics of a group of stars (e.g., cluster) in the Hertzsprung-Russell diagram?
    A)   luminosity and radius   C)   luminosity and surface temperature
    B)   surface temperature and mass   D)   mass and apparent magnitude
    Ans: C   Section: 19-7

122. Where on the Hertzsprung-Russell diagram do most local stars in our universe congregate?
    A)   in the supergiant area, where the most massive stars spend a significant time
    B)   in the giants area, where most stars spend the longest time of their lives
    C)   in the white dwarf area, the "graveyard" of stars
    D)   on the main sequence where stars are generating energy by fusion reactions
    Ans: D   Section: 19-7

123. What fraction of the stars in the night sky are main-sequence stars?
    A)   almost none of them, less than 1%   C)   almost all of them, about 90%
    B)   relatively few of them, about 20%   D)   roughly half of them, about 55%
    Ans: C   Section: 19-7

124. Compared to a star in the middle of the diagram, a star in the lower left part of the Hertzsprung-Russell diagram is
    A) brighter.   B) larger.   C) cooler.   D) smaller.
    Ans: D   Section: 19-7

125. What is the size of a star in the upper right part of the Hertzsprung-Russell diagram compared to one in the middle of the diagram?
    A)   It is fainter.
    B)   It is hotter.
    C)   There are no stars in the upper right part of the diagram.
    D)   It is larger.
    Ans: D   Section: 19-7

126. Using Fig. 19-14, Section 19-7, Freedman and Kaufmann, *Universe*, 7th ed., what can you conclude about the star Mira compared to the Sun?
    A)   Mira is hotter and bluer but intrinsically fainter than the Sun.
    B)   Mira is hotter than the Sun and intrinsically brighter
    C)   Mira is cooler, redder, and intrinsically fainter than the Sun.
    D)   Mira is cooler and redder but intrinsically brighter than the Sun.
    Ans: D   Section: 19-7

127. Measurements indicate that a certain star has a very high intrinsic brightness (100,000 times as bright as our Sun) and yet is relatively cool (3500 K). How can this be?
    A)   There must be an error in observation, since no star can have this form.
    B)   The star must be quite small.
    C)   The star must belong to the main sequence.
    D)   The star must be very large.
    Ans: D   Section: 19-7

128. A white dwarf is
    A)   an object intermediate between planets and stars, that will never become a star.
    B)   a star at the end of its life, with a size close to that of the Earth.
    C)   any main sequence star with a surface temperature between about 9000 K and 15,000 K.
    D)   a star at the beginning of its life, with a size two to ten times that of the Sun.
    Ans: B   Section: 19-7

129. If the surface temperature of white dwarf stars is four times that of the Sun, and energy output per unit area of a star depends on the fourth power of the temperature by the Stefan-Boltzmann relation, why then are white dwarfs intrinsically so faint?
    A)   because they are very small
    B)   because they have very thin atmospheres that do not emit continuum radiation but only line emissions, like a low density gas
    C)   because they are shrouded in very thick atmospheres
    D)   because they are moving rapidly away from the Sun, and their spectra are extremely redshifted, hence they appear faint at visible wavelengths
    Ans: A   Section: 19-7

130. The following are parameters of stars that astronomers obtained from their measurements. Which of these conclusions is obviously erroneous, on the basis of the positions of these alleged stars on the Hertzsprung-Russell diagram in Fig. 19-14 of Freedman and Kaufmann, *Universe,* 7th ed.? ($L_\odot$, $R_\odot$, are the luminosity and radius of the Sun, respectively)
    A) luminosity = 1 $L_\odot$, radius = 1/10 $R_\odot$, temperature = 20,000 K; conclusion: white dwarf star
    B) luminosity = 1/100 $L_\odot$, radius = 1/100 $R_\odot$, temperature = 20,000 K; conclusion: white dwarf star
    C) luminosity $\approx 10^4 L_\odot$, radius $\approx 100 R_\odot$, temperature ≈ 5000 K; conclusion: a supergiant star
    D) luminosity = 1 $L_\odot$, Radius = 1 $R_\odot$, Temperature = 6000 K; Conclusion: main sequence star
    Ans: A   Section: 19-7

131. In the Hertzsprung-Russell diagram of Fig. 19-14 of Freedman and Kaufmann, *Universe,* 7th ed., which of the following is the correct sequence of stars in order of increasing intrinsic brightness?
    A) Procyon B, Sirius B, the Sun, Deneb
    B) The Sun, Procyon B, Deneb, Sirius B
    C) Sirius B, Deneb, Procyon B, the Sun
    D) Deneb, the Sun, Sirius B, Procyon B
    Ans: A   Section: 19-7

132. In the Hertzsprung-Russell diagram of Fig. 19-14 of Freedman and Kaufmann, *Universe,* 7th ed., which of the following is the correct sequence of stars in order of increasing temperature?
    A) Sirius B, Deneb, Procyon B, the Sun   C) Deneb, the Sun, Sirius B, Procyon B
    B) the Sun, Procyon B, Deneb, Sirius B   D) Procyon B, Sirius B, the Sun, Deneb
    Ans: B   Section: 19-7

133. Using Fig. 19-14 of Freedman and Kaufmann, *Universe,* 7th ed., determine which of the following is the correct sequence of stars in order of increasing size or stellar radius.
    A) Mira, Betelguese, the Sun, Sirius B   C) Sirius B, the Sun, Betelguese, Mira
    B) Betelguese, Mira, the Sun, Sirius B   D) Sirius B, the Sun, Mira, Betelguese
    Ans: D   Section: 19-7

134. Using the Hertzsprung-Russell diagram in Fig. 19-14 of Freedman and Kaufmann, *Universe,* 7th ed., determine which type of star has the following characteristics: surface temperature of 40,000 K and luminosity 100,000 times that of the Sun.
    A) white dwarf   C) red giant
    B) main sequence red dwarf   D) blue main sequence star
    Ans: D   Section: 19-7

135. Using the Hertzsprung-Russell diagram in Fig. 19-14 of Freedman and Kaufmann, *Universe,* 7th ed., determine which type of star has the following characteristics: surface temperature 10,000 K and luminosity 1/100 times that of the Sun.
A) main sequence   B) red supergiant   C) white dwarf   D) red giant
Ans: C   Section: 19-7

136. Betelgeuse (the bright star in the constellation Orion) has a surface temperature of 3500 K and a luminosity 100,000 times that of the Sun. What is its approximate radius in terms of that of the Sun? (Hint: Use Fig. 19-14 of Freedman and Kaufmann, *Universe,* 7th ed.)
A) the same   B) 1000 times larger   C) 100 times larger   D) 10 times larger
Ans: B   Section: 19-7

137. What is the luminosity of a white dwarf star with the same surface temperature as the Sun? (See Fig. 19-15 of Freedman and Kaufmann, *Universe,* 7th ed.)
A) $10^{-2} \times$ the Sun's luminosity
B)   It will have the same brightness as the Sun, because it has the same surface temperature.
C) $10^{-4} \times$ the Sun's luminosity
D) $4 \times$ the Sun's luminosity
Ans: C   Section: 19-7

138. How much smaller (in radius) than the Sun is a white dwarf star whose temperature is the same as that of the Sun? (See Fig. 19-15 of Freedman and Kaufmann, *Universe,* 7th ed.)
A)   100 times smaller
B)   It will be the same size as the Sun, because it has the same temperature.
C)   10 times smaller
D)   2 times smaller
Ans: A   Section: 19-7

139. All of the statements comparing the Sun to the Giant stars are true *except* which of the following? (Refer to Figure 19-14, Freedman and Kaufmann, *Universe,* 7th edition.)
A)   The Giant stars are more luminous than the Sun.
B)   The Giant stars are larger than the Sun.
C)   The Giant stars are hotter than the Sun.
D)   The Giant stars have smaller absolute magnitudes than the Sun.
Ans: C   Section: 19-7

140. For a main sequence star of solar radius $R_\odot$, a surface temperature of 5000K gives about half the Sun's luminosity. What would a surface temperature of 20,000 K give for the approximate luminosity of a solar mass star?
A) $L_\odot$ B) $4\,L_\odot$ C) $16\,L_\odot$ D) $130\,L_\odot$
Ans: D   Section: 19-7 and Box 19-4

141. What is the physical reason that astronomers can find the luminosity class (I, II, III, IV, or V) of a star using the star's spectrum?
     A) The relative amounts of hydrogen, helium, and other elements are different for stars of different luminosity classes.
     B) The absorption lines in the spectrum are affected by the density and pressure of the star's atmosphere.
     C) The absorption lines in the spectrum are affected by the star's surface temperature.
     D) The wavelength of maximum emission (given by Wien's law) is affected by the size of the star.
     Ans: B   Section: 19-8

142. Of two stars of spectral class B5, one has broad hydrogen lines and the other has narrow hydrogen lines. How do these stars differ physically?
     A) The star with the narrow lines is a main sequence star, and the star with the broad lines is a giant or supergiant.
     B) The star with the narrow lines is a hot star, and the star with the broad lines is a cool star.
     C) The star with the narrow lines is a giant or supergiant, and the star with the broad lines is a main sequence star.
     D) The star with the narrow lines is a cool star, and the star with the broad lines is a hot star.
     Ans: C   Section: 19-8

143. One star has a spectral-luminosity class of B5 V (main sequence) and the other has a spectral-luminosity class of B5 Ia (supergiant). What difference do we see in the spectra of these two stars and why? (Note: Both the difference and the reason must be correct.)
     A) The main sequence star has broader hydrogen absorption lines, because its atmosphere is hotter than that of the supergiant.
     B) The main sequence star has narrower hydrogen absorption lines, because its atmosphere is cooler than that of the supergiant.
     C) The main sequence star has broader hydrogen absorption lines, because its atmosphere is denser and at higher pressure than that of the supergiant.
     D) The main sequence star has narrower hydrogen absorption lines, because its atmosphere is more compact (less physically extended) than that of the supergiant.
     Ans: C   Section: 19-8

144. A star with a surface temperature of 5000 K and a luminosity greater than 10^4 times that of the Sun is a member of which luminosity class? (See Fig. 19-16, Section 19-8, Freedman and Kaufmann, *Universe*, 7th ed.)
     A) I supergiant   B) III giant   C) V main sequence   D) II bright giant
     Ans: A   Section: 19-8

145. The star Hadar has a spectral classification of B1 III. This tells us that Hadar is a
     A) hot supergiant.   B) cool giant.   C) hot giant.   D) cool supergiant.
     Ans: C   Section: 19-8

146. The star Arcturus is classified as K2 III, which means that it is a
A) hot giant.   B) cool giant.   C) cool main sequence star.   D) cool supergiant.
Ans: B   Section: 19-8

147. The star Spica is classified as B1 V, which means that it is a
A)   cool main sequence star.   C)   hot supergiant.
B)   cool giant.   D)   hot main sequence star.
Ans: D   Section: 19-8

148. Barnard's star, one of our nearest neighbors, is classified as M5 V. This means that it is
A)   a cool giant.   C)   a cool supergiant.
B)   a hot main sequence star.   D)   a cool main sequence star.
Ans: D   Section: 19-8

149. Which of the following four spectral-luminosity classes would correspond to a red supergiant?
A) B7 I   B) G2 III   C) M3 V   D) M2 I
Ans: D   Section: 19-8

150. The star Elnath is classified as B7 III, and the star Al Na'ir is classified as B7 IV. This tells us that compared to Al Na'ir, Elnath is
A)   about the same intrinsic brightness, but considerably hotter.
B)   about the same intrinsic brightness, but considerably cooler.
C)   about the same temperature, but intrinsically much fainter.
D)   about the same temperature, but intrinsically much brighter.
Ans: D   Section: 19-8

151. The spectral-luminosity class of the star α Arae is B2 V, and that of π Herculi is K3 II. Using ONLY this information and not looking anything up in tables or diagrams, we know for sure
A)   that α Arae is hotter but intrinsically fainter than π Herculi.
B)   that α Arae is cooler and intrinsically fainter than π Herculi.
C)   only that α Arae is cooler than π Herculi.
D)   only that α Arae is hotter than π Herculi.
Ans: D   Section: 19-8

152. The spectral-luminosity class of the star Spica is B1 V, and that of the star τ Ceti is G8 V. From this (with luminosity measured in solar luminosities), we know for sure that
A)   τ Ceti is hotter but has the same luminosity as Spica.
B)   τ Ceti is cooler but has the same luminosity as Spica.
C)   τ Ceti is cooler and has a lower luminosity than Spica.
D)   τ Ceti is hotter and has a lower luminosity than Spica.
Ans: C   Section: 19-8

153. Spectroscopic parallax is the
    A)   apparent change in position of the absorption lines in a star's spectrum due to the Doppler shift, caused by Earth's motion around the Sun.
    B)   apparent change in position of a nearby star compared to distant background stars, due to the motion of the Earth around the Sun.
    C)   change in position of the absorption lines in a star's spectrum due to the Doppler shift, caused by the star's motion around the center of mass in a binary star system.
    D)   distance to a star measured using the spectral-luminosity class of the star and the inverse square law.
    Ans: D   Section: 19-8

154. Two stars, one classified A4 V and the other A4 III, have the same apparent magnitude. There is no significant amount of absorption of starlight by interstellar material. From this information we know that the A4 V star is
    A)   hotter than A4 III.   C)   cooler than A4 III.
    B)   farther from the Sun than A4 III.   D)   closer to the Sun than A4 III.
    Ans: D   Section: 19-8 and Box 19-2

155. Two stars, one classified A4 V and the other F8 V, have the same apparent magnitude. There is no significant amount of absorption of starlight by interstellar material. From this information we know that
    A)   the A4 V star is closer to the Sun than F8 V.
    B)   the A4 V star is smaller than F8 V.
    C)   the A4 V star is farther from the Sun than F8 V.
    D)   both stars are at the same distance from Sun.
    Ans: C   Section: 19-8 and Box 19-2

156. A particular star has an absolute magnitude of 0 and a spectral class similar to that of the Sun. Using Fig. 19-16 of Freedman and Kaufmann, *Universe,* 7th ed., how would this star be classified?
    A) G2 V   B) G2 III   C) G2 I   D) G-type white dwarf
    Ans: B   Section: 19-8

157. A particular star has an absolute magnitude of + 12 and a spectral class of A5. Using Figure 19-16 of Freedman and Kaufmann, *Universe,* 7th ed., how would this star be classified?
    A) A5 V   B) A-type white dwarf   C) A5 I   D) A5 III
    Ans: B   Section: 19-8

158. The star ζ Canis Majoris has an absolute magnitude of −2.4 and a spectral-luminosity class of B 2 V. The star γ Crucis has a spectral class of M4 and the same absolute magnitude as ζ Canis Majoris. Using Fig. 19-16 of Freedman and Kaufmann, *Universe,* 7th ed., the spectral-luminosity class of γ Crucis is probably
A) M4 Ia.   B) M4 II.   C) M-type white dwarf.   D) M4 V.
Ans: B   Section: 19-7 and 19-8

159. What proportion of visible stars in the night sky are multiple-star systems?
A)   about 25%, or 1/4
B)   less than 1%
C)   nearly 100%
D)   about 50%, or 1/2
Ans: D   Section: 19-9

160. What is the difference between an optical double star and a visual binary star?
A)   There is no difference—they are two names for the same thing.
B)   Optical double stars can be seen as separate stars only through a telescope, whereas visual binaries can be seen with the unaided eye (e.g., the star Mizar in the Big Dipper's handle).
C)   The stars in an optical double star are actually orbiting each other, whereas a visual binary is an illusion—the stars are at vast distances from each other and are not actually orbiting each other.
D)   An optical double is an illusion. The stars are at vast distances from each other and are not actually orbiting each other, whereas in a visual binary, the stars are actually orbiting each other.
Ans: D   Section: 19-9

161. In a particular binary star system, only one star is visible because the other star is too faint to see at that distance. An astronomer measures the size (semimajor axis) and period of the orbit of the visible star. From this information the astronomer can calculate
A)   nothing about the mass—both stars have to be visible to do so.
B)   the mass of each star.
C)   the sum of the masses of the two stars but not the mass of each star separately.
D)   the mass of the visible star but not that of the unseen star.
Ans: C   Section: 19-9

162. A particular star in a binary star system orbits the other in an elliptical orbit with a semimajor axis of 3 AU and a period of 5 years. What is the sum of the masses of the two stars in the system?
A) 0.9 M⊙   B) 1.1 M⊙   C) 13.9 M⊙   D) 0.07 M⊙
Ans: B   Section: 19-9

163. How do two unequal mass stars move around each other in a binary system?
    A) in a common elliptical orbit, always remaining diametrically opposite to each other through one of the foci of the ellipse
    B) in straight lines, back and forth past each other
    C) in elliptical orbits, about a common "center of mass"
    D) The low-mass star moves in a circular orbit around the stationary high-mass star.
    Ans: C   Section: 19-9

164. The point around which two stars of unequal mass in a binary system appear to revolve is
    A) closest to the more massive star.
    B) halfway between the two star centers.
    C) at the center of the more massive star.
    D) closest to the less massive star.
    Ans: A   Section: 19-9

165. Two stars in a binary system orbit around a common point that is
    A) always exactly midway between the two stars.
    B) always inside one of the stars.
    C) closer to the more massive star.
    D) closer to the less massive star.
    Ans: C   Section: 19-9

166. If two stars of unequal mass orbit each other under mutual attraction in circular orbits, what will be the location of the center of these orbits? (See Fig. 19-19, Freedman and Kaufmann, *Universe,* 7th ed.)
    A) a point halfway between the star centers
    B) a point between the two stars—closer to the more massive star
    C) a point between the stars—closer to the less massive star
    D) the center of the most massive star
    Ans: B   Section: 19-9

167. Which important stellar parameter can be determined by the study of binary stars?
    A) the age of the stars   C) surface temperatures of the stars
    B) stellar masses   D) the distance of the stars from Earth
    Ans: B   Section: 19-9

168. Observations of binary stars have helped astronomers to determine which important scientific parameter?
    A) the universal gravitational constant   C) the speed of light in deep space
    B) stellar masses   D) the sizes of stars
    Ans: B   Section: 19-9

169. An important aspect of binary star systems, as distinct from single stars, is that they allow a
    A)   verification of the Doppler shift.
    B)   measurement of the overall shapes of stars.
    C)   measurement of the universal gravitational constant.
    D)   measurement of the masses of stars.
    Ans: D   Section: 19-9

170. Astronomers measure the masses of stars by
    A)   measuring the star's brightness, temperature, and distance.
    B)   observing the star's brightness at different wavelengths (colors).
    C)   measuring the star's brightness and obtaining its radius using the HR diagram.
    D)   observing the motion of two stars in a binary star system.
    Ans: D   Section: 19-9

171. What is the only way to measure the mass of a star accurately?
    A)   Measure its gravitational effect on another object.
    B)   Measure its spectral type and luminosity class—then use the H-R diagram.
    C)   It is not possible to measure the mass of a star.
    D)   Measure its distance using trigonometric parallax and its brightness using photometry.
    Ans: A   Section: 19-9

172. Which one of the following statements is correct for an isolated star (i.e., a star that is not in a binary star system)?
    A)   It is not possible to measure the star's mass accurately.
    B)   There are several ways to measure its mass accurately.
    C)   Its mass can be measured accurately only if its luminosity and temperature can be measured.
    D)   Its mass can be measured accurately only if its distance can be found.
    Ans: A   Section: 19-9

173. The relationship between mass and luminosity of stars on the main sequence is that
    A)   the luminosity of stars rises to a peak at around a mass of 1 solar mass and decreases as mass increases beyond this limit.
    B)   the greater the stellar mass, the larger the luminosity.
    C)   luminosity is independent of the stellar mass.
    D)   the greater the stellar mass, the less the luminosity.
    Ans: B   Section: 19-9

174. Where do we find the most massive stars on the main sequence in a Hertzsprung-Russell diagram?
    A)   upper left
    B)   They all have approximately the same mass, because this is what defines the main sequence.
    C)   lower right
    D)   center, with lower mass stars on either side
    Ans: A   Section: 19-9

175. What is the mass of a main-sequence star that has a luminosity 1000 times greater than that of the Sun? (See Fig. 19-20, Freedman and Kaufmann, *Universe,* 7th ed.)
    A)   5 solar masses   C)   0.1 solar mass
    B)   1000 solar masses   D) 10^5 solar masses
    Ans: A   Section: 19-9

176. On the basis of the Hertzsprung-Russell diagram (Fig. 19-14, Freedman and Kaufmann, *Universe,* 7th ed.) and the mass-luminosity relationship for main sequence stars (Fig. 19-20), which of the following main sequence stars have the greatest mass?
    A) O   B) A   C) M   D) G
    Ans: A   Section: 19-7 and 19-9

177. Vega is an A0 V star with a surface temperature of about 10,000 degrees. Use Figures 19-14 and 19-20 of Freedman and Kaufmann, *Universe,* 7th ed., to estimate the mass of Vega.
    A)   between 3.0 and 5.0 solar masses   C)   about 10 solar masses
    B)   about 1.0 solar mass   D)   between 1.5 and 2.0 solar masses
    Ans: D   Section: 19-7 and 19-9

178. Using the Hertzsprung-Russell diagram in Fig. 19-14 of Freedman and Kaufmann, *Universe,* 7th ed., and the mass-luminosity relationship for main sequence stars shown in Fig. 19-20, which of the following is the correct sequence of stars in increasing order of mass?
    A)   Barnard's Star, Altair, the Sun, Regulus
    B)   Regulus, Barnard's Star, the Sun, Altair
    C)   Regulus, Altair, the Sun, Barnard's Star
    D)   Barnard's Star, the Sun, Altair, Regulus
    Ans: D   Section: 19-7 and 19-9

179. To determine the sum of the masses of a visual binary star system, we need to measure for the system
    A)   the temperatures and periods of the stars.
    B)   the distance from us and the semimajor axis of the orbit of one star relative to the other.
    C)   the period and the semimajor axis.
    D)   the temperatures and the distance from us.
    Ans: C   Section: 19-9

180. By studying the radial velocity curves of two visible stars in an edge-on binary system, we determine that the mass of Star 1 is three times the mass of Star 2.
    We also observe their period to be eight years and the semimajor axis of their relative orbit to be 4 AU. What are the masses of these stars?
    A) $M_A = M_\odot$; $M_B = 1/3\ M_\odot$
    B) $M_A = 3M_\odot$; $M_B = M_\odot$
    C) $M_A = 6M_\odot$; $M_B = 2M_\odot$
    D)   It is not possible to find both star masses from the information given.
    Ans: A   Section: 19-9

181. The spectrum of a very distant star shows spectral absorption lines of ionized helium, He II, and molecular absorption bands from titanium oxide, TiO. What would be your conclusion about this star?
    A)   The star must have a thick, cool atmosphere overlying a hot stellar surface.
    B)   There must be cool, interstellar gas containing TiO between the star and Earth.
    C)   There must be a very hot atmosphere containing helium gas overlying a much cooler stellar surface.
    D)   It is obviously the spectrum of a binary system, two stars close together, a hot star and a cooler companion, unresolved as separate stars from our distance but contributing separate spectra.
    Ans: D   Section: 19-10

182. The radial-velocity curve of a star in a binary star system is a plot against time of the
    A)   speed of the star in a direction perpendicular to the line of sight to the star.
    B)   temperature of the star as determined from the movement of the peak wavelength of its spectrum.
    C)   position of the star in celestial coordinates.
    D)   variation of Doppler shift of its spectral lines and hence of its speed toward or away from us.
    Ans: D   Section: 19-10

183. Absorption lines in the spectra of some binary stars are seen to change periodically from single to double lines and back again. Why is this?
   A)   Oscillations on the surfaces of the stars leads to Doppler-shifted lines.
   B)   Periodically, the magnetic field of one star produces Zeeman splitting of spectral lines in atoms of the second star.
   C)   The effect of the gravitational field of one star on the atoms of the second star produces spectral line shifts periodically.
   D)   Motion toward and away from Earth during their orbital motion results in Doppler shift of light from these stars at times and no shift when the stars are moving perpendicular to the line of sight.
   Ans: D   Section: 19-10

184. What is the physical reason for the appearance of periodic splitting and recombining of spectral lines in the spectra of binary stars?
   A)   distortion of atoms on one star by the gravitational force of the other star, leading to line splitting
   B)   Zeeman splitting of spectral lines on one star by the magnetic field of the second star
   C)   oscillations on the surfaces of the stars leading to Doppler-shifted lines
   D)   Doppler shift of light from stars orbiting each other, moving toward and away from Earth during this orbital motion
   Ans: D   Section: 19-10

185. An eclipsing binary system is
   A)   two stars whose spectral lines move back and forth, indicating relative motion.
   B)   a star that is periodically eclipsed by the Moon.
   C)   two stars whose combined light output when measured from Earth appears to vary periodically as the two stars move in front of one another.
   D)   two stars that are clearly seen as separate but associated in the sky.
   Ans: C   Section: 19-11

186. An eclipsing binary system is
   A)   two stars detected as such by movement of lines in their spectra by varying Doppler shifts.
   B)   two stars that periodically eclipse each other.
   C)   two stars clearly separated when viewed from Earth.
   D)   a star that is periodically eclipsed by the Moon.
   Ans: B   Section: 19-11

187. Suppose we observe the light curve of a totally eclipsing binary like that in Figure 19-24b in Freedman and Kaufmann, *Universe*, 7th edition. The brightness falls gradually from magnitude 5 to magnitude 9 and remains there for 12 hours before increasing gradually to magnitude 5. Then, after a while, it drops gradually to magnitude 6, remains there for 8 hours, and returns to magnitude 5. What conclusion can be drawn from this light curve?
    A)   The star with the higher temperature is the smaller star.
    B)   The star with the higher temperature is the larger star.
    C)   This system is experiencing tidal distortion.
    D)   The light curve is in error because we cannot have two minima of different durations.
    Ans: D   Section: 19-11

188. What condition is necessary for us to see eclipses of stars in binary star systems?
    A)   One of the stars must be much bigger than the other so that it can hide its smaller companion when the orbital plane is at a large angle to the line of sight.
    B)   The stars must have very similar surface temperatures whatever the inclination of their orbital plane to the line of sight, for us to see a significant eclipse.
    C)   The line of sight from Earth to the star system must be in or very close to the orbital plane of the stars.
    D)   The line of sight from Earth to the star system must be very close to the perpendicular to the orbital plane of the stars.
    Ans: C   Section: 19-11

189. Light intensity variations are detected from a star in which the intensity remains essentially constant, except for the periodic, short, and regular decreases by a fixed amount. What is the most likely explanation for this observation?
    A)   periodic ejection of a shell of absorbing gas and dust from the star, followed by its dispersion into interstellar space
    B)   eclipsing of one star by its companion in a binary star
    C)   periodic passage of a planet in front of the star's visible surface
    D)   pulsation of size, temperature, and intensity of a variable star
    Ans: B   Section: 19-11

190. Which of the following observations would not be an indication of a binary star system?
    A)   motion of the "star" in a straight line against the background field of stars
    B)   observation of the "star" image separating into two distinct images periodically
    C)   spectral lines from the "star" appearing to move back and forth periodically in position
    D)   The "star" appears to become periodically dimmer for a few hours at a time.
    Ans: A   Section: 19-11

191. How do two stars in a binary system orbit each other? (See Fig. 19-19, Freedman and Kaufmann, *Universe*, 7th ed.)
   A) They both follow elliptical orbits around a common point between the stars.
   B) The lower mass star orbits in an ellipse around the center of the larger mass star.
   C) The larger mass star orbits around the center of the smaller mass star.
   D) They both move on the same elliptical orbit around one of its foci.
   Ans: A   Section: 19-11

Chapter 20: The Birth of Stars

1. Certain stages of stellar evolution, such as birth of a protostar and post-main sequence red giant evolution, come about because of an imbalance between gravity and
   A) high-energy neutrino pressure.
   C) the centrifugal force from rotation.
   B) radiation intensity.
   D) internal gas pressure.
   Ans: D   Section: 20-1

2. Astronomers have been observing stars for about a century. What fraction is this of the typical lifetime of a normal main-sequence?
   A) 1 part in 10^{10} B) 1 part in 10^{12} C) 1 part in 10^5 D) 1 part in 10^8
   Ans: D   Section: 20-1

3. The total lifespan of the Sun is believed to be
   A) a few million years.   B) half a billion years.   C) 12 billion years.   D) infinite.
   Ans: C   Section: 20-1

4. The space between stars is now known to contain
   A) large quantities of dust that absorb light but no gas, either atomic or molecular.
   B) gas, made up of atoms, molecules, and dust particles.
   C) a perfect vacuum.
   D) variable amounts of gas but no dust, because dust forms only in planetary systems near stars.
   Ans: B   Section: 20-2

5. Compared to the air we breathe, how dense is the matter within a typical nebula, such as that in Orion, where star formation is taking place?
   A) about 10^{-16} times as dense
   B) about 10^{-19} times as dense
   C) about the same density—otherwise self-gravity could not form stars from this material
   D) about 10^{-10} times as dense
   Ans: A   Section: 20-2

6. Which of the following would NOT be found in higher-than-average densities in an interstellar nebula?
   A) electrons   B) neutrinos   C) dust   D) protons
   Ans: B   Section: 20-2

7. What is the similarity in physical principle between the mechanism at work in an emission nebula and that in a household fluorescent light bulb?
    A) Both depend on atomic ionization and subsequent recombination of atoms to produce light, mainly in specific spectral lines.
    B) The spectral lines they produce from hydrogen gas are the same in both the nebula and the fluorescent tube.
    C) Both depend on heating of a neutral gas to produce a continuum spectrum.
    D) Both depend on electrical energy to heat a gas; in a fluorescent bulb electric energy comes from the household supply, whereas in the emission nebula electrical energy arises from rapid motion of ionized gases.
    Ans: B   Section: 20-2

8. We see an emission nebula predominantly in
    A) blue light, originally emitted by stars within the nebula but scattered by dust.
    B) light emitted over a wide range of wavelengths by dust grains that have been heated by radiation from embedded stars.
    C) light emitted by molecules in the dense clouds of gas surrounding the stars in the nebula.
    D) the Balmer H_α red line, from recombination of electrons with nuclei in ionized hydrogen.
    Ans: D   Section: 20-2

9. The predominant color of an emission nebula is
    A) red, from the hydrogen Balmer H_α line.
    B) blue, from scattering of light from hot stars by dust particles.
    C) green-yellow, from the 530.3 nm-emission line of ionized iron, equivalent to that from the hot solar corona.
    D) a continuum of all colors, the combined light from all the stars in the nebula.
    Ans: A   Section: 20-2

10. What is the characteristic color of an emission nebula?
    A) red   B) blue   C) yellow   D) green
    Ans: A   Section: 20-2

11. What is the dominant spectral emission line from an emission nebula in visible light?
    A) H alpha
    B) There are no spectral line features emitted by this nebula, because the light is scattered continuum starlight from embedded stars.
    C) the sodium D lines.
    D) Lyman alpha
    Ans: A   Section: 20-2

12. What is the predominant atomic or molecular mechanism that produces the light we see from emission nebulae?
    A)   Radio energy from embedded stars excites atoms to high atomic states, and spectral lines are produced as these atoms return to their unexcited states.
    B)   Radiation from nearby stars heats the gas, and the gas then emits a continuum spectrum appropriate to its temperature.
    C)   Photons of UV and X radiation from very hot embedded stars accelerate electrons by collision and these accelerating electrons radiate at all wavelengths.
    D)   UV light from hot stars ionizes atoms, and the subsequent recombination of electrons with these ions produces spectral lines.
    Ans: D   Section: 20-2

13. What process makes an emission nebula glow?
    A)   electric currents caused by the flow of ionized gas, heating dust particles
    B)   free electrons emitting light as they pass close to, and are accelerated by, positively charged ions
    C)   light emitted when electrons jump between energy states in hydrogen atoms
    D)   high-energy electrons spiraling along magnetic field lines
    Ans: C   Section: 20-2

14. What causes the characteristic red color of an emission nebula?
    A)   thermal (blackbody) radiation with its peak in the visible red part of the spectrum
    B)   electrons jumping from the $n = 2$ energy state to the $n = 3$ energy state in hydrogen atoms
    C)   electrons jumping from the $n = 3$ energy state to the $n = 2$ energy state in hydrogen atoms
    D)   electrons jumping from the $n = 2$ energy state to the $n = 1$ energy state in hydrogen atoms
    Ans: C   Section: 20-2

15. Of the following components, which are responsible for the main spectral emission lines found in an emission nebula?
    A)   neutral helium, carbon, oxygen, and iron atoms
    B)   ionized helium atoms and electrons
    C)   protons, positrons, helium nuclei, and neutrinos
    D)   hydrogen atoms, protons, and electrons
    Ans: D   Section: 20-2

16. An H II region is a region of
    A)   ionized hydrogen around one or more O and B stars.
    B)   molecular hydrogen inside a giant molecular cloud.
    C)   neutral, atomic hydrogen in interstellar space.
    D)   gas and dust formed by the explosion of a massive star.
    Ans: A   Section: 20-2

17. Where are H II regions found?
    A)   around hot stars
    C)   around low-mass stars
    B)   in or near old open clusters
    D)   in globular star clusters
    Ans: A   Section: 20-2

18. What radiation ionizes the hydrogen in an H II region?
    A)   ultraviolet radiation from O and B stars
    B)   X rays from the coronas of solar-type stars
    C)   intense infrared radiation from pre–main-sequence stars
    D)   gamma rays from neutron stars embedded in the nebula
    Ans: A   Section: 20-2

19. Evidence of massive amounts of hydrogen gas surrounding some stars comes from
    A)   emission of characteristic red Balmer light from nebulosity around them.
    B)   theoretical calculations that correctly describe the process of stellar formation by gravitational contraction of hydrogen gas.
    C)   the reddening of the spectra of these stars because of absorption of blue light by hydrogen.
    D)   the blue glow of light preferentially scattered by hydrogen gas within the surrounding reflection nebulae.
    Ans: A   Section: 20-2

20. Long-exposure color photographs of the night sky often show regions that glow red, such as parts of the Orion Nebula. This distinctive red color is caused by
    A)   ionization and subsequent recombination of hydrogen atoms.
    B)   the emission of red and infrared light by warm dust grains.
    C)   the collective glow of many red giant stars in the region.
    D)   scattering of starlight by dust grains in the nebula.
    Ans: A   Section: 20-2

21. The bright stars at the center of an H II region (an emission nebula) are mostly
    A)   young O and B stars.
    C)   hot white dwarfs.
    B)   red supergiants.
    D)   T Tauri stars.
    Ans: A   Section: 20-2

22. The energy required to ionize the hydrogen gas in an emission nebula (H II region) comes from
    A)   UV radiation from hot O and B stars.
    B)   the intense radiation from supernovae (exploding stars).
    C)   collisions between gas clouds in interstellar space.
    D)   X rays from young T Tauri stars.
    Ans: A   Section: 20-2

23. A reflection nebula is made visible by
    A)   thermal energy emitted as a continuous spectrum by very hot gas, much like that emitted by a hot body on Earth.
    B)   blue light, preferentially scattered by tiny dust grains.
    C)   emission lines from hydrogen, which itself has been ionized by UV light from embedded stars.
    D)   light from embedded stars reflected over a wide range of wavelengths toward Earth, by crystals of water, methane, and ammonia ices.
    Ans: B   Section: 20-2

24. The distinctive color of a reflection nebula is
    A)   blue, caused by the preferential scattering of starlight by very small dust grains.
    B)   starlight of all colors from cool stars, predominantly in the red part of the spectrum, reflected by ice crystals of water, ammonia, and methane.
    C)   a mixture of several specific colors coming from fluorescence of atoms excited by ultraviolet radiation emitted by hot stars.
    D)   red, coming from the emission of light from hydrogen gas.
    Ans: A   Section: 20-2

25. The blue color of a reflection nebula is produced by
    A)   light emitted by the gas cloud that is Doppler-shifted as the cloud moves rapidly toward us.
    B)   the continuum emission of very hot gas and dust.
    C)   emission from specific transitions in hydrogen gas.
    D)   selective scattering from very small dust grains.
    Ans: D   Section: 20-2

26. The distinct blue color of the nebulosity around stars in young clusters, such as the Pleiades, is caused by
    A)   light emitted by very hot gas which has been heated by collisions in the interstellar gas.
    B)   preferential scattering of blue starlight by small dust grains in the interstellar material.
    C)   atoms of gas emitting light by fluorescence, having been excited by ultraviolet radiation from hot stars.
    D)   halos caused by refraction of starlight in ice crystals in the nebula, similar to halos seen occasionally in the Earth's atmosphere.
    Ans: B   Section: 20-2

27. In photographs, the Pleiades open star cluster is surrounded by a bluish haze (see Fig. 20-18, Freedman and Kaufmann, *Universe,* 7th ed.). What causes this blue light?
    A) starlight absorbed and reemitted by interstellar gas in the star cluster
    B) shock waves losing energy to interstellar gas in the star cluster, causing the atoms to emit light
    C) starlight scattered by the light-sensitive grains in the photographic plate when the picture was taken
    D) starlight scattered from interstellar dust in the star cluster
    Ans: D   Section: 20-2

28. What causes the characteristic blue color of a reflection nebula?
    A) scattering of starlight from dust grains within the nebula
    B) thermal (blackbody) radiation from dust grains heated to high temperatures by stellar UV
    C) electrons dropping from $n = 3$ to $n = 2$ in hydrogen atoms
    D) electrons dropping from $n = 2$ to $n = 1$ in hydrogen atoms
    Ans: A   Section: 20-2

29. Star clusters of the same type and structure appear to become fainter than expected, on the basis of the inverse square law alone, as distance from the Sun increases. This is because
    A) star clusters are systematically smaller and hence less bright, the farther they are from the galactic center and hence from the Sun.
    B) photons of light become "tired" and appear less bright, the farther they travel.
    C) some of the light is scattered and absorbed by interstellar dust and gas between distant clusters and the Earth.
    D) the cosmological redshift has moved some of the light into the infrared spectral region.
    Ans: C   Section: 20-2

30. The effect of interstellar dust on starlight is
    A) to dim and redden distant stars by preferentially scattering their blue light.
    B) to scatter the red light from stars preferentially, making them appear more blue than expected.
    C) almost nonexistent, because light does not interact with dust.
    D) to make stars appear less bright than expected by absorbing light about equally at all wavelengths.
    Ans: A   Section: 20-2

31. Evidence for the interstellar medium has been provided by all of the following *except one*. Which is the exception?
    A) the existence of interstellar clouds like the Horsehead Nebula in Orion
    B) unshifted spectral lines observed when examining a binary star system
    C) interstellar reddening
    D) the neutrino flux
    Ans: D   Section: 20-2

32. Astronomers use the symbol H II to mean
    A) neutral hydrogen.
    B) ionized hydrogen.
    C) molecular hydrogen (with two atoms)
    D) deuterium (hydrogen with a nucleus of two particles: one neutron and one proton)
    Ans: B   Section: 20-2

33. The ionization energy of hydrogen is 13.6 electron volts or 2.8×10^{-18} Joules. A photon emitted from a hot O or B star can ionize hydrogen if it has a wavelength no greater than
    A) 2.18×10^{-18} meters.   C) 6.54×10^{-10} meters.
    B) 5.69×10^{-11} meters   D) 9.12×10^{-8} meters.
    Ans: D   Section: 20-2 and Box 5-3

34. Hydrogen atoms can be ionized by light with a wavelength of 9.12×10^{-8} meters or shorter. What approximate temperature would a star need in order to have the *peak* of its spectrum at this wavelength?
    A) 32,000 K   B) 44,000 K   C) 51 million K   D) 4×10^{15} K
    Ans: A   Section: 20-2 and Box 5-2

35. The most likely places in which stars and planetary systems are forming in the universe are
    A) the rarified outer space between galaxies.
    B) regions of hot gas in the spiral arms of galaxies.
    C) gas and dust nebulae.
    D) the centers of galaxies.
    Ans: C   Section: 20-3

36. New stars are formed
    A) in huge, cool dust and gas clouds.
    B) from free space, out of pure energy.
    C) within supernova remnants.
    D) by condensation of gas near black holes in the centers of galaxies.
    Ans: A   Section: 20-3

37. What are the dimensions of a typical dark nebula of gas and dust within which a star might form?
    A)   a few thousand solar masses inside a diameter of about 10 parsecs, or about 30 light-years
    B)   about 10 solar masses inside a diameter of about 10 parsecs
    C)   1 or 2 solar masses inside a diameter of about 100 AU, about the size of the solar system
    D)   a few thousand solar masses inside about 1 AU, the Earth's orbit
    Ans: A   Section: 20-3

38. How is gas distributed in interstellar space?
    A)   uniformly distributed through space
    B)   in clumps concentrated in interstellar clouds
    C)   concentrated in thin walls throughout the universe
    D)   concentrated around existing stars because of the stars' gravitational pull
    Ans: B   Section: 20-3

39. The temperature inside a Bok globule, where star formation may be taking place, is
    A)   about 10,000 K.   C)   significantly less than 1 K.
    B)   about 100 K.   D)   about 10 K.
    Ans: D   Section: 20-3

40. Typical gas temperatures in dark Bok globules, the birthplaces of stars, are
    A)   just below freezing, at –3° C or 270 K.
    B)   100 K.
    C)   10 K.
    D)   just above that of the cosmic background radiation, at 3.5 K.
    Ans: C   Section: 20-3

41. A cocoon nebula is
    A)   a bright knot of ionized gas in the bipolar outflow from a young star.
    B)   a cloud of dust hiding a young protostar from sight.
    C)   a giant molecular cloud containing young prestellar objects.
    D)   a dark globule of dust and gas silhouetted against a bright H II region.
    Ans: B   Section: 20-3

42. What does a cocoon nebula do to deserve its name?
    A)   Its gravity prevents the evolving protostar from expanding rapidly and dissipating as a consequence of its very high temperature.
    B)   It enhances the visibility of a faint protostar by scattering the light from it, much as a mist spreads and enlarges the light from street lamps.
    C)   It hides protostars by absorbing the very large amounts of visible light emitted by them but reemits this energy as infrared radiation.
    D)   It absorbs all the electromagnetic radiation from protostars, rendering them invisible until they have melted and evaporated the dust and ionized the gas in the nebula.
    Ans: C   Section: 20-3

43. Protostars, when they FIRST form from the interstellar medium, are usually
    A)   detected easily because their light ionizes the surrounding interstellar gas, forming H II regions.
    B)   very bright in ultraviolet light due to numerous flares (like solar flares but hotter and brighter).
    C)   hidden from sight by dust clouds that emit infrared radiation.
    D)   detected by emission lines in their visible spectra, emitted by gas being blown off their surfaces into space.
    Ans: C   Section: 20-3

44. What would be the temperature inside a dense core that is about to collapse to form a star?
    A) 10 K   B) 1000 K   C) less than 1 K   D) 100 K
    Ans: A   Section: 20-3

45. What is the most abundant element in the universe?
    A) helium   B) hydrogen   C) carbon   D) oxygen
    Ans: B   Section: 20-3

46. Which is the second most abundant element in the universe (after hydrogen)?
    A) iron   B) carbon   C) nitrogen   D) helium
    Ans: D   Section: 20-3

47. Which are the two most abundant elements in the universe?
    A)   hydrogen and helium   C)   hydrogen and oxygen
    B)   nitrogen and oxygen   D)   hydrogen and carbon
    Ans: A   Section: 20-3

48. What fraction of the measured mass of the universe is hydrogen (as represented by "standard cosmic abundances" in the interstellar medium)?
    A) 25%   B) 98%   C) 1%   D) 74%
    Ans: D   Section: 20-3

49. What fraction of the measured mass of the universe is helium (as represented by "standard cosmic abundances" in the interstellar medium)?
    A) 25%   B) 1%   C) 8%   D) 74%
    Ans: A   Section: 20-3

50. A particular giant molecular cloud has a mass of 400,000 solar masses. What is the mass of hydrogen in this cloud?
    A)   100,000 solar masses   C)   392,000 solar masses
    B)   4000 solar masses   D)   300,000 solar masses
    Ans: D   Section: 20-3

51. A particular giant molecular cloud has a mass of 400,000 solar masses. What is the mass of helium in this cloud?
    A)   4000 solar masses   C)   392,000 solar masses
    B)   300,000 solar masses   D)   100,000 solar masses
    Ans: D   Section: 20-3

52. How does the temperature of an interstellar cloud affect its ability to form stars?
    A)   Star formation is so complicated that it is not possible to say how one quantity, such as temperature, affects it.
    B)   Higher temperatures inhibit star formation.
    C)   Higher temperatures help star formation.
    D)   Star formation is independent of the temperature of the cloud.
    Ans: B   Section: 20-3

53. What determines whether a particular region of an interstellar cloud can collapse and form a star?
    A)   only the temperature, because higher temperatures act to prevent collapse
    B)   the relative concentration of dust to hydrogen gas in the cloud, because the dust is the major trigger that initiates collapse
    C)   the amount of gravity pulling inward compared to gas pressure pushing outward
    D)   the amount of mass in the cloud alone, because this determines the strength of gravity, which will act unopposed on the cloud
    Ans: C   Section: 20-3

54. What condition is considered sufficient for an interstellar cloud to collapse and form a star or stars (i.e., if this condition holds then the cloud has to collapse)?
    A)   The cloud must be alone in space, far from the gravitational influence of stars or other interstellar clouds.
    B)   The cloud must be cooler than 100 K.
    C)   Gravity must be strong enough to reach all parts of the cloud.
    D)   Gravity must dominate gas pressure inside the cloud.
    Ans: D   Section: 20-3

55. Which of the following is NOT a required condition for gas and dust to begin to condense into a protostar?
    A) low mutual rotation, to avoid spin-off of material from the forming star
    B) low temperature, to maintain low gas pressure in the cloud
    C) higher than average density, to ensure that gravitational attraction is enhanced
    D) high temperature, to ensure that gas atoms and dust particles collide with sufficient energy to stick together
    Ans: D   Section: 20-3

56. An object that is formed by the gravitational collapse of an interstellar cloud, and is slowly contracting and heating up to become a star, is called
    A) a Herbig-Haro object.   C) a cocoon nebula.
    B) a red giant star.   D) a protostar.
    Ans: D   Section: 20-3

57. Protostars are
    A) stars made almost entirely out of protons.
    B) objects with masses less than about 0.08 solar masses, which do not have enough mass to become true stars.
    C) old stars, contracting after using up all of their available hydrogen fuel.
    D) very young objects, still contracting before becoming true stars.
    Ans: D   Section: 20-3

58. Protostars are stars
    A) that are slowly contracting and cooling.
    B) whose surfaces are slowly expanding while their cores are contracting.
    C) that are slowly contracting and heating up.
    D) that are slowly heating up and expanding.
    Ans: C   Section: 20-3

59. What is a protostar?
    A) a contracting sphere of gas produced by the collapse of an interstellar cloud with, as yet, no nuclear reactions occurring in its interior
    B) a shell of gas left behind from the explosion of a star as a supernova
    C) a small, cold, interstellar cloud before it collapses to become a star
    D) a star near the end of its life, just before it explodes as a supernova
    Ans: A   Section: 20-3

60. At what stage of its life does a star pass through the protostar phase?
    A) when it is expanding in size as a red giant or supergiant
    B) after all nuclear reactions have ended in its core
    C) before nuclear reactions begin in its core
    D) while it is converting hydrogen to helium in its core
    Ans: C   Section: 20-3

61. The source of a protostar's heat is
    A) gravitational energy, released as the star contracts.
    B) gravitational energy, released as the protostar expands.
    C) nuclear reactions converting helium to carbon and oxygen in its core.
    D) nuclear reactions converting hydrogen into helium in its core.
    Ans: A   Section: 20-3

62. The major source of energy in the pre–main-sequence life of the Sun was
    A) gravitational.   C) chemical burning of carbon atoms.
    B) nuclear fusion.   D) nuclear fission.
    Ans: A   Section: 20-3

63. A particular, dense interstellar cloud is about 10 pc (30 light-years) across and contains a few thousand solar masses of material. This cloud is classified as a
    A) Barnard object.   C) bipolar outflow.
    B) Herbig-Haro object.   D) giant molecular cloud.
    Ans: A   Section: 20-3

64. How large was the Sun when it first formed as a protostar, perhaps 1000 years after formation?
    A) the same diameter as it is now
    B) about 100 times its present diameter
    C) about 1000 times its present diameter
    D) about 20 times its present diameter
    Ans: D   Section: 20-3

65. How large and bright is a young protostar of 1 solar mass, whose age is about 1000 years, compared to the radius R and luminosity L of the Sun?
    A) $1 \times R$, the same size as the Sun, and $100 \times L$
    B) $20 \times R$, $100 \times L$
    C) $1 \times R$, $1 \times L$, because a protostar of this mass has already evolved to a Sun-like main-sequence star
    D) $20 \times R$, but still much fainter than the Sun, at $L/10$
    Ans: B   Section: 20-3

66. A star's evolutionary track is
    A) its movement when plotted on a Hertzsprung-Russell diagram, as it evolves in luminosity and temperature.
    B) its motion through the dark, dense cloud from which it was formed, marked by a visible channel swept free of dust and gas.
    C) the line across the Hertzsprung-Russell diagram denoting stars identified as main-sequence stars.
    D) its movement when plotted on a map of the galaxy as it takes part in the overall galactic rotation.
    Ans: A   Section: 20-3

67. If a protostar of one solar mass has a luminosity 100 times that of the Sun and a radius 20 times that of the Sun, what is its surface temperature? (The Sun's surface temperature is 5800 K.)
    A) 2000 K   B) 2900 K   C) 4100 K   D) 5800 K
    Ans: C   Section: 20-3

68. In which region of the Hertzsprung-Russell diagram will a newly formed protostar first appear when it begins to shine at visible wavelength?
    A)   at the center of the main sequence, because all protostars begin their lives at this position and move up or down it depending on the star's mass
    B)   lower right corner—very low luminosity and cool
    C)   top left corner—at the top of the main sequence, down which it will progress with time
    D)   upper right side—relatively large luminosity but cool
    Ans: D   Section: 20-4

69. A protostar of about 1 solar mass is gradually contracting and becoming hotter. This will cause its position on the Hertzsprung-Russell diagram to shift slowly
    A)   upward and toward the right.   C)   downward and toward the right.
    B)   downward and toward the left.   D)   upward and toward the left.
    Ans: B   Section: 20-4

70. For any star on the main sequence, the same star when it was a protostar was
    A)   larger and cooler.   C)   larger and hotter.
    B)   hotter but not necessarily larger. D)   cooler but not necessarily larger.
    Ans: A   Section: 20-4

71. How do low-mass protostars (< 4 solar masses) evolve in the H-R diagram?
    A)   temperature decreasing at approximately constant luminosity
    B)   temperature increasing at approximately constant luminosity
    C)   luminosity decreasing at approximately constant temperature
    D)   luminosity increasing at approximately constant temperature
    Ans: C   Section: 20-4 and Figure 20-9

72. Protostars with masses of less than about four times the mass of the Sun evolve at approximately constant surface temperature through most of their pre–main-sequence lifetimes. This is because
    A)   they contract too rapidly for their temperature and luminosity to change significantly.
    B)   they are not massive enough to contract significantly and luminosity remains constant.
    C)   the luminosity increases as the surface area decreases.
    D)   the luminosity decreases as the surface area decreases.
    Ans: D   Section: 20-4

73. How do massive protostars (4 solar masses) evolve on the H-R diagram?
    A)   Temperature decreases at approximately constant luminosity.
    B)   Temperature increases at approximately constant luminosity.
    C)   Luminosity decreases at approximately constant temperature.
    D)   Luminosity increases at approximately constant temperature
    Ans: B   Section: 20-4 and Figure 20-9

74. Protostars with masses of more than about 4 times the mass of the Sun maintain
    approximately constant luminosity through their pre–main-sequence lifetimes. This is
    because
    A)   the star contracts as its surface temperature decreases, and the change in surface
         area compensates for the change in energy emitted per unit area.
    B)   the surface temperature increases as the star contracts, and the change in energy
         emitted per unit area compensates for the change in surface area.
    C)   they contract too rapidly for their temperature and luminosity to change
         significantly.
    D)   they are too massive to contract significantly, thus keeping luminosity constant.
    Ans: B   Section: 20-4

75. How does a 15-solar-mass star evolve in the first 10^5 years after it becomes a protostar?
    A)   Its temperature remains relatively cool at about 4000 K, but its luminosity
         decreases by a factor of 100.
    B)   Its brightness and temperature remain approximately constant as it stabilizes into
         a nuclear-heated star on the main sequence.
    C)   Its brightness remains constant, while its surface temperature increases by a factor
         of 10.
    D)   Its brightness increases by about a factor of 10^4, because its temperature increases
         by a factor of 10, moving it upward along the main sequence.
    Ans: C   Section: 20-4 and Figure 20-9

76. If a protostar were able to contract (get smaller) without any change to its surface
    temperature, what would happen to its luminosity?
    A)   It would decrease, due to the smaller surface area of the protostar.
    B)   It would remain the same, because the temperature does not change.
    C)   It is not possible to predict the change in luminosity, because other factors are
         involved.
    D)   It would increase, due to the compression of the gas.
    Ans: A   Section: 20-4

77. The lowest mass that a protostar can have and still become a star (i.e., start thermonuclear reactions in its core) is
    A)   about half a solar mass.
    B)   slightly less than 1/100 of a solar mass.
    C)   slightly less than 1/10 of a solar mass.
    D)   8/10 of a solar mass.
    Ans: C   Section: 20-4

78. The smallest mass that a main-sequence star can have is about 0.08 solar mass. The reason for this is that
    A)   the temperature in the core of a contracting protostar of less than 0.08 solar masses does not get high enough for nuclear reactions to start.
    B)   protostars cannot form with masses less than 0.08 solar mass.
    C)   thermonuclear reactions begin so suddenly in stars of less than 0.08 solar mass, that the star is disrupted by an explosion.
    D)   protostars of less than 0.08 solar masses are not massive enough to contract.
    Ans: A   Section: 20-4

79. What is the lowest mass that an object can have and still be a star?
    A)   0.08 solar masses
    B)   0.02 solar masses
    C)   0.002 solar masses (twice Jupiter's mass)
    D)   0.80 solar masses
    Ans: A   Section: 20-4

80. A brown dwarf is
    A)   an object intermediate between a planet and a star, with not enough mass to begin nuclear reactions in its core.
    B)   a general name for objects similar to the planet Jupiter.
    C)   any star whose blackbody spectrum peaks in the brown region of the visible spectrum.
    D)   a star of less than about 1.5 solar masses at the very end of its life, after it has cooled to near-invisibility.
    Ans: A   Section: 20-4

81. Suppose that an astronomy news item announces the discovery of a brown dwarf. What is it that has been discovered?
    A)   a object too massive to be a planet but not massive enough to be a star
    B)   a protostar still embedded in the cloud of gas and dust from which it formed
    C)   a pre-stellar object undergoing gravitational collapse
    D)   a Pluto-like object in the Kuiper belt, beyond the edge of the planetary system
    Ans: A   Section: 20-4

82. Suppose that an astronomical observatory announces the discovery of an object with about 50 times the mass of Jupiter, a mass too low to become a main sequence star. What name would the observatory apply to this object?
    A) brown dwarf   B) white dwarf   C) infrared dwarf (IRD)   D) red dwarf
    Ans: A   Section: 20-4

83. An object that is too massive to be a planet but not massive enough to be a star is called a
    A) T Tauri star.   B) Herbig-Haro object.   C) brown dwarf.   D) red dwarf.
    Ans: C   Section: 20-4

84. Main-sequence stars do not have masses larger than about 200 solar masses. The reason that stars of larger mass do not exist is that
    A)   nothing can prevent such stars from collapsing directly into black holes.
    B)   the thermonuclear reactions in such stars proceed so rapidly that the star explodes.
    C)   such stars contract directly to become planet-like objects.
    D)   they rapidly become very luminous and are quickly disrupted by the resulting very high internal pressure.
    Ans: D   Section: 20-4

85. How does a massive star normally end its life?
    A)   It gradually shrinks to the size of the Earth.
    B)   We don't know, because its lifetime is longer than the age of the universe.
    C)   It collapses inward, and the whole star becomes a black hole.
    D)   It explodes.
    Ans: D   Section: 20-4

86. What is believed to be the maximum mass that a star can have?
    A)   There appears to be no physical limit.
    B)   about 1000 solar masses
    C)   about 200 solar masses
    D)   about 5 solar masses
    Ans: C   Section: 20-4

87. What prevents a star from having a mass greater than about 200 solar masses?
    A)   No interstellar clouds are found that contain more than 200 solar masses.
    B)   A star of larger mass would collapse under its own gravity, and the whole star would become a black hole.
    C)   Gas pressure becomes so high as a consequence of high temperatures, that the excess mass is pushed back into space.
    D)   The core of a larger-mass star would evolve rapidly and explode before the overall star finished contracting as a protostar.
    Ans: C   Section: 20-4

88. How long does it take for a 1-solar-mass star to pass through the pre–main-sequence phase?
    A)   200,000 years   C)   20,000 years
    B)   20,000,000 years   D)   20 billion years
    Ans: B   Section: 20-4

89. At approximately what temperature will nuclear reactions begin in the core of a pre–main-sequence star?
    A) 50 million K   B) 1 million K   C) 500,000 K   D) 5 million K
    Ans: D   Section: 20-4

90. What occurrence defines the end of the protostar phase of a star's life and the start of the main-sequence phase?
    A)   Convection begins in its interior.
    B)   The star stops accreting mass from the interstellar cloud.
    C)   The star begins to expand to become a red supergiant.
    D)   Nuclear reactions begin in its core.
    Ans: D   Section: 20-4

91. At what point in its evolution will a protostar stop shrinking and stabilize into a star?
    A)   when nuclear processes generate enough energy and internal pressure to resist gravitational contraction
    B)   when contraction leads to an increase in spin rate as a result of the conservation of angular momentum and the resulting centrifugal force begins to oppose the gravitational contraction
    C)   when gravitational contraction has heated up the gas to the point where radiation pressure opposes gravity for the first time
    D)   when the buildup of helium in the core stops the nuclear furnace
    Ans: A   Section: 20-4

92. What event occurs at the end of the protostar stage of a star's life?
    A)   Nuclear reactions begin in its core, converting hydrogen into helium, generating energy and increasing internal pressure.
    B)   It explodes, forming a supernova remnant.
    C)   It begins a long period of contraction, in which gravitational energy is converted into heat.
    D)   Gas is spun off from its equator, forming planets.
    Ans: A   Section: 20-4

93. Which part of the Hertzsprung-Russell diagram is occupied by protostars?
    A)   to the left of the main sequence
    B)   a band running from upper right to lower left
    C)   to the right of the main sequence
    D)   a band running from upper left to lower right
    Ans: C   Section: 20-4

94. What is the most important factor that determines the point in the Hertzsprung-Russell diagram where a protostar reaches the main sequence?
   A)   the initial luminosity of the protostar
   B)   the size of the interstellar cloud from which the protostar formed
   C)   the initial temperature of the protostar
   D)   the mass of the protostar
   Ans: D   Section: 20-4

95. What is the relationship between stellar mass and position on the main sequence of the Hertzsprung-Russell diagram?
   A)   The most massive stars appear in the center of the main sequence while less massive main sequence stars are brighter or dimmer than these stars as a consequence of their higher or lower temperatures.
   B)   The more massive the star, the higher up on the main sequence the star will appear.
   C)   The main sequence defines a line of stars whose masses are about 1 solar mass while stars of different masses appear on either side of the main sequence.
   D)   The less massive the star, the higher up on the main sequence the star will appear.
   Ans: B   Section: 20-4

96. What is the relationship between the mass of a protostar and the time needed for it to reach the main sequence, after it forms inside an interstellar cloud?
   A)   More massive protostars reach the main sequence in a shorter time than less massive protostars.
   B)   Less massive protostars reach the main sequence in a shorter time than more massive protostars.
   C)   The time needed is independent of the mass of the protostar.
   D)   The time needed is least for a protostar of approximately 4 solar masses and longer for protostars of either greater or less mass.
   Ans: A   Section: 20-4

97. How long did the Sun spend in the protostar phase of its life?
   A)   50 thousand years   C)   400 thousand years
   B)   20 million years   D)   4.6 billion years
   Ans: B   Section: 20-4

98. How much time does it take for a one solar mass protostar to finish accreting mass from the interstellar cloud?
   A) 100,000 years   B) 1 billion years   C) 10,000 years   D) 10,000,000 years
   Ans: A   Section: 20-4

99. Thermonuclear reactions convert hydrogen into helium in the core of a star during which phase of a star's life?
    A)   the protostar phase
    B)   the horizontal branch phase
    C)   the time when the star moves up the red giant branch for the first time
    D)   the main-sequence phase
    Ans: D   Section: 20-4

100. In the Hertzsprung-Russell diagram, how does the position of a typical star change while it is at the main-sequence phase of its evolution?
    A)   Stars move from upper right to lower left along the main sequence.
    B)   A star does not move on the H-R diagram while it is at this phase of its life.
    C)   Massive stars (> 4 solar masses) move toward the upper left as their luminosity increases, whereas lower-mass stars move toward the lower right as their temperature decreases, along the main sequence.
    D)   Stars move from upper left to lower right along the main sequence.
    Ans: B   Section: 20-4

101. At what stage of its evolutionary life is the Sun?
    A)   pre–main-sequence—variable star
    B)   main-sequence—middle age
    C)   post–main-sequence—red giant (cool) phase
    D)   just before supernova stage (perhaps 5 years)—late evolutionary stage
    Ans: B   Section: 20-4

102. What physical process is taking place inside stars that are in the main-sequence phase of their lives?
    A)   Hydrogen is being converted to helium in their cores.
    B)   Hydrogen is being converted to helium in a shell around a core where no nuclear reactions are occurring.
    C)   The gas in the star is contracting gravitationally without nuclear reactions taking place.
    D)   Helium is being converted to carbon in their cores.
    Ans: A   Section: 20-4

103. What is happening in a star that is on the main sequence on the Hertzsprung-Russell diagram?
    A)   The star is slowly shrinking and heating up as it slides up the main sequence from bottom right to top left in the H-R diagram.
    B)   Nuclear reactions have ceased, and the star is simply cooling down.
    C)   The star is generating internal energy by helium fusion, creating carbon.
    D)   The star is generating internal energy by hydrogen fusion, creating helium.
    Ans: D   Section: 20-4

104. How long will the Sun have been a main-sequence star when it finally begins to evolve toward the red giant phase?
    A) 10^7 years   B) 10^{11} years   C) 10^{10} years   D) 4.6×10^9 years
    Ans: C   Section: 20-4

105. The total time that the Sun will spend as a main-sequence star is
    A)   at least 200 billion years (2×10^{11} years)
    B)   about 10 billion years (10^{10} years)
    C)   about 10 million years (10^7 years)
    D)   about 1 million years
    Ans: B   Section: 20-4

106. Those interior regions of a protostar that are relatively cool are more likely to transport energy by
    A)   conduction, because the atoms are close enough together to act as a solid.
    B)   convection, because the hydrogen tends to form the H^- ion, a good absorber of radiation.
    C)   radiation, because the atoms move too slowly at these temperatures for convection to be effective.
    D)   radiation, because low temperature atoms produce copious amounts of visible light.
    Ans: B   Section: 21-4 and 18-5

107. A T Tauri star is at what stage of its stellar evolution?
    A)   a well-established main-sequence star
    B)   just before red giant phase—when variability begins
    C)   at the end of its life—decaying away and cooling
    D)   protostar—before main-sequence phase
    Ans: D   Section: 20-5

108. T Tauri stars are at what stage of stellar evolution?
    A)   early phase, just after the formation of the protostar
    B)   just after the red giant phase
    C)   post–main-sequence or later phases
    D)   main sequence or "middle age"
    Ans: A   Section: 20-5

109. A T Tauri star is
    A)   a low-mass protostar near the end of its pre–main-sequence lifetime.
    B)   a young, massive O or B star.
    C)   a low-mass protostar embedded in a cocoon of dust clouds.
    D)   a high-mass protostar surrounded by a rotationally flattened disk of gas and dust.
    Ans: A   Section: 20-5

110. Which of the following statements is characteristic of a T Tauri star?
    A) great age—near the end of its life as a star
    B) ejection of mass into space
    C) high mass—greater than about 3 solar masses
    D) nuclear reactions in the core
    Ans: B   Section: 20-5

111. What is a T Tauri star?
    A) a young, irregularly variable, G, K, or M type star that is ejecting gas
    B) a giant or supergiant star that varies regularly in brightness
    C) a giant or supergiant star that varies randomly in brightness
    D) a massive O or B type star that ionizes hydrogen in interstellar space
    Ans: A   Section: 20-5

112. A T Tauri star is
    A) a protostar that is ejecting mass near the end of its pre–main-sequence lifetime.
    B) a young, massive, O or B star.
    C) a young protostar embedded in a cocoon of dust clouds, visible only by infrared radiation.
    D) a high-mass yellow giant star that pulsates regularly in size and brightness.
    Ans: A   Section: 20-5

113. Which of the following is NOT a characteristic of T Tauri stars?
    A) nuclear reactions in the core   C) ejection of mass into space
    B) irregular variations in brightness   D) emission lines in the spectrum
    Ans: A   Section: 20-5

114. On a Hertzsprung-Russell diagram describing the stars in a young cluster, in which position would you expect to find the T Tauri stars?
    A) well above the main sequence and to the left of the diagram
    B) well below the main sequence
    C) just above and slightly to the right of the main sequence
    D) in the upper right of the diagram, well above the main sequence
    Ans: C   Section: 20-5

115. A Herbig-Haro object is
    A) the gas cloud produced by a supernova explosion.
    B) a dark nebula which obscures distant stars from our view.
    C) a young protostar emerging from its nebula.
    D) glowing interstellar gas, heated by a high-velocity jet of matter from an evolving star.
    Ans: D   Section: 20-5

116. Herbig-Haro objects are
   A)   dense dust clouds surrounding and being heated by massive protostars.
   B)   higher density knots of matter in protoplanetary disks around very young, low-mass stars.
   C)   regions of ionized gas on the edges of giant molecular clouds.
   D)   luminous knots of material at either end of bipolar jets emerging from young T Tauri stars.
   Ans: D   Section: 20-5

117. Herbig-Haro objects, bright, variable regions within nebulae, are now thought to be the result of
   A)   the initial condensation of matter into a protostar, producing an infrared and visible glow.
   B)   intense jets of material ejected from a young star, hitting parts of the nebula.
   C)   brightening of the gas surrounding a massive star as the precursor to a supernova explosion.
   D)   the hot atmosphere of a star as it is ejected in the dying phases of the star's life.
   Ans: B   Section: 20-5

118. What is the most important process causing a protostar to stop accreting mass?
   A)   Radiation and outflowing material from the protostar push infalling matter away from the protostar.
   B)   The dense core spins up as it collapses, and eventually the infalling matter is held away from the protostar by the centrifugal force.
   C)   Other protostars that have formed in the vicinity pass randomly through the infalling material and eventually disperse it.
   D)   All of the infalling matter has been used up in the accretion.
   Ans: A   Section: 20-5

119. What is a proplyd?
   A)   a protoplanetary disk around a young star
   B)   a protostar hidden inside a dense shell of dust
   C)   a bright nebula formed in the bipolar outflow from a T Tauri star
   D)   an amoeba-like creature thought to inhabit ethane lakes on Saturn's moon, Titan
   Ans: A   Section: 20-5

120. The Hubble Space Telescope has photographed disks of gas and dust around young, low-mass stars in the Orion Nebula. It is thought that planets may form from the material in disks such as these. What name has been given to these disks?
   A) stellar accretions   B) proplyds   C) cocoon nebulae   D) Barnard objects
   Ans: B   Section: 20-5

121. In the magnetic model for the bipolar outflow from a protostar
    A) magnetic field lines emanate from the poles of the protostar and carry material outward from the stellar interior.
    B) magnetic field lines through the circumstellar accretion disk become twisted and concentrated by the rotation of this disk.
    C) magnetic field lines associated with the galaxy as a whole are concentrated and shaped by their interaction with the magnetosphere of the protostar.
    D) the jets are formed along magnetic field lines, which go from the north magnetic pole of one protostar to the south magnetic pole of a second protostar which forms a close binary pair with the first.
    Ans: B   Section: 20-5 and Figure 20-15

122. When a giant molecular cloud collapses to form a group of stars, what is this stellar group called?
    A) a galaxy   B) a constellation   C) an open cluster   D) a globular cluster
    Ans: C   Section: 20-6

123. The characteristics of an open cluster of stars are
    A) many thousands of stars, all very old, with very little evidence of elements heavier than helium, and no evidence of dust or gas in their vicinity.
    B) many thousands of stars, of very different ages, but the same chemical composition.
    C) a few hundred stars, often very young and still embedded in the gas and dust from which they were formed.
    D) many thousands of stars, mostly binary, of different ages.
    Ans: C   Section: 20-6

124. If we plot the stars in a YOUNG star cluster on a Hertzsprung-Russell diagram, we would expect to see
    A) the more massive stars above the main sequence and the less massive stars on the main sequence.
    B) all of the stars above the main sequence because none have evolved to the main-sequence stage.
    C) all stars on the main sequence.
    D) the more massive stars on the main sequence and the less massive stars above the main sequence.
    Ans: D   Section: 20-6

125. An astronomer plots the H-R diagram of a star cluster and finds that it contains hot B-type stars on the main sequence and cooler G- and K-type stars noticeably above the main sequence. This cluster is
    A)   impossible, because one cannot have cool stars above the main sequence when hotter stars are on the main sequence.
    B)   of indeterminate age, because one cannot estimate the age of the cluster from the information given.
    C)   very young, because the G and K stars are still evolving toward the main sequence.
    D)   old, because the G and K stars are already evolving off (away from) the main sequence.
    Ans: C   Section: 20-6

126. When plotted on an H-R diagram, a particular star cluster has its more massive stars on the main sequence and its less massive stars above the main sequence. Can we find the age of this cluster (i.e., how long it is since its stars condensed from the interstellar medium)?
    A)   Yes, by finding the least massive star on the main sequence. The age of the cluster equals the time that this star spent as a protostar.
    B)   Yes, by finding the most massive star on the main sequence. The age of the cluster equals the time that this star spent as a protostar.
    C)   No.
    D)   Yes, by finding the least massive protostar. The age of the cluster equals the time that this star takes to reach the main sequence.
    Ans: A   Section: 20-6

127. What is the ultimate fate of an open star cluster?
    A)   The stars in it gradually sink toward the center, creating a globular cluster.
    B)   The shape of the cluster remains more or less as it is now while the stars in it age and die.
    C)   The stars in it escape one by one until the cluster no longer exists.
    D)   Over time the stars in it collide and merge, eventually creating a black hole.
    Ans: C   Section: 20-6

128. What is the ultimate fate of an open cluster (or galactic cluster) of stars?
    A)   It is torn apart by collisions with giant molecular clouds.
    B)   Its stars finish their lives and explode as supernovae, until eventually there are no stars left.
    C)   It gradually becomes more compact until the stars in it merge and collapse to become a supermassive black hole.
    D)   Its stars escape one by one until the cluster no longer exists.
    Ans: D   Section: 20-6

129. In an open cluster some of the lower mass stars may have had their sizes limited when the surrounding material they were accreting was blown away by ultraviolet radiation. What is the source of this UV radiation?
    A)   It sweeps generally through the galaxy.
    B)   It comes from supernova explosions from outside the cluster.
    C)   The more massive O and B stars in the cluster evolve more quickly and produce ultraviolet radiation while the less massive stars are still evolving toward the main sequence.
    D)   The ultraviolet radiation is emitted by the low mass stars themselves when they begin hydrogen burning.
    Ans: C   Section: 20-6

130. Which range of electromagnetic radiation is useful for observing new-born protostars within their gas and dust nebulas?
    A) visible   B) radio   C) highly penetrating X rays   D) infrared
    Ans: D   Section: 20-3 and 20-7

131. Which range of wavelengths of electromagnetic radiation is the most effective in the study of newborn protostars in their dust clouds and nebulae?
    A) gamma rays   B) radio   C) infrared   D) ultraviolet
    Ans: C   Section: 20-3 and 20-7

132. Which wavelength region is most useful for investigating dense cores inside giant molecular clouds?
    A) infrared   B) X rays   C) ultraviolet   D) optical (visual)
    Ans: A   Section: 20-7

133. The Orion Nebula is
    A)   a large interstellar gas and dust cloud containing many young stars.
    B)   a spiral galaxy in the constellation Orion.
    C)   a supernova remnant (material thrown out by an exploding star).
    D)   a red supergiant star surrounded by its retinue of planets.
    Ans: A   Section: 20-7

134. Infrared stars within the Orion Nebula are examples of which stage of stellar evolution?
    A)   protostar and young star   C)   red giant
    B)   supernova remnants   D)   planetary nebula
    Ans: A   Section: 20-7

135. Where in the universe would you look for a protostar?
    A)   in globular clusters of stars   C)   in dense dust and gas clouds
    B)   near black holes   D)   in the empty space between galaxies
    Ans: C   Section: 20-3 and 20-7

136. In which one of the following locations are clumps of gas most likely to be collapsing to form stars?
    A)   in the outer part of our solar system, in the Oort belt
    B)   giant molecular clouds
    C)   in hot, glowing H II regions
    D)   in a globular cluster
    Ans: B   Section: 20-7

137. Star formation takes place in
    A)   giant molecular clouds.
    B)   H II regions.
    C)   blue reflection nebulae.
    D)   hot, turbulent gas thrown out in a supernova explosion.
    Ans: A   Section: 20-7

138. Giant molecular clouds, which are major sites of star formation, can be up to
    A)   1000 pc across and contain 100 million solar masses of material.
    B)   10 times the size of the solar system and contain 2 to 3 solar masses of material.
    C)   100 pc across and contain 2 million solar masses of material.
    D)   10 pc across and contain a few thousand solar masses of material.
    Ans: C   Section: 20-7

139. What is the mass of a typical giant molecular cloud?
    A)   10 to 200 solar masses   C)   100,000 to 2,000,000 solar masses
    B)   1,000 to 20,000 solar masses   D)   10 million to 2 billion solar masses.
    Ans: C   Section: 20-7

140. What is a typical size for a giant molecular cloud?
    A)   100 light-years across   C)   10 light-years across
    B)   anything up to a light year across   D)   1000 light-years across
    Ans: A   Section: 20-7

141. A particular, dense interstellar cloud is about 100 pc across and contains 2 million solar masses of material. This cloud would probably be classified as a
    A)   giant molecular cloud.   C)   Herbig-Haro object.
    B)   cocoon nebula.   D)   Bok globule.
    Ans: A   Section: 20-7

142. Giant molecular clouds of H_2 and CO gas are found in which regions of our galaxy?
    A)   They appear to be uniformly spread throughout the galaxy, both in the spiral arms and above and below them.
    B)   above and below the plane of the spiral arms, over the galactic poles
    C)   at the center of the galaxy
    D)   along the spiral arms
    Ans: D   Section: 20-7

143. At what wavelengths have astronomers mapped and studied the distribution of the giant molecular clouds in space?
    A) long radio wavelengths, greater than 20 cm, because molecules are very efficient radio emitters
    B) visible light, using photography
    C) UV, because molecules are efficient UV emitters and the clouds are hot
    D) millimeter wavelengths, using radio telescopes
    Ans: D   Section: 20-7

144. In which part of the electromagnetic spectrum are molecules most easily detected?
    A) visible light   B) ultraviolet light   C) X rays   D) radio waves
    Ans: D   Section: 20-7

145. Which of the following molecules is likely to be the most common in interstellar space?
    A) H_2O, water   B) OH, hydroxyl   C) H_2 D) CO, carbon monoxide
    Ans: C   Section: 20-7

146. In star-forming regions in interstellar space, which molecule is the easiest to detect?
    A) carbon monoxide (CO)   C) ammonia (NH_3)
    B) formaldehyde (H_2CO)   D) hydrogen (H_2)
    Ans: A   Section: 20-7

147. Which of the following easily observed molecular species is used as a tracer for the fundamental but difficult-to-observe H_2 molecules in giant molecular clouds?
    A) H_2O B) CO   C) OH   D) CO_2
    Ans: B   Section: 20-7

148. How have molecules such as formaldehyde (H_2CO) been detected in interstellar clouds?
    A) by observing the chemical reactions in which they are created
    B) only by theoretical modeling, knowing that the component elements (H, C, O) are present
    C) by direct sampling by space probes
    D) by molecular emission lines
    Ans: D   Section: 20-7

149. Hydrogen in molecular form, H_2, is thought to be very abundant in gas clouds in space, but these molecules emit radiation relatively inefficiently because they are symmetrical molecules. Which other (asymmetrical) molecule occurs in close association with H_2 and is used as a probe for molecular clouds?
    A) CO   B) H_2O C) OH   D) CO_2
    Ans: A   Section: 20-7

150. An astronomer observes that there are 500 molecules of carbon monoxide per cubic meter in a particular interstellar cloud. What abundance of hydrogen gas (H_2) does the astronomer infer from this observation?
    A) 5,000,000 molecules of H_2 per cubic meter.
    B) 500,000,000 molecules of H_2 per cubic meter.
    C) 500 molecules of H_2 per cubic meter.
    D) 50,000 molecules of H_2 per cubic meter.
    Ans: A   Section: 20-7

151. When a carbon monoxide (CO) molecule emits a radio photon of 2.6-mm wavelength, what happens to the molecule?
    A) The molecule changes its rate of rotation.
    B) An electron in the molecule "flips" or reverses its direction of spin with respect to the plane of the molecule.
    C) An electron in the molecule jumps to a lower orbit.
    D) An electron in the molecule jumps to a higher orbit.
    Ans: A   Section: 20-7

152. Astronomers use millimeter wavelength radiation to find giant molecular clouds. What is the source of this millimeter radiation?
    A) vibrations of the hydrogen atoms in the H_2 molecule, the most abundant molecule in the giant molecular clouds
    B) emissions from the hot, O and B stars newly formed in the giant molecular cloud
    C) shock waves formed when solar winds from newly formed stars collide with the gas in the giant molecular cloud
    D) rotational energy changes in the CO molecule
    Ans: D   Section: 20-7

153. What is the relationship between a giant molecular cloud and an H II region?
    A) They are two names for the same entity.
    B) Within giant molecular clouds, H II regions surround ultraviolet-emitting stars (types O and B), which have ionized the hydrogen around them.
    C) Within H II regions, giant molecular clouds are concentrations of other molecules like CO and H_2O.
    D) Giant molecular clouds evolve into H II regions as the molecules other than hydrogen are used up in star formation.
    Ans: B   Section: 20-7

154. Which of the following mechanisms is thought to be ineffective and inefficient in the triggering of star birth in molecular clouds when compared to other mechanisms?
    A) gravitational contraction of a hot gas cloud
    B) collisions between two interstellar clouds
    C) supernova explosions and the resultant shock waves
    D) pressure waves in the spiral arms of a galaxy
    Ans: A   Section: 20-3, 20-7, and 20-8

155. Which of the following processes does NOT lead to star formation?
    A)   compression of a cold interstellar gas-and-dust cloud by the shock wave from a nearby supernova explosion
    B)   compression waves passing through interstellar clouds in the arms of spiral galaxies
    C)   compression of a hot interstellar gas cloud by its own gravity
    D)   compression of a cold part of a large interstellar cloud by another part which contains a group of hot, young, massive stars
    Ans: C   Section: 20-3, 20-7, and 20-8

156. Which of the following trigger mechanisms for the initiation of stellar formation in gas and dust clouds produces many low-mass stars and only a few high-mass, hot, O and B stars?
    A)   the passage of the cloud through a black hole
    B)   compression caused by the passage of the cloud through a galactic spiral arm
    C)   shock wave from a supernova explosion
    D)   gravitational condensation of the cloud
    Ans: C   Section: 20-8

157. What recent evidence has indicated that the initial condensation that occurred in a gas and dust cloud to produce the Sun was caused by a nearby supernova explosion?
    A)   the abnormal velocity of the Sun with respect to the spiral arm in which it is located, indicating a major disturbance in the past
    B)   radioactivity in meteorites
    C)   a vast shell of gas moving outward at a great speed from a position near to the Sun in our galaxy
    D)   a layer of the Earth's crust containing abnormal amounts of the rare metal iridium
    Ans: B   Section: 20-8

158. Which of the following trigger mechanisms for the initiation of stellar formation in gas and dust clouds produces many high mass O and B stars but only a few low-mass stars?
    A)   the passage of the cloud through a black hole
    B)   compression caused by the passage of the cloud through a galactic spiral arm
    C)   shock waves from a supernova explosion
    D)   gravitational condensation of the cloud
    Ans: B   Section: 20-8

159. There are several mechanisms that can trigger star formation in a cold, dark nebula. In each of these the key to star formation is
    A)   to bathe the cold, dark nebula in ultraviolet radiation and sweep away some of the colder material.
    B)   to compress the gas and dust so that gravitation will overcome the gas pressure.
    C)   to heat the gas so that gas pressure will overcome gravitation.
    D)   to subject the dark nebula to an intense magnetic field so that supersonic jets will form.
    Ans: B   Section: 20-8

Chapter 21: Stellar Evolution: After the Main Sequence

1. What places a limit on the lifetime of a star?
   A) loss of the mass, and therefore of nuclear fuel, of the star into space by stellar winds
   B) amount of available nuclear fuel it contains
   C) collisions between stars in a galaxy are sufficiently frequent that all stars will eventually be destroyed in this way.
   D) buildup of spin as it evolves and contracts means that the star will eventually spin apart
   Ans: B   Section: 21-1

2. What is happening in the interior of a star that is on the main sequence on the Hertzsprung-Russell diagram?
   A) Stars that have reached the main sequence have ceased nuclear "burning" and are simply cooling down by emitting radiation.
   B) The star is slowly shrinking as it slides down the main sequence from top left to bottom right.
   C) The star is generating energy by helium fusion, having stopped hydrogen "burning."
   D) The star is generating internal energy by hydrogen fusion.
   Ans: D   Section: 21-1

3. In which phase of a star's life are thermonuclear reactions converting hydrogen into helium in the core of a star?
   A) the main-sequence phase
   B) the horizontal branch phase
   C) as the star moves up the red giant branch for the first time
   D) the protostar phase
   Ans: A   Section: 21-1

4. All stars on the main sequence
   A) are at a late stage of evolution after the red giant stage.
   B) are changing slowly in size by gravitational contraction.
   C) generate energy by hydrogen fusion in their centers.
   D) have approximately the same age to within a few million years.
   Ans: C   Section: 21-1

5. What particular feature of stellar behavior is associated with the fact that a star is on the main sequence in the Hertzsprung-Russell diagram?
    A)   The star is generating internal energy by hydrogen fusion in its core.
    B)   The star is slowly shrinking, thereby releasing gravitational potential energy.
    C)   The star is generating energy by helium fusion in its core, having stopped hydrogen "burning."
    D)   The star has ceased nuclear "burning" and is simply cooling down by emitting radiation.
    Ans: A   Section: 21-1

6. At what stage of its evolutionary life is the Sun?
    A)   post-main sequence—red giant (cool) phase
    B)   before main sequence—variable star
    C)   main sequence—middle age
    D)   just before supernova stage
    Ans: C   Section: 21-1

7. Which group of stars in the H-R diagram would be labeled "zero-age main sequence"?
    A)   stars that have just collapsed from the interstellar medium
    B)   stars that are just beginning to convert helium into carbon in their cores
    C)   stars that contain no processed elements (elements heavier than hydrogen or helium)
    D)   stars that have just started converting hydrogen to helium in their cores
    Ans: D   Section: 21-1

8. Why are the majority of stars in the sky in the main-sequence phase of their lives?
    A)   This is the longest-lasting phase in each star's life.
    B)   Most stars die at the end of the main-sequence phase.
    C)   This is the only phase that is common to all stars.
    D)   Most stars in the sky were created at about the same time, so they are all in the same phase of their lives.
    Ans: A   Section: 21-1

9. Over which of the following stages of stellar evolution does the radius of a star remain approximately constant?
    A)   birth and initial formation   C)   asymptotic giant branch phase
    B)   red giant   D)   main-sequence phase
    Ans: D   Section: 21-1

10. How long will the Sun have spent as a main-sequence star when it finally begins to evolve toward the red giant phase?
    A) 1 billion years   B) 10^{11} years   C) 1 million years   D) 10^{10} years
    Ans: D   Section: 21-1

11. The total time the Sun will spend as a main-sequence star is
    A) about 1 million years.
    C) at least 200 billion years.
    B) about 10 billion years.
    D) about 4.5 million years.
    Ans: B   Section: 21-1

12. If you were to look at one kilogram of material taken from the surface of the Sun and 1 kilogram taken from the center, which of the following statements would be true of these two 1 kilogram masses?
    A) The kilogram from the surface would contain more hydrogen than the one from the center.
    B) Neither of them would contain any hydrogen.
    C) They both would contain the same amount of hydrogen.
    D) The kilogram from the surface would contain less hydrogen than the one from the center.
    Ans: A   Section: 21-1

13. What percentage of the mass of the Sun's core still remains as hydrogen after the thermonuclear furnace has transformed hydrogen into helium over its main-sequence lifetime?
    A) 75%   B) 35%   C) less than 1%   D) 25%
    Ans: B   Section: 21-1

14. Why does the core of the Sun contain more helium and less hydrogen than the surface material of the Sun?
    A) Thermonuclear reactions have converted much of the original hydrogen in the core into helium.
    B) The hydrogen has been lifted out of the core by the Sun's magnetic field.
    C) Helium is heavier than hydrogen and has sunk toward the center in a process of chemical differentiation.
    D) Helium condensed more easily, so the core became helium-rich when the Sun was first forming. Vast quantities of hydrogen were added only after the core became massive enough.
    Ans: A   Section: 21-1

15. What causes the core of a star to contract during the main-sequence phase of the star's life?
    A) The conversion of hydrogen into helium reduces the number of particles in the core.
    B) Convection in the outer layers carries energy out of the core more efficiently as the star ages.
    C) Helium has a larger atomic weight than hydrogen and exerts a stronger gravitational pull on the core.
    D) The rate of core hydrogen burning decreases as the hydrogen is used up, reducing the rate of energy generation.
    Ans: A   Section: 21-1

16. The evolution of a star is controlled mostly by its
    A) initial mass.
    B) location in the galaxy.
    C) surface temperature.
    D) chemical composition.
    Ans: A   Section: 21-1

17. What is the most important quantity on which the lifetime of a star depends?
    A) temperature of the star's corona
    B) abundance of heavy elements in the star
    C) star's speed of rotation
    D) mass of the star
    Ans: D   Section: 21-1

18. How is the length of a star's lifetime related to the mass of the star?
    A) Higher-mass stars run through their lives faster and have shorter lifetimes.
    B) The lifetimes of stars are too long to measure, so it is not known how their lifetimes depend on mass.
    C) Lower-mass stars run through their lives faster and have shorter lifetimes.
    D) A star's lifetime does not depend on its mass.
    Ans: A   Section: 21-1

19. Which of the following statements about the rate of stellar evolution is true?
    A) The more massive the original star, the faster the evolution.
    B) Star mass has no bearing upon stellar evolution, because all stars evolve at the same rate, controlled by nuclear fusion and core temperature.
    C) The chemical makeup of the original nebula is the major factor in deciding the rate of evolution.
    D) The more massive the original star, the slower the evolution, because there is more material for thermonuclear burning.
    Ans: A   Section: 21-1

20. Which of the following statements about the mass and lifetime of a star is true?
    A) Stars of about one solar mass have the shortest lives; less massive stars evolve slowly and live a longer time, whereas more massive stars have long lives because of the large amount of fuel they contain.
    B) The more massive the star, the faster it will evolve through its life.
    C) The mass of a star has no bearing on the length of a star's life or the speed of its evolution.
    D) The less massive the star, the shorter its life, because it has less hydrogen "fuel" to burn.
    Ans: B   Section: 21-1

21. The main-sequence lifetime of a star with half the mass of the Sun
    A)   could be longer or shorter than that of the Sun; it is not possible to tell from the information given.
    B)   is the same as that of the Sun, because mass does not affect the lifetime of a star.
    C)   is longer than that of the Sun.
    D)   is shorter than that of the Sun.
    Ans: C   Section: 21-1

22. A main-sequence star has a certain lifetime, t, because of thermonuclear "burning" of the hydrogen in the core of the star. How is this lifetime on the main sequence related to the mass M and luminosity L of the star?
    A) $t \propto M/L$ B) $t \propto ML$ C) $t \propto L/M$ D) $t \propto M^{3.5}$
    Ans: A   Section: 21-1

23. What is the expected main-sequence lifetime of a star with a mass of 15 solar masses? (See Table 21-1, Freedman and Kaufmann, *Universe,* 7th ed.)
    A)   10 billion years   C)   3 million years
    B)   less than 1 million years   D)   15 million years
    Ans: D   Section: 21-1

24. How long will a star whose mass is 0.75 the mass of the Sun spend on the main sequence? (See Table 21-1, Freedman and Kaufmann, *Universe,* 7th ed.)
    A)   25 billion years   C)   500 million years
    B)   3 million years   D)   10 billion years
    Ans: A   Section: 21-1

25. How long is the lifetime of a star with three times the Sun's mass compared to the lifetime of the Sun? (See Table 21-1, Freedman and Kaufmann, *Universe,* 7th ed.)
    A)   about 3 times as long   C)   about 1/15 as long
    B)   about 1/500 as long   D)   about 1/3 as long
    Ans: C   Section: 21-1

26. The star ζ Pegasi (in the constellation Pegasus, the Flying Horse) has a spectral luminosity class of B8 V, giving it a surface temperature of about 12,000 K. According to Table 21-1, Freedman and Kaufmann, *Universe,* 7th ed., the expected main-sequence lifetime of ζ Pegasi is
    A)   about 400,000 years.
    B)   about 400 million years.
    C)   much greater than 800 million years.
    D)   not defined in any way by the above information.
    Ans: B   Section: 21-1

27. If you were able to return to the Earth 1 million years into the future, which of the following views of the sky would be most likely?
    A)   All the present stars, both blue and red, would be visible, but nearby stars would have moved in position.
    B)   The sky would be very much as it is now, because 1 million years is a very short time in astronomical terms.
    C)   Nearby stars would have moved in position, and many blue stars would no longer be visible.
    D)   A few red stars would be missing because they would have evolved, but stars would be the same and in the same positions as today.
    Ans: C   Section: 21-1 and Box 19-1

28. The spiral galaxy in which we live is roughly 15 to 20 billion years old. For the stars that formed when the galaxy was very young (say, during the first billion years), which of the following statements is true? (See Table 21-1, Freedman and Kaufmann, *Universe,* 7th ed.)
    A)   Some stars of half the mass of the Sun are still on the main sequence, but most have finished their lives as stars.
    B)   All stars of half the mass of the Sun are still on the main sequence.
    C)   Some stars of 15 times the mass of the Sun are still on the main sequence, but most have finished their lives as stars.
    D)   All stars of three times the mass of the Sun are still on the main sequence.
    Ans: B   Section: 21-1

29. What is a red giant?
    A)   a large, red star burning hydrogen into helium in its core
    B)   a protostar in the "upper right" part of the Hertzsprung-Russell diagram
    C)   a large emission nebula
    D)   a star burning hydrogen into helium in a shell around the core
    Ans: D   Section: 21-1

30. In terms of nuclear reactions, what is the next stage of a star's life after the end of hydrogen burning in the core?
    A)   hydrogen burning in a thin shell around the core
    B)   helium burning in the core
    C)   carbon burning
    D)   death (it becomes either a supernova or a white dwarf)
    Ans: A   Section: 21-1

31. What is the next stage in a star's life after the main-sequence phase?
    A)   red giant
    B)   horizontal branch
    C)   protostar
    D)   death (i.e., either a supernova or a white dwarf)
    Ans: A   Section: 21-1

32. Compared to the composition of the early Sun, the composition of the gas in the core of a red giant star is
    A)   very different, with lots of H but almost no He after thermonuclear fusion.
    B)   very different, because thermonuclear fusion has transformed all the H and He into heavier elements.
    C)   significantly different, with a very high fraction of He and no H.
    D)   the same, with a high fraction of H compared to He, because these stars were produced from the same initial material.
    Ans: C   Section: 21-1

33. What makes a red giant star so large?
    A)   The helium-rich core has expanded, pushing the outer layers of the star outward.
    B)   The star has many times more mass than the Sun.
    C)   Red giants are rapid rotators, and centrifugal force pushes the surface of the star outward.
    D)   The hydrogen-burning shell is heating the envelope and making it expand.
    Ans: D   Section: 21-1

34. When a star leaves the main sequence and expands toward the red giant region, what is happening inside the star?
    A)   Hydrogen burning is taking place in a spherical shell just outside the core; the core itself is almost pure helium.
    B)   Hydrogen burning is taking place in a spherical shell just outside the core; the core has not yet started thermonuclear reactions and is still mostly hydrogen.
    C)   Helium burning is taking place in a spherical shell just outside the core; the core itself is almost pure carbon and oxygen.
    D)   Helium is being converted into carbon and oxygen in the core.
    Ans: A   Section: 21-1

35. What happens to the helium-rich core of a star after the core runs out of hydrogen?
    A)   It heats and expands.   C)   It cools and contracts.
    B)   It contracts and heats.   D)   It expands and cools.
    Ans: B   Section: 21-1

36. Within the deep interior of the Sun, which development will eventually lead to major changes as the Sun evolves off the main sequence toward the red giant phase of its life?
    A)   expansion of the core by the build-up of hydrogen in the nuclear furnace, pushing the outer regions of the Sun outward
    B)   the supernova explosion that will occur when the build-up of helium in the core exceeds a certain critical amount
    C)   slowing down of the nuclear furnace as the central core temperature drops with time
    D)   build-up of inactive helium by the transformation of hydrogen in the thermonuclear furnace
    Ans: D   Section: 21-1

37. What will be the diameter of the Sun when core helium burning begins?
    A) half its present size
    B) the size of the Earth
    C) about the size of the Earth's orbit
    D) twice its present size
    Ans: C   Section: 21-1

38. How large will the Sun be as a red giant?
    A) about 1.5 AU radius (out to Mars's orbit)
    B) about 1 AU radius (out to the Earth's orbit)
    C) about 1/2 AU radius (beyond Mercury's orbit)
    D) about 1/10 AU radius (1/4 of Mercury's orbit)
    Ans: B   Section: 21-1

39. Approximately what fraction of the Sun's main-sequence lifetime has been completed at this time? (See Section 21-1 and Table 21-1, Freedman and Kaufmann, *Universe*, 7th ed.)
    A) less than 10%   B) about 3/4   C) about 1/4   D) about half
    Ans: D   Section: 21-1

40. Which of the following are NOT very young stars or prestellar objects?
    A) protostars
    B) red giants
    C) T Tauri stars
    D) infrared emitting stars in gas and dust clouds
    Ans: B   Section: 21-1

41. What rates of mass loss are typical from red giant stars?
    A) 10^{-3} solar masses per year
    B) Red giant stars do not suffer mass loss.
    C) 1 solar mass per year
    D) 10^{-7} solar masses per year
    Ans: D   Section: 21-1

42. In the approximately five billion years since the Sun began its main sequence phase, its radius has increased by 6% and its surface temperature has increased by 5%. How has its luminosity changed?
    A) decreased by 10%
    B) decreased by 5%
    C) increased by 37%
    D) increased by 43%
    Ans: C   Section: 21-1 and Box 19-4

43. When the Sun entered the main sequence, its core was approximately 75% hydrogen and 25% helium, by mass. What was the ratio of hydrogen nuclei to helium nuclei?
    A) 3:1   B) 4:1   C) 12:1   D) 16:1
    Ans: C   Section: 21-1

44. The Kelvin-Helmholtz contraction supplies significant energy to a star
    A)   only in the stages before the main sequence.
    B)   after the core of a late main-sequence star runs out of hydrogen.
    C)   all during the main-sequence lifetime of star.
    D)   only when the outer edges of the star collapse inward.
    Ans: B   Section: 21-1

45. The majority of the elements heavier than hydrogen and helium in the universe are
    believed to have originated in
    A)   the original Big Bang.
    B)   the central cores of stars.
    C)   HII regions, under the action of Hα light.
    D)   giant molecular clouds.
    Ans: B   Section: 21-2

46. The temperature at which thermonuclear reactions begin to convert helium into carbon
    (helium burning) is
    A) 15 million K.   B) 1 million K.   C) 1 billion K.   D) 100 million K.
    Ans: D   Section: 21-2

47. Why does it require higher gas temperatures in the core of a star to produce nuclear
    fusion of helium compared to that required for hydrogen?
    A)   Higher speeds are needed between two He atoms to overcome the shielding effect
         of the 2 electrons around the nucleus compared to the 1 electron per nucleus of H.
    B)   The He nuclei need to be moving faster to avoid the more numerous and faster H
         nuclei with which they can combine with no energy generation.
    C)   Higher collision speeds are needed to overcome the extra electrostatic repulsion
         between doubly charged He nuclei.
    D)   Higher atomic speeds are required to strip off 2 electrons per helium atom rather
         than 1 electron per atom for hydrogen before fusion can take place.
    Ans: C   Section: 21-2

48. At which phase of a star's life will nuclear fusion reactions that convert helium into
    carbon and oxygen in the central core of a star occur?
    A)   during and immediately after the (first) red giant or supergiant stage
    B)   during the protostar stage, before the main sequence
    C)   in the red giant stage, before the helium flash
    D)   after the main-sequence phase, before the star becomes a red giant
    Ans: A   Section: 21-2

49. What is the dominant nuclear reaction during helium burning in a star?
    A)   4 He fusing into C   C)   3 He fusing into C
    B)   He + 4H combining into C   D)   2 He fusing into C
    Ans: C   Section: 21-2

50. In the helium burning stage of a star's later life, the major chemical element produced in this process is
   A)   beryllium—^{8}Be.   C)   heavy hydrogen—^{2}H.
   B)   the light isotope of helium—^{3}He.   D)   carbon—^{12}C.
   Ans: D   Section: 21-2

51. What are the products of helium burning in a star?
   A)   magnesium and silicon   C)   hydrogen and lithium
   B)   nitrogen and oxygen   D)   carbon and oxygen
   Ans: D   Section: 21-2

52. During helium burning, some ^{4}He combines with ^{16}O, similar the way in which it combines with ^{12}C to form ^{16}O. What is produced by the ^{16}O + ^{4}He reaction? (The periodic table shown in Box 5-5 of Freedman and Kaufmann, *Universe,* 7th ed., may be useful.)
   A) ^{22}Na—(light isotope of sodium)
   B) ^{20}Ne—(regular isotope of neon)
   C) ^{18}O—(heavy isotope of oxygen)
   D) ^{24}Mg—(regular isotope of magnesium)
   Ans: B   Section: 21-2

53. The Pauli exclusion principle, describing the quantum states of particles, states that no two identical particles (such as electrons) can have the same
   A)   speed.
   B)   position in space.
   C)   position in space and the same electrical charge.
   D)   location in space and the same speed.
   Ans: D   Section: 21-2

54. The Pauli exclusion principle
   A)   prevents high-mass stars from forming in low-mass interstellar clouds.
   B)   sets a limit to the crowding of electrons into any given small volume of space.
   C)   prevents two stars of the same spectral class from occupying the same binary star system.
   D)   limits the number of atoms that can become ionized in a star.
   Ans: B   Section: 21-2

55. Under what conditions does electron degeneracy occur?
   A)   when electrons become crowded too closely together
   B)   when thermonuclear reactions release more electrons than protons
   C)   when electrons and positrons annihilate, releasing energy
   D)   when ultraviolet light from hot, young O and B stars ionizes the interstellar medium
   Ans: A   Section: 21-2

56. Degeneracy occurs when
    A)   magnetic fields inhibit the motion of charged particles in sunspots.
    B)   solar wind particles ionize atoms in the Earth's upper atmosphere.
    C)   thermonuclear reactions halt the contraction of a protostar.
    D)   electrons inside a star resist being pushed closer together than a certain limit.
    Ans: D   Section: 21-2

57. Electron degeneracy, a result of the Pauli exclusion principle that prevents electrons from becoming crowded together beyond a certain limit, is important in
    A)   the core of a low-mass star just before the start of core helium burning.
    B)   the core of a low-mass star just before the start of core hydrogen burning.
    C)   the core of a low-mass star during core hydrogen burning.
    D)   a low-mass protostar evolving toward the main sequence.
    Ans: A   Section: 21-2

58. When is electron degeneracy pressure important in a star?
    A)   in a protostar evolving toward the main sequence
    B)   in a Cepheid variable that is burning helium in its core
    C)   just before the start of helium burning in the core
    D)   during core hydrogen burning
    Ans: C   Section: 21-2

59. If electrons are collectively compressed into a very small volume (e.g., within the core of a dying white dwarf star) where quantum mechanical considerations become important in preventing one electron from occupying space near to a second electron (Pauli exclusion principle), what is the result?
    A)   The electrons fall into orbit around one another in mutual pairs, reducing the restricted quantum space, thereby allowing further shrinkage of the star.
    B)   The electrons generate a very large pressure to oppose further compression.
    C)   Nuclear fusion occurs between electrons to produce energy, thereby heating the star's core.
    D)   Half of the electrons are transformed into antimatter (positrons) that annihilates electrons, producing a burst of energy and the explosion of the star.
    Ans: B   Section: 21-2

60. The helium flash results from
    A)   the high temperature in the helium core of a blue (spectral class O or B) supergiant star.
    B)   electron degeneracy or quantum crowding in the core of a low-mass red giant star.
    C)   the sudden release of energy in strong magnetic fields near a sunspot.
    D)   the sudden onset of nuclear reactions at the end of the protostar phase of a star's life.
    Ans: B   Section: 21-2

61. The helium flash is another name for
    A) the sudden appearance of helium during a supernova explosion (explosion of a star at the end of its life).
    B) a sudden onset of helium fusion reactions in red giant and supergiant stars of any mass.
    C) a sudden release of energy at the end of helium burning, due to core contraction.
    D) a sudden onset of helium fusion reactions in the core of a low-mass red giant star.
    Ans: D   Section: 21-2

62. A helium flash occurs in the cores of all stars
    A) that contain helium.   C) of fewer than 2 solar masses.
    B) of more than 2 solar masses.   D) that have become red giants.
    Ans: C   Section: 21-2

63. What unusual process is involved in the helium flash?
    A) An increase in temperature causes an increase in the nuclear reaction rate but has no effect on pressure.
    B) An increase in temperature causes an increase in the pressure with no increase in the nuclear reaction rate.
    C) An increase in the pressure causes a decrease in the temperature and the nuclear reaction rate.
    D) An increase in the nuclear reaction rate causes an increase in the temperature and the pressure.
    Ans: A   Section: 21-2

64. After the start of helium nuclear reactions in its core, what are the conditions in a star compared to those before these reactions began?
    A) The star is larger and cooler.   C) The star is smaller and cooler.
    B) The star is larger and hotter.   D) The star is smaller and hotter.
    Ans: D   Section: 21-2

65. What "safety valve" operates in the gas of normal (nondegenerate) stars?
    A) If the star gets too big, it will collapse into a black hole.
    B) If the stellar gas is suddenly heated, it will expand and cool.
    C) If the pressure gets too high, electrons will combine with protons to relieve the pressure.
    D) If thermonuclear reactions proceed too quickly, the star will run out of fuel before anything drastic happens.
    Ans: B   Section: 21-2

66. What is the "safety valve" that prevents normal (nondegenerate) stars from self-destructing?
    A)   If the pressure rises, the volume occupied by the matter will decrease, reducing the nuclear reaction rate.
    B)   If a part of a star is heated, it expands and cools.
    C)   If thermonuclear reactions proceed too quickly, the star will run out of fuel before anything drastic happens.
    D)   If the temperature rises, the thermonuclear reaction rate will increase.
    Ans: B   Section: 21-2

67. A degenerate-electron gas like that in the core of a red giant star lacks the "safety valve" of a normal gas. This is because
    A)   a rise in pressure releases more electrons, thus increasing the pressure further.
    B)   a rise in pressure reduces the number of electrons, causing the core to collapse.
    C)   a rise in temperature lowers the pressure, causing the star to contract.
    D)   a rise in temperature does not change the pressure, so the gas does not expand and cool.
    Ans: D   Section: 21-2

68. After the helium flash in a red giant star, the star contracts because
    A)   energy radiated to space during the helium flash cools the entire star, making it contract.
    B)   the electrons in the core become degenerate during the helium flash, reducing the volume occupied by the core.
    C)   the helium flash uses most of the helium in the star's core, reducing the energy produced in the core.
    D)   the star's deep interior expands and cools during the helium flash, reducing the energy produced by the hydrogen burning shell.
    Ans: D   Section: 21-2

69. After the helium flash in a low mass star
    A)   all nuclear reactions cease.
    B)   helium burning ceases in the core but hydrogen burning continues in the layers around the core.
    C)   helium burning begins in the core and hydrogen burning ceases in the layers around the core.
    D)   helium burning begins in the core and hydrogen burning continues in the layers around the core.
    Ans: D   Section: 21-2

70. Which way does a star of about 1 solar mass evolve, on the Hertzsprung-Russell diagram, at the end of its main-sequence lifetime?
    A)   toward lower luminosity and higher temperature—progressing through the main sequence toward the white dwarf stage
    B)   toward higher luminosity and lower temperature—away from the main sequence
    C)   toward higher luminosity and higher temperature—upward along the main sequence
    D)   toward lower luminosity and temperature—downward along the main sequence
    Ans: B   Section: 21-3

71. At what stage of evolution are the horizontal-branch stars, which have similar luminosities between 50 and 100 times that of the Sun but a range of temperatures?
    A)   because the horizontal branch is part of the main sequence, these stars are in the main-sequence stage
    B)   white dwarf stage
    C)   post–main-sequence stage
    D)   pre–main-sequence stage, evolving toward the main sequence
    Ans: C   Section: 21-3

72. Horizontal-branch stars, which have a range of temperatures with luminosities between 50 and 100 times that of the Sun, are in what stage of their lives?
    A)   hydrogen shell burning, with a degenerate helium core
    B)   core helium burning
    C)   gravitational contraction before the start of core hydrogen burning
    D)   core hydrogen burning
    Ans: B   Section: 21-3

73. The study of stars in clusters has helped astronomers to understand
    A)   the reason for differences in surface temperatures of stars.
    B)   the mechanism of mass loss in stars.
    C)   the action of nuclear fusion in stars.
    D)   stellar evolution—the development of stars with time.
    Ans: D   Section: 21-3

74. What are the main general features that make clusters of stars useful to astronomers?
    A)   The stars are at the same distance from Earth, were formed at approximately the same time, and were made from same chemical mix.
    B)   The stars are all at the same distance from Earth, have the same surface temperature, and joined the cluster at various times.
    C)   The stars all have the same apparent magnitude, the same surface temperatures, and the same sizes.
    D)   The stars all have the same intrinsic brightness but differ in size and surface temperature.
    Ans: A   Section: 21-3

75. In the HR diagram in Fig. 21-12 of Freedman and Kaufmann, *Universe,* 7th ed., the brightest stars in the Pleiades cluster are not on the main sequence but toward the upper right. Why is this?
    A)   These stars have not yet reached the main sequence and are in the T Tauri phase.
    B)   These stars have already evolved through the red giant phase, returned to the blue giant phase and are on their way to the white dwarf phase.
    C)   These stars have already become white dwarf stars, as shown by their position.
    D)   These blue supergiant stars have already begun to evolve toward the red supergiant phase.
    Ans: D   Section: 21-3

76. On the Hertzsprung-Russell diagram, in which direction does the position occupied by a star move after hydrogen burning ends in the star's core?
    A)   toward the upper left   C)   toward the lower right
    B)   toward the lower left   D)   toward the upper right
    Ans: D   Section: 21-3

77. In which direction in the Hertzsprung-Russell diagram does the position occupied by a star move when helium burning begins in the star's core?
    A)   toward the lower right   C)   toward the upper right
    B)   toward the lower left   D)   toward the upper left
    Ans: B   Section: 21-3

78. A globular cluster is a group of stars that has
    A)   many thousands of members, mostly binary, of different ages.
    B)   many thousands of members, all very old, with very few elements heavier than helium.
    C)   many thousands of members of different ages but with the same chemical composition.
    D)   a few hundred members, often still embedded in the gas from which they were formed.
    Ans: B   Section: 21-3

79. Which of the following statements is NOT true of a globular cluster?
    A)   It contains significant amounts of dust and gas surrounding the stars.
    B)   It has a round shape.
    C)   It can contain up to a million stars.
    D)   It contains only low-mass stars.
    Ans: A   Section: 21-3

80. Which of the following statements is NOT true of a globular cluster?
    A)   It does not contain main-sequence stars.
    B)   It can contain up to a million stars.
    C)   It has a round shape.
    D)   It contains only low-mass stars.
    Ans: A   Section: 21-3

81. Within a globular cluster, what would you expect to find in the population of stars?
    A)   a full range of stars from bright blue to dim red, with no bright red giant stars but significant amounts of dust and gas
    B)   a full mixture of bright blue supergiant and red giant stars, in addition to white dwarfs and dim red stars
    C)   mainly white dwarf stars surrounded by the remnant dust and gas from the planetary nebular stages of dying stars but no faint red stars, red giants, or bright blue stars
    D)   many red giants, white dwarfs, and dim red stars but no bright blue stars or dust and gas
    Ans: D   Section: 21-3

82. The Hertzsprung-Russell diagram of a globular cluster does NOT contain any stars with high luminosity and high temperature on the main sequence because
    A)   stars that will occupy this position on the main sequence have not yet evolved there from the protostar stage.
    B)   the stars that were in this position on the main sequence have undergone the usual splitting into binary stars, and hence appear lower down on the diagram.
    C)   these high-mass stars evolved away from the main sequence long ago.
    D)   this type of cluster contains only low-mass stars and has never had such stars on its main sequence.
    Ans: C   Section: 21-3

83. What would you expect to be the overall color of a globular cluster of stars?
    A)   blue, because of the contribution from young and very hot stars in the cluster
    B)   red, because of the emission of light by the hydrogen gas surrounding the stars in the cluster
    C)   blue, because of the scattering of starlight from the dust surrounding the stars in the cluster
    D)   red, because of the older population of stars in the cluster
    Ans: D   Section: 21-3

84. An astronomer studying a globular cluster plots its stars on a Hertzsprung-Russell diagram and finds that certain stars in the cluster lie on the horizontal branch. What does this astronomer immediately know about these stars?
    A)   They are still contracting toward the main sequence.
    B)   They are burning hydrogen into helium in their cores.
    C)   They are burning helium into carbon and oxygen in their cores.
    D)   They are burning helium into carbon and oxygen in a shell around their cores.
    Ans: C   Section: 21-3

85. The age of a cluster can be found by
    A)   observing its position in the sky with respect to the Sun.
    B)   measuring its speed of motion relative to the Sun.
    C)   carrying out a number count of the stars in the cluster.
    D)   determining the turnoff point on the main sequence of its HR diagram.
    Ans: D   Section: 21-3

86. How do astronomers know that globular clusters are old?
    A)   They do not contain any red giant stars.
    B)   There are no main-sequence stars in globular clusters.
    C)   There are no massive main-sequence stars in globular clusters.
    D)   Their stars have a high abundance of heavy elements.
    Ans: C   Section: 21-3

87. The age of a cluster of stars can be judged by the
    A)   total number of stars within the cluster.
    B)   amount of radioactive elements detected on star surfaces.
    C)   turnoff point on the main sequence of its Hertzsprung-Russell diagram.
    D)   number of novae per year occurring within the cluster.
    Ans: C   Section: 21-3

88. Of the following astronomical objects or systems, which is likely to be the oldest?
    A) globular cluster   B) the Pleiades   C) the Sun   D) a T Tauri star
    Ans: A   Section: 21-3

89. An astronomer plots the HR diagram of a star cluster and finds that it contains hot B-type stars on the main sequence and cooler G- and K-type stars noticeably above the main sequence. This cluster is
    A)   impossible, because one cannot have cool stars above the main sequence when hot stars are on the main sequence.
    B)   old, because the G and K stars are already evolving away from the main sequence.
    C)   of indeterminate age, because one cannot estimate the age of the cluster from the information given.
    D)   very young, because the G and K stars are still evolving toward the main sequence.
    Ans: D   Section: 21-3

90. How do the stars in a star cluster change with time?
    A)   The stars with the greatest heavy-element content evolve the most rapidly.
    B)   The highest-mass stars evolve the most quickly.
    C)   The lowest-mass stars evolve the most quickly.
    D)   All stars in it evolve at the same rate.
    Ans: B   Section: 21-3

91. The "turnoff" point for a star cluster is the point in the H-R diagram occupied by the
    A)   highest-mass main-sequence stars in the cluster.
    B)   stars undergoing (or about to undergo) the helium flash.
    C)   lowest-mass main-sequence stars in the cluster.
    D)   highest-mass stars that have not yet reached the main sequence.
    Ans: A   Section: 21-3

92. For an astronomer, what is the significance of the turn-off point in the Hertzsprung-Russell diagram of a star cluster?
    A)   It indicates the age of the star cluster.
    B)   It shows which stars pulsate in brightness (variable stars).
    C)   It indicates which stars might be about to explode as supernovae.
    D)   It provides a measure of the metal content of the star cluster.
    Ans: A   Section: 21-3

93. Suppose that, when the stars in a particular open star cluster are plotted in an H-R diagram, the luminosity of stars at the turnoff point is about five times the luminosity of the Sun. Approximately what is the age of this cluster? (See Figure 21-12 of Freedman and Kaufmann, *Universe,* 7th ed.)
    A)   100 million years   C)   500 million years
    B)   1 billion years   D)   4 billion years
    Ans: D   Section: 21-3

94. The stars at the turnoff point in the H-R diagram of the Hyades star cluster have an absolute magnitude of approximately M = + 2, whereas those at the turnoff point in the cluster M41 have M = 0. From this information, we can say with certainty that
    A)   the Hyades cluster is farther away than M41.
    B)   the Hyades cluster is older than M41.
    C)   the Hyades cluster has more stars in it than M41.
    D)   the Hyades cluster is younger than M41.
    Ans: B   Section: 21-3

95. From the time a star of more than one solar mass reaches the ZAMS until it leaves the main sequence, a star's evolution on the main sequence is
    A)   upward and to the left, along the main sequence.
    B)   downward and to the left, toward the white dwarves.
    C)   upward and to the right, but only very slightly.
    D)   straight upward as its luminosity increases.
    Ans: C   Section: 21-3 and Figure 21-8

96. After it leaves the main sequence, a star with a mass greater than one solar mass moves generally to the right on the HR diagram. This happens because
    A)   the star's surface temperature is increasing while its radius is decreasing.
    B)   the star's surface temperature is decreasing while its radius is increasing.
    C)   the star's core is expanding while its outer layers are contracting.
    D)   the star's core is expanding, causing its outer layers to expand as well.
    Ans: B   Section: 21-3

97. Suppose you pick 100 stars at random from the night sky and plot the apparent magnitude versus color ratio for these stars. What would this plot show you?
    A)   This is a color-magnitude diagram. By noting the turnoff point on the main sequence you could determine the age of the oldest star in the group.
    B)   Because we are not examining stars in a cluster, there will be no turnoff point. But you will have an HR diagram with main sequence, giants, and white dwarves.
    C)   Because we are not examining stars in a cluster, there will be no turnoff point. It will be an HR diagram, but with only 100 stars it is unlikely that more than one or two stars will be red giants.
    D)   Because we are plotting *apparent* magnitude versus color ratio for a group of unrelated stars, the plot will probably not show any particular pattern.
    Ans: D   Section: 21-3

98. The HR diagram for Open Clusters (see Figure 21-12, Freedman and Kaufmann, *Universe*, 7th ed.) shows the Sun at approximately the 10-billion-year mark on the main sequence. What is the meaning of this?
    A)   The present age of the Sun is approximately 10 billion years.
    B)   The Sun will change its position very little on the diagram during the rest of its main sequence lifetime and thus will still be near the 10-billion-year mark when it finishes its hydrogen burning.
    C)   The Sun will evolve a considerable distance up the main sequence, toward higher luminosities, before it leaves the main sequence.
    D)   The Sun will evolve a considerable distance down the main sequence, toward lower luminosities, before it leaves the main sequence.
    Ans: B   Section: 21-3

99. In describing a star, what does the adjective "metal-poor" mean?
    A) The star has a low abundance of all elements in its spectrum.
    B) The star has a low abundance of all elements heavier than hydrogen in its spectrum.
    C) The star may or may not have a low abundance of carbon in its spectrum, but it is definitely weak in iron.
    D) The star has a low abundance of all elements heavier than hydrogen and helium in its spectrum.
    Ans: D   Section: 21-4

100. Stars are formed from interstellar matter. Why are stars in open clusters metal-rich, whereas stars in globular clusters are metal-poor?
    A) Globular clusters have "burned" their heavy elements over their longer lifetime.
    B) Globular cluster stars are so widely spaced, that they have not interacted and collided to produce the supernova explosions that generate metals.
    C) Supernova explosions have blasted away the heavy elements in older globular cluster stars, leaving behind the metal-poor cores.
    D) Open clusters are young, and stars have been formed from material in which stellar evolution and supernova explosions in earlier stars have enriched heavy metal concentrations steadily with time.
    Ans: D   Section: 21-4

101. Which of the following stars are metal-poor?
    A) very young stars   C) population I stars
    B) population II stars   D) open cluster stars
    Ans: B   Section: 21-4

102. Which of the following stars would you classify as a population II star?
    A) a star with approximately the same abundance of heavy elements as the Sun
    B) any member of an open star cluster
    C) a star with very low abundance of heavy elements
    D) a star with a much higher abundance of heavy elements than the Sun
    Ans: C   Section: 21-4

103. The stars that formed first after the initial Big Bang
    A) were virtually all Population I stars.
    B) were virtually all Population II stars.
    C) were about the same mixture of Populations I and II, which we now observe.
    D) were an entirely different type of star, which has since evolved into Population I and Population II.
    Ans: B   Section: 21-4

104. ^{12}C and ^{16}O are among the most important elements in organic matter, including our bodies. What is the source of ^{12}C and ^{16}O in our solar system?
    A) They were a part of the cold, dark nebula from which the Sun condensed.
    B) They have been produced in the Sun as a part of the Sun's main sequence nuclear reactions.
    C) These elements were not present in the original solar nebula but have been produced since by radioactive decay.
    D) These elements were present in the original Big Bang and are thus a part of everything formed since then.
    Ans: A   Section: 21-4

105. The ^{12}C and ^{16}O, which now form part of living matter, were part of the cold, dark nebula from which the Sun formed. How did they get there?
    A) They were part of the original Big Bang and thus part of everything formed since then.
    B) They were formed by earlier generations of stars while they were on the main sequence.
    C) They were formed by earlier generations of stars while they were in their red giant phase.
    D) They were formed in an earlier supernova explosion and dissipated through space.
    Ans: C   Section: 21-4

106. When a star's evolutionary track on the Hertzsprung-Russell diagram carries it into the instability strip, what happens to the star?
    A) It collapses and forms a black hole.   C) It pulsates regularly in brightness.
    B) It pulsates randomly in brightness.   D) It explodes.
    Ans: C   Section: 21-5

107. What is a Cepheid variable star?
    A) a high-mass star that pulsates regularly in brightness
    B) one of several classes of stars that pulsate randomly in brightness
    C) a star that normally remains constant in brightness but occasionally flares up in brightness by several magnitudes
    D) a low-mass, horizontal-branch star that pulsates regularly in brightness
    Ans: A   Section: 21-5

108. Cepheid stars are
    A) white dwarf stars.
    B) stars at an early stage in stellar evolution.
    C) members of binary systems, in which one star periodically eclipses the other.
    D) stars that pulsate in brightness, size, and temperature.
    Ans: D   Section: 21-5

109. A Cepheid variable is a
   A)   type of eclipsing binary star.
   B)   low-mass red giant that varies in size and brightness in an irregular way.
   C)   high-mass giant or supergiant star that pulsates regularly in size and brightness.
   D)   variable-emission nebula near a T Tauri star.
   Ans: C   Section: 21-5

110. What scientific method is used to observe the pulsation in size of a Cepheid variable star?
   A)   This behavior has only been predicted theoretically; it has never been detected.
   B)   observation of the increase and decrease in the size of the star's image
   C)   observation of perturbations in the orbits of planets around these stars
   D)   Doppler shift of absorption lines in its spectrum
   Ans: D   Section: 21-5

111. What characteristic of Cepheid variables makes them extremely useful to astronomers?
   A)   Their absolute magnitude is related directly to their metal content (heavy element abundance).
   B)   Their absolute magnitude is directly related to their diameter.
   C)   Their absolute magnitude is related directly to their period of pulsation.
   D)   Their absolute magnitude is related directly to their surface temperature.
   Ans: C   Section: 21-5

112. What is the most important use of Cepheid variables for astronomers?
   A)   The diameter of a Cepheid variable can be found very easily.
   B)   The distance to a Cepheid variable can be found very easily.
   C)   The metal content of a Cepheid variable can be found very easily.
   D)   The characteristics of the pulsation of a Cepheid variable can be used to investigate conditions in the core of the star.
   Ans: B   Section: 21-5

113. The period of variability of a Cepheid variable star, which is easily measured, is directly related to which stellar parameter, thereby providing a reliable method for the measurement of distance to stars?
   A)   velocity away from Earth   C)   surface magnetic field
   B)   luminosity   D)   surface temperature
   Ans: B   Section: 21-5

114. RR Lyrae stars are
   A)   pulsating stars that vary regularly, all with periods of less than one day.
   B)   pulsars, with very rapid and regular brightness fluctuation caused by rapid rotation of stars with active regions on their surfaces.
   C)   eclipsing binary stars.
   D)   pulsating stars that vary irregularly, with periods of several hundred days.
   Ans: A   Section: 21-5

115. RR Lyrae variables are likely to be found in
    A) very young clusters, where high-mass stars are undergoing core hydrogen burning.
    B) giant molecular clouds, where protostars are forming from gas and dust clouds.
    C) young-to-intermediate-age clusters, where high-mass stars are undergoing central helium burning.
    D) globular clusters, where low-mass stars are undergoing core helium burning.
    Ans: D   Section: 21-5

116. What are the stars in the lower part of the instability strip called?
    A) Cepheid variables   B) RR Lyrae variables   C) protostars   D) T Tauri stars
    Ans: B   Section: 21-5

117. What are the stars in the upper part of the instability strip called?
    A) Cepheid variables   B) protostars   C) RR Lyrae variables   D) T Tauri stars
    Ans: A   Section: 21-5

118. Suppose a Cepheid variable has been identified by its spectrum as a Type I Cepheid, and its period of brightness variability is measured to be 30 days. Its apparent magnitude is +23.3. How far away is it? (See Figure 21-17, Freedman and Kaufmann, *Universe*, 7th ed.) The Sun's apparent magnitude is −26.7.
    A) 3.1×10^4 pc   B) 4.8×10^6 pc   C) 6.0×10^7 pc   D) 8.7×10^9 pc
    Ans: B   Section: 21-5 and Boxes 19-2 and 19-3

119. In a semidetached binary star system,
    A) the stars share the same outer atmosphere, but the cores of the two stars do not touch.
    B) one star fills its Roche lobe, while the other does not.
    C) one star orbits the center of mass, while the other moves freely through space.
    D) both stars fill their Roche lobes.
    Ans: B   Section: 21-6

120. The shape of the cross-section of the Roche lobes around a close binary star system, taken through the centers of the stars, is
    A) two unequal ellipses that touch at the center of the lobes.
    B) an ellipse, with a star at each focus.
    C) a sphere, centered on the center of mass of the star system.
    D) a figure-eight.
    Ans: D   Section: 21-6

121. The transfer of mass from the surface of one star onto the surface of another is most often observed in
    A) overcontact binaries.   C) contact binaries.
    B) detached binaries.   D) semidetached binaries.
    Ans: D   Section: 21-6

122. In some binary star systems, such as Algol, the less massive star is a red giant and the more massive star is on the main sequence. This is evidence that
    A)   mass transfer has occurred from one star to another.
    B)   the more massive star formed later, from a disk of gas surrounding the less massive star.
    C)   the more massive star captured the other one into orbit some time after the two stars had formed.
    D)   stars evolve differently in binary star systems, with less massive stars evolving faster than more massive stars.
    Ans: A   Section: 21-6

123. What is a Roche lobe?
    A)   the imaginary boundary around each star in a close binary system encompassing the mass gravitationally bound to that star
    B)   the imaginary boundary around each star in a close binary system which marks the limit outside of which planets cannot form
    C)   the imaginary boundary around each star in a close binary system which marks the limit inside of which planets cannot form because they would be torn apart by the star's gravity
    D)   the imaginary boundary around each star in a close binary system which marks the limit of each star's gravitational pull; as long as each star is within its own Roche limit the stars will have no effect on each other
    Ans: A   Section: 21-6

124. In some binary star systems, such as β (Beta) Lyrae, very little light is seen from the more massive star. This is because
    A)   the more massive star is still hidden in the dust clouds from which it formed.
    B)   the more massive star is a black hole, from which light cannot escape.
    C)   the more massive star is hidden by an accretion disk of material from the less massive star.
    D)   the orbit of the more massive star keeps it hidden behind the larger but less massive star as seen from the Earth.
    Ans: C   Section: 21-6

125. Which factor, more than any other, modifies the evolutionary tracks of stars in binary combinations compared to their single star counterparts?
    A)   tidal distortion of the shapes of the stars
    B)   radiation from one star heating the surface of the second star
    C)   mass exchange between the stars
    D)   reduction of the quantum mechanical limitation on continued shrinking of one star by the gravitational field of the second star
    Ans: C   Section: 21-6

126. Which of the following major perturbations can occur to a close binary system and radically alter the evolution and behavior of the two individual stars?
    A)   the eclipsing of the light from one star by the other, when viewed from Earth
    B)   the gravitational disturbance of one star's motion by its companion, to force it to move in an orbit
    C)   the heating of the localized areas of the atmosphere of one star by its companion
    D)   the transfer of matter from one star to its companion
    Ans: D   Section: 21-6

127. What very important phenomenon frequently occurs in binary star systems where stars are very close together?
    A)   The less massive star spirals slowly into its more massive companion because of tidal interactions.
    B)   The radiation from the hotter star will slowly heat and evaporate away the cooler star.
    C)   The less massive star, in its elliptical orbit, will repeatedly pass through the thin, extended atmosphere of the second star, producing periodic rises and falls in light output from the star system.
    D)   Mass lost from one star is deposited on its companion.
    Ans: D   Section: 21-6

128. The components of a binary star, particularly if they are close, can influence each other in various ways. Which of the following is NOT likely to be an effect of one star on its companion?
    A)   Mass can be transferred from one star to its companion.
    B)   Intense radiation from a hot star can produce nuclear reactions on the surface of a cooler companion and initiate a nova explosion.
    C)   The gravitational force of one star will make its companion move in an orbit, rather than remaining stationary.
    D)   A very hot star can heat part of its cooler companion to produce a hot spot.
    Ans: B   Section: 21-6

Chapter 22: Stellar Evolution: The Death of Stars

1. What are the main by-products of helium nuclear "burning" in red giant stars?
   A) hydrogen nuclei via photodisintegration
   B) carbon and oxygen nuclei
   C) The helium is transformed completely to γ rays, a form of pure electromagnetic energy.
   D) iron nuclei
   Ans: B   Section: 22-1

2. The nuclear process in which helium "burning" occurs in the deep interiors of red giant stars produces
   A) The nuclear mass is totally transformed by $E = mc^2$ into pure energy.
   B) iron nuclei.
   C) carbon and oxygen nuclei.
   D) hydrogen nuclei by the fission or splitting of helium nuclei.
   Ans: C   Section: 22-1

3. Helium nuclear reactions (helium burning) produce primarily
   A) iron.   C) oxygen and neon.
   B) carbon and silicon.   D) carbon and oxygen.
   Ans: D   Section: 22-1

4. Nuclear fusion reactions of helium nuclei (helium "burning") produce primarily
   A) beryllium and lithium nuclei. C) nitrogen and neon nuclei.
   B) iron nuclei.   D) carbon and oxygen nuclei.
   Ans: D   Section: 22-1

5. How bright will a star with the mass of the Sun become at the helium flash point, compared to its main-sequence luminosity?
   A) 10^6 times brighter   C) 10^3 times brighter
   B) about 50% brighter   D) 10 times brighter
   Ans: C   Section: 22-1 and Figure 22-1

6. The most important development in the interior of a star of moderate mass which leads to the red giant phase is
   A) a runaway nuclear furnace and eventual explosion in the star's interior, destroying the star and leaving only a rapidly expanding shell of gas.
   B) the cessation of hydrogen "burning" in the core, leading to core contraction and overall star expansion.
   C) expansion of the whole star, leading to lower temperatures throughout the star and the turnoff of the nuclear furnace in the core.
   D) contraction of the whole star, which quenches the nuclear furnace in the core and leads to cooling of the surface.
   Ans: B   Section: 22-1

7. The structure of the deep interior of a low-mass star near the end of its life is
    A)   a carbon-oxygen core, a shell undergoing fusion of helium nuclei, and a surrounding dormant hydrogen shell.
    B)   an inactive hydrogen core and a helium shell undergoing nuclear fusion, surrounded by a carbon-oxygen shell.
    C)   a turbulent mixture of hydrogen, helium, carbon, and oxygen in which only helium continues to undergo nuclear fusion.
    D)   a helium core surrounded by a thin hydrogen shell undergoing nuclear fusion, with very small concentrations of heavier nuclei.
    Ans: A   Section: 22-1

8. An asymptotic giant branch (AGB) star is a
    A)   star in its first red giant phase.   C)   cool main sequence star.
    B)   blue supergiant.   D)   red supergiant.
    Ans: D   Section: 22-1

9. In terms of a star's evolutionary life, an asymptotic giant branch (AGB) star is in the
    A)   helium core-burning phase.
    B)   helium shell-burning phase.
    C)   pre-main-sequence phase.
    D)   hydrogen shell-burning phase prior to helium ignition in the core.
    Ans: B   Section: 22-1

10. In which phase of a low-mass star's life does helium shell burning occur?
    A)   first red giant phase   C)   horizontal branch
    B)   main sequence   D)   asymptotic giant branch
    Ans: D   Section: 22-1

11. Helium nuclear reactions take place in a shell around the core of a low-mass star during its
    A)   protostar phase.   C)   asymptotic giant branch phase.
    B)   main sequence phase.   D)   horizontal branch phase.
    Ans: C   Section: 22-1

12. What is the last nuclear burning stage in the life of a low-mass star like the Sun?
    A)   fusion of hydrogen nuclei to form helium
    B)   fusion of silicon nuclei to form iron
    C)   fusion of iron nuclei with protons and neutrons to form heavy elements
    D)   fusion of helium nuclei to form carbon and oxygen
    Ans: D   Section: 22-1

13. A star ascending the red giant branch for the second time has
    A) no nuclear reactions in the core but a helium-burning shell outside the core, the whole surrounded by a dormant hydrogen shell.
    B) hydrogen fusion reactions occurring in the core.
    C) no fusion reactions anywhere in the star, because it has used up all its nuclear fuel.
    D) no nuclear reactions in the core but a hydrogen-burning shell outside the core.
    Ans: A   Section: 22-1

14. In the process of helium shell fusion in low-mass stars near the end of their lives, the star moves upward and to the right on the asymptotic giant branch of the Hertzsprung-Russell diagram. In this process, the star is
    A) contracting, cooling, and hence becoming less luminous.
    B) expanding, heating, and becoming more luminous.
    C) expanding, cooling, and becoming more luminous.
    D) contracting, becoming hotter and much less luminous.
    Ans: C   Section: 22-1

15. How much brighter than its main-sequence luminosity will a Sun-like star become at the asymptotic giant branch (AGB) phase of its life?
    A) twice as bright   C) 10 times brighter
    B) 10^3 times brighter   D) 10^4 times brighter
    Ans: D   Section: 22-1 and Figure 22-1

16. The characteristics of red supergiant stars are a
    A) brightness of 10,000 Suns and a diameter of about that of Mars's orbit.
    B) brightness of the Sun and size of about that of Mercury's orbit.
    C) brightness of about 1 million Suns and a diameter of the whole solar system.
    D) brightness of about 10,000 Suns and a diameter of 1/10 of that of the Sun.
    Ans: A   Section: 22-1

17. What will be the consequences for the planetary system when the Sun evolves to the asymptotic giant branch (AGB) phase of its evolution?
    A) The whole planetary system will melt and evaporate.
    B) The whole system will survive almost intact, but the planets will be driven outward from their present orbits by the intense solar wind.
    C) The planetary system will be slowly drawn into the core of the Sun by the gravitational field of the high-density core.
    D) The inner planets will melt and evaporate, but Jupiter and the outer planets will survive, after losing their outer atmospheres.
    Ans: A   Section: 22-1

18. Low-mass stars can undergo two evolutionary phases called red giant phases. What is the difference between them?
    A)   In the first, the primary production of energy is from hydrogen burning in the core. In the second, the primary production of energy is from helium burning in the core.
    B)   In the first, the primary production of energy is from helium burning in the core. In the second, the primary production of energy is from helium burning in a shell around the core.
    C)   In the first, the star's track on the HR diagram lies along the red giant branch. In the second, the track lies along the horizontal branch.
    D)   During the first red giant phase, the star moves up and to the right along the red giant branch. During the second red giant phase the star's track is down and to the left along the same red giant branch.
    Ans: B   Section: 22-1

19. The excess carbon in the surface layers of a "carbon star," compared to that at the surface of the Sun, is a result of
    A)   neutrinos, which escape easily from the core of a star but react with the cool hydrogen at its surface to form carbon.
    B)   helium flash, in which the explosion blasts carbon from the core into the surface layers.
    C)   dredge-up, in which the convective envelope transports material from a star's core to its surface.
    D)   mass loss, which strips away the outer envelope from an old star and reveals the carbon-rich core.
    Ans: C   Section: 22-2

20. Which of the energy-transporting processes in a star's interior also plays a role in moving heavy elements from their production region to the star's surface and from there into outer space?
    A)   Transport is not necessary because heavy elements are produced at the star's surface by fusion reactions in the late evolutionary phases of a star.
    B)   radiative diffusion, by radiation pressure
    C)   conduction
    D)   convection
    Ans: D   Section: 22-2

21. What process is necessary for a star with twice the Sun's mass to become a carbon star?
    A) dredge-up by convection of carbon that has been produced in the stellar core by nuclear fusion
    B) Nuclear fusion reactions on the surface of the star, producing carbon nuclei by combination of three helium nuclei during the helium flash.
    C) ejection of the outer hydrogen and helium layers by the helium flash in the star's interior, revealing the stellar carbon core.
    D) Nuclear fission reactions splitting magnesium nuclei (charge 12, atomic mass about 24) into carbon nuclei (charge 6, atomic mass about 12) on the star's surface.
    Ans: A   Section: 22-2

22. A star of twice the mass of the Sun reaches the asymptotic giant branch (AGB) phase of its life and begins to eject large amounts of carbon and heavier elements into space. What process occurs to make this component easy to detect, particularly at radio wavelengths?
    A) The carbon grains (soot!) are heated by radiation and re-emit a cool thermal continuum spectrum whose peak is at radio wavelengths.
    B) The carbon nuclei acquire electrons and become neutral but excited atoms which emit an easily detected spectrum as they de-excite.
    C) Carbon and oxygen nuclei have such high velocities that they undergo nuclear fusion in a shell surrounding the star to produce heavier elements whose emissions are at radio wavelengths.
    D) Carbon and oxgyen combine chemically to produce the easily detected CO molecule.
    Ans: D   Section: 22-2

23. Interstellar dust contains graphite dust, made of pure carbon, along with other materials. Most of this carbon probably
    A) came from T Tauri stars through stellar winds.
    B) came from carbon stars, through stellar mass loss.
    C) was produced in the Big Bang at the time of the creation of the universe.
    D) was produced in supernova explosions.
    Ans: B   Section: 22-2

24. During its lifetime the Sun will experience all of the following energy sources *except*
    A) Kelvin-Helmholtz gravitational contraction.
    B) hydrogen burning.
    C) helium burning.
    D) carbon burning.
    Ans: D   Section: 22-2

25. All of the ^{12}C in the universe, including that in our bodies, is believed to come from
    A)   the proton-proton chain of nuclear reactions in main-sequence stars.
    B)   the triple alpha process in helium burning in red giants.
    C)   supernova explosions.
    D)   several important sources, not just one.
    Ans: B   Section: 22-2, 18-1, 21-2

26. A planetary nebula is
    A)   a contracting spherical cloud of gas surrounding a newly formed star, in which planets are forming.
    B)   the expanding nebula formed by the supernova explosion of a massive star.
    C)   an expanding gas shell surrounding a hot, white dwarf star.
    D)   a disk-shaped nebula of dust and gas from which planets will eventually form, easily photographed around relatively young stars.
    Ans: C   Section: 22-3

27. A planetary nebula is
    A)   the spherical cloud of hot gas produced by a supernova explosion.
    B)   the disk of material in which planets are forming around a star other than the Sun.
    C)   a shell of ejected gases, glowing by fluorescence caused by ultraviolet light from a hot but dying central star.
    D)   a gas cloud surrounding a planet after its formation and before the formation of the planet's moons.
    Ans: C   Section: 22-3

28. A planetary nebula is
    A)   the nebula caused by the supernova explosion of a massive star.
    B)   a cloud of gas and dust surrounding newly formed planets from which their moons will eventually form.
    C)   the atmosphere of a red giant star slowly expanding away from the star's core to form a shell of gas.
    D)   a disk-shaped nebula of dust and gas rotating around a relatively young star, within which planets will eventually form.
    Ans: C   Section: 22-3

29. A planetary nebula is
    A)   the gas cloud surrounding a planet after its formation.
    B)   the spherical, rapidly expanding cloud of gas produced by a supernova explosion, containing heavy elements and radioactive nuclei.
    C)   a cloud of gas and dust grains surrounding a very young star, in which planets are expected to form by accretion.
    D)   a shell of gases ejected from the surface of a red giant star, glowing from fluorescence caused by UV light from the hot, central white dwarf star.
    Ans: D   Section: 22-3

30. Planetary nebulae are so-named because
    A)   these extended objects, often green-colored, looked like planets when first seen by nineteenth-century observers through their telescopes.
    B)   the ejected material is rich in carbon and oxygen, necessary elements for the manufacture of planets in the nebulae surrounding stars.
    C)   they rotate slowly and condense into planetary objects around a central star.
    D)   their spectra appear to be similar to the spectrum of the giant gas planets in our own solar system.
    Ans: A   Section: 22-3

31. The event that follows the asymptotic giant branch (AGB) phase in the life of a low-mass star is
    A)   the ejection of a planetary nebula.
    B)   core collapse and a supernova explosion.
    C)   helium flash and the start of helium burning in the core.
    D)   the onset of hydrogen burning in the core.
    Ans: A   Section: 22-3

32. A planetary nebula is created
    A)   over several hundred years, during mass transfer in a close binary star system.
    B)   in seconds, during the helium flash in a low-mass star.
    C)   slowly over 10,000 years or more, due to thermal pulses in a low-mass star.
    D)   in hours or less, during the explosion of a massive star.
    Ans: C   Section: 22-3

33. What happens to the surface of a low-mass star after the helium core and helium shell nuclear fusion "burning" stages are completed?
    A)   It stabilizes at the size of a red giant star, the radiation pressure from below balancing gravity from the core, to cool slowly for the rest of its life.
    B)   It is propelled slowly away from the core to form a planetary nebula.
    C)   It is spun off into space to form a spiral galaxy.
    D)   It contracts back onto the core and becomes hot enough to undergo further hydrogen fusion, leading to a very hot and active white dwarf star.
    Ans: B   Section: 22-3

34. The major source of light in the expanding shell of gas in a planetary nebula is
    A)   fluorescence of the atoms, caused by UV light from the hot central white dwarf star.
    B)   reflection and scattering of the light of the central white dwarf star from dust and gas in the shell.
    C)   thermal heating of the dust grains by radiation from the hot central star.
    D)   thermonuclear reactions in this hot gas, caused by the underlying explosion.
    Ans: A   Section: 22-3

35. The physical process believed to provide the energy for the ejection of a planetary nebula from a star is
    A)   transfer of hydrogen-rich material to the surface of a white dwarf from its companion in a binary star system.
    B)   a series of thermal pulses in a helium-burning shell.
    C)   a collision with another star.
    D)   core collapse and the ensuing shock wave.
    Ans: B   Section: 22-3

36. The typical diameter of a planetary nebula is
    A)   about 1000 ly.   C)   only about 3 to 5 stellar diameters.
    B)   about 1 AU.   D)   about 1 ly.
    Ans: D   Section: 22-3

37. The fraction of the mass of a red giant which is ejected as a shell in a planetary nebula is
    A)   almost the whole star, greater than 90%.
    B)   substantial, up to 40%.
    C)   extremely small, less than 1 part in 10^4.
    D)   small, close to 0.01, or 1%.
    Ans: B   Section: 22-3

38. What will be the mass of the Sun at the end of its asymptotic giant branch (AGB) phase, as a result of mass loss to space by its stellar wind?
    A)   0.6 solar masses
    B)   almost 1 solar mass, because mass loss is negligible for a low-mass star like the Sun
    C)   0.1 and 0.2 solar masses, because the Sun will lose most of its mass
    D)   0.9 solar masses
    Ans: A   Section: 22-3

39. In astronomical terms, planetary nebulae
    A)   exist around their central white dwarf stars for millions of years before slowly spreading into space.
    B)   are relatively long-lived, because they form when the original stars form and remain as slowly rotating shells for the whole of the star's lifetime of several billion years.
    C)   are very short-lived, with lifetimes of about 50,000 years.
    D)   are very long-lived objects, having been in existence since the Big Bang at the beginning of the universe.
    Ans: C   Section: 22-3

40. The shell of a planetary nebula is measured by the Doppler shift of emission lines to be expanding outward at a speed of 10 km/s and its diameter is measured to be 1 light-year. How long has the shell been expanding?
    A) 30,000 years   B) 30 million years   C) 30 years   D) 9.5×10^{11} years
    Ans: A   Section: 22-3

41. Out of all matter ejected into the interstellar medium each year by stars, planetary nebula shell ejections account for
    A) almost 100%.   B) just over half.   C) less than 1%.   D) about 15%.
    Ans: D   Section: 22-3

42. What fraction of the material returned to the interstellar medium of a galaxy by stars is contributed by planetary nebulae as they eject their shells?
    A)   15%
    B)   only about 1 part in a million
    C)   less than 1%
    D)   80%, or most of the returned material
    Ans: A   Section: 22-3

43. Which of the following important components does a planetary nebula contribute to the interstellar medium?
    A)   nuclei of elements like carbon, nitrogen, and oxygen, which are major components of planets such as our own
    B)   UV light that photoionizes hydrogen. This hydrogen, on recombination, produces the red Balmer-α light by which we see interstellar emission nebulae.
    C)   rotational motion from the original star, which serves to concentrate interstellar matter into new stars and planetary systems
    D)   new hydrogen nuclei, replenishing those which are lost when stars form
    Ans: A   Section: 22-3

44. What causes thermal pulses in low-mass stars?
    A)   Thermal pulses are the end result of the five-minute vibrations like those we observe on the Sun.
    B)   The internal structure of these low-mass stars becomes unstable as they cross the Instability Strip on the main sequence.
    C)   A helium shell flash occurs. This re-ignites the helium shell and triggers an expansion of the outer layers.
    D)   Spent nuclear "ash" from the helium burning shell falls onto the hydrogen burning core, causing it to flare up.
    Ans: C   Section: 22-3

45. Stars that have ejected a planetary nebula go on to become
    A) red giants.   B) white dwarfs.   C) protostars.   D) supernovae.
    Ans: B   Section: 22-4

46. The final remnant of the evolution of a red giant star that has ejected a planetary nebula is a
    A) blue supergiant.   B) neutron star.   C) supernova.   D) white dwarf star.
    Ans: D   Section: 22-4

47. The object seen at the center of a planetary nebula is
    A) an accretion disk around a black hole.
    B) a planet in the process of forming.
    C) composed almost entirely of neutrons, and is spinning rapidly.
    D) the former core of a red giant star, now a white dwarf star.
    Ans: D   Section: 22-4

48. A white dwarf is
    A) an object like Jupiter which was not massive enough to become a star.
    B) a low-mass star at the end of its life.
    C) a hot, main-sequence star.
    D) a type of protostar.
    Ans: B   Section: 22-4

49. At which phase of its evolutionary life is a white dwarf star?
    A) very late for a small mass star, the dying phase
    B) just at the main-sequence phase
    C) early phase, soon after formation
    D) post-supernova phase, the remnant of the explosion
    Ans: A   Section: 22-4

50. A white dwarf star is at what stage of its evolution?
    A) protostar phase, just after formation
    B) very late phase of evolution
    C) post-supernova stage, after the explosion of a star
    D) main-sequence phase, "middle-aged"
    Ans: B   Section: 22-4

51. A white dwarf star, the surviving core of a low-mass star toward the end of its life, can be found on the Hertzsprung-Russell diagram
    A) below and to the left of the main sequence.
    B) at the bottom end of the main sequence, along which it has evolved throughout its life.
    C) at the upper left end of the main sequence, because its surface temperature is extremely high.
    D) above and to the right of the main sequence, because it evolved there after its hydrogen-burning phase.
    Ans: A   Section: 22-4

52. Our Sun will end its life by becoming a
    A) black hole.   B) white dwarf.   C) molecular cloud.   D) pulsar.
    Ans: B   Section: 22-4

53. In which order will a single star of about 1 solar mass progress through its various stages of evolution?
    A)   T Tauri, main sequence, planetary nebula, white dwarf
    B)   planetary nebula, main sequence, neutron star, black hole
    C)   T Tauri, red giant, white dwarf, neutron star
    D)   planetary nebula, main sequence, red giant, white dwarf
    Ans: A   Section: Chapters 20-22

54. A white dwarf star is about the same size as
    A) the Earth.   B) the Sun.   C) the total solar system.   D) New York City.
    Ans: A   Section: 22-4

55. A white dwarf star is generating energy from what source?
    A)   It no longer generates energy but is cooling slowly.
    B)   nuclear fusion of heavy elements in the central core
    C)   gravitational potential energy as the star slowly contracts
    D)   nuclear fusion of hydrogen into helium
    Ans: A   Section: 22-4

56. One particular characteristic of a white dwarf star is its
    A)   very high surface temperature.
    B)   extremely low mass for a star, about 1/100 of a solar mass.
    C)   very low surface temperature, because it is at the end of its life.
    D)   spectrum, consisting simply of emission lines from hydrogen, helium, carbon, and oxygen.
    Ans: A   Section: 22-4

57. The energy generation process inside a white dwarf star is
    A)   the combining of protons and electrons to form neutrons within its core.
    B)   the helium flash—very efficient and rapid helium fusion.
    C)   nonexistent; a white dwarf star is simply cooling by radiating its original heat.
    D)   hydrogen fusion.
    Ans: C   Section: 22-4

58. Which characteristic is shared by all white dwarf stars without binary companions?
    A)   They are generating thermonuclear energy, but are maintaining a constant radius and so are not releasing gravitational energy.
    B)   They have stopped generating thermonuclear energy but continue to shrink, thereby releasing gravitational energy as heat.
    C)   They have never generated either thermonuclear or gravitational energy but are slowly cooling after their production in a supernova explosion.
    D)   They have ceased to generate energy by thermonuclear processes or gravitational contraction and are cooling down.
    Ans: D   Section: 22-4

59. The characteristics of interiors of white dwarf stars are
    A)   mainly helium nuclei, supported by electron degeneracy pressure in a volume with a radius about 11 times that of Earth, about the volume of Jupiter.
    B)   mostly hydrogen nuclei, supported by normal gas pressure because of the very high gas temperature, in a volume about the size of the Earth.
    C)   mainly carbon and oxygen nuclei, supported by electron degeneracy pressure in a volume about the size of the Sun.
    D)   mainly carbon and oxygen nuclei, supported by electron degeneracy pressure in a volume about the size of the Earth.
    Ans: D   Section: 22-4

60. Which physical phenomenon keeps a white dwarf star from collapsing inward on itself?
    A)   electron degeneracy or "quantum crowding"
    B)   normal gas pressure
    C)   convection currents or updrafts from the nuclear furnace
    D)   the physical size of the neutrons
    Ans: A   Section: 22-4

61. A white dwarf star is supported from collapse under gravity by
    A)   degenerate-electron pressure in the compact interior.
    B)   centrifugal force due to rapid rotation.
    C)   pressure of the gas, heated by nuclear fusion reactions in a shell around its core.
    D)   pressure of the gas, heated by nuclear fusion reactions in its core.
    Ans: A   Section: 22-4

62. Because it has ceased nuclear burning in its interior and therefore no longer generates energy, why is it that a white dwarf does not shrink rapidly under the force of gravity as it cools?
    A) The rapid reduction of radius before the white-dwarf phase produces a very rapid rotation, thereby generating a large centrifugal force which prevents the star from shrinking.
    B) The very low luminosity of a white dwarf means that it cools slowly and maintains a high temperature and therefore a high internal pressure which opposes gravity.
    C) The star has lost so much mass in earlier phases that the remaining mass generates insufficient gravitational force to produce further shrinkage.
    D) The electrons within it are in a degenerate state and will not allow further shrinkage.
    Ans: D   Section: 22-4

63. One physical characteristic of matter inside a white dwarf star is that it
    A) is composed only of electrons in a degenerate state.
    B) has extremely high density compared to ordinary stellar matter.
    C) is in the form of a hollow shell with a black hole at its center.
    D) is composed only of neutrons.
    Ans: B   Section: 22-4

64. The stars that eventually become white dwarfs are those that start life with masses of less than
    A) 1.4 solar masses.   C) 25 solar masses.
    B) 3 solar masses.   D) 4 solar masses.
    Ans: D   Section: 22-4

65. A white dwarf star, as it evolves, undergoes which of the following changes?
    A) Luminosity and size decrease, while its temperature remains constant.
    B) Its temperature remains constant, but its radius and luminosity decrease.
    C) It shrinks in size, the resulting release of gravitational energy maintaining both luminosity and temperature constant.
    D) Luminosity and temperature decrease, but its size remains constant.
    Ans: D   Section: 22-4

66. If two white dwarf stars have the same composition, then the more massive one always has a
    A) smaller radius than the less massive one.
    B) larger radius than the less massive one.
    C) higher temperature than the less massive one.
    D) lower temperature than the less massive one.
    Ans: A   Section: 22-4

67. White dwarf stars of different masses have radii or sizes for which
    A)   the more massive the star, the larger it is.
    B)   the sizes are the same for all stellar masses.
    C)   the sizes start out the same for all masses, but the more massive stars shrink
         fastest.
    D)   the more massive the star, the smaller it is.
    Ans: D   Section: 22-4

68. If you were to increase the mass of a white dwarf star in some way,
    A)   its radius would become smaller.
    B)   it would reject the mass, because the electrons within the star are in a degenerate
         state and generate a very large outward pressure.
    C)   its radius would become larger.
    D)   its radius would remain the same, because the electrons in the stellar material are
         in a degenerate state.
    Ans: A   Section: 22-4

69. One peculiar feature of the evolution of a white dwarf star is that
    A)   its size or radius slowly increases as it cools, until it becomes a red giant star.
    B)   it heats as it shrinks because of the release of gravitational energy, ending up as a
         very hot but very small star.
    C)   it shrinks as it cools, eventually to become a cold black hole in space.
    D)   its size remains constant as it cools and dies.
    Ans: D   Section: 22-4

70. As a white dwarf evolves, the direction of its motion on the Herzsprung-Russell diagram
    below the main sequence is upper right to lower left, which means that
    A)   its size must be increasing; therefore its luminosity is also increasing.
    B)   the release of gravitational energy heats the star as it shrinks and it will die as a
         hot but very small star.
    C)   its size or radius remains constant as it cools and becomes less luminous.
    D)   it shrinks as it cools, becoming a cold neutron star.
    Ans: C   Section: 22-4

71. There is a mass limit for a star in the white dwarf phase, the Chandrasekhar limit,
    beyond which the star can no longer support its own weight. This mass limit, in terms of
    solar mass, is
    A) 1.4.   B) 14.   C) 30.   D) 0.2.
    Ans: A   Section: 22-4

72. Which of the following types of stars or stellar remnants cannot have a mass larger than
    about 1.4 times the mass of the Sun?
    A) neutron star   B) red giant   C) black hole   D) white dwarf
    Ans: D   Section: 22-4

73. The two longest stages in the lifetime of a solar mass star, each lasting billions of years, are
    A) protostar and main sequence
    B) main sequence and red giant
    C) red giant and white dwarf
    D) main sequence and white dwarf
    Ans: D   Section: 22-4

74. Usually, ideal gases increase their pressure and volume when heated and decrease their pressure and volume when cooled. Do these rules apply to stars?
    A) No, stars never follow the rules for ideal gases, even approximately.
    B) Yes, stars in all stages follow these rules quite closely.
    C) No, protostars have cores of degenerate matter in which the pressure is independent of the temperature.
    D) No, white dwarfs are essentially degenerate matter in which the pressure is independent of the temperature.
    Ans: D   Section: 22-4 and 21-2 and Box 21-1

75. What is the mass limit above which the self-gravity of stars can overcome electron degeneracy pressure?
    A) 0.05 solar masses
    B) 1.4 solar masses
    C) 14 solar masses
    D) There is no limit, because nothing in nature can overcome this quantum mechanical limit.
    Ans: B   Section: 22-5

76. The supergiant stars Betelguese and Rigel in the Orion region of the sky appear particularly bright because
    A) they are in a region of low interstellar medium density and are not therefore heavily obscured compared to equivalent stars elsewhere.
    B) they are very close in our spiral arm.
    C) they are very luminous.
    D) their very high surface temperatures make them easy to see, even though they are intrinsically faint and far away, because most of their light is concentrated in the visible range.
    Ans: C   Section: 22-5

77. Which of the following will a high-mass star (say, 25 times the mass of the Sun) NOT do at or near the end of its life?
    A) emit copious amounts of neutrinos
    B) eject its outer layers and become a neutron star
    C) eject its outer layers and become a white dwarf
    D) convert silicon into iron in its core
    Ans: C   Section: 22-5

78. Which nuclear fusion cycle follows the helium fusion phase as a massive star evolves?
    A)   silicon "burning"   C)   iron "burning"
    B)   carbon "burning"   D)   oxygen "burning"
    Ans: B   Section: 22-5

79. A star of 25 solar masses spends roughly what percentage of its life as a main sequence star? (See Table 22-1, Freedman and Kaufmann, *Universe,* 7th ed.)
    A) about 10%   B) 91%   C) very little, less than 1%   D) about 50%
    Ans: B   Section: 22-5

80. Which force induces the core to condense and collapse in massive stars at the conclusion of each episode of nuclear fusion, such as the carbon, oxygen, and silicon fusion cycles?
    A)   gravity
    B)   the nuclear attractive force between nuclei and between neutrons and protons
    C)   gas pressure produced by the very high gas temperatures
    D)   electron degeneracy pressure
    Ans: A   Section: 22-5

81. During the late stages of evolution (e.g., oxygen burning) in massive stars, nuclear reactions produce many free neutrons. What very important effect do these neutrons have on the composition of the star?
    A)   The neutrons, being uncharged, escape from the star, thus carrying away energy from the core of the star and lowering its temperature.
    B)   The neutrons are captured by atomic nuclei and can produce heavy elements that would not form from nuclear fusion alone.
    C)   The neutrons are captured by atomic nuclei, causing the nuclei to split by fission reactions into lighter elements that would otherwise be very rare in the universe.
    D)   The neutrons decay into protons and electrons, thus increasing the amount of hydrogen in the core and extending the life of the star.
    Ans: B   Section: 22-5

82. The main product of silicon fusion reactions in the core of a massive star is
    A) carbon.   B) iron.   C) helium.   D) magnesium.
    Ans: B   Section: 22-5

83. The capture of free neutrons by heavy atomic nuclei is
    A)   easy, because neutron capture always produces a stable product nucleus.
    B)   easy, because the neutron has no electric charge.
    C)   difficult, unless the nucleus is already unstable.
    D)   difficult, unless the neutron is moving rapidly.
    Ans: B   Section: 22-5

84. Thermonuclear reactions release energy because
    A) the "ash" nucleus which is produced is less tightly bound than the "fuel" nucleus.
    B) the "ash" nucleus which is produced contains fewer protons than the "fuel" nucleus, and these protons have been converted into energy.
    C) the "ash" nucleus which is produced is more tightly bound than the "fuel" nucleus.
    D) the "ash" nucleus which is produced is moving faster than the "fuel" nucleus, and this excess kinetic energy shows up as heat.
    Ans: C   Section: 22-5

85. A sequence of thermonuclear fusion processes inside massive stars can continue to transform the nuclei of elements such as carbon, oxygen, etc. into heavier nuclei AND also generate excess energy, up to a limit beyond which no further energy-producing reactions can occur. The element that is produced when this limit is reached is
    A) silicon.   B) oxygen.   C) uranium.   D) iron.
    Ans: D   Section: 22-5

86. The sequence of thermonuclear fusion processes inside massive stars can transform elements such as carbon, oxygen, etc. into heavier elements AND generate excess energy, until iron has been produced. Why is it not possible for fusion reactions to release energy from iron nuclei?
    A) It has been found that iron nuclei never undergo fusion reactions.
    B) The magnetic properties of iron produce extra repulsion which, along with the electrostatic repulsion, prevents fusion of iron nuclei with protons.
    C) Iron is the heaviest possible element in nature and so, fusion of heavier elements is not possible.
    D) The electrostatic repulsion between the iron nucleus and the proton is so great that fusion requires extra energy, rather than releasing it.
    Ans: D   Section: 22-5

87. A high-mass star near the end of its life undergoes successive cycles of energy generation within its core in which gravitational collapse increases the temperature to the point where a new nuclear fusion cycle generates sufficient energy to stop the collapse. This process does not work beyond the silicon fusion cycle which produces iron. Why is this?
    A) The pressure from high-energy photons and neutrinos at the very high core temperatures reached at this stage of development is finally sufficient to halt the collapse.
    B) The density is so great that the iron nuclei are effectively touching one another and the collapse cannot continue.
    C) Fusion of iron nuclei into heavier nuclei requires energy rather than producing excess energy and therefore will not produce the additional gas pressure to halt the collapse.
    D) Electrostatic forces between the highly charged iron nuclei are sufficient to overcome the collapse and stabilize the stellar core.
    Ans: C   Section: 22-5

88. For a massive star, core hydrogen burning lasts for several million years. In contrast, core silicon burning lasts for only about
    A) 1 day.   B) 1 minute.   C) 600 years.   D) 1 year.
    Ans: A   Section: 22-5 and Table 22-1

89. The majority of massive stars, at the point in time when they explode as supernovae, have become (see Fig. 22-13, Freedman and Kaufmann, *Universe,* 7th ed.)
    A) red supergiants.   B) neutron stars.   C) blue supergiants.   D) white dwarfs.
    Ans: A   Section: 22-5

90. Carbon fusion in massive stars combines helium and carbon to produce oxygen. This is followed by oxygen fusion in which oxygen is burned to produce sulfur. Why is a higher temperature required for oxygen fusion than for carbon fusion?
    A)   Because of extensive mass loss between the carbon fusion and oxygen fusion stages, higher temperatures are required for nuclear reactions in the relatively rarified stars in which oxygen fusion takes place.
    B)   Larger nuclei, like oxygen, have more protons and are therefore repelled more strongly from other nuclei. Thus faster speeds (at higher temperatures) are required to bring these nuclei together than are required for smaller nuclei.
    C)   Free neutrons are required in greater numbers to enable the oxygen reaction, and this requires higher temperatures to produce them.
    D)   The enormous neutrino flux in the core of a massive star inhibits nuclear reactions. High temperatures are necessary to force these neutrinos out of the star so nuclear reactions can proceed.
    Ans: B   Section: 22-5

91. After the material in the core of a massive star has been converted to iron by thermonuclear reactions, further energy can be released to heat the core ONLY by
    A)   gravitational contraction.
    B)   thermonuclear fusion of iron into heavier elements.
    C)   nuclear fission or splitting of nuclei.
    D)   absorption of neutrinos.
    Ans: A   Section: 22-6

92. At the end of the life of a massive star, during the process of core collapse, the time taken from the start of collapse to the attainment of nuclear density is about
    A) 1/4 second.   B) 1/2000 second.   C) 8 minutes.   D) a few hours.
    Ans: A   Section: 22-6

93. The core collapse phase at the end of the life of a massive star is triggered when
    A)   the helium flash and thermal pulses have expelled the star's envelope.
    B)   nuclear fusion has produced a significant amount of iron in its core.
    C)   the core becomes as dense as an atomic nucleus.
    D)   the density reaches a threshold at which electron degeneracy pressure begins to play a role.
    Ans: B   Section: 22-6

94. What is photodisintegration?
    A)   heating and ejection of mass from the surface of a normal star by the radiation from a neutron star orbiting it
    B)   destruction of a star by the pressure of radiation inside it
    C)   splitting apart of atomic nuclei by high-energy gamma rays
    D)   ejection of a neutron or proton from an atomic nucleus, accompanied by the emission of a gamma ray
    Ans: C   Section: 22-6

95. Which of the following processes does NOT happen as a result of core collapse at the end of the life of a massive star?
    A)   The core density approaches the density of an atomic nucleus.
    B)   Great numbers of neutrinos are produced.
    C)   Electrons combine with protons to form neutrons.
    D)   The silicon core is converted to iron by fusion reactions.
    Ans: D   Section: 22-6

96. The very last nuclear process to occur at the center of a massive star (at the end of its life) is
    A)   silicon burning, resulting in the production of iron.
    B)   the helium flash.
    C)   the photodisintegration of nuclei by gamma rays.
    D)   the capture of electrons by protons to produce neutrons.
    Ans: D   Section: 22-6

97. Which of the following processes is NOT involved in the supernova explosion of a massive star?
    A)   passage of a shock wave through the star's envelope
    B)   helium flash in the star's core, when 3 helium nuclei combine
    C)   photodisintegration of nuclei by gamma rays
    D)   collapse of the star's core
    Ans: B   Section: 21-2 and 22-6

98. Just before the outer layers of a high-mass star are thrown into space in a supernova explosion, the density in its core is about that
    A)   of iron metal, 7.5×10^3 kg/m^3.
    B)   of degenerate gases in white dwarf stars, about 10^3 kg/m^3.
    C)   at the center of the Sun, about 1.5×10^5 kg/m^3.
    D)   of nuclear matter in a normal nucleus, about 4×10^{17} kg/m^3.
    Ans: D   Section: 22-6

99. Which of the following is NEVER a consequence of a supernova explosion?
    A)   condensation of matter into a solid nuclear star composed entirely of neutrons
    B)   triggering of star formation by shock waves moving through interstellar space
    C)   formation of a planetary nebula
    D)   manufacture of the nuclei of heavy elements
    Ans: C   Section: 22-3 and 22-6

100. What fraction of the mass of a 25 M$_\odot$ main sequence star is ejected into space during its lifetime?
    A)   almost all of it, greater than 80%
    B)   only a small fraction, about 1/100
    C)   between 1/4 and 1/2
    D)   only its outer atmosphere, less than 1 part in 10^4
    Ans: A   Section: 22-6

101. How much energy is released in the supernova explosion of a massive star?
    A)   almost as much energy as the Sun emits over its entire lifetime
    B)   almost as much energy as the entire galaxy emits over its lifetime
    C)   10,000 times as much energy as the Sun emits over its entire lifetime
    D)   100 times as much energy as the Sun emits over its entire lifetime
    Ans: D   Section: 22-6

102. What is the source of most of the heavy elements on the Earth and in our own bodies?
    A)   explosive nucleosynthesis during supernova explosions of massive stars
    B)   nuclear reactions during the formation of the Universe (the Big Bang)
    C)   cosmic ray interactions with hydrogen and helium nuclei in interstellar clouds
    D)   thermonuclear fusion reactions in the cores of massive stars
    Ans: A   Section: 22-6

103. It is now thought that most elements in the universe heavier than iron in the periodic table
    A)   are produced by the nuclear reactions in the central cores of high-mass stars a few 100 years before the star explodes into a supernova.
    B)   were produced in the Big Bang explosion at the beginning of our Universe.
    C)   are produced by the successive capture of high-speed neutrons within low-mass star cores because neutrons are uncharged and can approach other nuclei without electrostatic repulsion.
    D)   are produced by nuclear reactions in the shock wave regions surrounding supernova explosions.
    Ans: D   Section: 22-6

104. Very heavy elements beyond iron in the periodic table are formed in the interiors of massive stars by what process in general?
    A)   triple α process
    B)   neutron capture
    C)   splitting of heavier elements by nuclear fission
    D)   CNO cycle of nuclear fusion
    Ans: B   Section: 22-6

105. The next element in the periodic table after tin (chemical symbol Sn) is antimony (chemical symbol Sb). If ^{122}Sn captures a neutron, the result will be
    A) ^{123}Sn.   B) ^{123}Sb.   C) ^{121}Sn.   D) ^{122}Sb.
    Ans: A   Section: 22-6 and Box 5-5

106. Photodisintegration, the fissioning of iron nuclei into helium nuclei due to high energy gamma radiation, occurs only at the very end of the life of a massive star. Why can this not occur earlier? Each of the following answers is correct *except*
    A)   Iron nuclei do not exist in anything but trace amounts before this stage.
    B)   Gamma radiation of sufficient energy is not produced before this stage.
    C)   The fissioning of an iron nucleus requires energy, and the energy-rich environment that allows this to happen does not exist before this stage.
    D)   Under the conditions of the previous stages of evolution, iron (^{26}Fe) disappears as quickly as it is formed by combining with helium (^{4}He) to produce zinc (^{30}Zn).
    Ans: D   Section: 22-6

107. A typical supernova, in the hours following its explosion, is as bright as
    A)   1000 typical spiral galaxies.   C)   1000 Sun-like stars.
    B)   an entire galaxy.   D)   a million Sun-like stars.
    Ans: B   Section: 22-7

108. The luminosity of a typical supernova star, during the initial phases of the explosion, increases by a factor of
    A) 10^6 B) 2–3, because the star is already very bright   C) 10^3 D) 10^9
    Ans: D   Section: 22-7

109. In what year did the light arrive at Earth from the most recent supernova visible to the unaided eye?
    A) 1604 AD   B) 1987 AD   C) 1054 AD   D) 1572 AD
    Ans: B   Section: 22-7

110. Just before it exploded, the star that became supernova SN 1987A was
    A) a B3 I supergiant.   B) an M2 I supergiant.   C) a pulsar.   D) a white dwarf.
    Ans: A   Section: 22-7

111. The star that exploded to form the supernova SN 1987A probably had, before it blew up, a mass of
    A)   about 20 solar masses.   C)   about 1.4 solar masses.
    B)   less than 1 solar mass.   D)   about 40 to 50 solar masses.
    Ans: A   Section: 22-7

112. How did supernova SN 1987A differ from most other observed supernovae?
    A)   It declined in brightness much faster than most supernovae.
    B)   It occurred in an external galaxy, not in our Milky Way galaxy.
    C)   The star was a blue supergiant when it blew up, rather than the expected red supergiant.
    D)   It reached a maximum luminosity ten times that of a normal supernova.
    Ans: C   Section: 22-7

113. Which of the following is NOT true for supernova SN 1987A?
    A)   It did not become as bright intrinsically as originally expected.
    B)   Observations of the star were made before it blew up.
    C)   It was a white dwarf exploding after mass transfer from a companion star in a binary star system.
    D)   A burst of neutrinos was detected from the supernova.
    Ans: C   Section: 22-7

114. What is the source of energy that allowed supernova 1987A to continue to brighten slowly for a few months after its initial explosion?
    A)   radioactive decay of specific nuclei produced in the explosion
    B)   thermonuclear reactions between iron nuclei and protons, neutrons, and helium nuclei
    C)   thermonuclear reactions between hydrogen nuclei in the shell of gas surrounding the supernova, triggered by the shock wave from the explosion.
    D)   slow gravitational compression of the remnant core of the supernova and the consequent release of gravitational potential energy
    Ans: A   Section: 22-7

115. A blue (hot) supergiant is 10 times larger in diameter than the Sun, but a red (cool) supergiant of the same luminosity has a diameter 1000 times that of the Sun. How does the surface temperature of the blue supergiant compare to that of the red supergiant?
    A) They have the same luminosity, so they must have the same surface temperature.
    B) The surface temperature of the blue supergiant is 10 times the surface temperature of the red supergiant.
    C) The surface temperature of the blue supergiant is 100 times the surface temperature of the red supergiant.
    D) The surface temperature of the blue supergiant is 1000 times the surface temperature of the red supergiant.
    Ans: B   Section: 22-7 and Box 19-4

116. The neutrino is
    A) a very small asteroid-like body orbiting the Sun that is very difficult to see.
    B) a heavy nuclear particle, easily detected.
    C) an elusive subatomic particle, having very little or no mass and difficult to detect.
    D) another name for an antielectron or positron.
    Ans: C   Section: 22-8 and 18-4

117. Which of the following properties does the neutrino NOT possess?
    A) travels at or very close to the speed of light
    B) highly penetrating through any matter
    C) electrical charge equal to that of the electron
    D) zero or extremely small mass
    Ans: C   Section: 22-8 and 18-4

118. What new method has recently provided astronomers with new information about the behavior of stars beneath their surfaces, for example, the collapse of the inner core of a star undergoing supernova explosion and the nuclear reactions in the interior of the Sun?
    A) neutrino astronomy   C) X-ray astronomy and photography
    B) visible light spectroscopy   D) radio astronomy
    Ans: A   Section: 22-8

119. What was the effective "neutrino energy luminosity" (energy carried away by neutrinos) of the SN 1987A supernova for a few seconds following the explosion compared to relatively well-known electromagnetic luminosities?
    A) 1 million times greater than that of the observable universe
    B) 10 times greater than the total observable universe.
    C) 10 times greater than the total output of the stars in our galaxy
    D) 1 million times greater than the luminosity of our Sun
    Ans: B   Section: 22-8

120. Neutrino detectors for astronomical purposes are built and operated deep underground to
    A)   shield them against other high-energy radiation from space or from natural radioactivity
    B)   reduce the effect of rotational speed produced by Earth's rotation, because the sensitive neutrino detection techniques are adversely affected by Doppler shifts.
    C)   utilize the gravitational focusing of neutrinos that occurs in the Earth's core.
    D)   ensure that they are absolutely light-tight, because they depend on the detection of very faint flashes of light.
    Ans: A   Section: 22-8

121. One technique for the detection of neutrinos from outer space involves the reaction of neutrinos with protons in a water tank, with the resulting high-speed positrons then generating Cerenkov radiation in the water. How is this Cerenkov radiation produced?
    A)   by the passage of the charged positron through the water at a speed greater than the speed of light in a vacuum
    B)   by the recombination of the positron with a proton to produce neutral hydrogen and Balmer series line emissions
    C)   by the charged positron moving in the water faster than the speed of light in water
    D)   by the annihilation of a negative electron in the water by the positron, to produce radiation
    Ans: C   Section: 22-8

122. The Cerenkov radiation used to detect neutrinos from supernova SN 1987A in water tanks was produced by
    A)   electrons and antielectrons (positrons) colliding and annihilating.
    B)   nuclear fusion in the neutrino detector.
    C)   neutrons ejected from nuclei by the neutrinos.
    D)   electrons traveling faster than the speed of light in water.
    Ans: D   Section: 22-8

123. The detection of neutrinos from supernova SN 1987A occurred three hours before the detection of the burst of visible light. What caused this time lag?
    A)   The result proved that neutrinos travel faster in vacuum than light does.
    B)   The space between the supernova and the Earth is not a perfect vacuum, but is filled with very rarified gas and dust. This impedes the passage of light (very slightly) but not of neutrinos.
    C)   The neutrinos and the light were produced at the same time, but the light bounced back and forth between the core and the outer layers several times before these layers expanded to the point that they became transparent.
    D)   The neutrinos were produced earlier (when the core collapsed) and the light was produced three hours later (when the shock wave reached the outer layers).
    Ans: D   Section: 22-8

124. Where are supernovae detected?
    A)   only in spiral galaxies, never in ellipticals
    B)   in our galaxy and many others
    C)   only in our galaxy
    D)   only in elliptical galaxies, never in spirals
    Ans: B   Section: 22-7 and 22-9

125. A Type II supernova is the
    A)   explosion of a single massive star after silicon burning has produced a core of iron nuclei.
    B)   explosion of a red giant star as a result of the helium flash in the core.
    C)   collapse of a blue supergiant star to form a black hole.
    D)   explosion of a white dwarf in a binary star system after mass has been transferred to it from its companion.
    Ans: A   Section: 22-9

126. A Type Ia supernova is the
    A)   explosion of a massive star that has lost its hydrogen-rich outer layers through a stellar wind or mass transfer in a binary star system.
    B)   explosion of a white dwarf in a binary star system after mass has been transferred onto it from its companion.
    C)   collapse of a blue supergiant star to form a black hole.
    D)   explosion of a massive star after silicon burning has produced a core of iron nuclei.
    Ans: B   Section: 22-9

127. A Type Ib supernova is believed to result from the
    A)   collapse of a blue supergiant star to form a black hole.
    B)   explosion of a massive star that has lost its hydrogen-rich outer layers through a stellar wind or by mass transfer in a binary star system.
    C)   explosion of a white dwarf in a binary star system after matter transferred to it from its companion has increased its mass above the Chandrasekhar limit.
    D)   explosion of a massive, hydrogen-rich star after silicon burning has produced a core of iron nuclei.
    Ans: B   Section: 22-9

128. What is the main observational difference between a Type I and a Type II supernova?
   A)   Hydrogen lines are prominent in the spectrum of a Type II supernova but absent in that of Type I.
   B)   The spectrum of a Type II supernova shows strong lines of both hydrogen and helium, whereas that of Type I shows only hydrogen.
   C)   The spectrum of a Type I supernova shows strong lines of both hydrogen and helium, whereas that of Type II shows only hydrogen.
   D)   Hydrogen lines are prominent in the spectrum of a Type I supernova but absent in that of Type II.
   Ans: A   Section: 22-9

129. Type II supernovae show prominent lines of hydrogen in their spectra, whereas hydrogen lines are absent in spectra of Type Ia supernovae. Why is this? (HINT: Think about the type of star that gives rise to each of the two types of supernova.)
   A)   Massive stars have burned all of their hydrogen into heavier elements, whereas low-mass stars still have large hydrogen-rich envelopes.
   B)   Massive stars contain large amounts of hydrogen, whereas white dwarfs are mostly carbon and oxygen.
   C)   White dwarfs have a thick surface layer of hydrogen, whereas neutron stars contain no hydrogen at all.
   D)   Massive stars contain large amounts of hydrogen, whereas neutron stars contain no hydrogen at all.
   Ans: B   Section: 22-9

130. Can a white dwarf explode?
   A)   Only if another star collides with it; and stars are so far apart in space that this is unlikely ever to have happened in our galaxy.
   B)   Yes, but only if nuclear reactions in the white dwarf core reach the stage of silicon burning, producing iron.
   C)   No; white dwarfs are held up by electron degeneracy pressure, and this configuration is stable against collapse or explosion.
   D)   Yes, but only if it is in a binary star system.
   Ans: D   Section: 22-9

131. A supernova of Type Ia has a much higher peak luminosity than a supernova of Type II. When we measure luminosity we are including the energy of all of the following *except*
   A) ultraviolet radiation.   B) gamma rays.   C) neutrinos.   D) X rays.
   Ans: C   Section: 22-9 and Figure 5-7

132. The estimated rate at which supernova explosions occur in a spiral galaxy such as our own is almost once every
   A) 20 years.   B) 30,000 years.   C) 5 years.   D) 300 years.
   Ans: A   Section: 22-10

133. The most recent supernova explosion known to have occurred in our own galaxy
    A)   gave rise to the Crab Nebula.
    B)   created the Gum Nebula.
    C)   was seen in 1987 (supernova 1987A).
    D)   created the supernova remnant Cassiopeia A.
    Ans: D   Section: 22-10

134. What is remarkable about the supernova remnant Cassiopeia A?
    A)   It contains a binary neutron star system, in which one neutron star is significantly more massive than the other.
    B)   It shows that a supernova occurred in our galaxy about 300 years ago, but there is no record of any supernova having been seen at that time.
    C)   It is the nearest supernova remnant, located only about 300 light-years from the Earth.
    D)   It is bright at all wavelengths from radio through visible light to X rays.
    Ans: B   Section: 22-10

135. Measurements suggest that light first arrived at Earth from the Cassiopeia A supernova about 300 years ago and that this supernova is about 10,000 light years away from Earth. When did the explosion actually occur?
    A)   It is not possible to say when it occurred from the information given.
    B)   300 years ago, or about 1700 AD
    C)   9700 years ago, or about 7700 BC
    D)   10,300 years ago, or about 8300 BC
    Ans: D   Section: 22-10

136. Measurements from distant galaxies indicate that supernovae should occur at a rate of five per century in a spiral galaxy such as the Milky Way but only three have been recorded in this galaxy in the past thousand years. Why is this?
    A)   Most supernovae produce X rays and radio waves, and not visible light, and hence were invisible to earlier observers.
    B)   The majority of supernovae must have occurred in the plane of the Milky Way and hence were hidden from Earth by the dense gas and dust in the Milky Way plane.
    C)   Observers were not watching the sky carefully enough, particularly through the Dark Ages and over the past few centuries.
    D)   The Milky Way galaxy is somehow different, with much lower numbers of very massive stars in general, so many fewer stars have undergone supernova explosions.
    Ans: B   Section: 22-10

137. From observations of supernova explosions in distant galaxies, it is predicted that there should be about five supernovae per century in our galaxy, whereas we have seen only about one every 300 years from Earth. Why is this?
    A)   Most supernovae occur in the Milky Way, which can be seen only from the southern hemisphere where, until recently, there were no observers of the sky.
    B)   Our galaxy is peculiar in that the majority of stars are old, well beyond the supernova stages of evolution.
    C)   The majority of supernovae produce no visible light, only radio and X-ray radiation, which we have only been able to observe for the past three decades.
    D)   Most supernovae occur in the galactic plane where interstellar dust obscures our view of them from Earth.
    Ans: D   Section: 22-10

138. When a supernova explosion results from core collapse in a massive star it appears to leave behind
    A)   a rapidly expanding shell of gas and a central neutron star or black hole.
    B)   a rapidly rotating shell of gas, dust, and radiation, but no central object.
    C)   a rapidly expanding shell of gas and a compact white dwarf star at its center.
    D)   nothing, the explosion changes all the matter completely into energy, which then radiates into space at the speed of light.
    Ans: A   Section: 22-10

139. Supernova remnants are *least* likely to be discovered when observers are attempting to detect them by looking for
    A) radio waves.   B) X rays.   C) visible light.   D) neutrinos.
    Ans: D   Section: 22-10

Chapter 23: Neutron Stars

1. Ancient Chinese astronomers recorded the appearance of what phenomenon in 1054 AD?
   A) a nearby nova explosion, in our Galaxy
   B) a brilliant auroral display covering the whole Earth.
   C) a supernova, visible in daylight
   D) a bright binary star undergoing eclipse
   Ans: C   Section: 23-1

2. Which major astronomical event was apparently recorded faithfully by Chinese astronomers in the Sung Dynasty in 1054 AD?
   A) a supernova explosion in our Galaxy, visible even in daylight
   B) the passage of the planet Venus across the face of the Sun, a solar transit
   C) the discovery of the planet, Mercury
   D) the total eclipse of the Sun in that year
   Ans: A   Section: 23-1

3. The existence of stars composed almost entirely of neutrons was first predicted by
   A) Stephen Hawking, in 1985.
   B) Jocelyn Bell, in 1967.
   C) Albert Einstein, in 1908.
   D) Fritz Zwicky and Walter Baade, in 1933.
   Ans: D   Section: 23-1

4. The diameter of a typical neutron star of 1 solar mass is predicted to be approximately
   A) 1 km.
   B) that of the Sun.
   C) that of an average city, about 30 km.
   D) that of Earth, 12,800 km.
   Ans: C   Section: 23-1

5. What is the relationship between neutron stars and the Chandrasekhar Limit?
   A) The Chandrasekhar Limit is an upper mass limit for the stability of any massive system. It applies to any system, no matter how it was formed, including neutron stars.
   B) The Chandrasekhar Limit applies only to systems stabilized by degenerate electrons. Neutron stars are stabilized by the pressure of the neutron degeneracy.
   C) The Chandrasekhar Limit applies specifically to the neutron degeneracy and thus to neutron stars.
   D) The Chandrasekhar Limit applies to radius, not mass. Thus as long as a neutron star is big enough, it will not be affected by the Chandrasekhar Limit.
   Ans: B   Section: 23-1 and 22-4

6. What stage of the evolutionary life of a star does the Crab Nebula represent?
   A)   late stage, the remnant of a stellar explosion
   B)   a black hole, the very late stages of evolution of a massive star
   C)   a middle-age, main-sequence star, surrounded by an extended atmosphere
   D)   the early, star-forming stage, surrounded by its protostar nebula
   Ans: A   Section: 23-2

7. The Crab Nebula is
   A)   a supernova remnant.
   B)   a planetary nebula surrounding a hot star.
   C)   the active nucleus of a spiral galaxy.
   D)   a cool prestellar gaseous nebula.
   Ans: A   Section: 23-2 and Figure 1-6

8. The Crab Nebula is a nearby example of what type of physical phenomenon?
   A)   spiral galaxy, a collection of 100 billion stars
   B)   remnant of a supernova explosion
   C)   gas and dust cloud, the formation region for new stars
   D)   planetary nebula, a shell of gas leaving an old star
   Ans: B   Section: 23-2 and Figure 1-6

9. Among the following locations in the universe, where would you expect to find a pulsar?
   A)   at the center of the galaxy   C)   in the Orion Nebula
   B)   at the center of the Sun   D)   in the Crab Nebula
   Ans: D   Section: 23-2

10. The first pulsar was detected using
    A)   the infrared satellite IRAS
    B)   a British radio telescope
    C)   the unaided eye, by Chinese astronomers
    D)   the 200-inch telescope at Mount Palomar
    Ans: B   Section: 23-2

11. In what year was the first pulsar discovered?
    A) 1978   B) 1967   C) 1960   D) 1930
    Ans: B   Section: 23-2

12. The first pulsar was discovered by
    A)   the Hubble Space Telescope, soon after it was launched, in 1990.
    B)   Johannes Kepler, in 1604.
    C)   an English graduate student, Jocelyn Bell, in 1967.
    D)   the Astronomer Royal in Newton's time, Sir Edmund Halley, in 1606.
    Ans: C   Section: 23-2

13. A pulsar is most probably formed
    A)   in the core of a star as it evolves through its main sequence phase.
    B)   in the center of a supernova explosion.
    C)   within a huge gas cloud, by collisions between stars.
    D)   just after the formation of a protostar by gravitational condensation.
    Ans: B   Section: 23-2

14. The discovery of the Crab Pulsar, with a period of only 1/30 second, ruled out a number
    of possible explanations for pulsars. These included all of the following *except one.*
    Which one was the exception?
    A)   eclipsing binaries   C)   variable stars
    B)   rapidly shifting dark dust clouds   D)   rotating white dwarfs
    Ans: B   Section: 23-2

15. Which of the following astronomical objects are most closely associated with pulsars?
    A) neutron stars   B) black holes   C) red giant stars   D) white dwarf stars
    Ans: A   Section: 23-3

16. What is a pulsar?
    A)   a pulsating white dwarf star, fluctuating rapidly in brightness
    B)   a rapidly rotating neutron star, producing beams of radio energy and in some
         cases, light and X rays
    C)   a rotating black hole, producing two jets of gas in opposite directions and pulses
         of gravitational energy
    D)   a Cepheid variable star with a period of a few days
    Ans: B   Section: 23-3

17. A pulsar is
    A)   a pulsating star, in which size, temperature, and light intensity vary regularly.
    B)   a binary star in which matter from one star is falling onto the second star.
    C)   a rapidly rotating neutron star, emitting beams of radio radiation and in some
         cases X rays and visible light.
    D)   an object at the center of each galaxy, providing energy from its rapid rotation.
    Ans: C   Section: 23-3

18. A pulsar is
    A)   an interstellar beacon manufactured by little green persons (LGPs).
    B)   a type of variable star, pulsating rapidly in size and brightness.
    C)   a rapidly spinning neutron star.
    D)   an accretion disk around a black hole, emitting light as matter is accumulated on
         the disk.
    Ans: C   Section: 23-3

19. Pulsars, emitting very regular radio and sometimes visible light pulses, are what type of object?
    A) rapidly rotating neutron stars
    B) close binary star systems in which the stars are undergoing rapid and regular eclipses as seen from Earth
    C) black holes, with material falling regularly into them
    D) pulsating variable stars
    Ans: A   Section: 23-3

20. The pulsation periods of most pulsars are in the range
    A) of 1/1000 second and a few seconds.
    B) of 10^{-6} and 10^{-3} second.
    C) from minutes to hours.
    D) from many hours to a few days.
    Ans: A   Section: 23-3, 23-6

21. A neutron star will be detected from Earth as a pulsar by its regular radio pulses ONLY if
    A) Earth lies in the plane of the neutron star's magnetic equator, halfway between its magnetic poles.
    B) Earth lies almost directly in line with the magnetic axis of the neutron star at some time during the star's rotation.
    C) Earth lies directly above the rotation axis of the rotating neutron star.
    D) Earth lies in the neutron star's "equator," the plane perpendicular to its spin axis.
    Ans: B   Section: 23-3

22. Which of the following descriptions does NOT represent a property of neutron stars?
    A) emitters of relatively narrow beams of radio energy and other electromagnetic radiation
    B) rotation rates from one to thirty times each second
    C) strong gravitational fields but weak magnetic fields
    D) composed almost entirely of neutrons
    Ans: C   Section: 23-3

23. The very strong magnetic field of a neutron star is created by
    A) a burst of neutrinos produced by the supernova explosion, because this would be the equivalent of a very large electrical current flowing for a short time.
    B) the collapse of a star, which significantly intensifies the original weak magnetic field of the star.
    C) differential rotation of the neutron star, its equator rotating faster than the poles, similar to sunspot formation.
    D) turbulence generated in electrical plasmas during the collapse of a star, even though this star had no magnetic field originally.
    Ans: B   Section: 23-3

24. The strength of the magnetic field around a typical neutron star is
    A) about a million (10^6) gauss, similar to the strongest magnetic fields ever produced on Earth.
    B) about a trillionth (10^{-12}) of a gauss, or about a trillion times weaker than the Earth's magnetic field.
    C) about 1 gauss, similar to the magnetic field strength of the Sun.
    D) about a trillion (10^{12}) gauss, or about a million times stronger than the strongest magnetic fields ever produced on Earth.
    Ans: D   Section: 23-3

25. The pulsed nature of the radiation at all wavelengths that is seen to come from a pulsar is produced by
    A) the mutual orbiting and eclipsing of two very hot stars in a close binary system.
    B) the rapid pulsation in size and hence brightness of a small white dwarf star.
    C) the rapid rotation of a neutron star that is producing two oppositely directed beams of radiation.
    D) extremely hot matter that is rapidly orbiting a black hole just prior to descending into it.
    Ans: C   Section: 23-3

26. The source of the beams of electromagnetic radiation (including light in some cases) emitted by pulsars is
    A) the surface of a normal star that has a white dwarf companion. The white dwarf creates a hot spot on the normal star that emits a beam of light as the stars rotate around each other.
    B) charged particles spiraling along the magnetic axes of rotating neutron stars and, because they are being accelerated, emitting electromagnetic radiation.
    C) jets of material flowing out along the rotation axis of the accretion disk around a black hole, collisions in the jets heating the material to produce electromagnetic radiation.
    D) electrons flowing out along the rotation axis of an accretion disk around a neutron star, the electrons emitting light because they are being accelerated.
    Ans: B   Section: 23-3

27. The charged particles that emit the beams of electromagnetic radiation from a pulsar are believed to be
    A) iron and other nuclei pulled from the neutron star's crust by its intense magnetic fields.
    B) plasma (ionized gas) spiraling onto the neutron star from a normal stellar companion.
    C) electrons and hydrogen and helium nuclei from the neutron star's ionized atmosphere.
    D) electron-positron pairs created by very strong electric fields near the neutron star's surface.
    Ans: D   Section: 23-3

28. Neutron stars are believed to be created primarily by
    A)   explosions of main-sequence stars.
    B)   all types of supernovae.
    C)   type II supernovae, i.e., explosions of high-mass stars.
    D)   type Ia supernovae, i.e., exploding white dwarfs.
    Ans: C   Section: 23-3

29. What is believed to be the reason that no pulsar has yet been detected in the remnant of Tycho's supernova of 1572?
    A)   Supernovae prior to 1967 did not produce pulsars.
    B)   It was a Type Ia supernova.
    C)   Any neutron star that may have formed is still hidden in debris and is not yet visible.
    D)   It was a Type II supernova.
    Ans: B   Section: 23-3

30. Some pulsars are found outside the gaseous remnant of the supernova explosion in which they were born. What is believed to be the reason for this?
    A)   The supernova explosion was asymmetrical, and ejected gas in only one broad direction.
    B)   The supernova explosion was asymmetrical and gave a strong "kick" to the pulsar.
    C)   The gaseous remnant is more massive than the neutron star and lags behind it as the galaxy rotates.
    D)   Galactic rotation creates a "wind" of interstellar gas that pushes on the gaseous remnant but leaves the neutron star unaffected.
    Ans: B   Section: 23-3

31. Astronomers originally rejected the idea that white dwarfs could rotate fast enough to be responsible for pulsar radiation. But they soon accepted the idea that neutron stars could produce pulsar radiation. Why this difference?
    A)   The earlier rejection was mistaken. With sufficient evidence astronomers have come to believe that both white dwarfs and neutron stars can produce pulsar radiation.
    B)   There are two types of white dwarfs: those that produce Type Ia supernova and those that do not. The earlier rejection applied to the second type. It is now believed that the Ia supernova type white dwarfs, along with neutron stars, can produce pulsar radiation.
    C)   Neutron stars are smaller and even more dense than white dwarfs. Thus they can rotate at tremendous rates without flying apart.
    D)   Neutron stars are held together by nuclear forces that are much stronger than the gravitational forces operating in white dwarfs. Thus the surface of a neutron star can pulse in and out much more quickly than the surface of a white dwarf.
    Ans: C   Section: 23-3

32. Visible pulses are seen to accompany radio pulses only from neutron stars, which are
    A) relatively young, like the Crab or Vela pulsars.
    B) part of binary star systems.
    C) high above the galactic plane, where visible light is not obscured by interstellar dust and gas.
    D) relatively old, because young pulsars are surrounded by a supernova remnant that absorbs the visible light.
    Ans: A   Section: 23-4

33. As time progresses, the pulse rate for most solitary pulsars is
    A) slowing down, because rotational energy is being used to generate the pulses.
    B) absolutely constant, pulsars providing ideal frequency standards or clocks.
    C) varying periodically as the neutron star undergoes periodic expansions and contractions.
    D) speeding up, as the neutron star slowly contracts under gravity.
    Ans: A   Section: 23-4

34. The main reason for the observed slowdown of Crab pulsar is
    A) the slow expansion and redistribution of mass, similar to a spinning skater who spreads her arms outward.
    B) a slow buildup of the magnetic field as rotational energy is transferred to magnetic energy.
    C) the loss of rotational energy through the emission of beams of charged particles.
    D) friction between the stellar surface and the surrounding nebular material.
    Ans: C   Section: 23-4

35. The energy radiated by the Crab Nebula is supplied by the Crab pulsar. The resulting luminosity of the Crab Nebula is
    A) very much greater than the luminosity of the Crab pulsar.
    B) about 1/4 to 1/3 of the luminosity of the Crab pulsar.
    C) very much smaller than the luminosity of the Crab pulsar.
    D) approximately equal to the luminosity of the Crab pulsar.
    Ans: A   Section: 23-4

36. How can the luminosity of the Crab Nebula be so much greater than that of the Crab pulsar?
    A) The Crab Nebula has a different source of energy, not related to the Crab pulsar.
    B) The energy radiated from the Crab Nebula comes from charged particles emitted by the pulsar, not from the luminosity (photons) emitted by the pulsar.
    C) The energy radiated by the Crab pulsar is magnified by laser action in the nebula.
    D) The energy now being radiated from the Crab Nebula was deposited in it by the original supernova explosion, and does not come from the present-day pulsar.
    Ans: B   Section: 23-4

37. The Crab pulsar now spins at a rate of 30 times per second (period = 0.033 s). If its rate of "spin-down" were to remain constant at the present rate, how long would it be before the Crab pulsar was spinning only 25 times per second (period = 0.04 s)? (See Section 23-4, Freedman and Kaufmann, *Universe*, 7th ed.)
    A) 640 years.   B) 4500 years.   C) 2.3×10^5 years.   D) 1.3×10^6 years.
    Ans: A   Section: 23-4

38. Synchrotron radiation is emitted whenever
    A)   charged particles are forced to move along curved paths within a magnetic field.
    B)   matter and antimatter meet and annihilate.
    C)   charged particles are accelerated in straight lines into dense gas such as the outer atmosphere of a star.
    D)   charged particles move at speeds faster than the speed of light in any medium.
    Ans: A   Section: 23-4

39. All of the following are emitted in large numbers from the vicinity of pulsars *except one*. Which is the exception?
    A) electrons   B) visible light   C) X rays   D) neutrinos
    Ans: D   Section: 23-4

40. Is there a relationship between the age of a pulsar and its rotation rate?
    A)   No. Pulsars all have the same rotation rate. But we do not believe they were all formed at the same time.
    B)   No. All pulsars are believed to have formed at the same time (in the Big Bang at the beginning of the universe). So the different rotation rates cannot be attributed to different ages.
    C)   Yes. The faster they spin the older they are.
    D)   Yes. The slower they spin the older they are.
    Ans: D   Section: 23-4

41. The interior of a neutron star is believed to consist of
    A)   almost entirely neutrons, but with some protons, electrons, and some nuclei in the innermost part.
    B)   an inner part with entirely neutrons and an outer part with a mixture of neutrons and neutron-rich nuclei.
    C)   entirely neutrons.
    D)   almost entirely neutrons, but with some protons and electrons.
    Ans: D   Section: 23-5

42. The neutrons in the interior of a neutron star are believed to exist in a
    A)   normal fluid state.   C)   superfluid state.
    B)   superfluid and superconducting state. D)   superconducting state.
    Ans: C   Section: 23-5

43. The interior of a neutron star is believed to consist of
    A) superconducting neutrons and superfluid electrons.
    B) superfluid neutrons and superconducting protons.
    C) superfluid neutrons and superconducting electrons.
    D) superconducting neutrons and superfluid protons.
    Ans: B   Section: 23-5

44. Glitches are occasionally observed by astronomers studying pulsars. What are these glitches?
    A) clumps of denser material in the jets of particles emitted along the magnetic poles
    B) sudden flares caused by matter falling onto the surface of the neutron star
    C) secondary pulses of radiation occasionally interspersed with the primary pulses
    D) sudden increases in rotation rate
    Ans: D   Section: 23-5

45. The pulsation rate of the pulsar within the Vela supernova remnant has increased abruptly several times since its discovery (see Fig. 23-7, Freedman and Kaufmann, *Universe,* 7th ed.). What is the presently accepted explanation for this speed-up?
    A) The pulsar is a rotating neutron star that is occasionally spun up by the interaction of its powerful magnetic field with passing stars.
    B) The pulsar is a rotating neutron star whose surface slows down because of energy loss to radiation, but whose superfluid interior continues to rotate. Friction between these surfaces occasionally spins up the crust.
    C) The pulsar is a pulsating white dwarf that occasionally undergoes an abrupt change in its oscillating mode.
    D) The pulsar is a rotating neutron star with a solid, rotationally flattened crust. As the pulsar's rotation slows down, the crust readjusts through a "starquake" that causes the pulsar to spin up slightly.
    Ans: B   Section: 23-5

46. The thickness of the solid crust of a 1.4-solar-mass neutron star whose radius is about 11 km is approximately
    A) 20 cm.   B) 20 m.   C) 300 m.   D) 4 mm.
    Ans: C   Section: 23-5 and Figure 23-8

47. What is the escape velocity of matter from the surface of a 1-solar-mass neutron star with a diameter of 28 km? (See Box 7-2, Freedman and Kaufmann, *Universe,* 7th ed.)
    A) about 0.46 of the speed of light
    B) quite small, much less than 1/10 of the speed of light
    C) 10 times greater than the speed of light
    D) about ¾ the speed of light
    Ans: A   Section: 23-5 and Box 7-2

48. Astronomers believe neutron stars may have atmospheres. What form of evidence do we have for this?
    A) observation of a banded structure such as we see on Jupiter and Saturn
    B) occultation observations during which another star is eclipsed by the neutron star, and absorption lines are seen, which are due to absorption by the neutron star's atmosphere
    C) dips in the X-ray spectrum emitted by the neutron star suggesting that these wavelength ranges are absorbed by an atmosphere
    D) interruptions in the magnetic activity on the neutron star, which seem to be due to clouds or storms or other atmospheric phenomena
    Ans: C   Section: 23-5

49. The spectra from the atoms in the atmosphere of a neutron star are very different from spectra observed elsewhere. Why is this?
    A) A neutron star is basically one giant nucleus, and the electrons in the atmosphere move in electron energy levels around the entire star.
    B) The intense magnetic field distorts the shapes of atoms, making them ellipsoidal instead of spherical, and distorting their spectra as well.
    C) The extreme conditions around neutron stars give rise to new forms of atoms with spectra never before observed.
    D) The atmosphere of a neutron star is dominated by the magnetic jets that propel atoms to relativistic velocities and thus extreme Doppler shifts for their spectra.
    Ans: B   Section: 23-5

50. The fastest pulsars, called millisecond pulsars, have periods of about 1/1000 second. The reason they pulse so much faster than (for example) the Crab and Vela pulsars is that they
    A) were formed from much more massive stars than were the Crab and Vela pulsars, and were spun up more as their cores collapsed to a smaller volume.
    B) are normal pulsars, whereas the Crab and Vela pulsars have been slowed down from millisecond speeds over their long lifetimes.
    C) are a totally different phenomenon, involving a black hole rather than a neutron star.
    D) were spun up by mass transferred on to them from a companion in a binary star system.
    Ans: D   Section: 23-6

51. The Black Widow pulsar is unusual because it appears to
    A) be a solitary millisecond pulsar with no companion star.
    B) be eating away at its companion star.
    C) have been eaten away by its companion star.
    D) be a black hole surrounded by the remnants of its former companion star.
    Ans: B   Section: 23-6

52. Which of the following *cannot* result from the evolution of a binary star system containing at least one high-mass star which will produce a Type II supernova and neutron star.
    A) One star, having evolved to a pulsar, is emitting high-energy particles that erode its companion.
    B) One star, having evolved to a pulsar, is bombarded with infalling mass from the other star when it expands as a red giant and overflows its Roche lobe.
    C) One star, having evolved to a pulsar, is bombarded with high-energy particles from its red giant companion. This bombardment eats away at the pulsar and destroys it.
    D) Both stars, having evolved to the neutron star stage, spiral in toward each other and collide.
    Ans: C   Section: 23-6

53. Pulsating X-ray sources are believed to be
    A) white dwarf stars with intense magnetic fields; the X rays are generated by flares like those on the Sun, but much stronger.
    B) black holes in binary systems, with the X rays emitted from an accretion disk around the black hole.
    C) neutron stars in binary systems, emitting X rays because of mass transfer onto the neutron star from its normal companion.
    D) the same as regular radio and visible-light-emitting pulsars but observed in X rays.
    Ans: C   Section: 23-7

54. Pulsating X-ray sources with periods of a few seconds are caused by
    A) the pulsation in radius, temperature, and hence luminosity of a hot Cepheid variable star with a surface temperature hot enough to emit X rays.
    B) the eclipsing of an X-ray-emitting star with a very hot surface by a cool companion in a close binary system.
    C) matter falling onto the surface of a very hot, rotating white dwarf star from an ordinary companion star in a binary system, producing an X-ray-emitting hot spot that disappears periodically behind the white dwarf.
    D) matter falling violently onto the surface of a rotating neutron star from a close companion in a binary star system, causing an X-ray hot spot that disappears periodically behind the neutron star.
    Ans: D   Section: 23-7

55. The X rays from pulsating X-ray sources are believed to arise from
    A) hot spots in an accretion disk around a rapidly precessing neutron star, created when the jets of charged particles from the neutron star's poles pass across the accretion disk.
    B) a hot spot on a normal star, caused by intense radiation from an orbiting neutron star.
    C) hot spots on a neutron star's equator, caused by matter falling inward from an accretion disk around the neutron star.
    D) hot spots at the magnetic poles of a neutron star, caused by matter from a companion star traveling down the neutron star's magnetic field.
    Ans: D   Section: 23-7

56. Why do we believe that pulsating X-ray sources are neutron stars that are members of close binary systems?
    A) The spectra of pulsating X-ray sources are always characterized by periodic Doppler shifts.
    B) All pulsating X-ray sources are in the millisecond range, suggesting that they have been "spun up" by infalling matter from a close binary companion.
    C) The source of the intense X rays must be large amounts of gas not found on a neutron star. This must be pulled in from a close binary companion.
    D) All pulsating X-ray sources show a periodic "turnoff" as the neutron star disappears behind its companion.
    Ans: C   Section: 23-7

57. The pulsation frequency of a pulsating X-ray source is related to
    A) the rotation rate of the neutron star.
    B) the rotation rate of the close binary companion.
    C) the orbital period of the binary pair.
    D) the rotation rate of the accretion disk around the neutron star.
    Ans: A   Section: 23-7

58. When a typical nova explodes, it brightens in a few hours by a factor of
    A) 2 to 5.   B) 10^4 to 10^6.   C) 10^8 to 10^{10}.   D) 10 to 100.
    Ans: B   Section: 23-8

59. How much fainter than a supernova is a typical nova?
    A) 1,000,000 times   B) 10 times   C) 100,000,000 times   D) 10,000 times
    Ans: D   Section: 23-8

60. A nova is a sudden brightening of a star that occurs when
   A)   material from a companion star is transferred onto the surface of a white dwarf in a binary system and is subsequently blasted into space by a runaway thermonuclear explosion, leaving the white dwarf intact to repeat the process.
   B)   the electron-degenerate iron core of a massive star collapses after its mass becomes larger than the Chandrasekhar mass limit.
   C)   material from a companion star is transferred onto a neutron star in a binary system, causing the neutron star to collapse into a black hole.
   D)   material from a companion star is transferred onto the surface of a white dwarf star in a binary system, after which runaway carbon fusion reactions cause the entire white dwarf to be destroyed in an explosion.
   Ans: A   Section: 23-8

61. The nova phenomenon, an occasional and sometimes repeated intense brightening of a star by a factor of about 10^6, is caused by
   A)   the beam of radiation from a nearby pulsar illuminating the surface of a red giant star and inducing rapid and intense heating.
   B)   hydrogen "burning" explosively on the surface of a white dwarf star after mass transfer from a companion star in a binary system.
   C)   the capture and rapid compression of matter by a black hole.
   D)   the explosion of a single massive star at the end of its thermonuclear burning phases.
   Ans: B   Section: 23-8

62. The mechanism that gives rise to the phenomenon of the nova is
   A)   material falling into a black hole and being condensed to the point where a thermonuclear explosion is produced.
   B)   the complete disintegration of a massive star because of thermonuclear runaway in the star's interior.
   C)   the impact and subsequent explosion of a large comet nucleus on a star's surface.
   D)   matter from a companion star falling onto a white dwarf in a close binary system, eventually causing a nuclear explosion on the dwarf's surface.
   Ans: D   Section: 23-8

63. The difference between a nova and an X-ray burst is that
   A)   a nova involves an explosion on the surface of a neutron star, whereas an X-ray burst involves an explosion on the surface of a white dwarf.
   B)   a nova involves an explosion on the surface of a neutron star, whereas an X-ray burst involves the complete collapse of a neutron star to form a black hole.
   C)   a nova involves an explosion on the surface of a white dwarf, whereas an X-ray burst involves an explosion on the surface of a neutron star.
   D)   a nova involves the complete explosive destruction of a white dwarf, whereas an X-ray burst involves an explosion on the surface of the white dwarf.
   Ans: C   Section: 23-8

64. X-ray bursters are objects in the sky that emit sudden bursts of X rays in addition to a steady, low-level, X-ray emission. These bursts of X rays are believed to be caused by
    A) material transferred onto the surface of a neutron star in a binary system, then subsequently ignited in a thermonuclear explosion that leaves the neutron star intact to repeat the process.
    B) material from a companion star pulled into an accretion disk around a black hole, with periodic clumps of material falling from the disk into the black hole to produce the X rays.
    C) material transferred onto the surface of a neutron star, causing the neutron star to collapse suddenly into a black hole.
    D) material transferred onto the surface of a white dwarf in a binary star system, producing a thermonuclear explosion at the surface while leaving the white dwarf intact to repeat the process.
    Ans: A   Section: 23-8

65. The X-ray bursts from an X-ray burster are caused by
    A) explosive hydrogen burning on the surface of a neutron star.
    B) hot spots caused by material falling onto the poles of a rotating neutron star.
    C) explosive photodisintegration of iron nuclei on the surface of a neutron star.
    D) explosive helium burning on the surface of a neutron star.
    Ans: D   Section: 23-8

66. What is the difference between a nova and an X-ray burster? Each one of the following answers is correct *except one*. Which one is the exception?
    A) A nova involves stars in a close binary system, whereas an X-ray burster involves an individual star not in a binary system.
    B) A nova is produced by a white dwarf, whereas an X-ray burster is produced by a neutron star.
    C) A nova involves the nuclear explosion of hydrogen, whereas an X-ray burster involves the nuclear explosion of helium.
    D) The system that emits X-ray bursts emits a constant stream of X-rays between bursts, whereas a system that produces nova does not.
    Ans: A   Section: 23-8

67. A mass of about 2 solar masses is imploded inward by a supernova explosion. What is the result of this implosion?
    A) a star a little smaller than the size of the Sun, its size governed by gas pressure from the hot interior of the star
    B) a white dwarf star, its size governed by electron degeneracy pressure
    C) a neutron star, its size governed by neutron degeneracy pressure
    D) a black hole with infinitely small radius, because nothing can prevent such a mass from collapsing completely
    Ans: C   Section: 23-9

68. What is the upper limit to the mass of a neutron star beyond which neutron degeneracy pressure is unable to withstand the force of gravity and the neutron star is crushed out of existence into a black hole?
    A)   1.4 solar masses   C)   about 100 solar masses
    B)   20 solar masses   D)   about 3 solar masses
    Ans: D   Section: 23-9

69. The pressure within a neutron star that opposes the inward force of gravity comes from
    A)   gas pressure, very similar to that described by the ideal gas equation.
    B)   degenerate electron pressure.
    C)   both degenerate electron pressure and degenerate neutron pressure.
    D)   both degenerate neutron pressure and the repulsive hard core aspect of the nuclear force between neutrons.
    Ans: D   Section: 23-9

Chapter 24: Black Holes

1. Which statement best describes the "fabric" of space and time as outlined by the classical physics of Newton?
   A) Space is expanding uniformly, whereas the rate of passage of time is slowing down as the universe ages.
   B) Space becomes "curved" and time slows down near a source of gravity, as measured by a distant observer.
   C) The shape of space and the rate of time variation depends on the relative velocities of observer and observed.
   D) Space is perfectly uniform and is mapped by a fixed network, whereas time passes at a uniform rate for all observers.
   Ans: D   Section: 24-1

2. What is "special" about the special theory of relativity?
   A) It deals only with objects that are at rest relative to one other.
   B) It deals only with objects moving in a straight line at constant speed.
   C) It deals only with motion at speeds significantly less than the speed of light.
   D) It deals with motion at constant velocity and accelerated motion but excludes all other effects; in particular, it excludes gravity.
   Ans: B   Section: 24-1

3. In order to use the theory of special relativity to describe an object's motion, the object must be moving
   A) at a constant speed in a straight line; how fast it is moving is not important.
   B) in a constant direction; how the speed changes is not important.
   C) close to the speed of light; if this is true then how speed and direction change is not important.
   D) at a constant speed; whether the direction of motion changes is not important.
   Ans: A   Section: 24-1

4. Which of the following is a correct and complete statement of Einstein's first postulate of special relativity?
   A) Your description of physical reality will be the same provided that your speed remains constant, though the direction of this speed can vary.
   B) Your description of physical reality is the same regardless of the direction in which you move.
   C) Your description of physical reality is the same regardless of how you move.
   D) Your description of physical reality will be the same regardless of your velocity, provided that this velocity is constant.
   Ans: D   Section: 24-1

5. Suppose you are in a jet airliner traveling at a constant speed of 400 km/h in a constant direction. All windows are blocked so you cannot see outside, and there are no vibrations from the engines. What experiment can you do to determine that you are in fact moving?
   A)   Measure the speed of a sound wave traveling up the aisle (toward the nose of the plane) and another traveling down toward the tail, and calculate the difference between the two results.
   B)   None. All experiments will give the same results as when you are at rest on the ground.
   C)   Suspend a ball by a thread from the ceiling and measure the angle the thread makes with the vertical.
   D)   Drop a small rock and measure the distance it moves backward down the aisle as it falls.
   Ans: B   Section: 24-1

6. Suppose you are in the Space Shuttle in orbit around the Earth at a speed of 7 km/s, and at some particular time your direction of travel is straight toward the Sun. The speed of light in a vacuum is 300,000 km/s. What speed will you measure for the light from the Sun?
   A)   300,000 km/s
   B)   300,014 km/s because your speed is added to that of the light and relativistic contraction has shortened your reference meter sticks
   C)   299,993 km/s because relativistic contraction has shortened all distances, including your reference meter sticks
   D)   300,007 km/s because your speed is added to that of the light
   Ans: A   Section: 24-1

7. Two rocket ships are traveling past the Earth at 90% of the speed of light in opposite directions (i.e., they are approaching each other). One turns on a searchlight beam, which is seen by scientists aboard the second spaceship. What speed do the scientists measure for this light? (c = speed of light in a vacuum)
   A) 1.8 c (equal to 2 × 0.9 c)   B) 0.9 c   C) 1.9 c (equal to c + 0.9 c)   D) c
   Ans: D   Section: 24-1

8. You are standing on the gangplank of your spaceship on Mars when you see an identical spaceship go past Mars at 90% of the speed of light. When you look closely at this spaceship, how do you find that it compares to your own spaceship?
   A) The moving spaceship looks shorter, and time on it appears to run more slowly than on yours.
   B) The moving spaceship looks longer, and time on it appears to run faster than on yours.
   C) The moving spaceship looks shorter, and time on it appears to run faster than on yours.
   D) The moving spaceship looks longer, and time on it appears to run more slowly than on yours.
   Ans: A   Section: 24-1 and Box 24-1

9. If you see an object moving past you at 90% of the speed of light, you will measure the length of this object to be
   A) unchanged from when it is at rest.
   B) shorter than if it were at rest while it is traveling toward you, longer than if it were at rest when it is traveling away from you.
   C) shorter than if it were at rest.
   D) longer than if it were at rest.
   Ans: C   Section: 24-1 and Box 24-1

10. Suppose you are in a rocket ship traveling toward the Earth at 95% of the speed of light. Compared to when your ship was at rest on Mars, you measure the length of your spaceship to be
   A) the same as when it was on Mars.
   B) longer than when it was on Mars.
   C) You can't tell. Your life processes have slowed down too much for you to measure the length.
   D) shorter than when it was on Mars.
   Ans: A   Section: 24-1 and Box 24-1

11. Fred and Joanne both measure the length of a particular spaceship to be 100 m when it is on the Earth. Joanne then gets into the spaceship and, after visiting the Moon, hurtles past the Earth at a speed close to the speed of light. Fred, still on the Earth, measures the length of the moving spaceship to be about 90 m. At the same time, Joanne (using her own meter-stick) measures the length of the spaceship to be
   A) We can't tell from the information given.
   B) 100 m, because she is "at rest" on the spaceship.
   C) about 90 m, because of the motion of the spaceship.
   D) about 110 m, because both she and the spaceship are moving.
   Ans: B   Section: 24-1 and Box 24-1

12. A child on a playground swing is swinging back and forth (one complete oscillation) once every four seconds, as seen by her father standing next to the swing. At the same time, a spaceship hurtles by at a speed close to the speed of light. According to special relativity (and ignoring the Doppler effect for this question), a person on the spaceship finds that the time for one full swing is
    A)   less than 4 seconds when the spaceship is approaching the swing and longer than 4 seconds when it is moving away.
    B)   more than 4 seconds.
    C)   equal to 4 seconds.
    D)   less than 4 seconds.
    Ans: B   Section: 24-1 and Box 24-1

13. Suppose that you are on the Earth and see a spaceship with a clock on it hurtling past you at 80% of the speed of light. As it goes by, the second hand on the ship's clock ticks off 5 seconds. How much time elapsed on your clock while this was happening?
    A)   5 seconds—the same as on the ship's clock
    B)   more than five seconds if the spaceship is approaching you, or less than five seconds if it is moving away
    C)   more than 5 seconds
    D)   less than 5 seconds
    Ans: C   Section: 24-1 and Box 24-1

14. Suppose you are on board a spaceship that is passing the Earth at 80% the speed of light. You see a clock on the Earth tick off five seconds. How much time elapsed on your clock while this was happening?
    A)   5 seconds—the same as on the Earth's clock
    B)   less than 5 seconds if you are approaching the Earth, or more than 5 seconds if you are moving away
    C)   less than 5 seconds
    D)   more than 5 seconds
    Ans: D   Section: 24-1 and Box 24-1

15. If you stay on the Earth while a friend races off in a rocket at a speed close to the speed of light then, according to special relativity, you will see a clock on the rocket appear to tick more slowly than the one on your wall. If your friend looks back at your clock then, according to the same theory, the friend will see your clock appear to tick
    A)   at the same speed as the clock on the rocket.
    B)   faster or slower than the clock on the rocket, depending on the direction of travel of the rocket compared to Earth.
    C)   more slowly than the clock on the rocket.
    D)   faster than the clock on the rocket.
    Ans: C   Section: 24-1 and Box 24-1

16. A person is standing beside the open doorway of an empty barn. A pole of the same length as the barn is lying on the ground outside the barn. A second person picks up the pole and runs toward the barn at 90% of the speed of light, with the pole pointing toward the barn (a very athletic person!). How long does the pole appear to be to the person standing by the door, compared to the barn?
    A)   19% of the length of the barn   C)   44% of the length of the barn
    B)   90% of the length of the barn   D)   81% of the length of the barn
    Ans: C   Section: 24-1 and Box 24-1

17. A pole is lying on the ground outside a barn. The length of the pole is the same as the length of the barn. A person picks up the pole and runs toward the barn at 90% of the speed of light, with the pole pointing toward the barn (a very athletic person!). How long does the barn appear to be compared to the pole, as seen by the person running?
    A)   The barn appears to be 19% of the length of the pole.
    B)   The barn appears to be 5.3 times longer than the pole.
    C)   The barn appears to be 2.3 times longer than the pole.
    D)   The barn appears to be 44% of the length of the pole.
    Ans: D   Section: 24-1 and Box 24-1

18. At what speed would an object have to be traveling for its length to appear to a stationary observer to have decreased to 1/3 of its length when seen at rest?
    A)   0.11 c, or 11% of the speed of light   C)   0.33 c, or 1/3 c
    B)   0.94 c, or 94% of the speed of light   D)   0.89 c, or 89% of the speed of light
    Ans: B   Section: 24-1 and Box 24-1

19. Suppose that a particular kind of subatomic particle lives on average for exactly 1.0 microsecond (1.0×10^{-6} s) before it decays, when this particle is created at rest in the laboratory. If a beam of such particles is created that travels at 97% of the speed of light as measured by a scientist standing beside the beam, what lifetime does the scientist measure for these particles?
    A)   4.1 microseconds   C)   16.9 microseconds
    B)   0.24 microsecond   D)   0.06 microsecond
    Ans: A   Section: 24-1 and Box 24-1

20. During a stop on Jupiter's satellite Europa to investigate a possible liquid ocean under the ice, you spot a spaceship passing Europa at 97% of the speed of light. While you see 2 seconds tick past on the spaceship's clock, how much time ticks by on your own clock?
    A) 8.2 seconds.   B) 33.8 seconds.   C) 0.12 seconds.   D) 0.48 seconds.
    Ans: A   Section: 24-1 and Box 24-1

21. During a stop on Jupiter's satellite Europa to investigate a possible liquid ocean under the ice, you spot a spaceship passing Europa at 97% of the speed of light. A person on the spaceship sees 2 seconds tick past on your clock. How much time does this person see elapse on the clock on board his spaceship?
    A) 0.48 seconds   B) 8.2 seconds   C) 33.8 seconds   D) 0.12 seconds
    Ans: B   Section: 24-1 and Box 24-1

22. To "spin up" the rotation of a neutron star, infalling material from the binary companion impacts the surface at half the speed of light. Suppose the infalling material includes radioactive particles with a half-life T_0 measured when the particle is at rest. What is the half-life of these particles measured by an observer on the neutron star?
    A) $0.5\, T_0$ B) $0.87\, T_0$ C) $1.15\, T_0$ D) $2\, T_0$
    Ans: C   Section: 24-1

23. A clock is moving across your line of sight with its face turned toward you. Each of the following statements about this clock, as seen by you, is true *except one*. Which statement is *incorrect*?
    A)   The clock will run slow compared to a clock in your hand.
    B)   The clock will appear shorter than it would if it were at rest.
    C)   The clock will appear thinner, front to back, than it would if it were at rest.
    D)   The clock will appear more dense than it would if it were at rest.
    Ans: C   Section: 24-1

24. Einstein's principle of equivalence in his general theory of relativity asserts that
    A)   the behavior of all types of atoms in a gravitational field is equivalent.
    B)   all objects are attracted toward all other objects in the universe by gravitational forces.
    C)   being at rest in a gravitational field is equivalent to being in an upwardly accelerated frame of reference in a gravity-free environment.
    D)   if person B is in a rapidly moving reference frame (moving at constant velocity), then person B will observe exactly the same effects for person A as person A observes for person B.
    Ans: C   Section: 24-1

25. Which is the correct sequence for the following end-points of stellar evolution, in order of increasing maximum mass?
    A)   neutron star, black hole, white dwarf   C)   black hole, neutron star, white dwarf
    B)   white dwarf, neutron star, black hole   D)   white dwarf, black hole, neutron star
    Ans: B   Section: 24-2

26. Which of the following objects does NOT represent the endpoint of a star's evolutionary life?
    A) black hole   B) neutron star   C) red giant   D) supernova
    Ans: C   Section: 24-2

27. In what way is the general theory of relativity more general (deals with more situations) than the special theory?
    A)   It includes accelerated motion but not gravitation.
    B)   It includes accelerated motion and gravitation.
    C)   It includes only constant, unaccelerated motion.
    D)   It includes only motion at the speed of light.
    Ans: B   Section: 24-2

28. Suppose a satellite were placed in orbit around (and very close to) a neutron star. Which theory would you need to use to describe how it moves?
    A)   Kepler's laws   C)   Newton's theory of gravitation
    B)   general theory of relativity   D)   special theory of relativity
    Ans: B   Section: 24-2

29. According to Einstein's general theory of relativity, a clock that ticks at a regular rate far from a source of gravity will appear to tick
    A)   at the same rate in a gravitational field if it is an atomic clock but at a slower rate if it is a mechanical clock.
    B)   at the same rate wherever it is placed in a gravitational field.
    C)   faster, the closer it comes to the source of gravity.
    D)   slower, the closer it comes to the source of gravity.
    Ans: D   Section: 24-2

30. According to Einstein's theory of general relativity, if you watch a clock from a distant location as it is moved closer to a source of gravity, you will see the clock
    A)   slow down.
    B)   run faster.
    C)   only change its rate if it is moving rapidly but maintain its standard rate if stationary in a gravity field.
    D)   maintain the same rate, because time is unaffected by gravity.
    Ans: A   Section: 24-2

31. How does a gravitational field affect the passage of time?
    A)   Gravity has no effect on the passage of time.
    B)   Clocks in a gravitational field run faster than clocks outside the field.
    C)   Gravity makes time stop.
    D)   Clocks in a gravitational field run slower than clocks outside the field.
    Ans: D   Section: 24-2

32. Suppose you are far from a planet that has a very strong gravitational field, and you are watching a clock on the surface of the planet. During the time in which your own clock ticks out a time of 1 hour, how much time does the clock on the planet tick out?
    A)   more than 1 hour
    B)   no time at all
    C)   exactly 1 hour, the same as your clock
    D)   less than 1 hour
    Ans: D   Section: 24-2

33. Suppose that, from a stationary spaceship, you identify a source of hydrogen (H_α) light on the surface of a planet that has a very strong gravitational field. When you observe an equivalent H_α light source on your spaceship, the wavelength is 656.3 nm. How long is the wavelength you measure when you look at the light source on the planet?
    A)   shorter than 656.3 nm
    B)   the same wavelength of 656.3 nm, but the frequency of the light appears lower
    C)   656.3 nm, the same as your light source, but the source appears very faint because the radiation has been weakened by the gravity field
    D)   longer than 656.3 nm
    Ans: D   Section: 24-2

34. Light traveling away from the surface of a neutron star becomes strongly redshifted. What name is given to this effect?
    A)   cosmological redshift   C)   Zeeman effect
    B)   Doppler shift   D)   gravitational redshift
    Ans: D   Section: 24-2

35. Spectral lines detected from the surfaces of white dwarf stars are slightly redshifted with respect to the equivalent spectral absorption lines in the laboratory. Why is this?
    A)   The rapid rotation of these stars produces a redshift of light from atoms on their surfaces.
    B)   The extremely high temperature of the star surface affects the atomic energy levels and therefore the spectral lines produced by the atoms.
    C)   The steady shrinkage of white dwarf stars as they evolve is reflected in Doppler redshift of the surface spectrum.
    D)   Photons are gravitationally redshifted by the intense gravity field of the star.
    Ans: D   Section: 24-2

36. What happens to the wavelength of light as it travels outward through the gravitational field of a planet, a star, or other massive object?
    A)   It stays the same but the intensity of the light decreases.
    B)   It stays the same but the energy of each photon decreases.
    C)   It decreases.
    D)   It increases.
    Ans: D   Section: 24-2

37. According to Newton's law of gravity, why does the Earth orbit the Sun?
    A) Matter contains quarks, and the Earth and Sun attract each other with the "color force" between their quarks.
    B) Space around the Sun is curved.
    C) The Earth and the Sun are continually exchanging photons of light in a way that holds the Earth in orbit.
    D) The Sun exerts a gravitational force on the Earth across empty space.
    Ans: D   Section: 24-2

38. According to general relativity, why does the Earth orbit the Sun?
    A) Space around the Sun is curved and the Earth follows this curved space.
    B) The Sun exerts a gravitational force on the Earth across empty space.
    C) Matter contains quarks, and the Earth and Sun attract each other with the "color force" between their quarks.
    D) The Earth and the Sun are continually exchanging photons of light in a way that holds the Earth in orbit.
    Ans: A   Section: 24-2

39. What is the correct explanation of the bending of a beam of light as it passes close to a massive object like the Sun?
    A) The gravitational field interacts with the electromagnetic field of the photons to bend the light.
    B) It is traveling across and must follow the curved space surrounding a massive object.
    C) The gravitational field of the massive object changes the refractive index of the nearby space, leading to bending of the light.
    D) The photons of light are attracted by the gravitational field of the massive object.
    Ans: B   Section: 24-2

40. Which of the following is NOT a test of general relativity but rather a test of special relativity?
    A) Light travels in a curved path in a gravitational field.
    B) The wavelength of light increases as it leaves a region of stronger gravitational field.
    C) The length of a moving object decreases when observed by a stationary observer.
    D) The perihelion position of Mercury precesses more quickly than is predicted by Newtonian theory.
    Ans: C   Section: 24-2

41. A black hole is so named because
    A)   the gravitational field is so high that the wavelength of its emitted light is shifted into the infrared and radio regions of the spectrum.
    B)   it emits no visible light because it is so cold, its energy being held in an intense gravity field.
    C)   its spectrum has the same shape as that of a laboratory blackbody at a temperature of about 1000 K.
    D)   no light can escape from it on account of its powerful gravitational field.
    Ans: D   Section: 24-2

42. Black holes are so named because
    A)   they emit a perfect blackbody spectrum.
    B)   no light or any other electromagnetic radiation can escape from inside them.
    C)   all their electromagnetic radiation is gravitationally redshifted to the infrared, leaving no light in the optical region.
    D)   they emit no visible light, their only spectral lines being in the radio and infrared.
    Ans: B   Section: 24-2

43. Why are black holes called black holes?
    A)   Nothing, not even electromagnetic radiation, can escape from inside them.
    B)   Only nonvisible radiation longer than about 1,000 nm wavelength (infrared and radio radiation) can escape from them.
    C)   They are always surrounded by an accretion disk which absorbs all light escaping from the inside of the black hole.
    D)   They emit an electromagnetic spectrum which matches that of a perfect blackbody.
    Ans: A   Section: 24-2

44. What is the likely final fate of a star that has a mass of 15 solar masses after completing its nuclear fusion burning phases?
    A)   It undergoes fission and immediately splits into two to become a binary star system.
    B)   The degeneracy of the electrons within the star prevents collapse beyond the diameter of a white dwarf.
    C)   It condenses to the point where it is composed completely of neutrons, the degeneracy of which prevents further shrinkage.
    D)   It collapses and becomes a black hole.
    Ans: D   Section: 24-2 and 23-9

45. Suppose that a neutron star of 2.8 solar masses is part of a binary star system in which the other star is a normal giant star. What would happen if half a solar mass of material were transferred onto the neutron star from its companion?
    A)   The neutron star would collapse and become a black hole.
    B)   The increased gravitational force would transform the neutrons into quarks, and the neutron star would re-establish equilibrium as a quark star of smaller diameter.
    C)   The neutron degeneracy pressure inside the neutron star would increase to balance the increased gravitational force within the neutron star.
    D)   The neutron star would explode as a supernova.
    Ans: A   Section: 24-2

46. A black hole can be thought of as
    A)   strongly curved space.
    B)   a star with a temperature of 0 K, emitting no light.
    C)   the point at the center of every star, providing the star's energy by gravitational collapse.
    D)   densely packed matter inside a small but finite volume.
    Ans: A   Section: 24-2

47. What would happen to the gravitational force on the Earth if the Sun were to be replaced by a 1-solar-mass black hole?
    A)   It would become extremely high, sufficient to pull the Earth into it.
    B)   It would double in strength.
    C)   It would be much less, because the gravitational field of a black hole exists only very close to it.
    D)   It would remain as it is now.
    Ans: D   Section: 24-2

48. If the Sun were replaced by a 1-solar-mass black hole, then the Earth would
    A)   continue to orbit the black hole in precisely its present orbit.
    B)   move into an elliptical orbit passing close to the black hole, with its farthest distance from the black hole equal to 1 AU.
    C)   spiral quickly into the black hole.
    D)   head off into interstellar space along a straight line at a tangent to its original orbit around the Sun.
    Ans: A   Section: 24-2

49. What prevents a neutron star from collapsing and becoming a black hole?
    A) Gravity in the neutron star is balanced by an outward force due to neutron degeneracy.
    B) Neutron stars are held up by the centrifugal force due to their rapid rotation.
    C) Neutron stars are solid, and like other solid spheres they are held up by the repulsive force between atoms in the solid.
    D) Gravity in the neutron star is balanced by an outward force due to gas pressure, as in the Sun.
    Ans: A   Section: 24-2

50. What is believed to be the maximum mass for a neutron star?
    A)   150 solar masses   C)   3 solar masses
    B)   12 solar masses   D)   1.4 solar mass
    Ans: C   Section: 24-2

51. The gravitational redshift of light leaving the surface of Sirius B is $\Delta\lambda/\lambda = 3.0 \times 10^{-4}$. What velocity of Sirius B (relative to the Earth) would be needed to produce an equivalent Doppler shift?
    A)   90 km/sec away from Earth   C)   300 km/sec away from Earth
    B)   90 km/sec toward Earth   D)   300 km/sec toward Earth
    Ans: A   Section: 24-2 and Box 5-6

52. In a binary star system, an unseen component is found to have a mass of about 8 solar masses. If this were a normal star, then it would be visible, so it must be a collapsed object. Theoretical considerations tell us that it must be
    A) a white dwarf.   B) a black hole.   C) a neutron star.   D) a brown dwarf.
    Ans: B   Section: 24-3

53. What method is used by astronomers to infer the existence in space of a dark object with a mass of about 5 solar masses such as a black hole?
    A) The measurement of the effect of its gravitational force on a companion object in a binary system.
    B) The measurement of the gravitational redshift of spectral lines in the spectrum of the object.
    C) The estimation of the luminosity of the object and the application of the mass-luminosity relationship.
    D) The photography or imaging of a region from which no light or radiation at all appears to come.
    Ans: A   Section: 24-3

54. Which effect has been useful (and successful) in the search for and identification of black holes in the universe?
    A)   their magnetic fields and their influence on nearby matter.
    B)   the effect of their angular momentum or spin on nearby matter.
    C)   the influence of their intense gravitational field on atoms and molecules that are emitting light from the event horizons of the black holes.
    D)   their gravitational influence on nearby matter, particularly companion stars.
    Ans: D   Section: 24-3

55. X rays that come from the vicinity of a black hole actually originate from
    A)   well inside the event horizon.
    B)   its exact center, or singularity.
    C)   relatively far away from the black hole, where matter is still relatively cool.
    D)   just outside the event horizon, on the accretion disk.
    Ans: D   Section: 24-3

56. If a black hole is truly black and has an escape velocity greater than the speed of light such that no light can escape it, where do the X rays come from in the black hole candidates so far identified?
    A)   from stars behind the black hole, whose light is focused and concentrated by gravitational focusing to the point where it becomes X-ray radiation.
    B)   The black hole is only black to visible radiation traveling at the speed of light, but because X rays travel faster than the speed of light, they can escape.
    C)   from the normal star accompanying the black hole, its ordinary light being blueshifted into the X-ray spectral region by the intense gravity of the black hole.
    D)   from the matter surrounding the black hole, which is highly condensed and hence very hot because of the intense gravitational field.
    Ans: D   Section: 24-3

57. At first it was always thought that nothing could escape from a black hole, yet astronomers are locating black hole candidates by the X rays they emit. Why do they see X rays coming from a black hole?
    A)   The X rays come from highly compressed matter in the accretion disk outside the event horizon of the black hole.
    B)   The black hole modifies spacetime around it so much that particles and X rays are created in the vacuum itself, just outside the event horizon.
    C)   The X rays are produced by vibrations of the black hole itself, and therefore they come from the event horizon, and not from inside the black hole.
    D)   X rays are not light or matter, therefore they can escape from inside the black hole.
    Ans: A   Section: 24-3

58. The intense X rays emitted by a suspected black hole are generated by what physical mechanism?
    A)   the deceleration of matter as it abruptly stops at the event horizon of the black hole
    B)   frictional and compressional heating as material moves into the hole
    C)   Light emitted by hot gas is extremely blueshifted to become X rays by the motion of the gas into the black hole.
    D)   excitation of atoms and molecules by the extreme gravitational field of the hole
    Ans: B   Section: 24-3

59. One object that is believed to be a black hole in our galaxy is
    A)   the central star in the Ring Nebula in Lyra.
    B)   the central star in the Crab Nebula.
    C)   the undetected tenth planet in our solar system, whose presence has been inferred from its gravitational influence on the outer planets.
    D)   Cygnus X-1, a powerful X-ray source.
    Ans: D   Section: 24-3

60. The first black hole candidate, Cygnus X-1, was discovered while astronomers were using the
    A)   Uhuru X-ray satellite.
    B)   VLA radio interferometric array in New Mexico.
    C)   IRAS infrared satellite.
    D)   Hubble Space Telescope.
    Ans: A   Section: 24-3

61. How has mass of the black hole candidate Cygnus X-1 been estimated?
    A)   from the periodic wobble in its own X-ray spectrum
    B)   from the observed size and estimated density of the object
    C)   from the periodic wobble it produces in the spectral lines of its normal companion star
    D)   from the gravitational redshift, where the more massive the object, the greater the redshift of its spectral lines
    Ans: C   Section: 24-3

62. What is believed to be the mass of the black hole candidate Cygnus X-1?
    A)   30 solar masses   C)   7 solar masses
    B)   1 billion solar masses   D)   1 solar mass
    Ans: C   Section: 24-3

63. Probably the best candidate for a black hole in a binary star system at the present time, based on the accuracy of measuring its mass, is (see Freedman and Kaufmann, *Universe,* 7th ed., Chapter 24)
    A) A0620-00.   B) LMC X-3.   C) Cygnus X-1.   D) HDE 226868.
    Ans: A   Section: 24-3

64. Why is Cygnus X-1 thought to be a black hole?
    A)   It has pulled matter from its companion star into an accretion disk around itself.
    B)   No light has ever been observed to come from it.
    C)   It emits X rays that flicker on time scales of a hundredth of a second.
    D)   It is physically smaller than the Earth, but its mass is too large to be a neutron star or white dwarf.
    Ans: D   Section: 24-3

65. The X-ray source Cygnus X-1 is a black hole candidate located in a binary star system. The X-ray source is believed to occupy a volume smaller than the Earth. This size is deduced from
    A)   its luminosity and spectral class.
    B)   the shortness of its orbital period.
    C)   the short time period of the rapid flickering in its X-ray brightness.
    D)   its distance from the Earth and the angle it subtends in the sky.
    Ans: C   Section: 24-3

66. The diameter of the black hole candidate Cygnus X-1 has been estimated by
    A)   combining the amount of energy received at the Earth per second with the distance to the source to estimate the total energy emitted per second.
    B)   measuring how quickly it flickers in intensity.
    C)   measuring how long it takes to block off the light from its companion star during an eclipse (i.e., as it passes in front of its companion star as seen from the Earth).
    D)   combining its distance with its angular diameter to find its physical size.
    Ans: B   Section: 24-3

67. If an astronomical source of electromagnetic radiation is observed to flicker, with intensity changes in as short a time as 1/30 second, how large is the emitting region?
    A)   10,000 km, a little smaller than the Earth
    B)   1/30 light-year
    C) 9×10^6 km, about 6 times the size of the Sun
    D)   10,000 m, about the size of a small city or town
    Ans: A   Section: 24-3

68. Which of the following would NOT be considered a possible mechanism for the production of a black hole with a mass of a few solar masses?
    A)   coalescence of a binary pair of dead stars which spiral into one another after losing rotational energy as gravitational radiation
    B)   slow gravitational condensation of a massive gas cloud
    C)   accretion of mass onto a white dwarf or neutron star from the companion star in a binary star system
    D)   one member of a binary star exploding as a type II supernova, leaving a black hole
    Ans: B   Section: 24-3

69. A flickering signal is received from a source the size of the Sun. What frequencies are possible for this flicker?
    A)   any frequency at all depending on the source mechanism
    B)   0.21 cycles per second or more
    C)   0.21 cycles per second or less
    D)   0.42 cycles per second or more.
    Ans: C   Section: 24-3

70. Pairs of jets carrying material and radiation outward in opposite directions have been detected (or inferred) for each of the following types of objects *except one*. Which is the exception?
    A)   stellar mass black hole candidates   C)   protostars
    B)   supermassive black hole candidates   D)   white dwarfs
    Ans: D   Section: 24-3, 24-4, 20-5

71. Evidence for the existence of supermassive black holes has now been found
    A)   in every known galaxy.
    B)   nowhere in our observable universe, though the existence of such black holes has been predicted by theory.
    C)   in several dozen galaxies.
    D)   in only one galaxy, our own Milky Way galaxy.
    Ans: C   Section: 24-4

72. The existence of supermassive black holes in the centers of many galaxies has been inferred by what definitive measurement?
    A)   the measurement of extremely dark regions of space in the centers of galaxies, from which no radiation is seen
    B)   measurement of very rapid orbital motion of objects around a very massive central object
    C)   bending of light from stars on the far sides of galaxies by a very massive central object, as seen from Earth
    D)   detection of very specific electromagnetic emissions predicted by theory to be emitted by a massive black hole
    Ans: B   Section: 24-4

73. What is believed to be the mass of the black hole candidate at the center of the galaxy NGC 4261?
    A) 120 $M_\odot$ B) 120,000 $M_\odot$ C) 1.2 million $M_\odot$ D) 1.2 billion $M_\odot$
    Ans: B   Section: 24-4

74. The mass of the candidate black hole at the center of the galaxy NGC 4261 was estimated from the
    A) application of Kepler's laws to the orbital speed of objects close to this center.
    B) intensity of X rays from it and the speed at which the X rays flicker.
    C) amount of mass that is disappearing into it per year.
    D) periodic shift in the wavelengths of spectral lines from a companion object around which the black hole is orbiting.
    Ans: A   Section: 24-4

75. Where would you look for a supermassive black hole?
    A) in an orbit around a normal star in our galaxy
    B) at the center of the universe
    C) at the center of a supernova remnant
    D) in the center of a galaxy
    Ans: D   Section: 24-4

76. A primordial black hole is a black hole
    A) created during the formation of the universe.
    B) not in orbit around a normal star.
    C) created during the formation of the solar system.
    D) at the center of a galaxy.
    Ans: A   Section: 24-4

77. What name is given to any black hole that was created in the Big Bang (the creation of the universe)?
    A) supermassive black hole   C) primordial black hole
    B) original black hole   D) primeval black hole
    Ans: C   Section: 24-4

78. What separates a black hole from the rest of our universe?
    A) its event horizon   C) a crystalline crust
    B) the surface of its ergosphere   D) a singularity
    Ans: A   Section: 24-5

79. Where would you look for an event horizon?
    A) at the edge of the visible universe
    B) at the photosphere of a star (e.g., the Sun)
    C) around a black hole
    D) in the magnetosphere of a neutron star
    Ans: C   Section: 24-5

80. What is the event horizon of a black hole?
    A)   the "surface" from the inside of which nothing can escape
    B)   the "surface" at which all "events" or activity appear to happen because of general relativity
    C)   the infinitesimally small volume at the center of the black hole that contains all of the black hole's mass
    D)   the "surface" inside which any object entering will leave with greater energy than that with which it entered
    Ans: A   Section: 24-5

81. What is actually located at the event horizon of a black hole, to define this entity?
    A)   an infinitely dense concentration of mass
    B)   a magnetic field of immense strength
    C)   a sphere of photons
    D)   nothing
    Ans: D   Section: 24-5

82. At what location in the space around a black hole does the escape velocity become equal to the speed of light?
    A)   at the point where escaping X rays are produced
    B)   at the point where clocks are observed to slow down by a factor of 2
    C)   at the event horizon
    D)   at the singularity
    Ans: C   Section: 24-5

83. The escape velocity for any object at the event horizon around a black hole is
    A)   not quite but almost the speed of light.
    B)   much less than the speed of light.
    C)   infinite.
    D)   equal to the speed of light.
    Ans: D   Section: 24-5

84. What feature distinguishes a black hole from all other objects in the universe?
    A)   It emits large quantities of X rays.
    B)   The escape velocity from this object is greater than the speed of light.
    C)   The shape of its gravitational field is always different from that of an ordinary massive object, even at large distances from it.
    D)   Its total mass exceeds 3 solar masses.
    Ans: B   Section: 24-5

85. The escape velocity of matter from the center of a black hole whose mass is 3 solar masses is
    A)   quite small.   C)   exactly equal to the speed of light.
    B)   much greater than the speed of light.   D)   about half the speed of light.
    Ans: B   Section: 24-5

86. The only parts of a non-rotating black hole that are necessary for its complete description are
    A) the escape velocity of matter and the diameter of its core.
    B) its center, or singularity, and its "surface" or event horizon.
    C) the gravitational field and the curvature of space at its center.
    D) its semimajor axis and its orbital eccentricity.
    Ans: B   Section: 24-5

87. The event horizon of a non-rotating black hole is located at the
    A) distance of a Schwarzschild radius from its center
    B) outer surface of the ergosphere.
    C) position of maximum X-ray emission
    D) singularity at its center
    Ans: A   Section: 24-5

88. What is the Schwarzschild radius of a black hole?
    A) the radius of the singularity
    B) the distance from the singularity to the point from which the X rays are emitted
    C) the maximum distance from the singularity from which nothing can escape from the black hole
    D) the distance from the singularity to the point where any object entering the black hole will gain energy before leaving again
    Ans: C   Section: 24-5

89. The Schwarzschild radius of a black hole is the distance from the singularity (center) to
    A) the point where the gravitational field becomes zero.
    B) the event horizon, from which light cannot escape.
    C) the outside radius of the massive solid body forming the black hole.
    D) the accretion disk, from which X rays originate and from which light can still escape.
    Ans: B   Section: 24-5

90. The words "Schwarzschild radius" refer to
    A) the distance to which gas is ejected in a planetary nebula.
    B) half the diameter of a neutron star.
    C) half the diameter of the singularity in a black hole.
    D) the distance from the center of a black hole at which the escape velocity becomes equal to the speed of light.
    Ans: D   Section: 24-5

91. The radius of the event horizon of a black hole, the Schwarzchild radius,
    A)   is constant, because the general theory of relativity states that the size of a black hole is independent of its mass.
    B)   is smaller, the more massive the black hole, because the matter will be more condensed.
    C)   will not depend on its mass but will depend on the material from which it was formed, a "hydrogen" black hole being smaller than an "iron" black hole.
    D)   is larger, the more massive the black hole.
    Ans: D   Section: 24-5

92. How does the diameter of a black hole (size of the event horizon) depend on the mass inside the black hole?
    A)   The greater the mass, the smaller the diameter.
    B)   The greater the mass, the greater the diameter up to the mass limit for a black hole; above that mass the black hole collapses.
    C)   The diameter does not depend on the mass.
    D)   The greater the mass, the greater the diameter.
    Ans: D   Section: 24-5 and Box 24-2

93. What is the Schwarzschild radius of a 2-solar-mass black hole?
    A) 6000 km   B) 6 m   C) 60 km   D) 6 km
    Ans: D   Section: 24-5 and Box 24-2

94. If the Schwarzschild radius of a 2-solar-mass black hole is 6 km, what is it for a 5-solar-mass black hole?
    A) 150 km   B) 15 m   C) 15,000 km   D) 15 km
    Ans: D   Section: 24-5 and Box 24-2

95. What happens to the Schwarzschild radius of a black hole if you double its mass?
    A)   The Schwarzschild radius is doubled.
    B)   The Schwarzschild radius is quadrupled (4 times).
    C)   The Schwarzschild radius decreases to 1/4 the size.
    D)   The Schwarzschild radius is halved.
    Ans: A   Section: 24-5 and Box 24-2

96. What happens to the radius of the event horizon of a black hole if you triple its mass?
    A)   It decreases to 1/3 the size.   C)   It decreases to 1/9 the size.
    B)   It becomes 3 times bigger.   D)   It becomes 9 times bigger.
    Ans: B   Section: 24-5 and Box 24-2

97. What is a singularity?
    A)   any point at the Schwarzschild radius from a black hole
    B)   a point of infinite density
    C)   a particle-antiparticle pair
    D)   a tunnel into another universe
    Ans: B   Section: 24-5

98. In reference to black holes, a singularity is
    A)   the name given to a hot-spot emitting X rays just beyond the event horizon
    B)   a place just outside the event horizon of a rotating black hole, where it is
          impossible to remain at rest
    C)   a place where a non-zero mass occupies zero volume.
    D)   a place where the escape velocity equals the speed of light
    Ans: C   Section: 24-5

99. What is the law of cosmic censorship?
    A)   No astronomer shall criticize the Galactic Empire.
    B)   Black holes have no hair; nothing can remain for more than a fraction of a second
          just outside the event horizon of a black hole.
    C)   Information entering a black hole is lost forever from our universe.
    D)   There can be no naked singularities; every black hole must be surrounded by an
          event horizon.
    Ans: D   Section: 24-5

100. Which of the following statements correctly describes "cosmic censorship"?
     A)   It is not possible to measure both the mass and the electric charge of a black hole
           with unlimited precision; if our knowledge of one increases, then our knowledge
           of the other decreases.
     B)   The only way into or out of a singularity is through an event horizon.
     C)   Black holes cannot have magnetic fields.
     D)   It is not possible to measure any property of a black hole other than its mass, its
           electric charge, and its spin.
     Ans: B   Section: 24-5

101. The supermassive black hole candidate in the center of the galaxy NGC 4261 is
     estimated to have a mass of 1.2×10^9 M$_\odot$. What is the Schwarzschild Radius of such a
     black hole?
     A) 1.6×10^9 m, a little larger than the Sun
     B)   24 AU, a little larger than Jupiter's orbit
     C)   0.95 pc, more than half the distance to the nearest star
     D)   1600 pc, about one-tenth of the way across our galaxy
     Ans: B   Section: 24-5

102. Suppose you discover a naked singularity without its surrounding event horizon. What effect would such an object have on the neighboring region of space?
    A)   The "black hole" would no longer be black and would probably be very bright.
    B)   Without the shielding effect of the event horizon, the black hole's gravity would begin pulling in stars and, indeed, whole galaxies to merge with it.
    C)   The singularity would probably be spinning rapidly, because any infalling material from the accretion disk would now reach the singularity after a short journey.
    D)   The effects of a naked singularity are completely unpredictable.
    Ans: D   Section: 24-5

103. How many properties of the matter inside a black hole can be measured from outside the black hole?
    A) 4   B) only 1   C) 3   D) 6
    Ans: C   Section: 24-6

104. Which of the following can you never know about a black hole?
    A)   the total amount of matter (the mass) inside it
    B)   the type of material inside it
    C)   its angular momentum (spin)
    D)   its net electric charge
    Ans: B   Section: 24-6

105. The only physical properties necessary to describe a black hole and its interaction with the rest of the universe completely are
    A)   its mass, the chemical or atomic structure of the matter within it, and its overall size.
    B)   its mass, its angular momentum or spin, and its temperature.
    C)   its mass, its electric charge, and its angular momentum or spin.
    D)   the size of its event horizon, the strength of its magnetic field, and the size of its solid core.
    Ans: C   Section: 24-6

106. Which properties of the matter inside a black hole can be measured from outside the black hole?
    A)   mass, electric charge, angular momentum, and average atomic weight.
    B)   only the mass
    C)   mass and angular momentum
    D)   mass, electric charge, and angular momentum
    Ans: D   Section: 24-6

107. Take two identical, nonrotating, 5-solar-mass black holes and place them side by side. Add one solar mass of pineapples to the left-hand one and one solar mass of radioactive uranium to the right-hand one (without changing their electric charge or their rotation). Afterward, how do these two black holes differ?
    A)   The left-hand one will smell better.
    B)   The right-hand one is radioactive, emitting alpha particles, electrons, and gamma rays.
    C)   The right-hand one has a stronger gravitational field because of the denser matter inside it.
    D)   They do not differ at all.
    Ans: D   Section: 24-6

108. Take two identical, nonrotating, 5-solar-mass black holes and place them side by side. Add one solar mass of neutrons to the left-hand one and one solar mass of protons to the right-hand one (without changing the rotation of the black holes). Afterward, how do these two black holes differ?
    A)   They will not differ at all.
    B)   The left-hand one has a stronger gravitational field because a neutron is heavier than a proton.
    C)   The light particles, electrons and neutrinos, from the decay of the neutrons into protons escape from the left-hand one.
    D)   The left-hand one is electrically neutral and the right-hand one will have an enormous electric charge.
    Ans: D   Section: 24-6

109. Black holes cannot possess magnetic fields because
    A)   black holes cannot spin.
    B)   any magnetic field would have been radiated away during the collapse.
    C)   black holes cannot contain moving electric charges.
    D)   the original object could not have collapsed to form a black hole if it had any magnetic field.
    Ans: B   Section: 24-6

110. What happens to the magnetic field of a star that collapses to become a black hole?
    A)   The magnetic field is radiated away; black holes can never have magnetic fields.
    B)   The magnetic field becomes compressed and intensified by a factor equal to the ratio of the star's original diameter to the diameter of the event horizon.
    C)   The magnetic field becomes infinite.
    D)   The magnetic field becomes weaker by a factor equal to the ratio of the star's original diameter to the diameter of the event horizon.
    Ans: A   Section: 24-6

111. In reference to black holes, the word "ergosphere" refers to
    A) the entire universe outside the black hole.
    B) the entire region inside the event horizon.
    C) a region just outside the event horizon of a rotating black hole, where it is impossible for anything to remain at rest.
    D) the region occupied by the accretion disk, where matter from a companion star collects around a black hole.
    Ans: C   Section: 24-6

112. How do rotating black holes DIFFER from nonrotating black holes?
    A) Rotating black holes have a region just inside the event horizon in which nothing can be at rest.
    B) Rotating black holes have a region just outside the event horizon in which nothing can be at rest.
    C) Rotating black holes have a magnetic field due to the spin of electrically charged matter.
    D) Not at all—the only property that distinguishes one black hole from another is mass, not spin.
    Ans: B   Section: 24-6

113. Which of the following properties of a massive rotating star will be enhanced if the star collapses into a black hole?
    A) the intensity of light emitted by it   C) electric charge
    B) angular rotation speed   D) mass
    Ans: B   Section: 24-6

114. One day, while straying dangerously close to a black hole, you notice that you must keep your spaceship moving; no matter how hard you try to remain at rest you are inevitably drawn into the black hole unless you keep moving. What does this tell you about this specific black hole (other than that it is something that you should leave)?
    A) It is rotating.   C) It has an off-axis magnetic field.
    B) It is a naked singularity.   D) It is electrically charged.
    Ans: A   Section: 24-6

115. One consequence of the no-hair theorem ("Black holes have no hair") is that
    A) matter that falls into a black hole does not retain any measurable properties at all, when observed by an outside observer.
    B) matter that falls into a black hole retains no properties except its mass, as measured by an outside observer.
    C) certain kinds and shapes of matter (i.e., long strings) cannot fall into a black hole.
    D) matter that falls into a black hole does not retain any properties except its mass, spin, and electric charge, as measured by an outside observer.
    Ans: D   Section: 24-6

116. How many fundamentally different types of black holes would you expect there to be?
    A)   three: those with mass, those with angular momentum, and those with electric charge
    B)   two: those that rotate and those that don't
    C)   two: those that have mass and those that don't
    D)   one: all identifying properties of matter are destroyed when a black hole is created
    Ans: B   Section: 24-6

117. Suppose that a large piece (e.g., 5 solar masses) of purple, magnetized iron is rotating five times per day. If this object were able to collapse gravitationally to form a black hole, which one of the following properties could an outside observer measure for the matter inside the black hole?
    A) magnetic field   B) color   C) rotation   D) composition
    Ans: C   Section: 24-6

118. The matter in an accretion disk is in orbit around a black hole, but friction within the disk causes the matter to spiral slowly into the black hole. What will change in terms of the observable properties of the black hole as this process continues?
    A)   Both the mass and the angular momentum of the black hole will increase.
    B)   The mass, the angular momentum, and the diameter of the singularity will increase.
    C)   Only the mass will increase.
    D)   Nothing will change.
    Ans: A   Section: 24-6

119. The opening illustration of Chapter 24 (Freedman and Kaufmann, *Universe*, 7th ed.) depicts a rotating black hole with an accretion disk. Magnetic field lines connect the black hole with the disk. What, if anything, can be transferred between the rotating black hole and its accretion disk?
    A)   Particles and energy can be transferred, but only from the disk to the black hole, never from the hole to the disk.
    B)   Particles and energy can be transferred in either direction.
    C)   Rotational energy and angular momentum can be transferred from the black hole to the accretion disk.
    D)   Nothing can be transferred in either direction.
    Ans: C   Section: 24-6

120. You guide your spacecraft into an orbit a few AU from a black hole. You know its mass is four or five solar masses, but you want to measure it more precisely. How would you do this?
    A)   Actually, the mass of a black hole cannot be determined precisely because it is impossible to see beyond the event horizon. So your estimate of four or five solar masses is as good a value as you can hope for.
    B)   You can measure the period and the semimajor axis of your orbit and then use Newton's form of Kepler's Third Law.
    C)   You cannot use Newton's form of the Third Law. Because of General Relativity, you must use a relativistic form of Kepler's Third Law.
    D)   You must move in toward the black hole and mark the distance as you cross the event horizon. From this distance the mass can be calculated.
    Ans: B   Section: 24-6

121. If you were to enter the event horizon of a black hole,
    A)   you could, with a powerful rocket, move outward within the black hole (thereby avoiding the singularity until your fuel ran out), but you could never escape back out through the event horizon.
    B)   there would be nothing you could do to prevent yourself from falling directly into the singularity at the center.
    C)   you could escape again provided that the black hole was spinning.
    D)   you could avoid the singularity by going into orbit around it, but you could never move outward again from any particular orbit.
    Ans: B   Section: 24-6

122. What appears to happen to a clock as it approaches and reaches the event horizon around a black hole, when viewed by a remote observer?
    A)   It speeds up because of the intensified gravitational field.
    B)   It appears to slow down and stop.
    C)   Time appears to pass at a much faster rate, the rate becoming infinitely fast at the event horizon.
    D)   It ticks uniformly, because nothing changes the progress of time.
    Ans: B   Section: 24-7

123. A space freighter accidentally drops a steel beam while passing a black hole, and the beam starts falling toward the black hole with the long axis of the beam pointing toward the black hole. What happens to the beam as it approaches the event horizon?
    A)   It begins to rotate faster and faster.
    B)   It is stretched in length.
    C)   Nothing happens to its length or rotation; it simply falls faster and faster.
    D)   It is compressed in length.
    Ans: B   Section: 24-7

124. Suppose it were possible to lower a yellow sodium lamp slowly toward the event horizon of a black hole. What would you see while watching from a safe distance?
    A)   The light from the lamp would change from yellow to green and then to blue.
    B)   The light from the lamp would remain unchanged because the lamp is moving slowly.
    C)   The light from the lamp would remain yellow, but the lamp would emit increasingly less light.
    D)   The light from the lamp would change from yellow to orange and then to red.
    Ans: D   Section: 24-7

125. As you are investigating a black hole from a safe distance, a rivet pops out of the tailfin of your spaceship and falls toward the black hole. Will you ever see the rivet enter the event horizon?
    A)   No, it will be compressed to zero size and disappear from sight before it reaches the event horizon.
    B)   No, it will appear to stop and hover forever just above the event horizon.
    C)   Yes, but light from it will be so blueshifted that you would need X-ray eyes to see it.
    D)   Yes, you will see it fall faster and faster until it disappears as it falls through the event horizon.
    Ans: B   Section: 24-7

126. A laborer repairing the clock tower on a space station orbiting a black hole accidentally drops the clock in such a way that it accelerates toward the black hole. What does this person see while watching the clock?
    A)   The hands of the clock move slower and slower until they stop moving as the clock appears to come to a stop at the event horizon.
    B)   The hands of the clock move faster and faster until the clock disappears as it plunges through the event horizon.
    C)   The hands of the clock keep normal time, because time is absolute and the same everywhere.
    D)   As the clock nears the event horizon, the hands begin to move randomly as time becomes jumbled near the black hole.
    Ans: A   Section: 24-7

127. If you were watching a friend (or better still, an enemy!) who has fallen as far as the event horizon of a black hole, what would you measure as his heartbeat (apart from effects caused by his adrenaline level)?
    A)   It would appear to be normal because gravity has no effect on time intervals.
    B)   It would appear to have slowed down somewhat, but not much, because of the change of the speed of light in the gravity field.
    C)   It would appear to be zero, his heart would appear to have stopped.
    D)   It would appear to have speeded up to an incredible rate.
    Ans: C   Section: 24-7

128. In terms of black holes, what is a wormhole?
    A) a direct connection from a black hole to another part of spacetime
    B) a long, thin black hole known as a "string," created by unstable electric fields within the black hole
    C) a hole through a solid object, such as a planet, created by the passage of a small black hole through the object
    D) a "tunnel" of undistorted space through an event horizon allowing objects to enter and leave a black hole without being torn apart
    Ans: A   Section: 24-7

129. Which statement describing wormholes is correct?
    A) A wormhole connects one black hole to a second black hole when the two form a binary pair.
    B) A wormhole connects our universe with another universe.
    C) Because wormholes, once established, are permanent, a wormhole could be used as a time travel machine.
    D) A wormhole, once established, collapses almost immediately.
    Ans: D   Section: 24-7

130. A light wave is emitted from the accretion disk surrounding a black hole and moves toward the hole and away from an observer. This observer will see
    A) the beam of light moving faster than c as it accelerates toward the hole.
    B) the beam of light slow down and stop as it reaches the event horizon.
    C) that the wavelength of the light is gravitationally blueshifted and Doppler redshifted, and the two effects just cancel as the light reaches the event horizon.
    D) that the wavelength of the light is gravitationally blueshifted as it falls toward the event horizon.
    Ans: D   Section: 24-7 and 24-2

131. A virtual particle is a particle
    A) whose time of existence is too short for us to know that this particle ever existed.
    B) that never does anything wrong.
    C) that, if it comes in contact with ordinary matter, will be annihilated to form pure energy.
    D) like a photon or a graviton that is made up of waves.
    Ans: A   Section: 24-8

132. Sometimes particle-antiparticle pairs are created and then annihilate so quickly that we cannot know that they ever existed. What are these particles (or antiparticles) called?
    A) relativistic particles   C) field particles
    B) temporary particles   D) virtual particles
    Ans: D   Section: 24-8

133. If nothing can ever leave a black hole, can the mass of a black hole ever decrease?
    A)   No.
    B)   Yes, if antiparticles enter a black hole and annihilate with matter already inside the black hole.
    C)   Yes, if the matter inside the black hole is radioactive (e.g., uranium), because then alpha particles, electrons, and gamma rays are constantly leaving the black hole.
    D)   Yes, if particle-antiparticle pairs are created outside the event horizon and one particle enters the event horizon while the other escapes.
    Ans: D   Section: 24-8

134. Black holes with which of the following masses are most likely to have evaporated within the lifetime of our universe?
    A)   supermassive, similar to those at the centers of galaxies
    B)   very low mass, about that of Mount Everest
    C)   low mass, about that of the Earth
    D)   the mass of a star, about 5 solar masses
    Ans: B   Section: 24-8

135. Which one of the following statements about the evaporation of black holes is correct?
    A)   The rate at which a black hole evaporates is higher for a lower-mass black hole.
    B)   The rate at which a black hole evaporates is higher for a higher-mass black hole.
    C)   Black holes do not evaporate.
    D)   The rate at which a black hole evaporates is independent of the mass of the black hole.
    Ans: A   Section: 24-8

136. How are antiparticles and virtual particles related?
    A)   All antiparticles are virtual particles.
    B)   All virtual particles are antiparticles.
    C)   All virtual particle pairs include a particle and its antiparticle.
    D)   All particle–antiparticle pairs are virtual pairs.
    Ans: C   Section: 24-8

Chapter 25: Our Galaxy

1. Who was the first to look at the Milky Way with a telescope?
   A)   Johannes Kepler   C)   Sir Isaac Newton
   B)   Sir William Herschel   D)   Galileo Galilei
   Ans: D   Section: Introductory

2. Why are we able to see only a relatively small part of our galaxy, the Milky Way Galaxy?
   A)   There are so many stars in our galaxy that the more distant ones are hidden behind the nearer ones.
   B)   Distant stars are obscured by dust in interstellar space.
   C)   Expansion of the universe has carried the more distant stars out of our view.
   D)   Distant stars are obscured by gas in interstellar space.
   Ans: B   Section: 25-1

3. In the 1790s, Sir William Herschel tried to measure the Sun's position in our galaxy by
   A)   counting the density of stars in different directions along the Milky Way.
   B)   comparing our galaxy to photographs of the Andromeda galaxy.
   C)   measuring the locations of globular clusters around the galaxy.
   D)   measuring distances to star clusters and H II regions in the disk of the galaxy.
   Ans: A   Section: 25-1

4. In the eighteenth century, Sir William Herschel used star counts in regions of the sky along the Milky Way to estimate the position of the center of the Milky Way. He incorrectly concluded that the Sun was close to that center. The reason for this erroneous conclusion was
   A)   that Herschel counted all stars in each star field, and included many that were outside our galaxy, thus confusing the distribution.
   B)   that the redshift of the more distant stars made them invisible to Herschel.
   C)   that he had no knowledge of the large quantity of dust between stars, that obscured the more distant regions of the galaxy.
   D)   that he mistook globular clusters for stars and these are distributed uniformly around the Sun.
   Ans: C   Section: 25-1

5. The unknown factor that misled Herschel into concluding that the stars of the Milky Way were distributed with the Sun at the center of the galaxy was
    A) hot hydrogen gas in the galaxy, whose emission hid the more distant stars.
    B) the fact that most of the "stars" that he measured were in fact distant galaxies distributed uniformly around the Sun.
    C) gravitational bending of light by the mass of the galaxy, which distorted the relative positions of the stars.
    D) the presence of significant interstellar dust, which obscured the more distant stars and thereby localized his observations.
    Ans: D   Section: 25-1

6. When distances were carefully measured from Earth to globular clusters above and below the Milky Way plane (where our view of them is not obscured by interstellar dust and gas), their distribution was found to be
    A) in a relatively flat disk almost perpendicular to the plane of the galaxy, with relatively higher density of clusters toward its center.
    B) spherically symmetric about a point in the constellation Sagittarius and concentrated in that direction.
    C) concentrated in the plane of the Milky Way and clustered around the Sun's position, indicating that the Sun is close to the galaxy's center.
    D) uniformly distributed throughout space, with no concentration in any area of the Milky Way.
    Ans: B   Section: 25-1

7. Interstellar dust obscures our view of distant regions of space at optical wavelengths. Which of the following statements is true concerning this dust obscuration?
    A) Distant regions are severely obscured only in the plane of the galaxy.
    B) Distant regions are obscured roughly uniformly over the whole sky.
    C) Distant regions are obscured randomly over the whole sky, individual absorbing dust clouds showing no preference for one particular direction or plane.
    D) Distant regions are obscured the least in the plane of the galaxy, and are strongest when we look out into the galactic halo, at right angles to this plane.
    Ans: A   Section: 25-1

8. Which component of our galaxy accounts for interstellar extinction—the dimming of light from distant objects?
    A) molecules such as H_2 and CO, which are strong absorbers, in molecular clouds.
    B) dust
    C) the so-called dark matter, because its absorbing properties render it invisible in the galaxy.
    D) cool hydrogen gas
    Ans: B   Section: 25-1

9. The one component of the material of the Milky Way Galaxy that prevents us from seeing and photographing the galactic center at optical wavelengths is
   A) very cold hydrogen gas.   C) interstellar dust.
   B) the glare of light from nearby stars.   D) hot hydrogen gas.
   Ans: C   Section: 25-1

10. Variable stars, such as Cepheid variables and RR Lyrae stars, are used in what important measurement in astronomy?
    A) rotation speeds of galaxies   C) distance measurement
    B) surface temperature measurement   D) the keeping of accurate time
    Ans: C   Section: 25-1

11. Cepheid stars are useful to astronomers as indicators of
    A) white dwarf star behavior.
    B) distance, particularly to stars in our galaxy and to nearby galaxies.
    C) stars with very high speed motion.
    D) the mechanics of eclipsing variable stars.
    Ans: B   Section: 25-1

12. The period-luminosity relationship for Cepheid variable stars, relating variability to absolute overall brightness, thereby providing identifiable beacons throughout our local space, was discovered by
    A) Harlow Shapley.   C) Edwin Hubble.
    B) Henrietta Leavitt.   D) Sir Isaac Newton.
    Ans: B   Section: 25-1

13. A classical Cepheid variable star is seen to vary regularly with a period of 25 days. How much brighter than the Sun would this star appear to be if it were to replace the Sun in our solar system? (See Fig 25-4, Freedman and Kaufmann, *Universe,* 7th ed.)
    A) 4   B) 10,000   C) 1000   D) 10^2
    Ans: B   Section: 25-1

14. The method used by Harlow Shapley in 1917 to estimate the Sun's location in our galaxy was the measurement of
    A) the locations of globular clusters around the galaxy.
    B) the density of stars in different directions along the Milky Way.
    C) distances to open star clusters and H II regions in the disk of the galaxy.
    D) the structure of the Andromeda galaxy and a comparison of this to the structure of our galaxy.
    Ans: A   Section: 25-1

15. Harlow Shapley first located the center of our galaxy in 1917 by
    A)   observing the distribution of hydrogen gas, measured by 21-cm radio emission.
    B)   measuring the positions of supernova explosions throughout the galaxy.
    C)   redshift measurements on stars in the galactic plane and disk.
    D)   observing the distribution of globular clusters in the galactic halo.
    Ans: D   Section: 25-1

16. What useful purpose did RR Lyrae stars serve for Harlow Shapley in locating the galactic center?
    A)   Their brightness variations allowed accurate distances to be measured.
    B)   They emit copious amounts of infrared radiation, and are thus visible through interstellar dust, which obscured visible light.
    C)   They are concentrated in the galactic center and so defined its direction.
    D)   They are important spiral arm tracers, and thus defined the shape of the galaxy.
    Ans: A   Section: 25-1

17. Harlow Shapley determined the position of the Sun in the galaxy by measuring the distances to 93 globular clusters of stars. How did Shapley obtain the distances to these very distant clusters?
    A)   He measured the apparent brightnesses and pulsation periods of RR Lyrae stars in the clusters.
    B)   He plotted the apparent brightnesses and spectral classes of a sample of the stars in each cluster on a Hertzsprung-Russell diagram.
    C)   He measured the proper motion and radial velocity of each globular cluster.
    D)   He measured the apparent brightness of the brightest red giant stars in each cluster.
    Ans: A   Section: 25-1

18. Approximately how far is the Sun from the center of our galaxy?
    A) 49 kpc   B) 2 kpc   C) 8 kpc   D) 160 kpc
    Ans: C   Section: 25-1

19. Harlow Shapley's original estimate of the distance from the Sun to the galactic center was incorrect because it did not take interstellar extinction into account. This original estimate was
    A)   too large because light scattering and absorption by dust made nearer stars look dim—as though they were more distant.
    B)   too large because scattering by dust made stars look redder—as though they were highly Doppler shifted and thus more distant.
    C)   too small because gas and dust tend to reflect light back into the path of the beam, thus making stars look brighter and nearer.
    D)   too large because scattering by dust made stars look redder—as though they were red giants of larger luminosity and thus farther away.
    Ans: A   Section: 25-1

20. The distance to the globular cluster M55 has been determined to be 6500 pc by analysis of RR Lyrae stars in the cluster. How do the apparent brightnesses of these stars compare with the apparent brightness of the Sun? (Calculate $b/b_\odot$)
    A) 5.6×10^{-17}
    B) 2.5×10^{-7}
    C) 2.4×10^{-6}
    D)   There is no reason to believe all RR Lyrae stars in M55 have the same apparent brightness.
    Ans: A   Section: 25-1 and Box 19-2

21. What would be the wavelength of maximum emission of interstellar dust grains at a temperature of 65 K? (See Wien's law, Section 5-4, Freedman and Kaufmann, *Universe*, 7th ed.)
    A) $450\,\mu m$ B) $22.5\,\mu m$ C) $45\,\mu m$ D) $2.25\,\mu m$
    Ans: C   Section: 25-2 and Box 25-2

22. Interstellar matter blocks our view of the disk of our galaxy
    A)   not at all at any wavelength.
    B)   more-or-less equally at all wavelengths from radio waves to light waves.
    C)   most at radio wavelengths, where hydrogen absorbs radio waves efficiently, and least at optical wavelengths.
    D)   more at optical wavelengths, less in the infrared, and not at all at radio wavelengths.
    Ans: D   Section: 25-2

23. The dimensions of the disk of our Milky Way Galaxy are
    A)   diameter 80,000 light-years; thickness, 6,500 light-years.
    B)   diameter 6,500 light-years; thickness 2000 light-years.
    C)   diameter 2000 light-years; thickness, 160,000 light-years.
    D)   diameter 160,000 light-years; thickness, 2000 light-years.
    Ans: D   Section: 25-2

24. The diameter of our galaxy is about
    A) 50 kpc.   B) 2 kpc.   C) 8 kpc.   D) 160 kpc.
    Ans: A   Section: 25-2

25. The ratio of thickness to diameter of the Milky Way Galaxy is
    A) 1/800.   B) 1/3.25.   C) 1/80.   D) 1/40.
    Ans: C   Section: 25-2

26. Where is the solar system located in our galaxy?
    A)   It is not in a galaxy, but in intergalactic space.
    B)   in the galactic halo
    C)   in the galactic disk
    D)   in the galactic nucleus
    Ans: C   Section: 25-2

27. Where in space would you look for a globular cluster?
    A)   in the Milky Way halo, orbiting the galactic center in a long elliptical orbit
    B)   in the galactic disk, moving in a circular orbit around the galactic center
    C)   in the asteroid belt
    D)   only in elliptical galaxies, because they are composed of old stars
    Ans: A   Section: 25-2

28. Where would you look in our galaxy to find older, metal-poor stars?
    A)   in the disk and spiral arms
    B)   everywhere in the galaxy
    C)   in the globular clusters in the galactic halo
    D)   only at the galactic center
    Ans: C   Section: 25-2

29. In our galaxy, young metal-rich stars are found
    A)   in the disk and spiral arms.
    B)   everywhere in the galaxy.
    C)   only at the galactic center.
    D)   in the globular clusters, in the galactic halo.
    Ans: A   Section: 25-2

30. Observation of the different components of the Milky Way Galaxy indicates that the
    spiral arms contain very different populations of stars and other material from those in
    globular clusters. In what way are they different?
    A)   Spiral arms contain young stars, dust and gas within which star formation
          continues, whereas globular clusters contain older star populations, with no dust
          and gas and no on-going star formation.
    B)   Globular clusters contain dust and gas and are the only locations where star
          formation continues in the galaxy at the present time. The older stars in the spiral
          arms have no surrounding dust or gas.
    C)   Both spiral arms and globular clusters contain about the same populations of stars
          both young and old but, in contrast to the spiral arms, there is no dust and gas, no
          star formation, and there are no nova explosions in globular clusters.
    D)   Spiral arms contain older, more developed, and hence brighter and bluer stars,
          whereas globular clusters are composed largely of young, red stars in the early
          stages of formation and development.
    Ans: A   Section: 25-2

31. Which of the following types of stars is not found in the halo of our galaxy?
    A) O-type stars   B) Population II stars   C) K-type stars   D) RR Lyrae stars
    Ans: A   Section: 25-2

32. The disk of the Milky Way appears bluish because of the light from the many O and B type stars found there. What color tint would you expect globular clusters to take on?
    A)   white— that is, a random mixture of all the visible colors
    B)   red
    C)   green
    D)   blue
    Ans: D   Section: 25-2

33. Where in the Milky Way would you expect most star formation to be taking place?
    A) globular clusters   B) the halo   C) the disk and spiral arms   D) the bulge
    Ans: C   Section: 25-2

34. The Milky Way is an example of which type of galaxy?
    A) irregular   B) elliptical   C) lenticular (S0)   D) spiral
    Ans: D   Section: 25-3

35. How is cool neutral hydrogen gas, H I, detected in the spiral arms of galaxies?
    A)   by its Balmer line emissions from hydrogen gas
    B)   by its absorption of infrared radiation from distant galaxies
    C)   by its ultraviolet Lyman α hydrogen-line emissions
    D)   by its 21-cm radio emissions
    Ans: D   Section: 25-3

36. Radio waves of 21-cm wavelength originate from which component of the interstellar medium?
    A)   ionized atomic hydrogen   C)   carbon monoxide, CO
    B)   neutral atomic hydrogen   D)   molecular hydrogen, H_2
    Ans: B   Section: 25-3

37. What happens when the electron in a hydrogen atom flips its direction of spin, from parallel to antiparallel to that of the proton?
    A)   Nothing—this is a forbidden transition and never occurs.
    B)   The atom emits a photon of 656.3 nm wavelength (H_α), in the red region of the spectrum.
    C)   The atom emits a photon of 121.5 nm wavelength (L_α), in the UV region of the spectrum.
    D)   The atom emits a photon of 21-cm wavelength, in the radio region of the spectrum.
    Ans: D   Section: 25-3

38. What atomic transition occurs in atoms of hydrogen gas in the galactic spiral arms to produce 21-cm radio emission?
    A) the change in the vibrational state of the H atoms in the H_2 molecule
    B) the transition from the n = 2 to n = 1 level in atomic hydrogen
    C) the inversion of the electron spin relative to the proton spin, from parallel to anti-parallel
    D) the change in rotation about an axis perpendicular to the molecular axis in the molecule H_2
    Ans: C   Section: 25-3

39. What quantum transition occurs inside a cool hydrogen atom to produce a 21-cm radio photon?
    A) The electron combines with the proton in the nucleus to become a neutron, producing energy.
    B) An electron reverses the direction of its motion in orbit around the proton.
    C) An electron in the ground atomic state reverses its direction of spin with respect to that of the proton.
    D) An electron falls from the level n = 100 to the level n = 99 in the atom.
    Ans: C   Section: 25-3

40. The major advantages of the measurement of the 21-cm radio emission from hydrogen gas for investigating the spiral structure of our galaxy are
    A) that Doppler shift of this narrow-wavelength line emission is caused by the temperature of the hot hydrogen gas and therefore can be used to measure the distribution and temperature of this important component of the Milky Way.
    B) that it is relatively easily absorbed by hydrogen gas in the Milky Way, so that measurements are not confused by emission of this radiation from other galaxies beyond the Milky Way. It originates only from cold hydrogen gas, and can be used to map this important component.
    C) that this emission can easily penetrate the Milky Way gas and dust and comes only from hot gas, and hence can be used to map the distribution of hot hydrogen gas.
    D) that radio waves easily penetrate the Milky Way dust and gas and it is a very narrow line emission, thus its Doppler shift can be used to measure gas motions.
    Ans: D   Section: 25-3

41. When we measure the narrow line emissions of hydrogen at 21-cm radio wavelength along a particular line of sight through the disk of our galaxy, we can tell the distances to different hydrogen clouds because
    A)   clouds at different distances have different Doppler shifts because of the rotation of the galaxy.
    B)   the further away the gas cloud, the greater the delay in the arrival time of the 21-cm emission.
    C)   clouds that are further away have smaller angular sizes.
    D)   the emission is weaker from clouds that are further away.
    Ans: A   Section: 25-3

42. The spiral-arm structure of the Milky Way Galaxy has been measured and evaluated most effectively by observations of
    A)   Lyman UV radiation from hot hydrogen gas.
    B)   observations of globular clusters in the halo of the galaxy.
    C)   21-cm radiation from interstellar hydrogen and the positions of young stars.
    D)   Balmer emission lines of visible radiation from hydrogen.
    Ans: C   Section: 25-3

43. Which type of radiation has been most effective in evaluating the spiral structure of our galaxy?
    A)   neutrinos from exploding supernovas, because they can easily penetrate gas and dust clouds
    B)   21-cm radio emission from the "spin-flip" transitions in cool hydrogen gas
    C)   synchrotron radiation from electrons moving in magnetic fields
    D)   Lyman α ultraviolet hydrogen emission from hot hydrogen gas
    Ans: B   Section: 25-3

44. Which of the following components of the galaxy best outline the spiral arms of the galaxy?
    A)   young O and B stars, dust, and gas   C)   predominantly solar-type stars
    B)   globular clusters   D)   white dwarf stars
    Ans: A   Section: 25-3

45. The stellar components of the galaxy that act as tracers for the mapping of spiral arm structure in the Milky Way are
    A)   supernova explosions, because they are very luminous and can be seen through considerable dust and gas.
    B)   old, red giant stars and white dwarfs.
    C)   globular clusters.
    D)   bright, population I stars and emission nebulae surrounding them.
    Ans: D   Section: 25-3

46. Which kind of stars are the major source of energy for the heating of the dust clouds and the H II emission nebulae within the planes of the Milky Way and other galaxies?
    A) hot, young O and B stars, via their UV radiation
    B) the numerous old, red giant K and M stars, via their IR heat radiation
    C) very hot white dwarf stars, the remnants of planetary nebulae in the gas clouds
    D) the very many nova and supernova explosions of stars within the gas and dust clouds
    Ans: A   Section: 25-3

47. Which of the following is NOT useful for mapping the locations and shapes of the spiral arms of our galaxy?
    A) the distribution of globular clusters
    B) the distribution of O and B stars
    C) the distribution of emission nebulae (H II regions)
    D) the distribution of molecular clouds
    Ans: A   Section: 25-3

48. What is the distribution of molecular clouds in our galaxy and other similar galaxies?
    A) They occur primarily in the spiral arms.
    B) They are distributed uniformly throughout the disk.
    C) They are concentrated close to the galactic center.
    D) They are distributed throughout the halo, with greater density toward the center.
    Ans: A   Section: 25-3

49. A map of our galaxy deduced from radio observations of the 21-cm line emission from cool hydrogen gas reveals
    A) two spiral arms, one on each side of the galaxy.
    B) two spiral arms, which wrap around the galaxy several times.
    C) a smooth distribution of stars, characteristic of an elliptical galaxy.
    D) at least four spiral arms and several short arm segments.
    Ans: D   Section: 25-3

50. The Milky Way galaxy appears to have a spiral structure with
    A) four separate major arms.
    B) one "arm," wound around the nucleus four times.
    C) two major arms, wound twice around the nucleus.
    D) three loosely wound arms.
    Ans: A   Section: 25-3

51. If a spacecraft were to travel outward from the Sun in a direction opposite to the galactic center, how many and which spiral arms would it have to cross before reaching intergalactic space? (See Fig. 25-14, Freedman and Kaufmann, *Universe,* 7th ed.)
    A)   none—because this direction takes the spacecraft out of the plane of the galaxy
    B)   four—the Sagittarius, Centaurus, and Cygnus arms and then the Centaurus arm again
    C)   two—the Sagittarius and Centaurus arms
    D)   two—the Perseus and Cygnus arms
    Ans: D   Section: 25-3

52. Recent observations suggest that the Milky Way
    A)   may be an irregular galaxy, with chaotic distribution of matter within it.
    B)   may have vast stellar streams in a plane perpendicular to the galaxy's disk, formed by a collision of the Milky Way with another large spiral galaxy.
    C)   may be an elliptical galaxy, with little structure.
    D)   may have a central bar, formed by an elongation of the central bulge.
    Ans: D   Section: 25-3 and Figure 25-14

53. Which physical process in the interstellar medium is most efficient at stopping us from seeing large distances in the disk of our galaxy at ultraviolet wavelengths?
    A)   absorption of ultraviolet light by molecules in the interstellar medium
    B)   absorption of UV light at the wavelength of the hydrogen-alpha line in the Balmer series
    C)   ionization of hydrogen gas by ultraviolet light
    D)   absorption and scattering of ultraviolet light by dust grains
    Ans: C   Section: 25-3

54. Which physical process is thought to have created the Local Bubble near our Sun in the galaxy?
    A)   a nearby supernova explosion
    B)   neanderthal campfires
    C)   the solar wind
    D)   hot O and B stars in the solar neighborhood
    Ans: A   Section: 25-3

55. The Sun's location in our galaxy is
    A)   in the disk of the galaxy, inside a spiral arm or segment of a spiral arm.
    B)   in the disk of the galaxy, between and well away from any spiral arm.
    C)   We cannot tell where we are located because our view is too severely blocked by interstellar dust.
    D)   in the halo, somewhat above and outside of the spiral arms.
    Ans: A   Section: 25-3

56. Where is the Sun located in our galaxy? (i.e., What is our address in the universe?) (See Fig. 25-14, Freedman and Kaufmann, *Universe*, 7th ed.)
    A)   in the Centaurus arm, between the galactic center and the Orion arm
    B)   in the Sagittarius arm, which is between the Centaurus and Orion arms
    C)   in or close to the Orion arm, which is between the Sagittarius and Perseus arms
    D)   in the Perseus arm, between the Orion and Cygnus arms
    Ans: C   Section: 25-3

57. A neutral hydrogen atom consists of a proton and an electron. The energy of the atom is
    A)   the same regardless of the relative spin orientations of the two particles.
    B)   highest when the proton spin and the electron spin are perpendicular to each other.
    C)   highest when the two spin directions are parallel.
    D)   highest when the two spin directions are antiparallel.
    Ans: C   Section: 25-3

58. If we aim a radio telescope at a distant spiral arm of our galaxy we will probably observe a 21-cm line. If we point a large optical telescope at this same region we will probably not be able to detect the neutral hydrogen, which gives rise to the 21-cm radio signal. Why not?
    A)   Neutral hydrogen is incapable of emitting visible radiation.
    B)   The H_α line—the primary emission of neutral hydrogen—has a much smaller energy than the 21-cm radio wave, and thus is harder to detect.
    C)   There is little energy in the depths of space to excite visible radiation from neutral hydrogen.
    D)   The visible light emitted by neutral hydrogen is all absorbed by H II gas regions before reaching the solar system.
    Ans: C   Section: 25-3

59. We aim our radio telescope at a distant region of our galaxy and detect 21-cm radio waves with no Doppler shift. Each of the following is a possible explanation *except one*. Which is the exception?
    A)   The neutral hydrogen in this region is not moving relative to the Earth.
    B)   The neutral hydrogen in this region is moving perpendicularly across our line of sight.
    C)   The neutral hydrogen in this region is in a circular orbit around the galactic center at the same radius as the solar system.
    D)   The neutral hydrogen in this region is moving away from us instead of toward us.
    Ans: D   Section: 25-3

60. Which of the following statements correctly describes the rotation of our galaxy?
    A)   Objects in the disk have random orbits with no net rotation of the disk about the center of the galaxy, and the halo rotates differentially (objects further from the center take longer to complete an orbit than objects closer to the center).
    B)   The disk rotates differentially (objects further from the center take longer to complete an orbit than objects closer to the center), and the halo rotates differentially (objects further from the center take longer to complete an orbit than objects closer to the center).
    C)   The disk rotates like a solid object (objects at all distances take the same time to complete an orbit), and the halo objects have random orbits with no net rotation of the halo about the center of the galaxy.
    D)   The disk rotates differentially (objects further from the center take longer to complete an orbit than objects closer to the center), and the halo objects have random orbits with no net rotation of the halo about the center of the galaxy.
    Ans: D   Section: 25-4

61. The speed of the Sun in its orbit around the galaxy is deduced from observations of
    A)   the galactic center, about which the Sun is orbiting.
    B)   Cepheid variables between spiral arms, because distances can easily be measured to them.
    C)   the orbital motions of stars near the Sun.
    D)   globular clusters in the galactic halo and distant galaxies.
    Ans: D   Section: 25-4

62. The most important reason why globular clusters are useful for finding the speed of the Sun in its orbit around the galaxy is that
    A)   globular clusters on average rotate at the same speed as the Sun around the center of the galaxy.
    B)   globular clusters are bright and easily seen at large distances.
    C)   globular clusters are distributed uniformly around the galaxy.
    D)   globular clusters on average do not rotate around the center of the galaxy.
    Ans: D   Section: 25-4

63. If the Sun were traveling around the galactic center along with companion stars (all in circular orbits) as depicted in Fig. 25-15 (Freedman and Kaufmann, *Universe*, 7th ed.), from which of the stars described below would you measure Doppler shift of their light? (Hint: Think about relative velocities and orbital velocities at different orbital distances from the galactic center.)
    A)   stars at the same orbital distance as the Sun
    B)   stars in directions at 45° angles from the Sun's direction of motion
    C)   none of them, because they are all moving along with the Sun and have no relative velocity with respect to it
    D)   stars directly between the Sun and the galactic center
    Ans: B   Section: 25-4

64. The time taken for the Sun to orbit the galactic center once in its motion in the galaxy is
    A) 230 million years.
    B) about ½ million years.
    C) 1.3×10^{11} years.
    D) 2.3 million years.
    Ans: A   Section: 25-4

65. The Sun, in its orbit around the center of our galaxy, moves a distance equal to the diameter of the Earth in a time of about (see Section 25-4, Freedman and Kaufmann, *Universe*, 7th ed.)
    A) one hour.   B) one minute.   C) one day.   D) one second.
    Ans: B   Section: 25-4

66. The present estimate for the mass of our galaxy is approximately
    A) 10^{11} M$_\odot$.   B) 10^{10} M$_\odot$.   C) 10^{12} M$_\odot$ or more.   D) 10^{9} M$_\odot$ or less.
    Ans: C   Section: 25-4

67. How is the mass of the galaxy estimated?
    A) by observing the bending of light from distant galaxies as it passes near the Milky Way center.
    B) by observing its movement toward neighboring galaxies because of gravitational attraction
    C) by counting stars and assuming an average stellar mass
    D) by applying Newton's extension of Kepler's laws to the motion of the Sun and other stars
    Ans: D   Section: 25-4

68. Which two parameters of star motion in the Milky Way are represented by its rotation curve?
    A) orbital speed of the stars as a function of their age
    B) orbital period of the stars as a function of their distance from the galactic center
    C) orbital speed as a function of star distance from the galactic center
    D) star position above or below the galactic plane as a function of distance from the galactic center
    Ans: C   Section: 25-4

69. Which parameter is plotted against distance from the galactic center in the rotation curve of a galaxy?
    A) the thickness of the galactic disk
    B) the mass of cool hydrogen gas
    C) the speed of stars orbiting the galactic center
    D) the mass of matter inside the distance from the galactic center
    Ans: C   Section: 25-4

70. Much of the mass of our galaxy appears to be in the form of "dark matter" of unknown composition. At present this matter can be detected only because
    A)   it bends light from distant galaxies and quasars.
    B)   it emits synchrotron radiation.
    C)   its gravitational pull affects orbital motions of matter in the galaxy.
    D)   it blocks out the light from distant stars in the plane of our galaxy.
    Ans: C   Section: 25-4

71. The possible presence of a very large amount of unseen ("dark") matter in the halo of our galaxy is deduced from
    A)   the unexpected absence of luminous matter (stars, etc.) beyond a certain distance.
    B)   the rotation curve of our galaxy, which indicates higher than expected orbital speeds in the outer regions of the galaxy.
    C)   the rotation curve of our galaxy, which shows that orbital speeds in the outer parts of the galaxy decrease in a way that follows Kepler's law.
    D)   the unexpected high amount of interstellar absorption in certain directions.
    Ans: B   Section: 25-4

72. What fraction of the mass of our galaxy is in a form that we have been able to see?
    A)   about 10%
    B)   100%. Who ever heard of matter that can't be seen?
    C)   about 50%
    D)   about 90%
    Ans: A   Section: 25-4

73. What fraction of the mass of our galaxy appears to be in the form of dark matter, which we cannot see but can detect through its gravitational influence?
    A)   about 50%
    B)   0%. Who ever heard of matter that can't be seen?
    C)   about 90%
    D)   about 10%
    Ans: C   Section: 25-4

74. What is microlensing?
    A)   the focusing of starlight by the gravitational fields of "small" objects such as brown dwarfs
    B)   the beaming of radiation by accretion disks
    C)   the use of small telescopes to enhance contrast by eliminating scattered light
    D)   the focusing of starlight by planetary atmospheres
    Ans: A   Section: 25-4

75. What is microlensing?
    A)   a minute shift in the apparent position of a star as an object passes in front of it
    B)   a slow brightening of a star as an object passes in front of it
    C)   the temporary disappearance of a star as an object passes in front of it
    D)   a gradual reduction in brightness of a star as an object passes in front of it
    Ans: B   Section: 25-4

76. Because the rotation curve for the Milky Way galaxy is approximately flat, a star in a circular orbit 13,000 kpc from the galactic center has the same orbital speed as the Sun, namely 220 km/sec. How much mass is interior to this star's orbit?
    A) 9.0×10^{10} M$_\odot$ B) 1.5×10^{11} M$_\odot$ C) 9.0×10^{11} M$_\odot$ D) 1.5×10^{12} M$_\odot$
    Ans: B   Section: 25-4 and Box 25-2

77. Which of the following has *not* been proposed as a candidate for dark matter?
    A)   massive compact halo objects   C)   dark nebulae
    B)   weakly interacting massive particles   D)   neutrinos
    Ans: C   Section: 25-4

78. Astronomers have found the existence of spiral arms in galaxies difficult to account for because
    A)   the inner part of a galaxy rotates in a shorter time than the outer parts, so the arms should have wound up so tightly that they would have disappeared over the lifetime of the galaxy.
    B)   the arms should have been destroyed by collisions with other galaxies over the galaxy's lifetime.
    C)   the outer regions of a galaxy including the spiral arms have no significant rotation, so the arms should have fallen into the center of the galaxy.
    D)   the outer parts of a galaxy rotate faster than the inner parts, so the arms should have straightened out into spokes like those of a bicycle wheel.
    Ans: A   Section: 25-5

79. The density wave that produces the spiral arm in the Milky Way Galaxy is similar in properties to a
    A)   light wave.   C)   compression wave.
    B)   wave on a stretched string.   D)   gravitational wave.
    Ans: C   Section: 25-5

80. According to the density-wave theory of spiral structure in galaxies,
    A)   collisions between galaxies create waves like the ripples around a rock dropped into a pond, and these are twisted into a spiral pattern by the galaxy's rotation.
    B)   collisions between stars send shock waves propagating through the disk of the galaxy.
    C)   star-formation regions propagate through the interstellar medium and get stretched into a spiral structure by differential rotation.
    D)   stars and interstellar clouds spend more time in regions of higher density, thus maintaining the higher density of the region.
    Ans: D   Section: 25-5

81. One difficulty with the density wave theory is that
    A)   the theory fails to explain why a given spiral pattern lasts only a small fraction of the lifetime of a galaxy.
    B)   it fails to provide a mechanism for star formation.
    C)   there is no mechanism proposed to provide the energy output necessary to sustain the density wave.
    D)   it fails to explain the distribution of Population I and Population II stars in the galaxy.
    Ans: C   Section: 25-5

82. In the self-propagating star formation theory
    A)   spiral arms are formed and sustained primarily by the actions of solar mass stars because there are so many more of them than there are high mass stars.
    B)   spiral arms are poorly defined because they are formed and sustained primarily by the actions of short-lived massive stars.
    C)   the passage of dust clouds through the spiral arms triggers star formation.
    D)   spiral structure results with thin, well-defined arms.
    Ans: B   Section: 25-5

83. In which constellation in our sky is the center of our Milky Way Galaxy located?
    A) Hercules   B) Ursa Major   C) Sagittarius   D) Lyra
    Ans: C   Section: 25-6

84. The center of our Milky Way Galaxy can be observed most easily at which of the following wavelengths?
    A)   ultraviolet light.   C)   infrared and radio radiation.
    B)   hydrogen Balmer H_α light.   D)   highly penetrating gamma rays.
    Ans: C   Section: 25-6

85. If the Sun were to be at or close to the galactic center, the intensity of starlight in the nighttime sky on Earth would be
    A) very much fainter than at present because neighboring stars would be obscured by dense dust and gas clouds.
    B) extremely intense from the dense field of nearby stars, equivalent to about 200 full Moons.
    C) about twice as bright as at present, because neighboring stars would be mostly bright, young blue stars in about the same numbers as the present, older, and less bright red giant neighbors to the Sun.
    D) about the same as it is now, because neighboring stars would still be relatively far away.
    Ans: B   Section: 25-6

86. What is the significance of the object Sagittarius A* ("Sagittarius A-star") in our galaxy?
    A) It appears to be a jet of material ejected from an accretion disk around a supermassive black hole in the galactic nucleus.
    B) It is a globular cluster passing close to the galactic nucleus, and the RR Lyrae stars in it allow the distance to the galactic center to be calculated.
    C) It is a bright, high-speed cloud of gas close to the galactic nucleus, which allows the mass of the nucleus to be calculated.
    D) It appears to be the actual nucleus of the galaxy.
    Ans: D   Section: 25-6

87. What type of object has been proposed to explain the tremendous activity detected at the center of our galaxy?
    A) a giant molecular cloud   C) a rapidly rotating neutron star
    B) a supermassive black hole   D) a supernova explosion
    Ans: B   Section: 25-6

88. Which of the following locations in our universe has been suggested as the site of a supermassive black hole?
    A) the center of the Ring Nebula in Lyra, an old star
    B) the center of the Crab Nebula, an old supernova remnant
    C) the center of the universe, as defined by the universal expansion of the observable universe
    D) the center of our galaxy
    Ans: D   Section: 25-6

89. What evidence now exists for a supermassive black hole at the center of our galaxy?
    A) a very dark void in an otherwise bright region of space near the galactic center, indicating the presence of a black hole
    B) observations of intense inflow of matter toward the center of the galaxy, as seen by light, Doppler-shifted toward the red, emitted by this matter
    C) very bright and very energetic X-ray emissions from the galactic center
    D) very rapid motion of matter close to the nucleus of the galaxy, requiring a very massive body to hold it in orbit
    Ans: D   Section: 25-6

90. The possible presence of a supermassive black hole at the center of our galaxy has been deduced from
    A) powerful magnetic fields in the huge filaments arching away from (or toward) the center.
    B) the number of globular clusters that are concentrated near to the galactic center.
    C) gravitational radiation being emitted from stars as they are swallowed by the black hole.
    D) the very high orbital speed of stars close to the galactic center.
    Ans: D   Section: 25-6

91. What is the evidence that indicates to some astronomers that a supermassive black hole exists at the center of our galaxy?
    A) No electromagnetic radiation at all comes from the precise position of the galactic center and it just looks like a dark void in space.
    B) measurement of stars orbiting the galactic center at very high speeds, which would rapidly move out of the galaxy unless some very massive object holds them in orbit
    C) Doppler shift of light from stars in the near neighborhood of the galactic center that indicates that the stars are falling inward at very high speeds
    D) The Sun's motion in space shows that, if Kepler's Law holds for its orbit around the galactic center, there must be a very massive object at this center.
    Ans: B   Section: 25-6

92. What appear to be the characteristics of the object at the center of our galaxy?
    A) three million solar masses in a volume the size of our solar system
    B) five billion solar masses in a volume smaller then Jupiter's orbit
    C) twenty solar masses in a volume the size of the Sun
    D) several trillion solar masses in a volume two light years in diameter
    Ans: A   Section: 25-6

93. If the galactic center is now thought to contain a supermassive black hole, why is the Sun not falling into it under the black hole's extreme gravity?
    A)   because the inward force exerted on the Sun from the black hole is offset by the force exerted outward by the hidden "dark" matter beyond the Sun's orbit
    B)   because its mass is so small that even this extreme mass concentration at the galactic center will not exert a significant force upon it
    C)   because it has sufficient velocity that it can orbit the galactic center in a circle
    D)   because the mutual gravitational forces of local stars in the Orion spiral arm are sufficient to overcome the strong inward force and keep the Sun moving in its orbit
    Ans: C   Section: 25-6

94. The most important electromagnetic bands for studying the galactic center do *not* include which one of the following?
    A) infrared   B) visible   C) radio   D) X ray
    Ans: B   Section: 25-6

95. The star S2 orbits Sagittarius A* with a period of 15.2 years and a semimajor axis of 950 AU. What does Kepler's Third Law suggest as the total amount of mass inside the orbital radius of S2?
    A) $1.3 \times 10^6 \, M_\odot$ B) $2.6 \times 10^6 \, M_\odot$ C) $3.7 \times 10^6 \, M_\odot$ D) $9.4 \times 10^9 \, M_\odot$
    Ans: C   Section: 25-6

Chapter 26: Galaxies

1. The famous nineteenth-century observational astronomer, Lord Rosse, who built the largest telescope in the world and discovered the spiral nature of many so-called "nebulae" with it, did so in which country?
   A) U.S.A.   B) Ireland   C) England   D) Germany
   Ans: B   Section: 26-1

2. The idea that some of the "nebulae" that are observed in the sky might be "island universes"—immense collections of stars far beyond the Milky Way—was first proposed by
   A)   Immanuel Kant in 1755.   C)   Edwin Hubble in 1923.
   B)   Lord Rosse in 1845.   D)   Albert Einstein in 1909.
   Ans: A   Section: 26-1

3. Which concept concerning the diffuse objects observed by Herschel was proposed by Kant in the 1700s and confirmed by observations made in 1845 by the Earl of Rosse with his world-class telescope in Ireland?
   A)   The diffuse objects observed by Herschel and known as planetary nebulae were in fact planets orbiting other stars in our galaxy.
   B)   Many of the diffuse objects in our sky are moving rapidly away from our galaxy.
   C)   All of the diffuse nebulae seen in the sky are gas clouds in our Milky Way Galaxy.
   D)   Many of the nebulae in the sky are separate entities beyond our Milky Way Galaxy.
   Ans: D   Section: 26-1

4. The Andromeda Galaxy (M31) is best described as
   A)   an extension of the Milky Way.
   B)   a spiral collection of stars, dust, and gas, 200,000 light-years across.
   C)   a gaseous nebula, extending for 6° across our sky.
   D)   a vortex surrounding a black hole.
   Ans: B   Section: 26-1

5. Which of the following fundamental astronomical questions did Curtis and Shapley debate in 1920 in their famous confrontation?
   A)   whether the Sun was at the center of the Milky Way Galaxy
   B)   whether the universe was expanding outward in all directions
   C)   whether the spiral "nebulae" were part of the Milky Way Galaxy or more distant, separate entities
   D)   whether the Theory of General Relativity could be used to explain the behavior of our universe
   Ans: C   Section: 26-1

6. The event that settled the Shapley-Curtis debate about "spiral nebulae" was
   A) Albert Einstein showing that gravity can bend the path of light.
   B) Arno Penzias and Robert Wilson detecting the cosmic microwave background radiation.
   C) Edwin Hubble measuring the distance to the Andromeda galaxy.
   D) Edwin Hubble showing that the universe is expanding.
   Ans: C   Section: 26-1

7. It is the year 1920 and you are conducting a survey of the astronomy community on the question: "What is the nature of the spiral nebulae?" What response are you likely to receive?
   A) The overwhelming opinion is that spiral nebulae are relatively small objects in the outer part of the Milky Way Galaxy.
   B) The overwhelming opinion is that spiral nebulae are large, distant galaxies somewhat like the Milky Way.
   C) There is a deep division of opinion between these two views of the nature of spiral nebulae.
   D) Because spiral nebulae have just been discovered, no one has much of an opinion about them yet.
   Ans: C   Section: 26-1

8. The 1920 Shapley-Curtis debate on the nature of spiral nebulae was inconclusive. What was really needed to provide an answer to the question was
   A) a better idea of the size of the Milky Way Galaxy.
   B) a better understanding of interstellar extinction.
   C) distances to spiral nebulae.
   D) a clearer idea of star formation.
   Ans: C   Section: 26-1

9. The observation by Hubble that demonstrated for the first time that the Andromeda "nebula" was at a very large distance from the Sun, and outside our galaxy, was
   A) that the "nebula" appeared to be rotating night by night around a center that was not the center of our galaxy.
   B) that Cepheid variable stars appeared to be very faint in the "nebula."
   C) that stars with characteristics similar to those of our Sun appeared to be absent in this "nebula."
   D) that globular clusters appeared to be distributed in a halo around the "nebula," a sure sign of a separate galaxy.
   Ans: B   Section: 26-2

10. What was the implication of the observation by Edwin Hubble that the Cepheid variable stars that he measured in the Andromeda Nebula appeared to be very faint compared with what was expected?
    A) The Andromeda Nebula was very far away, and was in fact a galaxy not a nebula.
    B) The observed period was affected by the intense gravitational field of the nebula as predicted by General Relativity, leading to incorrect luminosity determination.
    C) He had discovered a new class of intrinsically faint Cepheid variable stars.
    D) Dust and gas in the nebula had severely reduced the light from these stars.
    Ans: A   Section: 26-2

11. The method used by Hubble to determine the distance to the Andromeda Galaxy (M31), thereby establishing the concept of separate and individual galaxies throughout the universe, was the
    A) measurement of the redshift of the whole galaxy.
    B) observation of the apparent brightnesses of supernovas in M31.
    C) measurement of stellar parallax, or apparent motion of stars because of Earth's orbital motion.
    D) observation of Cepheid variable stars.
    Ans: D   Section: 26-2

12. Distances to a nearby galaxy can be determined most accurately by
    A) using pulsating stars as beacons.
    B) measuring the chemical compositions of the brightest stars.
    C) measuring the shifts of spectral lines from stars in this galaxy.
    D) measuring the total amount of energy received from the galaxy.
    Ans: A   Section: 26-2

13. Variable stars, such as Cepheid variables and RR Lyrae stars, are used in what important measurement in astronomy?
    A) the keeping of accurate time
    B) the measurement of the gravitational fields of supermassive black holes by their effect upon the star's pulsation rate
    C) the measurement of the surface temperatures of stars
    D) the measurement of distances to galaxies
    Ans: D   Section: 26-2

14. In determining the distance to a galaxy by using observations of a Cepheid variable star, which of the following is NOT needed?
    A) the star's velocity via the Doppler effect
    B) the Cepheid's period of variability
    C) the type of spectrum of the Cepheid; metal-rich or metal-poor
    D) the star's average brightness or apparent magnitude
    Ans: A   Section: 26-2

15. The intrinsic brightness (represented by luminosity) of a Cepheid variable star compared to that of the Sun is
    A)   several thousand times larger.
    C)   about 10 times larger.
    B)   significantly less.
    D)   about the same.
    Ans: A   Section: 26-2

16. How does the intrinsic brightness or luminosity of a Cepheid variable star compare to that of our Sun?
    A)   much less, about 1/10, because it is a variable star
    B)   larger, by 100
    C)   about the same
    D)   much larger, by 10^4
    Ans: D   Section: 26-2

17. The observational fact about a Cepheid variable star that leads to a measurement of its distance from the Earth is that its period of variation is directly related to its
    A)   absolute magnitude or luminosity.
    B)   apparent magnitude.
    C)   speed away from us, using the relativistic effect upon pulsation period.
    D)   surface temperature.
    Ans: A   Section: 26-2

18. The significant feature of a Cepheid variable is that there is a relationship between two intrinsic parameters, the first being easily measured, the second being the parameter that is required. These parameters are
    A)   variation of spectral color and distance to the star.
    B)   period of brightness variation and spectral color.
    C)   period of brightness variation and luminosity.
    D)   amplitude of brightness variation and luminosity.
    Ans: C   Section: 26-2

19. A Cepheid variable star with a pulsation period of a few days is seen in the spiral arm of a galaxy. Its apparent brightness is measured as 10^4 times fainter than an equivalent Cepheid star with the same period 1000 ly away from the Sun in our galaxy. Assuming no light absorption between galaxies, what is the distance to the far Cepheid, and hence to the galaxy?
    A)   100,000 ly (100 times further away)
    C) 10^7 ly (10^4 times further away)
    B)   10 ly (100 times closer)
    D)   10,000 ly (10 times further away)
    Ans: A   Section: 26-2, 21-5, and 19-2

20. The typical diameter of a spiral galaxy is about
    A) 10^5 light-years.   B) 10^7 light-years.   C) 100 light-years.   D) 1 light-year.
    Ans: A   Section: 26-2

21. The Cepheid variables that Hubble observed in M31 were metal-rich Type I Cepheids. They had an apparent magnitude of about 18 and thus an apparent brightness relative to the Sun ($b/b_\odot$) of about 1.3×10^{-8}. What approximate periods would these Cepheids need in order to yield a distance to M31 of about 750 kpc?
    A) less than one day   B) 3 days   C) 10 days   D) 70 days
    Ans: D   Section: 26-2

22. The Milky Way in which the Sun resides is an example of which type of galaxy?
    A)   an elliptical galaxy
    B)   a normal spiral galaxy
    C)   a barred spiral galaxy
    D)   an irregular galaxy
    Ans: B   Section: 26-3

23. Who developed the classification system that divides galaxies into spiral, elliptical, and irregular, and classifies spirals by the size of their nuclear region and the tightness of winding of their arms?
    A)   Ejnar Hertzsprung
    B)   Sir John Herschel
    C)   Henrietta Leavitt
    D)   Edwin Hubble
    Ans: D   Section: 26-3

24. In the Hubble Classification Scheme for spiral galaxies, the tightness of the winding of the spiral arms appears to be directly related to
    A)   the overall intrinsic size of the galaxy, or the diameter across the spiral arms.
    B)   the number of globular clusters in the halo of the galaxy.
    C)   the age of the galaxy, as determined from the age of its individual stars.
    D)   the size of the central bulge of the galaxy.
    Ans: D   Section: 26-3

25. A particular galaxy has a nuclear region of more-or-less uniform brightness from which long lanes of stars curve outward. What type of galaxy is this?
    A) lenticular   B) spiral   C) elliptical   D) irregular
    Ans: B   Section: 26-3

26. What does a spiral galaxy look like when seen edge-on?
    A)   round, but without spiral arms because they are hidden
    B)   a thick line curved into a spiral shape
    C)   a thick, flat line with a bulge in the center
    D)   a thick, flat line
    Ans: C   Section: 26-3

27. What is the basic shape of a spiral galaxy?
    A)   a round, thin disk of uniform brightness with its edges bent up and down into a
         spiral shape
    B)   a round, flat disk with long lanes of stars that curve outward in a spiral shape from
         the very center of the galaxy
    C)   approximately spherical with long lanes of dark dust clouds curving through it in
         a spiral pattern
    D)   a round, flat disk containing long lanes of stars that curve outward in a spiral
         shape from the edge of a round, nuclear region of uniform brightness
    Ans: D   Section: 26-3

28. Why do the spiral arms show up so clearly in spiral galaxies?
    A)   Stars are spread uniformly over the galaxy but the dust forms a spiral pattern,
         absorbing starlight; the spiral arms are the dust-free regions between the dust
         lanes.
    B)   Stars are spread almost uniformly throughout the disk of the galaxy outside the
         nuclear bulge, but the brightest stars occur only in the spiral arms, making the
         arms stand out.
    C)   There are many more stars in the arms than in the regions between the arms, so
         the arms stand out distinctly.
    D)   Stars occur only in the spiral arms (and the nuclear bulge), with essentially none
         between the arms, making the arms stand out brightly.
    Ans: B   Section: 26-3

29. How do spiral galaxies rotate?
    A)   We don't know; they rotate too slowly for us to have seen any motion in the time
         since galaxies were discovered.
    B)   They don't rotate; if they did the spiral pattern would soon disappear.
    C)   The arms trail the rotation (point back).
    D)   The arms lead the rotation (point forward).
    Ans: C   Section: 26-3

30. The Hubble classification for a spiral galaxy with a prominent central bulge and smooth,
    broad spiral arms is
    A) Sc.   B) E0.   C) SBa.   D) Sa.
    Ans: D   Section: 26-3

31. The Hubble classification for a spiral galaxy with a moderate-sized nuclear region and
    moderately well-defined spiral arms is
    A) Sb.   B) E3.   C) SBa.   D) Sa.
    Ans: A   Section: 26-3

32. The Hubble classification for a spiral galaxy with a tiny central bulge and narrow, well-defined, loosely wound spiral arms is
   A) E0.   B) SBa.   C) Sa.   D) Sc.
   Ans: D   Section: 26-3

33. The Hubble classification for a galaxy having loosely wound spiral arms originating at the ends of a bar through the central bulge is
   A) Sb.   B) SBa.   C) S0.   D) SBc.
   Ans: D   Section: 26-3

34. According to the Hubble classification scheme, an Sa galaxy has
   A)   a round or spherical appearance with a smooth light distribution.
   B)   a large central bulge and broad, smooth, tightly wound spiral arms.
   C)   an irregular shape with no obvious disk or spiral arms.
   D)   a small central bulge and loosely wound spiral arms.
   Ans: B   Section: 26-3

35. According to the Hubble classification scheme, an Sc galaxy has
   A)   a large central bulge and tightly wound spiral arms.
   B)   a small central bulge and well-defined but loosely wound spiral arms.
   C)   an irregular shape with no obvious disk or spiral arms.
   D)   a round or spherical appearance with a smooth light distribution.
   Ans: B   Section: 26-3

36. An astronomer studying a distant cluster of galaxies finds that several of the galaxies are spiral-shaped, with a large nuclear region and tightly wound arms. How should the astronomer classify these galaxies?
   A) Sc   B) SBb   C) Sb   D) Sa
   Ans: D   Section: 26-3

37. An astronomer studying a distant cluster of galaxies finds that several of the galaxies are spiral-shaped, with a nuclear region of moderate size and moderately wound arms. How should the astronomer classify these galaxies?
   A) Sa   B) Sb   C) SBc   D) Sc
   Ans: B   Section: 26-3

38. An astronomer studying a distant cluster of galaxies finds that several of the galaxies are spiral-shaped, with a small nuclear region and loosely wound but well-defined arms. How should the astronomer classify these galaxies?
   A) Sa   B) SBa   C) Sc   D) Sb
   Ans: C   Section: 26-3

39. Which of the following statements concerning spiral galaxies is true and provides a possible reason for the differences between different classes of spiral galaxies, Sa, Sb, and Sc?
    A) the fraction of their total mass which in the form of dust and gas is different; Sa has the lowest fraction whereas Sc has the highest
    B) the rate of star formation in their central bulges is different; the rate is highest for Sa type and lowest for Sc type
    C) the ratio of dust to gas in the interstellar medium is different in these types of galaxies; Sa has the most dust whereas Sc has the most gas
    D) the fraction of their total mass which in the form of dust and gas is different; Sa has the highest fraction whereas Sc has the lowest
    Ans: A   Section: 26-3

40. What is a barred spiral galaxy?
    A) a galaxy in which the arms form straight bars instead of spiral curves
    B) a spiral galaxy with a straight bar instead of a nuclear bulge
    C) a galaxy with a bar extending across the entire diameter and the arms starting at intervals along the bar
    D) a galaxy with a bar through the nuclear bulge, and the spiral arms starting from the ends of the bar
    Ans: D   Section: 26-3

41. What assignment is given to a galaxy with a large nuclear bulge and tightly wound arms starting from a bar through the central part of the galaxy?
    A) SBa   B) SBc   C) Sb   D) SBb
    Ans: A   Section: 26-3

42. What assignment is given to a galaxy with a moderately sized nuclear bulge and moderately wound arms starting from a bar through the central part of the galaxy?
    A) SBb   B) SBc   C) Sb   D) SBa
    Ans: A   Section: 26-3

43. What classification is given to a galaxy with a small nuclear bulge and loosely wound arms starting from a bar through the central part of the galaxy?
    A) SBc   B) SBa   C) SBb   D) Sb
    Ans: A   Section: 26-3

44. What is an SBc galaxy?
    A)   a galaxy with a moderately sized nuclear bulge, moderately wound arms, and a circular ring around the nuclear bulge
    B)   a galaxy with a small nuclear bulge and loosely wound arms starting from a bar through the central part of the galaxy
    C)   a galaxy with a moderately sized nuclear bulge and moderately wound arms starting from a bar through the central part of the galaxy
    D)   a galaxy with a large nuclear bulge and tightly wound arms starting from a bar through the central part of the galaxy
    Ans: B   Section: 26-3

45. How many barred spirals are there compared to ordinary spirals?
    A)   There are about half as many barred spirals as ordinary spirals.
    B)   There are about six times as many barred spirals as ordinary spirals.
    C)   There are about twice as many barred spirals as ordinary spirals.
    D)   There are about one-tenth as many barred spirals as ordinary spirals.
    Ans: C   Section: 26-3

46. What is the ratio of barred spirals to ordinary spirals in our universe?
    A) 1:100, very few spirals are barred   B) 10:1   C) 2:1   D) 1:2
    Ans: C   Section: 26-3

47. How does the number of barred spirals in the universe compare to the number of ordinary spirals?
    A)   Ordinary spirals outnumber barred spirals.
    B)   The question is meaningless—barred spirals are simply ordinary spirals seen edge-on.
    C)   Barred spirals outnumber ordinary spirals.
    D)   There are about equal numbers of barred spirals and ordinary spirals.
    Ans: C   Section: 26-3

48. Why does the central bulge of a spiral galaxy appear red when compared to the color of the spiral arms?
    A)   UV light from the very hot stars in the bulge has excited hydrogen gas, which is emitting the red Balmer H_α light as a consequence.
    B)   There is no star formation there, and the star population is dominated by old, long-lived, low-mass red stars.
    C)   The light from the stars in this region is not Doppler-shifted by galactic rotation, in contrast to that from spiral-arm stars.
    D)   Dust surrounding the bulge has preferentially scattered the blue light from the bulge stars.
    Ans: B   Section: 26-3

49. What is an elliptical galaxy?
    A)   a galaxy with an elliptical outline and a smooth distribution of brightness (no spiral arms)
    B)   a spiral galaxy seen from an angle (not face-on), giving it an elliptical profile
    C)   any galaxy with an elliptical halo when observed at radio wavelengths
    D)   a spiral galaxy with an elliptical central bulge, and the spiral arms starting from the ends of the ellipse
    Ans: A   Section: 26-3

50. Do the shapes of elliptical galaxies really reflect their true shape?
    A)   No. The shapes of most of them have been severely distorted by gravitational lensing around the super-massive black hole at their centers.
    B)   No, they may all be the same shape but viewed either edge-on, face-on, or in between these two cases.
    C)   No, because we cannot see the outlying spherical shells of material detected by radio telescopes around elliptical galaxies.
    D)   Yes. The shapes we see have been shown to be their true 3-dimensional shape.
    Ans: B   Section: 26-3

51. Which of the following statements is NOT characteristic of elliptical galaxies?
    A)   They are almost devoid of interstellar gas and dust.
    B)   They stopped forming stars billions of years ago.
    C)   Different elliptical galaxies appear to be flattened by different amounts.
    D)   They have a disk and central bulge, but no spiral arms.
    Ans: D   Section: 26-3

52. The Hubble classification for a galaxy with a circular outline and a smooth distribution of brightness is
    A) Sa.   B) Sc.   C) E7.   D) E0.
    Ans: D   Section: 26-3

53. The Hubble classification for a very flat elliptical galaxy is
    A) SBc.   B) Sc.   C) E0.   D) E7.
    Ans: D   Section: 26-3

54. What name is given to a galaxy with a smooth distribution of brightness and a very elongated shape?
    A) Sc.   B) SBc.   C) E7.   D) E0.
    Ans: C   Section: 26-3

55. What is an E3 galaxy?
    A)   a galaxy with a smooth light distribution and a moderately elongated elliptical shape, without a disk or central bulge
    B)   a galaxy with a smooth light distribution and a very elongated elliptical shape, without a disk or central bulge
    C)   a galaxy with a smooth light distribution and a moderately elongated elliptical shape, having a pronounced disk and central bulge
    D)   a galaxy with an irregular light distribution and a very elongated shape
    Ans: A   Section: 26-3

56. According to the Hubble classification scheme, an E4 galaxy has
    A)   an irregular shape.
    B)   a disk and central bulge, with a smooth light distribution and no spiral arms.
    C)   a round or spherical shape with a smooth light distribution and no disk or central bulge.
    D)   an elliptical shape (flattened circle) with a smooth light distribution.
    Ans: D   Section: 26-3

57. According to the Hubble classification scheme, an E3 galaxy
    A)   is flatter looking than an E5 galaxy.
    B)   has more tightly wound spiral arms than an E5 galaxy.
    C)   is rounder looking than an E5 galaxy.
    D)   has a shorter central bar in its disk than an E5 galaxy.
    Ans: C   Section: 26-3

58. According to the Hubble classification scheme, an E6 galaxy
    A)   has a shorter central bar in its disk than an E2 galaxy.
    B)   has more tightly wound spiral arms than an E2 galaxy.
    C)   is flatter looking than an E2 galaxy.
    D)   is rounder looking than an E2 galaxy.
    Ans: C   Section: 26-3

59. Which one of the following statements does NOT correctly describe a typical elliptical galaxy?
    A)   They have a central bulge and a disk, but no spiral arms.
    B)   They have a smooth light distribution with various degrees of flattening compared to a circular shape.
    C)   They contain primarily low-mass stars.
    D)   They cover the widest range of masses, from the smallest to the largest galaxies in the universe.
    Ans: A   Section: 26-3

60. Which of the following galaxy types contain little or no interstellar dust or gas?
    A) ellipticals   B) barred spirals   C) spirals   D) irregular galaxies
    Ans: A   Section: 26-3

61. In which of the following types of galaxies is star formation no longer occurring?
A) irregular galaxies   B) spirals   C) barred spirals   D) ellipticals
Ans: D   Section: 26-3

62. Which of the following types of galaxies contains primarily population II, low-mass, long-lived stars?
A) ellipticals   B) irregular galaxies   C) lenticular galaxies   D) spirals
Ans: A   Section: 26-3

63. An elliptical galaxy contains mostly what kind of stars?
A)   stars of all ages, but all metal-poor
B)   primarily young, metal-rich stars
C)   primarily old, metal-poor stars
D)   stars of all ages, from young, metal-rich stars to old, metal-poor stars
Ans: C   Section: 26-3

64. An astronomer studying a galaxy finds that its spectrum shows only old, low-mass, population II stars, and photographs of the galaxy show little or no interstellar dust or gas. What kind of galaxy is this astronomer studying?
A)   a spiral galaxy   C)   a barred spiral galaxy
B)   an elliptical galaxy   D)   an irregular galaxy
Ans: B   Section: 26-3

65. The largest galaxies in the universe come from which classification group?
A)   giant elliptical galaxies
B)   irregular galaxies
C)   lenticular galaxies
D)   large spiral galaxies like the Milky Way Galaxy
Ans: A   Section: 26-3

66. At visible wavelengths, which galaxies are the brightest in the universe?
A)   giant elliptical galaxies
B)   lenticular galaxies
C)   starburst galaxies
D)   large spiral galaxies like the Milky Way Galaxy
Ans: A   Section: 26-3

67. The largest range of sizes of galaxies is found in which class of galaxies?
A) barred spiral   B) elliptical   C) irregular   D) spiral
Ans: B   Section: 26-3

68. Which class of galaxies has the greatest range of sizes from largest to the smallest in our universe?
A) ellipticals   B) spirals   C) lenticular galaxies   D) irregular galaxies
Ans: A   Section: 26-3

69. The type or group of galaxies that contains both the largest and smallest galaxies in the universe is
    A)   the ellipticals.
    B)   the barred spirals.
    C)   the Sc type galaxies.
    D)   the irregulars.
    Ans: A   Section: 26-3

70. The biggest and intrinsically brightest galaxies in the universe are members of which group?
    A) large spirals   B) ellipticals   C) barred spirals   D) irregular galaxies
    Ans: B   Section: 26-3

71. Are there types of galaxies in which we can see completely through their centers?
    A)   No. The intense gravity generated by the central black hole will bend light beams passing through all galaxies, even if they have few stars.
    B)   Yes. Dwarf galaxies have very few stars that are not closely packed, even near their centers.
    C)   No. All galaxies have dense central bulges and most contain a central black hole.
    D)   Yes. Space has been cleared through the centers of some very massive galaxies by their central supermassive black holes, producing a tunnel.
    Ans: B   Section: 26-3

72. Which observation of elliptical galaxies provides a measure of the relative motions of stars and of the degree of randomness of their motions within these galaxies?
    A)   the redshift of spectral lines in their spectra
    B)   the broadening of spectral lines in their spectra
    C)   the relative brightnesses of central bulges and extended disks of these galaxies
    D)   the shapes of the galaxies
    Ans: B   Section: 26-3

73. The Hubble classification for a galaxy having a disk and central bulge, with a smooth light distribution but no spiral arms, is
    A) irregular.   B) S0.   C) SBa.   D) E0.
    Ans: B   Section: 26-3

74. What is a lenticular (S0) galaxy?
    A)   A galaxy with a lot of gas and dust and no particular structure.
    B)   A spiral galaxy with fuzzy and poorly formed spiral arms.
    C)   A galaxy with a smooth brightness profile, and lacking the central bulge and disk of a spiral galaxy.
    D)   A galaxy with a disk and central bulge like a spiral galaxy, but with no spiral arms.
    Ans: D   Section: 26-3

75. The Hubble classification scheme for an S0 galaxy is
    A) a large central bulge with tightly wound spiral arms.
    B) a small central bulge with loosely wound spiral arms.
    C) a disk and central bulge, with a smooth light distribution and no spiral arms.
    D) a round or spherical shape, with a smooth light distribution and no disk or central bulge.
    Ans: C   Section: 26-3

76. An astronomer studying a cluster of galaxies finds a galaxy that is round and has a disk and central bulge like a spiral galaxy, but has no spiral arms. How should the astronomer classify this galaxy?
    A) E0, elliptical
    B) Sa, extreme spiral
    C) irregular type I, underdeveloped spiral
    D) S0, lenticular
    Ans: D   Section: 26-3

77. How are the Magellanic Clouds, the two nearby satellite galaxies of our own galaxy, classified?
    A) globular clusters   C) elliptical galaxies
    B) irregular galaxies   D) spiral galaxies
    Ans: B   Section: 26-3

78. The Magellanic Clouds seen from the Southern hemisphere are examples of what type of objects?
    A) lenticular galaxies   C) planetary nebulae
    B) irregular galaxies   D) globular clusters
    Ans: B   Section: 26-3

79. Which of the following sequences shows the correct order of galaxy type in terms of the extent of rotational motion, from the least to the most rotation?
    A) Sb spiral, S0 lenticular, E7 elliptical, E0 elliptical
    B) S0 lenticular, E0 elliptical, E7 elliptical, Sb spiral
    C) E7 elliptical, E0 elliptical, S0 lenticular, Sb spiral
    D) E0 elliptical, E7 elliptical, S0 lenticular, Sb spiral
    Ans: D   Section: 26-3

80. To an astronomer, what is a "standard candle"?
    A) a standard light source that can be placed in a telescope, to which the brightnesses of stars and other objects can be compared
    B) any type of object whose absolute magnitude is known
    C) any galaxy whose redshift has been measured accurately
    D) an accurately defined brightness scale for stars and galaxies, such as the magnitude scale
    Ans: B   Section: 26-4

81. "Standard candles," which are important for finding distances to remote galaxies, are
    A)   standard laboratory light sources with which the brightness of a galaxy can be compared.
    B)   heat sources used for calibrating infrared observations of galaxies.
    C)   stars and other objects of known intrinsic brightness.
    D)   laboratory light sources with a well-known spectrum for calibration of stellar and galactic spectra.
    Ans: C   Section: 26-4

82. Which of the following objects are NOT used as "standard candles" for distance measurement to distant galaxies?
    A)   supernova explosions   C)   hot white dwarf stars
    B)   RR Lyrae stars   D)   Cepheid variable stars
    Ans: C   Section: 26-4

83. How would an astronomer, ancient or modern, use a "standard candle"?
    A)   She would use its faint light to illuminate the setting dials of her telescope.
    B)   She would use it to measure time using its slow but steady melting.
    C)   She would use it to generate a known and extremely reproducible standard spectrum for comparison with stellar spectra.
    D)   She would measure distance by comparing its apparent brightness with its known absolute brightness.
    Ans: D   Section: 26-4

84. Which of the following properties would NOT be important for a type of astronomical object being considered for use as a "standard candle" for distance estimation?
    A)   It must be a stable source of light over long periods.
    B)   It must be very bright.
    C)   It must be easily identifiable by some easily observed property.
    D)   It must have known and reproducible luminosity.
    Ans: A   Section: 26-4

85. How far out into space can we observe and identify Cepheid variables with the Hubble Space Telescope?
    A) about 30 Mpc   B) about 200 Mpc   C) about 600 kpc   D) about 60 pc
    Ans: A   Section: 26-4

86. What is the brightest standard candle found so far, and therefore the one that can be seen to the greatest distance?
    A)   Cepheid variables   C)   RR Lyrae stars
    B)   Type Ia supernovae   D)   Type II supernovae
    Ans: B   Section: 26-4

87. Type Ia supernovae are frequently used as standard candles for the measurement of distances to galaxies, but they are not all equally luminous. What additional relationship between properties of supernovae is used to determine specific luminosities for individual supernovae?
    A) the more blue the spectrum of the supernova, the more luminous the supernova
    B) the faster the rise of light intensity during the explosion, the more luminous the supernova
    C) the slower the decay of intensity after the explosion, the more luminous the supernova
    D) the faster the decay of intensity after the explosion, the more luminous the supernova
    Ans: C   Section: 26-4

88. The Tully-Fisher relation provides a method of determining distances to galaxies by estimating the galaxy luminosity from a measurement of which parameter relating to the 21-cm atomic hydrogen radio emission line?
    A) its position and Doppler shift   C) its width
    B) the split between its two components D) its intensity
    Ans: C   Section: 26-4

89. In the 1970s it was discovered that, among spiral galaxies, the wider the 21-cm radio emission line is, the brighter the galaxy. What name is given to this relation?
    A) the Schwarzschild law   C) the Tully-Fisher relation
    B) the Hubble law   D) the mass-luminosity relation
    Ans: C   Section: 26-4

90. What is the Tully-Fisher relation?
    A) the more distant the galaxy, the fainter it appears
    B) the more distant the galaxy, the greater the recessional velocity
    C) the brighter the Cepheid, the longer the pulsation period
    D) the brighter the galaxy, the wider the 21-cm radio emission line
    Ans: D   Section: 26-4

91. Which spectral feature originating in a galaxy is used in the Tully-Fisher relation, by measuring its width, to determine the intrinsic luminosity of the galaxy?
    A) the 2.3 mm microwave emission line from the molecule CO, which is closely associated with molecular hydrogen
    B) the Lyman L_α ultraviolet line from atomic hydrogen
    C) the 21-cm radio emission line from atomic hydrogen gas
    D) the Balmer H_α red line from atomic hydrogen
    Ans: C   Section: 26-4

92. Of the following distance measurement techniques, which one can be used to find the farthest distances?
    A)   RR Lyrae variable star measurement
    B)   parallax measurement
    C)   Cepheid, population I, variable star measurement
    D)   Type Ia supernova apparent brightness measurement
    Ans: D   Section: 26-4

93. How does the maser technique work in providing a direct distance measurement to distant galaxies at intermediate distances (5–10 Mpc range) in the universe?
    A)   velocity measurements of sources on either side of the galaxy from Doppler shift of the very narrow maser spectral lines combined with very precise angular motions of equivalent sources in front of the galaxy, measured with radio interferometry
    B)   velocity measurements of sources on either side of the galaxy from Doppler shift of the very narrow maser spectral lines combined with observations of rates of intensity flickering of these small sources
    C)   velocity measurements of sources on either side of the galaxy from Doppler shift of the very narrow maser spectral lines combined with very precise angular separation between the sources and the centers of the galaxies by radio interferometry
    D)   very precise angular motions of sources in front of the galaxy measured with radio interferometry combined with observations of the rates of flickering of intensity of these small sources
    Ans: A   Section: 26-4

94. The Tully-Fisher Relationship relies upon broadening of the 21-cm radio line in distant spiral galaxies. What causes this broadening?
    A)   thermal motion of the gases in the galaxy
    B)   random motions of the stars in the galaxy
    C)   the rotation of the galaxy
    D)   the general expansion of the universe (Hubble flow)
    Ans: C   Section: 26-4

95. The Tully-Fisher Relationship can be used to measure the luminosity of (and thus the distance to)
    A)   elliptical galaxies.   C)   globular clusters.
    B)   spiral galaxies.   D)   Type II supernovae.
    Ans: B   Section: 26-4

96. Parallax and masers are two techniques for measuring distances in astronomy. Although very different from each other, they share a characteristic that is different from the other main measuring techniques. This is that
    A) they can both be used to measure the same set of objects and can thus check each other.
    B) the relative motion of the distant objects is not important, thus avoiding the complication of the Earth's motion.
    C) each is independent of the results of any other distance measuring technique.
    D) only these two techniques are correct for relativistic as well as Newtonian situations.
    Ans: C   Section: 26-4

97. The following distance measuring techniques, arranged in order of the distance for which they are most effective, from smallest to greatest, are
    A) Cepheid variables, spectroscopic parallax, Type Ia supernovae, Tully-Fisher Relation.
    B) spectroscopic parallax, Tully-Fisher Relation, Cepheid variables, Type Ia supernovae.
    C) spectroscopic parallax, Cepheid variables, Tully-Fisher Relation, Type Ia supernovae.
    D) Cepheid variables, spectroscopic variables, Type Ia supernovae, Tully-Fisher Relation.
    Ans: C   Section: 26-4

98. Who first discovered the fact that the majority of galaxies are moving away from the Earth?
    A) Albert Einstein   B) Karl Jansky   C) V. M. Slipher   D) Edwin Hubble
    Ans: C   Section: 26-5

99. Who first showed that the recessional speeds of galaxies increase with increasing distance from the Earth?
    A) Edwin Hubble   B) Karl Jansky   C) V. M. Slipher   D) Albert Einstein
    Ans: A   Section: 26-5

100. Which of the following did Edwin Hubble NOT contribute to our understanding of galaxies and their behavior?
    A) observations of Cepheid variable stars in spiral "nebulae" and their interpretation
    B) a relationship between distance to galaxies and their apparent velocity of recession
    C) determination of the ages of galaxies and the correct sequence of evolutionary progress of galaxies
    D) a classification scheme for galaxy types
    Ans: C   Section: 26-2, 26-3, and 26-5

101. The primary evidence for the Expanding Universe concept is
    A) the redshift of light from distant galaxies, which increases with distance of the galaxy from Earth.
    B) the slow increase in the Earth-Moon separation with time.
    C) observation of supernova explosions.
    D) the discovery of black holes in binary stars.
    Ans: A   Section: 26-5

102. The Hubble relationship shows a proportionality between the distance to a galaxy and the
    A) width of the 21-cm radio emission line from hydrogen.
    B) parallax angle change of the galaxy as the Earth moves through one year.
    C) angular diameter of the galaxy as seen from Earth.
    D) overall redshift of a galaxy's spectrum.
    Ans: D   Section: 26-5

103. Which of the following speeds does Hubble's law describe?
    A) the speeds of individual galaxies in the Local Group and other nearby galaxy clusters
    B) the speeds of individual clusters of galaxies in our own local supercluster
    C) the speeds of stars in our own galaxy
    D) the speeds of superclusters of galaxies
    Ans: D   Section: 26-5

104. The Hubble relation links which two characteristics of distant objects in the universe?
    A) distance and velocity of recession
    B) the state of organization of stars in clusters and the age of the clusters
    C) stellar mass and luminosity
    D) luminosity and surface temperature
    Ans: A   Section: 26-5

105. Hubble's law describes how two properties of distant galaxies are related to each other. What are these two properties?
    A) distance and velocity of recession
    B) brightness and recession velocity
    C) brightness and the width of the 21-cm radio emission line of hydrogen
    D) distance and brightness
    Ans: A   Section: 26-5

106. The Hubble Law, representing observations of distant galaxies in the universe, relates which two parameters?
  A)   the mass of a distant galaxy and its luminosity
  B)   the luminosity of a distant galaxy and the width of the 21-cm radio line of hydrogen
  C)   the distance to a distant galaxy and its recession velocity
  D)   the mass of a distant galaxy and its recession velocity
  Ans: C   Section: 26-5

107. The Hubble distance-velocity relation states that
  A)   all objects appear to have the same velocity away from the Sun, irrespective of distance from the Sun.
  B)   all distant objects are moving toward the Sun, the most distant objects fastest.
  C)   the further a distant object is from the Sun, the faster it appears to be moving away from the Sun.
  D)   mutual gravitational attraction of all objects in the universe means that all objects appear to be moving toward the Sun, the closest ones traveling fastest.
  Ans: C   Section: 26-5

108. For which objects in the universe has the Hubble relation been shown to hold experimentally?
  A)   stars in the near neighborhood of the Sun, in our galaxy
  B)   stars in the distant spiral arms of our galaxy
  C)   galaxies in the Local Group, in the near vicinity of the Milky Way
  D)   distant galaxies
  Ans: D   Section: 26-5

109. What is the Hubble flow?
  A)   Distant galaxies are all moving toward us on one side of the sky and away from us on the other, as part of the universal flow of galaxies through the universe.
  B)   Distant galaxies are all moving away from us at approximately the same speed.
  C)   Distant galaxies are all moving away from us, with speed decreasing with increasing distance.
  D)   Distant galaxies are all moving away from us, with speed increasing with increasing distance.
  Ans: D   Section: 26-5

110. Because of the expansion of space, we see all distant galaxies moving away from us, with more distant galaxies moving faster. An observer in one of these distant galaxies would see
    A) all galaxies moving away from the observer, with more distant galaxies moving faster.
    B) all galaxies on one side of the observer moving toward the observer, and all galaxies on the other side moving away from the observer, with more distant galaxies moving faster.
    C) all galaxies moving away from the observer, with closer galaxies moving faster.
    D) all galaxies moving toward the observer, with more distant galaxies moving faster.
    Ans: A   Section: 26-5

111. In the verification of the Hubble law for the expansion of the universe and the determination of the constant H_0, the greatest difficulty has been
    A) measurement of recession velocities of distant galaxies by Doppler shift.
    B) accurate determination of distances to very distant galaxies.
    C) allowance for the fact that the high gravitational fields of the supermassive black holes within distant galaxies can redshift light (gravitational redshift).
    D) identification of distant objects as galaxies, rather than very bright stars.
    Ans: B   Section: 26-5

112. What method is used to determine the distances of very remote galaxies?
    A) use of their spectral redshifts and the Hubble law
    B) measurement of the angular size of the galaxy and an assumption about the actual physical size of the galaxy
    C) measurement of the apparent brightness and period of Cepheid variable stars within the galaxies
    D) comparison of their apparent and absolute magnitudes
    Ans: A   Section: 26-5

113. The expansion of the universe takes place
    A) between all objects, even between the atoms in our bodies, although the expansion of a person is too small to be measured reliably.
    B) only between objects separated by a vacuum; as a result, our bodies do not expand but the Earth-Moon system does.
    C) only over distances about the size of a galaxy or larger; consequently, our galaxy expands but the solar system does not.
    D) primarily in the huge voids between clusters of galaxies: "small" objects like galaxies or the Earth do not expand.
    Ans: D   Section: 26-5

114. Even though the Hubble law for galactic motions indicates that the spectra of all galaxies should show redshift as a consequence of the general expansion of the universe, the Andromeda Galaxy M31 appears to show a blueshift in its spectrum. Why is this?
    A) M31 has an abnormally powerful black hole at its center which gravitationally blueshifts its entire spectrum.
    B) The mutual attraction between M31 and the Milky Way Galaxy has overcome the general Hubble flow.
    C) Young giant spiral galaxies such as M31 do not follow the normal Hubble flow because they have formed relatively recently.
    D) One side of M31 is heavily obscured by dust and gas and the blueshift simply shows the Doppler shift of the other side of the galaxy, produced by galactic rotation.
    Ans: B   Section: 26-5

115. What does the Hubble law tell us, if H_0 is a constant?
    A) $H_0 \times$ recessional speed = distance   C) distance $\times$ recessional speed = H_0
    B) recessional speed = H_0 = constant   D) recessional speed = $H_0 \times$ distance
    Ans: D   Section: 26-5

116. What is Hubble's law, if V is recession velocity, d is the distance to a galaxy, and H_0 is a constant?
    A) $V = H_0$ = constant   B) $V = H_0\, d$ C) $H_0\, V = d$ D) $Vd = H_0$
    Ans: B   Section: 26-5

117. The mathematical form of the Hubble law for the expanding universe concept relates the velocity of recession, V, to the distance of the observed object d (with H_0 the Hubble Constant) as follows:
    A) $V = H_0/d$.   B) $d = H_0\, V$.   C) $V = H_0\, d$.   D) $V = H_0/d^2$.
    Ans: C   Section: 26-5

118. Based on the most accurate measurements to date, what is believed to be the value of Hubble's constant?
    A) between 50 and 60 km/s/Mpc   C) between 70 and 75 km/s/Mpc
    B) between 100 and 120 km/s/Mpc   D) between 80 and 90 km/s/Mpc
    Ans: C   Section: 26-5

119. On the basis of the distance to the Coma cluster of galaxies (90 Mpc) and the Hubble relation, using for the Hubble constant H_0 the value 71 km/sec per million parsecs, what would be the approximate wavelength shift of the Balmer H_α spectral line at 656.3 nanometers emitted by a galaxy in the cluster because of the general expansion of the universe? (See Box 26-2, Freedman and Kaufmann, *Universe*, 7th ed.)
    A) 1.40×10^{-2} nm   B) 2.80×10^{-3} nm   C) 140.0 nm   D) 14.0 nm
    Ans: D   Section: 26-5

120. One astronomer (astronomer A) claims that the Hubble constant is 84 km/s/Mpc, while another (astronomer B) claims that it is 63 km/s/Mpc. If, based on the Hubble constant, astronomer A claims that a particular galaxy is 3 billion light years away, then astronomer B would claim that it is
A)   4.00 billion light years away.   C)   3.75 billion light years away.
B)   2.25 billion light years away.   D)   2.00 billion light years away.
Ans: B   Section: 26-5

121. The Hercules cluster of galaxies shown in Fig. 26-19 (Freedman and Kaufmann, *Universe,* 7th ed.) is at a distance of 650 million light years from our galaxy. Using a Hubble constant of 23 km/s/Mly, at what wavelength will the Balmer H_α spectral line, with rest wavelength = 656.3 nm, be seen in the spectrum of a galaxy in this cluster?
A) 623.6 nm   B) 689.0 nm   C) 656.7 nm   D) 32.7 nm
Ans: B   Section: 26-5

122. If the elliptical galaxy in Hydra, whose image and spectrum are shown at the bottom of Fig. 26-14 (Freedman and Kaufmann, *Universe,* 7th ed.), were to be at a distance of 3 billion light-years, what would be the value of Hubble's constant H_0? (Be careful with units.)
A)   about 215 km/s/MLy   C)   about 20,000 km/s/MLy
B)   about 20 km/s/MLy   D)   about 66 km/s/MLy
Ans: B   Section: 26-5

123. Suppose that a particular galaxy is 400 million parsecs from the Earth. What is the recessional velocity of this galaxy? Take Hubble's constant to be 71 km/s/Mpc.
A) 5.7 km/s   B) 175,000 km/s   C) 5.7 million km/s   D) 28,400 km/s
Ans: D   Section: 26-5

124. An astronomer studying the spectrum of a distant galaxy finds that its recessional velocity is 14,000 km/s. What is the distance to the galaxy? Take Hubble's constant to be 71 km/s/Mpc.
A) 98 Mpc   B) 980,000 Mpc   C) 1,970 Mpc   D) 197 Mpc
Ans: D   Section: 26-5

125. Suppose an astronomer discovers a distant quasar whose recessional velocity is 1/3 the speed of light. If Hubble's constant is 71 km/s/Mpc, how far away is the quasar?
A) 7,000,000 Mpc   B) 1,410 Mpc   C) 141 Mpc   D) 70 Mpc
Ans: B   Section: 26-5

126. Which one of the following formulas is not valid when the speed of the object under consideration becomes large—say, 10% of the speed of light?
   A) $v = H_0 d$
   B) $z = v/c$
   C) $z = \Delta\lambda/\lambda$
   D)   All the equations above are generally valid at all speeds.
   Ans: B   Section: 26-5 and Box 26-2

127. For galaxies in the Hydra cluster, the recessional velocity is 61,000 km/sec. What is the shift in frequency for the Balmer H_α line, the rest wavelength of which is 656.3 nm?
   A) 92 nm   B) 133 nm   C) 151 nm   D) 584 nm
   Ans: C   Section: 26-5 and Box 26-2

128. Our galaxy is
   A)   one member of a large, regular cluster of thousands of galaxies.
   B)   one member of a small cluster of galaxies.
   C)   an isolated galaxy, not a member of any cluster.
   D)   one member of a large, irregular cluster of thousands of galaxies.
   Ans: B   Section: 26-6

129. What is the Local Group?
   A)   a group of about 100 stars within 100 light years of the Sun, which appear to have been formed in a star cluster at about the same time from similar material
   B)   the planets Mars, Earth, and Venus, which are similar in physical properties and in orbital positions around the Sun
   C)   a group of galaxies clustered around the Andromeda Galaxy M31, apparently gravitationally bound to it but separate from the Milky Way
   D)   a cluster of about 30 galaxies of which the Milky Way is a member
   Ans: D   Section: 26-6

130. The Local Group is
   A)   the name of the spiral arm of our galaxy in which the Sun is located.
   B)   a cluster of galaxies in which the Milky Way is located.
   C)   a star cluster to which the Sun belongs.
   D)   the family of planets around the Sun.
   Ans: B   Section: 26-6

131. In the Local Group of galaxies, how many other galaxies are known to be within 10^6 light-years of our own Milky Way Galaxy? (See Figure 26-17, Freedman and Kaufmann, *Universe,* 7th ed.)
   A) 11   B) 21   C) 5   D) 15
   Ans: A   Section: 26-6

132. What is a rich cluster of galaxies?
     A)   a cluster with a high metal content
     B)   a cluster with more spiral galaxies than ellipticals
     C)   a cluster (like our local group) that contains at least two large galaxies
     D)   a cluster containing thousands of galaxies
     Ans: D   Section: 26-6

133. What is a poor cluster of galaxies?
     A)   a cluster containing a few dozen galaxies
     B)   a cluster with very little gas or dust
     C)   a cluster with a low metal content
     D)   a cluster with very few spirals compared to other types of galaxies
     Ans: A   Section: 26-6

134. A rich, regular cluster of galaxies differs from a rich, irregular cluster by
     A)   having its galaxies distributed in a regular, highly flattened system (like a disk).
     B)   lacking the giant elliptical galaxies often found in irregular clusters.
     C)   having fewer spirals and more ellipticals and S0 galaxies than an irregular cluster.
     D)   containing fewer galaxies than an irregular cluster.
     Ans: C   Section: 26-6

135. What is the galaxy content of a rich, regular cluster of galaxies, like the Coma cluster?
     A)   mostly ellipticals and S0 galaxies, with relatively few spirals and irregulars
     B)   entirely elliptical galaxies
     C)   mostly spirals and irregulars, and very few ellipticals and S0 galaxies
     D)   more-or-less even distribution of spirals, ellipticals, irregulars, and S0 galaxies
     Ans: A   Section: 26-6

136. What is the galaxy content of a rich, irregular cluster of galaxies, like the Hercules cluster?
     A)   entirely elliptical galaxies
     B)   more-or-less equal numbers of spirals and ellipticals
     C)   many more ellipticals than spirals
     D)   many more spirals than ellipticals
     Ans: B   Section: 26-6

137. The total number of galaxies in a rich, regular cluster of galaxies such as the Coma cluster, is believed to be
     A)   over a million galaxies.   C)   about 10,000 galaxies.
     B)   several dozen galaxies.   D)   about 1000 galaxies.
     Ans: C   Section: 26-6

138. What is the famous Virgo cluster of galaxies?
    A)   a cluster of unknown type centered on a very bright quasar near the edge of the visible universe
    B)   a rich, irregular cluster of over 1,000 galaxies
    C)   a rich, regular cluster of thousands of galaxies
    D)   the nearest cluster beyond the Local Group, containing about 3 dozen galaxies
    Ans: B   Section: 26-6

139. What is distinctive about the Coma cluster of galaxies?
    A)   It is the cluster in which our Milky Way Galaxy is located.
    B)   It contains many quasars.
    C)   It is the nearest rich, regular cluster.
    D)   It is moving very rapidly toward the Local Group of galaxies, which contains the Milky Way Galaxy.
    Ans: C   Section: 26-6

140. If the estimated distance from the Earth to the Coma cluster of galaxies is about 300 million light-years (see Fig. 26-16, Freedman and Kaufmann, *Universe*, 7th ed.), what is its velocity of recession?
    A) 14 km/s   B) 6,600 km/s   C) 0.072 km/s   D) 21,000 km/s
    Ans: B   Section: 26-6

141. The light that arrives at Earth from the Coma cluster of galaxies has traveled for approximately how long?
    A)   300 million years   C)   30 million years
    B)   300 billion years   D)   92 million years
    Ans: A   Section: 26-6

142. Suppose we were to detect radio signals from an intelligent civilization in the Coma cluster of galaxies. If we sent a message to this civilization, how long would it take for us to get a reply?
    A)   300 million years   C)   150 million years
    B)   75 million years   D)   600 million years
    Ans: D   Section: 26-6

143. How are galaxies spread throughout the universe?
    A)   They are grouped into clusters that are spread more-or-less evenly throughout the universe.
    B)   They are grouped into clusters that in turn are grouped into clusters of clusters (superclusters).
    C)   Galaxies are densest near the Milky Way Galaxy and become less and less numerous the further we look out into the universe.
    D)   Galaxies are spread more-or-less evenly throughout the universe.
    Ans: B   Section: 26-6

144. The overall distribution of galaxies through space is now found to be
    A) galaxies clustered together in several high-density centers, with very little matter between them
    B) galaxies concentrated on the surfaces of huge open spaces or voids, like soap bubbles.
    C) galaxies concentrated around one position in space, presumably the original site of the Big Bang.
    D) galaxies distributed uniformly throughout space, out to the furthest distances.
    Ans: B   Section: 26-6

145. Galaxies are distributed through the universe in
    A) clusters, which are grouped into linked superclusters around huge voids (like soap bubbles).
    B) isolated clusters containing anywhere from a few dozen galaxies to thousands of galaxies.
    C) isolated superclusters, each of which contain dozens of clusters of galaxies.
    D) a random scattering of small clusters of galaxies similar to the Local Group.
    Ans: A   Section: 26-6

146. What is a supercluster of galaxies?
    A) It is a cluster of galaxies that is packed much more densely than normal clusters, giving it a significantly higher mass.
    B) It is another name for the whole universe.
    C) It is a cluster of galaxies that is spread out over a larger-than-normal volume of space.
    D) It is a cluster of galaxy clusters.
    Ans: D   Section: 26-6

147. How are clusters of galaxies spread throughout the universe?
    A) They are distributed more-or-less evenly (i.e., at random) throughout the universe.
    B) They are distributed over the surfaces of large voids, making the universe look like a large collection of soap bubbles.
    C) They are distributed with increasing density of galaxies toward some point which must be the original site of the Big Bang.
    D) They are distributed into long lines that cover the universe like a gigantic network of strings.
    Ans: B   Section: 26-6

148. Which common household phenomenon represents the closest analogy to the distribution of galaxies in our universe?
    A) a bowl of sugar crystals, uniformly distributed, close-packed, and evenly spaced apart
    B) lemonade in a glass, surrounding small moving gas bubbles, the bubble's motion being similar to the Hubble flow
    C) ice crystals forming on a cold, flat window in regular patterns
    D) soap films surrounding air bubbles in soap suds
    Ans: D   Section: 26-6

149. In discussing galaxies and the universe, astronomers often talk about "voids." What are voids?
    A) holes in some galaxies in dense clusters of galaxies where a collision with another, smaller, galaxy has removed the stars from that region
    B) volumes of space hundreds of millions of light years across that contain almost no galaxies
    C) the large expanses of space between galaxies, where there is essentially no gas or dust
    D) regions within clusters of galaxies that seem to be devoid of matter
    Ans: B   Section: 26-6

150. Gravity is a long-range force, and its effect can be seen in each of the following cases *except one*. Which is the exception?
    A) globular clusters move in orbits about the center of the Milky Way
    B) the most recently discovered member of the Local Group, Canis Major Dwarf, a close companion of the Milky Way galaxy, is being disrupted by tidal forces from the Milky Way
    C) clusters of galaxies are bound systems
    D) superclusters of galaxy clusters are bound systems
    Ans: D   Section: 26-6

151. The source of the hot, intergalactic gas in many rich, regular clusters of galaxies appears to be
    A) jets of gas ejected by supermassive black holes at the centers of the galaxies.
    B) bursts of star formation in merging galaxies.
    C) collisions between galaxies in the cluster.
    D) supernovae (exploding stars).
    Ans: C   Section: 26-7

152. Large clouds of very hot gas that emit vast quantities of X rays are detected between the galaxies in rich clusters of galaxies. How has this gas been heated?
    A)   by the intense radiation from nearby galaxies
    B)   by the compression of gas as it falls into an unseen supermassive black hole between the galaxies
    C)   by the annihilation of antimatter in this region of space by matter ejected by nearby galaxies
    D)   by the collision of two galaxies
    Ans: D   Section: 26-7

153. Many rich, regular clusters of galaxies contain substantial amounts of very hot, intergalactic gas. Where is this gas believed to have come from?
    A)   supernovae (exploding stars)
    B)   the result of shell ejection on numerous planetary nebulae from stars between the galaxies
    C)   collisions between galaxies in the cluster
    D)   ejection of material by supermassive black holes at the centers of the galaxies
    Ans: C   Section: 26-7

154. What is the dominant radiation that we see from the intergalactic matter in rich clusters of galaxies?
    A)   X rays from very hot gas
    B)   infrared radiation from dust
    C)   21-cm radio radiation from cool, neutral hydrogen gas
    D)   ultraviolet light from electrons spiraling in magnetic fields
    Ans: A   Section: 26-7

155. What is the typical temperature of the intergalactic gas in rich clusters of galaxies?
    A)   10 to 100 million K   C)   10 to 100 K
    B)   10,000 to 20,000 K   D)   1 to 10 billion K
    Ans: A   Section: 26-7

156. What is the likely fate of our Milky Way within about the next 6–8 billion years?
    A)   It will collide with the Andromeda Galaxy, triggering new star birth in gas and dust clouds.
    B)   It will continue to move away from its near neighbor galaxy, M31 in Andromeda, allowing its spiral arms to straighten to form a central bar.
    C)   Its rate of rotation will slow and its spiral arms will dissipate into intergalactic space as the galaxy becomes an elliptical galaxy.
    D)   It will slowly condense under the action of the central supermassive black hole, causing its spin rate to increase.
    Ans: A   Section: 26-7

157. What would happen if the Andromeda galaxy (a spiral about the same size as ours) collided with our own Milky Way Galaxy?
    A)   The two galaxies would pass through each other, the stars sailing past each other unharmed, while the interstellar gas and dust clouds would collide and stop, thereby becoming extremely heated.
    B)   The two galaxies would pass through each other almost unchanged, with essentially no interactions at all.
    C)   The supermassive black holes of the two galaxies would collide and explode, the resulting radiation essentially destroying their stars, planets, and any life forms that there may have been (including us).
    D)   All of the gas and dust clouds and a great many of the stars would collide with each other, stopping both galaxies and creating a galactic merger.
    Ans: A   Section: 26-7

158. What is a starburst galaxy?
    A)   a galaxy with streams of stars arching out from one region, as if from an explosion
    B)   a galaxy with an unusually large number of newborn and young stars
    C)   a galaxy that is still in the process of formation from the intergalactic medium, and is undergoing its first episode of star formation
    D)   a galaxy with stars moving radially outward in all directions from the explosion of the accretion disk of its central supermassive black hole
    Ans: B   Section: 26-7

159. A starburst galaxy appears to be a galaxy in which
    A)   essentially all of the star formation took place in a single, billion-year-long burst early in the life of the galaxy.
    B)   a central, supermassive black hole is throwing jets of gas and stars out from the nucleus into intergalactic space.
    C)   most of the energy from the galaxy is being produced by supernovae.
    D)   a collision with another galaxy has produced a burst of star formation.
    Ans: D   Section: 26-7

160. What is believed to be the origin of starburst galaxies?
    A)   The galaxies are slower-rotators than other galaxies, and the slower-speed collisions between interstellar clouds produce more star formation.
    B)   A recent collision with another galaxy has triggered a wave of star formation.
    C)   A recent series of supernovae has compressed the interstellar medium and started a new wave of star formation.
    D)   The galaxies are newly formed and are undergoing their initial, rapid star formation
    Ans: B   Section: 26-7

161. One of the consequences of the collision of two galaxies appears to be
    A) the disappearance of one of the galaxies into the central supermassive black hole of the other.
    B) almost nothing, because stars are widely separated in each galaxy and the probability of star-to-star collisions is very small.
    C) a burst of vigorous star birth.
    D) a very large explosion, similar to but much larger than a supernova.
    Ans: C   Section: 26-7

162. Which of the following statements is most likely to be true when discussing galactic motions and interactions?
    A) Galaxies are so widely separated that they never interact or collide.
    B) Galaxies are so closely packed in the universe that they are always interacting with one another.
    C) The universe is composed of one giant galaxy of which all observed stars are members; thus, the question of interaction between galaxies is irrelevant.
    D) Galaxies occasionally collide with one another, particularly within clusters of galaxies.
    Ans: D   Section: 26-7

163. What is believed to be the origin of giant elliptical galaxies?
    A) They grew by devouring smaller galaxies in galactic cannibalism.
    B) They have grown continuously since their formation, by accreting intergalactic gas.
    C) Collisions between galaxies in the cluster produce a smooth distribution of stars throughout the cluster; these sink by gravity to the cluster center and form giant elliptical galaxies.
    D) They formed that way and have remained unchanged ever since.
    Ans: A   Section: 26-7

164. We have observed each one of the following as evidence of colliding galaxies *except one*. Which is the exception?
    A) very strong x-ray emission coming from rich clusters of galaxies
    B) starburst galaxies that contain hot gas, many newborn stars, and relatively young globular clusters
    C) streams of hydrogen gas connecting two or more galaxies
    D) a distribution of black hole candidates throughout a galaxy suggesting many star mergers as a result of a galactic collision
    Ans: D   Section: 26-7

165. Which of the following techniques have been successful in identifying good candidates for black holes in our galaxy?
    A) detection of X rays from binary stars undergoing mass exchange, where the masses of component stars have been determined
    B) detection of extremely redshifted starlight from regions in the nearby spiral arm of the galaxy
    C) detection of extremely dark points in the sky, from which no light at all is seen
    D) gravitational lensing of light from stars to produce two very close and identical images
    Ans: A   Section: 26-8

166. Which single major problem perhaps puzzles astronomers the most as they attempt to interpret the properties and behavior of clusters of galaxies?
    A) the presence of star formation in many galaxies, long after it is expected to have died out
    B) the missing-mass problem, with at least 10 times more mass needed for galactic cluster stability than is observed in visible material
    C) the structure and motion of spiral arms in galaxies in many clusters
    D) the excessive rate of supernova occurrence in galaxies in some clusters
    Ans: B   Section: 26-8

167. How much of the mass of a galaxy plays a role in emitting radiation into space?
    A) 10%   B) 50%   C) only about 1%   D) almost 100%
    Ans: A   Section: 26-8 and Introduction, Chapter 26

168. Which one of the following statements is true about clusters of galaxies?
    A) The mass observed in the galaxies of the cluster is about ten times larger than the amount needed to hold the cluster together, and this is causing the cluster to collapse.
    B) The mass observed in the galaxies of the cluster is typically almost exactly equal to that needed to hold the cluster together.
    C) The mass observed in the galaxies of the cluster is many thousands of times too small to hold the cluster together.
    D) The mass observed in the galaxies of the cluster is about ten times too small to hold the cluster together.
    Ans: D   Section: 26-8

169. Which of the following has NOT provided a means by which astronomers can infer the presence of dark matter in the universe?
    A) observation of the bending of light from remote galaxies as it passes through intervening clusters of galaxies, producing gravitational lensing
    B) measurement of the orbital speeds of stars in the outer regions of galaxies
    C) measurement of the orbital speeds of stars near possible supermassive black holes at the centers of galaxies
    D) measurement of the line-of-sight speeds of individual galaxies in clusters of galaxies
    Ans: C   Section: 26-8

170. One of the big puzzles about the properties and behavior of large clusters of galaxies is that
    A) they appear to be spread uniformly throughout space in all directions, which is difficult to explain with the Big Bang Theory.
    B) there appears to be insufficient mass in the luminous matter (star, etc.) to hold the cluster together gravitationally.
    C) each one appears to consist of the same type of galaxy, some made up totally of spiral galaxies whereas others contain only ellipticals.
    D) they appear not to take part in the general expansion of the universe, in contrast to single separate galaxies, probably because they are gravitationally bound to one another.
    Ans: B   Section: 26-8

171. One of the recently discovered components of clusters of galaxies, which may have some bearing upon the "missing-mass" problem, is
    A) large numbers of cool, dark "brown dwarf" stars, previously unknown, within the galaxies.
    B) X-ray measurements of substantial amounts of very hot, intergalactic gas in clusters.
    C) very large, cool molecular clouds within and surrounding the galaxies, detected by radio astronomy.
    D) large numbers of small but massive black holes within every galaxy.
    Ans: B   Section: 26-8

172. How has the hot, X-ray-emitting intergalactic gas in galaxy clusters affected the "missing mass" problem for these clusters?
    A) It supplies the mass needed to solve the problem.
    B) It supplies about 1/10 of the "missing mass," leaving 9/10 still missing.
    C) It is very tenuous gas and supplies almost no mass at all; therefore it has almost no effect on the "missing mass" problem.
    D) It supplies ten times too much mass—now the problem is how clusters so massive can be so large.
    Ans: B   Section: 26-8

173. If most of the mass of a galaxy is located near the center of the galaxy, then in the OUTER PART of this galaxy we would expect the orbital speeds of stars to decrease with increasing distance from the center. This is an example of
    A) Kepler's third law.   C) Newton's third law.
    B) Wien's law.   D) Hubble's law.
    Ans: A   Section: 26-8

174. Most of the light from a galaxy comes from the inner parts. IF THIS MEANS that most of the galaxy's mass is also in the inner region, then how would we expect the galaxy's speed of rotation to behave in its outer region?
    A) The rotation speed should decrease smoothly with increasing distance from the center, following a Keplerian curve.
    B) The rotation speed should decrease sharply to zero at the outer edge of the visible galaxy.
    C) The rotation speed should increase with increasing distance from the center.
    D) The rotation speed should not change appreciably with increasing distance from the center (i.e., a "flat" rotation curve).
    Ans: A   Section: 26-8

175. The rotation curve of a galaxy is a graph showing the galaxy's speed of rotation at different distances from the center. The observed rotation curve in the OUTER PARTS of a typical large spiral galaxy
    A) decreases suddenly to zero at the outer edge of the visible galaxy.
    B) decreases smoothly with increasing distance from the center, following a Keplerian curve.
    C) is quite flat (roughly the same speed at all distances).
    D) increases drastically with increasing distance from the center, as shown by the spiral arms.
    Ans: C   Section: 26-8

176. What evidence is there for considerable extra mass within galaxies which does not produce visible light—the so-called dark matter?
    A) The rotation curve of galaxies, showing orbital speeds of material, remains flat to large distances from the galactic centers, and does not follow a Kepler-type curve.
    B) the appearance of many very dark spots within the galaxy, evidence of numerous low-mass black holes scattered throughout the galaxy
    C) widespread evidence for gravitational lensing of background stars in a galaxy by massive but invisible objects in the foreground
    D) intense output of X rays from very hot gas between the stars, originating in otherwise dark regions
    Ans: A   Section: 26-8

177. Dark, unknown forms of matter appear to make up about what fraction of the mass of a typical rich cluster of galaxies?
A) 10%   B) much less than 1%   C) 90%   D) half
Ans: C   Section: 26-8

178. What fraction of the mass required by the cluster's observed gravity, as shown by the speeds of galaxies in the cluster, is represented by the mass of the presently observable matter in a typical rich cluster of galaxies?
A) 10%   B) 100%, or all of the galaxy   C) about 1%   D) 90%
Ans: A   Section: 26-8

179. In order for gravitational lensing of a distant quasar to occur, the galaxy producing the lensing must
A)   be rotating rapidly in order to produce the requisite curvature of space to bend the light beam.
B)   be almost perfectly placed on a line between Earth and the quasar.
C)   contain a supermassive black hole at its center.
D)   be a dwarf galaxy, otherwise the quasar's light cannot pass through it and reach Earth.
Ans: B   Section: 26-8

180. In observations of a double quasar image produced by gravitational lensing, fluctuations on the intensity of one image appear to be delayed compared to equivalent variations on the other image. Why is this?
A)   Rotation of the lensing galaxy has delayed the beam of light on one side compared to the other because of the Doppler effect.
B)   One beam has had to pass through material with a greater refractive index than for the other beam within the lensing galaxy.
C)   The gravitational field of the lensing object slows down the light on one beam compared to the other.
D)   The optical path through the gravitational lens producing one image is longer than that for the other image.
Ans: D   Section: 26-8

181. As much as 90% of the matter in the universe may be unseen "dark matter." Where is this dark matter?
A)   It seems to be rather uniformly distributed throughout the universe.
B)   It is concentrated in the centers of galaxies, and may, in fact, be related to black holes at galactic centers.
C)   It is concentrated in the planes of galaxies, but extending far beyond the visible galactic plane.
D)   It appears to be concentrated in spherical haloes around galaxies, but extending several times the radius of visible matter.
Ans: D   Section: 26-8, 25-4

182. As we look deeper and deeper into space (and thus farther and farther back in time) the composition of rich clusters of galaxies
    A)   is about the same mix of ellipticals and spirals that we find in the Virgo cluster and other nearby rich clusters.
    B)   increases in the ratio of ellipticals to spirals.
    C)   increases in the ratio of spirals to ellipticals.
    D)   contains increasing numbers of large irregular galaxies, replacing spirals and ellipticals altogether.
    Ans: C   Section: 26-9

183. Which of the following is UNLIKELY to contribute to the "missing mass" in galaxies or between galaxies?
    A)   the very abundant but elusive neutrinos, which might have a small rest mass
    B)   a large number of faint, red, low-mass stars
    C)   clouds of X-ray-producing hot gas
    D)   young, massive, blue supergiant stars, still hidden in their cocoon nebulae
    Ans: D   Section: 26-9

184. Why are the gravitational lens image arcs of a distant galaxy photographed around the center of a cluster of galaxies significantly more blue in color than the cluster galaxies themselves?
    A)   The gravitational lensing also produces differential refraction which renders the outer arcs blue and the inner ones, which are among the nearby galaxies, red, like an atmospheric halo around the Sun.
    B)   We are seeing a more distant galaxy at an earlier stage in its evolution, and it is intrinsically more blue on account of star formation in galaxies early in the life of the universe.
    C)   We are seeing the more distant galaxy at an earlier stage in its evolution when the Hubble motion had not redshifted its spectrum as much as for nearer, and hence, later galaxies.
    D)   The lensing process shifts light toward the blue as predicted by General Relativity.
    Ans: B   Section: 26-9

185. Which parameter is now thought to be vital in the evolution of a pregalactic gas cloud into an elliptical rather than a spiral galaxy?
    A)   the presence of other evolving galaxies nearby
    B)   the initial rate of star birth
    C)   the presence of supernova explosions to trigger star birth within the galactic cloud
    D)   the presence of a black hole around which the galaxy can form
    Ans: B   Section: 26-9

186. In which of the following types of galaxy is star formation no longer occurring?
    A)   E0 elliptical galaxy   C)   Sc spiral galaxy
    B)   Irregular I-type galaxy   D)   SBb barred spiral galaxy
    Ans: A   Section: 26-9

Chapter 27: Quasars, Active Galaxies, and Gamma-Ray Bursters

1. Astronomy with a radio telescope was initiated by
    A)   the British Broadcasting Corporation in England.
    B)   an amateur astronomer Grote Reber, after Jansky detected radio energy from the galaxy.
    C)   Marconi in Europe.
    D)   the National Science Foundation and the American Astronomical Society.
    Ans: B   Section: 27-1

2. One of the three astronomical objects that were first detected at radio wavelengths by Grote Reber in the 1930s and 1940s was
    A) the galactic center.   B) the Moon.   C) Jupiter.   D) the Sun.
    Ans: A   Section: 27-1

3. The discovery of the peculiar galaxy Cygnus A was a surprise to astronomers because
    A)   it was discovered first at X-ray wavelengths, only later being seen optically.
    B)   it has a redshift as high as those of the most distant quasars.
    C)   it is very faint at visible wavelengths but extremely bright at radio wavelengths.
    D)   it was so bright at optical wavelengths that no one expected it to be a galaxy.
    Ans: C   Section: 27-1

4. The major surprise about Cygnus A, one of the first three sources of strong radio emission detected by Grote Reber in the late 1930s, when examined with a large optical telescope, was that
    A)   it was at the center of our galaxy.
    B)   it was a supernova remnant.
    C)   it corresponded to no optical source at all.
    D)   it was a relatively faint yet very distant object at optical wavelengths.
    Ans: D   Section: 25-1

5. An intense radio source is found to coincide with a starlike object whose spectrum contains a pattern of intense emission lines in the visible range that matches that of the Lyman UV hydrogen spectral lines, but is very redshifted. What is this object?
    A)   a quasar   C)   the exploding shell of a supernova
    B)   a black hole   D)   a pulsar
    Ans: A   Section: 27-1

6. The specific characteristics that identify most quasars are
   A) starlike appearance, very high redshifts, and hence very large distances, indicating very energetic sources.
   B) that they look like elliptical galaxies, but with high spectral redshifts.
   C) spiral galaxy appearance, and very high spectral blueshift, indicating that they are coming toward the Sun at high speed.
   D) starlike appearance, and very high spectral blueshift, indicating that they are approaching the Sun very fast.
   Ans: A   Section: 27-1

7. Quasars appear to be
   A) very distant, intrinsically bright objects, moving away from Earth at very high speeds.
   B) very distant, intrinsically faint objects, moving toward Earth very rapidly.
   C) relatively close, very bright objects moving away from Earth.
   D) very distant and intrinsically bright objects moving in random directions at high speeds.
   Ans: A   Section: 27-1

8. Quasars all appear to be
   A) moving away from us at very high speeds, at up to 90% of the speed of light.
   B) moving across our line of sight at very high speeds, as seen from time-lapse photographs.
   C) extremely massive objects in our galaxy, their intense surface gravity having redshifted their spectra.
   D) moving toward us at high speeds, as high as 90% of the speed of light.
   Ans: A   Section: 27-1

9. All quasars appear to be
   A) moving in random directions, at high speeds.
   B) very distant, intrinsically faint objects.
   C) relatively close, very bright objects.
   D) moving away from Earth at very high speeds.
   Ans: D   Section: 27-1

10. The observed characteristics of a quasar are
    A) starlike image, spectrum highly redshifted, often an intense radio emitter.
    B) starlike image, with a highly variable Doppler spectrum that shifts from red to blue, and often a very bright radio source.
    C) diffuse circular image, no redshift of the spectrum, often a very bright radio source.
    D) starlike image, extremely blueshifted spectrum, often an intense radio emitter.
    Ans: A   Section: 27-1

11. The typical optical spectrum of a quasar shows
    A) very redshifted emission lines superimposed upon a weak continuum of radiation.
    B) a series of very blueshifted emission lines, with no continuum component.
    C) a continuum of radiation crossed by a sequence of very redshifted absorption lines.
    D) a sequence of highly blueshifted absorption lines upon a continuum of radiation.
    Ans: A   Section: 27-1

12. Which of the following astronomical objects can be described as follows: "Starlike in appearance, its spectrum showing very high redshift, energy output of about 1000 galaxies from a small region about 1 light year across"?
    A) a giant molecular cloud
    B) a quasar
    C) the center of our galaxy
    D) a supernova explosion in a neighboring galaxy
    Ans: B   Section: 27-1

13. A starlike object seen on deep sky photographs coincides with an intense radio source and has a spectrum in which the characteristic Lyman pattern of hydrogen spectral lines is seen in the visible spectral range which has been shifted from the ultraviolet range. What is this object?
    A) a black hole   B) a pulsar   C) a quasar   D) a supernova explosion
    Ans: C   Section: 27-1

14. Astronomers initially had difficulty identifying the emission lines in quasar spectra at optical wavelengths because
    A) the lines are created by elements that do not exist on Earth.
    B) no one expected violet and ultraviolet spectral lines to be shifted so far toward the red.
    C) quasars are receding from us at extremely high speeds, and this smears out the emission lines, making them hard to measure.
    D) they were emission lines from ionized atoms which had not been seen before.
    Ans: B   Section: 27-1

15. The emission lines in quasar spectra were difficult to identify at first because
    A) emission lines of such intensity were not expected from astronomical sources.
    B) no one expected far-ultraviolet spectral lines to be shifted to visible wavelengths.
    C) they were very faint and could not be measured accurately.
    D) they arise from elements that do not exist on Earth.
    Ans: B   Section: 27-1

16. The extreme redshifts of quasar spectra are caused by
    A) very high recession speeds of the sources away from our galaxy.
    B) the high gravitational fields at the surfaces of these quasars (gravitational redshift).
    C) absorption of all but the red parts of the quasar spectrum by intergalactic matter.
    D) Zeeman effects from the very intense magnetic fields in the vicinity of the source.
    Ans: A   Section: 27-1

17. Which observations of quasars convinced astronomers that they were very distant objects?
    A) their extremely red spectrum, reddened by extreme interstellar absorption of the blue part of the spectrum, meaning that the source must be very far away
    B) their extreme faintness at visible wavelengths, the inverse square law for visible light showing that they must be very distant
    C) They appeared as pointlike star images under the highest magnification, meaning that they must be very far away.
    D) extreme redshift of visible Balmer and UV Lyman hydrogen emission lines, indicating high recessional velocities and hence, by the Hubble Law, very large distances
    Ans: D   Section: 27-1

18. The unusual feature that was noted in the optical spectra of the faint starlike objects that coincided in position with the intense sources of radio energy known as quasars was
    A) sets of spectral lines that indicated simultaneous motion of sources toward and away from the Sun, possibly a rapidly expanding shell of material around the radio source.
    B) the extreme redshift of emission lines that indicated high recessional velocities and hence great distances, requiring extremely high energy output in order to be detected.
    C) the extreme blueshift, meaning that these stars in our galaxy are coming toward the Earth at very high velocities.
    D) the periodic variation of the Doppler shift from red to blue, indicating a light source oscillating back and forth over a few weeks.
    Ans: B   Section: 27-1

19. The distance to the bright quasar 3C 273 is estimated to be
    A) 20,000 light-years.   C) 2 billion light-years.
    B) just beyond our Milky Way.   D) 3 million light-years.
    Ans: C   Section: 27-1

20. Those quasars that have the highest observed redshifts have recession velocities of
    A)   more than 90% of the speed of light.
    B)   about one-quarter of the speed of light.
    C)   70–80% of the speed of light.
    D)   almost half the speed of light.
    Ans: A   Section: 27-1

21. The highest redshifts ($z = \Delta\lambda/\lambda_0$) that have been observed for quasars are in the range of
    A) $z = 11$ to 12.   B) $z = 5$ to 6.   C) $z = 8$ to 9.   D) $z = 4$ to 5.
    Ans: B   Section: 27-1

22. What is the distance to a quasar having a redshift of $z = 3.0$? (See Table 27-1, Freedman and Kaufmann, *Universe,* 7th ed.)
    A) 1500 Mpc   B) 3500 Mpc   C) 500 Mpc   D) 2500 Mpc
    Ans: B   Section: 27-1 and Table 27-1

23. The quasar PKS 1247+3406 has a redshift $z = 4.897$. What is its recession speed away from our galaxy? (See Table 27-1, Freedman and Kaufmann, *Universe,* 7th ed.)
    A) 4.897 c   B) 1.06 c   C) 0.204 c   D) 0.94 c
    Ans: D   Section: 27-1 and Table 27-1

24. The hydrogen Balmer H_α line with laboratory wavelength 656.3 nm is identified in emission in the spectrum of a quasar at 1968.9 nm. What is its velocity with respect to us? (See Table 27-1, Freedman and Kaufmann, *Universe,* 7th ed.)
    A)   15/17c, or 88% of the speed of light
    B)   0.8 of the speed of light, away from us
    C)   The line identification or the measured redshift must be wrong, otherwise this measurement would imply that the object's speed is twice the speed of light, which is impossible.
    D)   0.8 of the speed of light, toward us
    Ans: B   Section: 27-1 and Table 27-1

25. The spectrum of the quasar PKS 2000-330 contains the UV Lyman L_α line which has been shifted into the visible region of the spectrum by a cosmological redshift of $z = 3.773$. What is the redshift, $\Delta\lambda_0$, of this radiation in nanometers?
    A) 45.85 nm   B) 458.5 nm   C) 701.5 nm   D) 635 nm
    Ans: B   Section: 27-1 and 5-8

26. When the quasar 3C 273 was first discovered, astronomers noted several unusual features. Which of the following was *not* one of these unusual characteristics?
    A) 3C 273 was a faint starlike object that coincided with an intense radio source.
    B) A luminous jet protruded from one side.
    C) The object was ringed with multiple but identical images of a distant galaxy, suggesting gravitational lensing.
    D) The spectrum contained emission lines that could not be immediately identified.
    Ans: C   Section: 27-1

27. The energy output of a bright quasar is equivalent to
    A) 1000 times that of the Sun.
    B) 10^6 solar-type stars.
    C) that of the Milky Way Galaxy.
    D) 1000 bright galaxies.
    Ans: D   Section: 27-2

28. The fact that quasars can be detected from distances where even the biggest and most luminous galaxies cannot be seen means that
    A) they must be intrinsically far more luminous than the brightest galaxies.
    B) they must be in directions where intergalactic absorption by dark matter is minimum, allowing us to see them.
    C) they must be in directions where gravitational focusing by the masses of nearer galaxies makes them visible from Earth.
    D) they have not been as redshifted by their motion as have galaxies, and hence they can still be seen.
    Ans: A   Section: 27-2

29. A quasar is now thought to be
    A) the central core of an active galaxy.
    B) a very active, very distant star.
    C) a long-lived supernova explosion.
    D) a nearby star, ejected with great violence out of a galaxy.
    Ans: A   Section: 27-2

30. Evidence obtained over the last few years indicates that quasars are most probably
    A) the central nuclei of very distant, very active galaxies.
    B) the remnant cores of exploding stars or supernovae.
    C) evidence of very intense star-building activity in certain distant dust and gas clouds.
    D) the focused image of a distant galaxy by the gravitational lens effect of a closer galaxy.
    Ans: A   Section: 27-2

31. Recent spectral observations of the faint light from the regions surrounding several quasars seem to indicate that quasars may be
    A)   rapidly rotating neutron stars within the remnants of a supernova explosion.
    B)   the super-luminous centers of active galaxies.
    C)   very luminous stars surrounded by extensive planetary systems.
    D)   very active nearby stars with extensive atmospheres, which are moving rapidly for some reason.
    Ans: B   Section: 27-2

32. Recent evidence indicates that quasars
    A)   are isolated objects not associated with galaxies.
    B)   occur only in elliptical galaxies.
    C)   occur only in spiral galaxies.
    D)   occur in both spiral and elliptical galaxies.
    Ans: D   Section: 27-2

33. In the 1960's American astronomer Halton Arp suggested an alternative interpretation of quasars. This led to a decade or more of debate in the astronomy community. Arp's suggestion was
    A)   that quasars are very far away and produce enormous amounts of energy.
    B)   that quasars are relatively close and produce only moderate amounts of energy.
    C)   that quasars are black holes that shoot out jets of radiation, and that we see intense radiation because we happen to be in line with the beam.
    D)   that quasars are at the centers of giant elliptical galaxies that are, in turn, in the centers of rich clusters of galaxies.
    Ans: B   Section: 27-2

34. In the 1960's Halton Arp suggested that quasars are relatively close and produce only moderate amounts of energy. One problem with this interpretation is that
    A)   the blackbody curves for quasars suggest that they should produce large amounts of radiation.
    B)   if they are closer, then the emission lines should be more intense compared with absorption lines.
    C)   they would not obey the Hubble redshift relationship.
    D)   the mass-luminosity relationship would be violated for quasars.
    Ans: C   Section: 27-2

35. The quasar 3C 273 is believed to have a luminosity of about 2.5×10^{13} $L_\odot$ at a distance of 620 Mpc. Suppose instead that it were a normal galaxy with a luminosity a thousand times smaller. How far away would it have to be to have the same apparent brightness it has now?
    A) 620 kpc   B) 6.2 Mpc   C) 19.6 Mpc   D) 620×10^9 pc
    Ans: C   Section: 27-2 and Box 19-2

36. An electron moving in a magnetic field in space is forced to follow a spiral pattern. As it does so it will emit
    A)   nothing, because such electrons are in equilibrium.
    B)   synchrotron radiation, mostly radio waves.
    C)   X rays.
    D)   visible light, mostly blue in color.
    Ans: B   Section: 27-3

37. A moving electron in a magnetic field in space follows a spiral pattern, emitting what type of radiation as it does so?
    A)   Synchrotron radiation.
    B)   Lyman radiation.
    C)   No radiation at all, because they are moving smoothly without acceleration.
    D)   Cerenkov radiation.
    Ans: A   Section: 27-3

38. Synchrotron radiation is produced whenever
    A)   electrons move in spirals in a magnetic field.
    B)   atoms in a molecule vibrate back and forth.
    C)   electrons jump from level to level in an atom.
    D)   light passes into a transparent medium, such as glass.
    Ans: A   Section: 27-3

39. Synchrotron radiation is produced by what mechanism?
    A)   the heating of matter by compression as it spirals into a black hole
    B)   the radioactive decay of an atomic nucleus
    C)   the slowing down of charged particles as they enter a dense medium such as a star atmosphere or the Earth's atmosphere
    D)   the acceleration of high-energy charged particles as they spiral along in a magnetic field
    Ans: D   Section: 27-3

40. Seyfert galaxies are
    A)   the largest galaxies in the universe.
    B)   active galaxies, with very bright, starlike nuclei.
    C)   irregular galaxies seen from the southern hemisphere.
    D)   very small elliptical galaxies.
    Ans: B   Section: 27-3

41. Seyfert galaxies are
    A)   elliptical galaxies whose nuclei resemble quasars.
    B)   spiral galaxies whose nuclei resemble quasars.
    C)   giant irregular galaxies that have neither spiral arms nor the smooth shape of elliptical galaxies.
    D)   active galaxies, most of whose energy is emitted at radio wavelengths by two widely spaced lobes above the galactic poles.
    Ans: B   Section: 27-3

42. A spiral galaxy with a bright, starlike nucleus showing strong emission lines is called
    A)   a quasar.   C)   a BL Lacertae object.
    B)   a gravitational lens.   D)   a Seyfert galaxy.
    Ans: D   Section: 27-3

43. Seyfert galaxies are considered to be a distinct class of galaxies because
    A)   they are completely devoid of structure, appearing to be amorphous spheres of gas and dust.
    B)   they are in the constellation of Seyfert in the southern hemisphere sky.
    C)   they are very close to the Milky Way and appear to be gravitationally bound to it.
    D)   they have hot and very bright and variable, starlike central cores.
    Ans: D   Section: 27-3

44. A radio galaxy is any galaxy that
    A)   has two lobes, one on each side of the galaxy, which emit synchrotron radiation at radio wavelengths.
    B)   emits large amounts of energy from the whole galaxy at radio wavelengths.
    C)   is invisible at optical wavelengths (ordinary light), and is detected only at radio wavelengths.
    D)   has a bright, compact nucleus that emits large amounts of thermal energy at radio wavelengths.
    Ans: A   Section: 27-3

45. The most likely mechanism for the many double radio sources that are now detected in distant space is
    A)   two oppositely directed jets of matter, ejected from a small source in the center of a galaxy.
    B)   two pulsars on opposite sides of a quasar.
    C)   two black holes on either side of a small galactic nucleus.
    D)   two radio stars in the spiral arms of a galaxy, symmetrically placed around the galactic nucleus.
    Ans: A   Section: 27-3

46. Many bright radio sources at very large distances from the Sun appear to emit energy from two relatively widely spaced sources. What mechanism is thought to produce these double radio emission regions?
    A)   These sources are two galaxies orbiting each other, like binary stars.
    B)   two oppositely directed beams of light and radio energy illuminating the intergalactic dust and gas
    C)   They are in fact a single source and its reflection in a dense intergalactic gas and dust "mirror" or plasma sheet.
    D)   Two oppositely directed plasma jets from a central source produce radio energy as the plasma slows down.
    Ans: D   Section: 27-3

47. The mechanism that appears to generate two extensive regions of radio emission near active galaxies is
    A)   the double image of a single source behind the galaxy, produced by gravitational lensing by the galaxy.
    B)   two small black holes orbiting around the center of the galaxy.
    C)   two oppositely directed jets of energetic particles.
    D)   two very hot gas clouds, emitting 21-cm radio waves.
    Ans: C   Section: 27-3

48. The radio emission from the jets in a double radio source is
    A)   21-cm emission from neutral hydrogen atoms.
    B)   recombination radiation from electrons recombining with protons as the gas cools in the outer parts of the jets.
    C)   synchrotron radiation from relativistic electrons spiraling in magnetic fields.
    D)   thermal emission from very hot matter ejected from the accretion disk around the central black hole.
    Ans: C   Section: 27-3

49. What is now considered to be the origin and mechanism for the production of the double lobes of radio emission that appear on either side of many galaxies?
    A)   the explosion of a supermassive star and the ejection outward in two opposite directions of very hot gas, which is emitting thermal energy
    B)   material streaming inward to a black hole, perpendicular to and on opposite sides of the accretion disk
    C)   two oppositely directed jets of relativistic particles spiraling around magnetic fields
    D)   radio emission from two halves of a galactic halo containing many globular clusters, which generate radio-noise
    Ans: C   Section: 27-3

50. In which direction(s) are the jets of matter ejected from a supermassive black hole in order to produce the many effects surrounding quasars and active galaxies?
    A)   in two opposite directions across the accretion disk and rotating with it
    B)   in a single direction above the accretion disk, the precession of which sweeps the jet along the surface of a cone
    C)   tangential to the accretion disk in two opposite directions, 180° apart, the matter being spun off by the rapid disk rotation
    D)   in two opposite directions, perpendicular to the accretion disk of the black hole
    Ans: D   Section: 27-3

51. Observationally, the biggest difference between quasars and other active galaxies such as Seyferts and radio galaxies appears to be that
    A)   Seyferts and radio galaxies have bright nuclei, but do not have ejected jets of material from their nuclei.
    B)   quasars appear to be located inside elliptical galaxies, whereas Seyferts and radio galaxies are all inside spirals.
    C)   Seyferts and radio galaxies do not have the bright, starlike nuclei of quasars.
    D)   Seyferts and radio galaxies are less powerful than quasars.
    Ans: D   Section: 27-3

52. Synchrotron radiation, a type of nonthermal radiation, is found in the emission from
    A)   the nucleus of a Seyfert galaxy such as NGC 7742.
    B)   the nucleus of a giant elliptical radio galaxy such as M87.
    C)   the jet emanating from M87.
    D)   radio lobes around Seyfert galaxies.
    Ans: C   Section: 27-3

53. M87 is a giant elliptical radio galaxy. Its radio emission is primarily from
    A)   the galactic nucleus.
    B)   the lobes outside the galaxy.
    C)   the jet leading from the nucleus to the lobes.
    D)   the entire galaxy, including the jet and the lobes.
    Ans: B   Section: 27-3

54. Blazars or BL Lacertae objects are
    A)   elliptical galaxies whose nuclei resemble quasars.
    B)   spiral galaxies whose nuclei resemble quasars.
    C)   giant irregular galaxies which have neither spiral arms nor the smooth shape of elliptical galaxies.
    D)   active galaxies, most of whose energy is emitted by two widely spaced radio lobes.
    Ans: A   Section: 27-4

55. A blazar or BL Lacertae object is
    A)   an eclipsing binary star in which one component is believed to be a neutron star or a black hole.
    B)   a rapidly spinning neutron star.
    C)   an active galactic nucleus.
    D)   an emission nebula containing a young T Tauri star.
    Ans: C   Section: 27-4

56. The spectrum of a BL Lacertae object shows
    A)   absorption lines of highly ionized atoms.
    B)   doubled emission lines, split by the Doppler shift of oppositely directed jets of material.
    C)   strong, highly redshifted emission lines.
    D)   a continuum with very faint emission and absorption lines that are all but rendered invisible by the intense synchronous radiation.
    Ans: D   Section: 27-4

57. A starlike object showing an almost featureless continuum spectrum would be
    A)   a gravitational lens.   C)   a Seyfert galaxy.
    B)   a quasar.   D)   a BL Lacertae object.
    Ans: D   Section: 27-4

58. Observations indicate that blazars are
    A)   quasars that have absorbed or merged with a smaller galaxy within a cluster of galaxies.
    B)   distant spiral galaxies undergoing an intense burst of star formation.
    C)   radio galaxies whose jets and radio lobes point almost directly at the Earth.
    D)   black holes in binary star systems, where matter pulled from the companion star forms a hot accretion disk around the black hole.
    Ans: C   Section: 27-4

59. To what does the phrase "superluminal motion" refer?
    A)   the motion of relativistic electrons in magnetic fields
    B)   the apparent motion of jets of gas at speeds faster than light
    C)   the apparent motion of arcs of light caused by gravitational lensing
    D)   the motion of galaxies at redshifts z > 1
    Ans: B   Section: 27-4

60. The apparent motion of objects at speeds greater than that of light ("superluminal motion") is caused by
   A)   objects moving almost directly toward us at speeds close to (but less than) that of light.
   B)   gravitational lensing.
   C)   objects moving almost directly toward us at speeds greater than that of light.
   D)   the expansion of space, carrying distant galaxies away from us at apparent speeds greater than that of light.
   Ans: A   Section: 27-4

61. Which of the following objects is NOT classified as an active galaxy?
   A) blazars   B) barred spirals   C) quasars   D) Seyfert galaxies
   Ans: B   Section: 27-4

62. The typical time of variation in the brightness of quasars and blazars can be as short as
   A) a few seconds.   B) about a month.   C) about a year.   D) about a day.
   Ans: D   Section: 27-4

63. Relatively rapid fluctuations (within 1 day) in the electromagnetic output of quasars and blazars is an indication of
   A)   objects moving in front of them, from our point of view.
   B)   the rapid rotation of the sources.
   C)   the relatively small size of the emitting regions.
   D)   their relative closeness to the Milky Way.
   Ans: C   Section: 27-4

64. What observational fact convinces astronomers that the source of energy in a typical quasar is physically very small?
   A)   the extremely high redshift of its spectrum
   B)   the appearance of all quasars as starlike objects in our sky
   C)   the extreme distance of all quasars
   D)   the rapid variation of the intensity of the source
   Ans: D   Section: 27-4

65. Which observations of the radiation from quasars indicate that they are physically very small objects compared to galaxies?
   A)   starlike appearance on photographs, with little structure
   B)   They emit most of their radiation in the infrared and radio range.
   C)   extremely high redshift of their light
   D)   rapid fluctuations in output, often in less than one day
   Ans: D   Section: 27-4

66. How can astronomers determine the size of an emission region in a very distant and unresolvable source?
    A)   by measuring brightness variability, because an object cannot vary more rapidly than the time taken for light to cross the source
    B)   by using radio interferometry, because this technique can resolve far greater detail than optical imaging
    C)   by measuring the redshift of its spectrum, because this will be dependent upon the source size
    D)   by measuring the object's mass and by using a reasonable value for the average density for matter, calculate its volume and hence its diameter
    Ans: A   Section: 27-4

67. Why is it that, when we observe an extragalactic source whose diameter is about one light-day, we are unlikely to see fluctuations in light output in times shorter than about one day?
    A)   because the light from different parts of the source will be Doppler-shifted by different amounts, allowing us to see only an average shift
    B)   because light from the back of an object, one light day further from us than the front, cannot be received by us earlier than one day after the front
    C)   because absorption of light by intergalactic matter will smooth out rapid fluctuations within the beam
    D)   because it is inconceivable that a source of this size could vary on such a short time scale
    Ans: B   Section: 27-4

68. The surprising observational fact about quasars is that they appear
    A)   to be the largest known structures in the universe, although they produce only modest amounts of energy.
    B)   to be moving rapidly toward us, while emitting large amounts of energy.
    C)   to be associated with ancient supernova explosions.
    D)   to produce the energy output of 1000 galaxies in a volume similar to that of our planetary system.
    Ans: D   Section: 27-4

69. Which observational fact about quasars and their behavior is perhaps the most extraordinary?
    A)   velocities of recession of up to 9/10 of the speed of light
    B)   distances from the Sun of up to 18 billion light-years
    C)   incredibly powerful radio emitters, such that simple receivers can detect them, from vast distances across the universe
    D)   energy output equivalent to 1000 galaxies from a volume as small as our planetary system
    Ans: D   Section: 27-4

70. Consider the diagram of superluminal motion in Figure 27-15, Freedman and Kaufmann, *Universe*, 7th ed. Suppose the motion of the blob of material continued on in a straight line at 5/6 for an additional 5 years to position C. Viewed from the earth, the speed of the blob would then appear to be
    A) 5/6 c.
    B) 11/12 c.
    C) 1.5 c.
    D) incalculable! In this case the light from the *final* position C would arrive at Earth before the light from the *initial* position A.
    Ans: C   Section: 27-4

71. A radio galaxy, viewed from a position so that the observer is looking down one of the jets toward the galaxy, is a
    A) blazar.   B) quasar.   C) Seyfert Type 1.   D) Seyfert Type 2.
    Ans: A   Section: 27-4

72. What is the Eddington limit for any object?
    A) the mass beyond which the gravitational force on an accretion disk overcomes the rotational motion due to conservation of angular momentum
    B) the speed of light
    C) the maximum pressure that the electrons, nuclei, and photons in the object can withstand before the object collapses into a black hole
    D) the luminosity beyond which the outward force due to radiation pressure on matter exceeds the inward force due to gravity
    Ans: D   Section: 27-5

73. What would the mass of a supermassive black hole at the center of a quasar need to be, in terms of the solar mass, in order to produce a luminosity of 10^{12} times that of our Sun, assuming that this luminosity is at the Eddington limit?
    A) 10^9 B) 3.3×10^7 C) 10^{12} D) 3.3×10^8
    Ans: B   Section: 27-5

74. What recent evidence now indicates that several nearby galaxies may contain supermassive black holes at their centers?
    A) extreme redshift of light from stars near the centers of these galaxies, caused by gravitational redshift from a very massive object
    B) spectroscopic observations of stars near the centers of these galaxies, showing extremely high orbital velocities, which will require large-mass objects to retain the stars in orbit
    C) The rotation curve of these galaxies shows no decrease in orbital velocity of stars as the radius of orbit increases out to the observable limit of the galaxy, indicating an unseen source of gravity.
    D) observation that these galaxies are rushing rapidly toward each other (and toward the Milky Way!), presumably because of gravitational attraction
    Ans: B   Section: 27-5

75. What evidence seems to indicate the presence of a supermassive black hole at the center of our neighboring galaxy, M31, the Andromeda Galaxy?
    A)   very intense X-ray emission from a very small central core of the galaxy
    B)   spectroscopic measurements of very high and symmetrical Doppler shifts from material orbiting very rapidly near to the galaxy center, obviously under control of an object with a very powerful gravitational field
    C)   a small but very dark region on detailed photographs of M31, showing an area from which light cannot escape
    D)   the slow but measurable motion of our galaxy toward M31 under the intense gravitational force of the black hole
    Ans: B   Section: 27-5

76. The "central engine" of an active galaxy appears to be
    A)   stars falling into a supermassive black hole, their remnants being thrown out in all directions.
    B)   supernova explosions in an extremely dense star cluster at the center of the galaxy.
    C)   the violent merger of two galaxies, in which the collision throws out jets of matter along the rotation axis of the larger galaxy.
    D)   a supermassive black hole at the center of an accretion disk, with jets of material being ejected perpendicular to the disk.
    Ans: D   Section: 27-5

77. What appears to be the central energy-generating system or "engine" that is producing prodigious amounts of energy in the centers of galaxies, active galaxies, and quasars?
    A)   a steady series of supernova explosions, the late evolutionary stages of massive stars
    B)   a supermassive black hole, where matter is compressed upon falling into the hole and heated to extremely high temperatures
    C)   There is no central "engine" in these sources. Their high gravity has focused radiation from many sources beyond them by gravitational lensing, and thus they appear to be very bright.
    D)   a very rapidly rotating core of matter, where friction between it and the surrounding matter causes tremendous heat and energy output
    Ans: B   Section: 27-5

78. The luminosity of the Milky Way Galaxy is about $3 \times 10^{10} \, L_\odot$. Suppose all of this luminosity is due to a black hole and accretion disk at the center of the galaxy which is assumed to be a its Eddington Limit. What would this suggest for the mass of this black hole (in solar masses)?
    A) 30,000   B) 3×10^5 C) 10^5 D) 3×10^{10}
    Ans: C   Section: 27-5

79. Suppose a rotation curve is made of the region close to the center of a galaxy. At a distance of four parsecs from the center the radial velocity is 328 km/sec. How much mass is within this four parsec radius (in solar masses)?
    A) 10^6 B) 10^8 C) 2.4×10^{11} D) 1.2×10^{17}
    Ans: B   Section: 27-5 and Box 4-4

80. What is the relationship between blazars (intense, rapidly varying nonthermal sources of polarized radio radiation) and double-lobed radio sources?
    A)   A blazar is an early view of a superluminous supernova, which will eventually evolve into a double radio source as matter expands outward.
    B)   A blazar appears to be what is left in space after all the surrounding matter has been devoured by a black hole, whereas a double radio source still has matter spiralling into the black hole.
    C)   A blazar is now considered to be the end-on view of a double radio source, looking along one of the relativistic particle jets emitted from the central core.
    D)   A blazar is the central "engine" that generates the energy for the relativistic particle beams that produce the double radio lobes.
    Ans: C   Section: 27-6

81. If double radio sources, quasars, and blazars are considered to be the same basic object, why do they appear to us to have very different and distinct properties?
    A)   because the relativistic particles in the double jets are different in each case: electrons in double radio sources, protons in quasars, and quarks in blazars
    B)   because they are at different distances from us, and we see more detail and different properties on those that are closer to us
    C)   because we are viewing them at different angles to the line of the double jets emitted from their cores
    D)   because they are of different ages
    Ans: C   Section: 27-6

82. In the "unified model" of active galaxies, the main difference between quasars, blazars, and radio galaxies appears to be that
    A)   the mass of the central black hole is different in each case—largest in quasars, less in blazars, and least in radio galaxies.
    B)   the rate at which matter is falling into the central black hole is different in each case—highest in quasars, less in blazars, and lowest in radio galaxies.
    C)   the galaxy type is different in each case—spiral for blazars, elliptical for quasars, and irregular for radio galaxies.
    D)   we see the accretion disk around the central black hole from a different angle in each case—face-on for blazars, edge-on for radio galaxies, and in between for quasars.
    Ans: D   Section: 27-6

83. Quasars, blazars, and double radio sources may well be the same kind of object, their different appearance simply being caused by
   A)   their age: BL Lac objects that evolve through a double radio source phase end up as a quasar.
   B)   their orientation: In blazars the jets point toward and away from us, in double radio sources they point sideways, and quasars are in between.
   C)   their position in the universe: Quasars are in our galaxy, double radio sources are associated with other galaxies, and BL Lac objects are within the vast voids of space between galaxies.
   D)   their size: Quasars are star-sized, double radio sources larger, and BL Lac objects are galaxy-sized.
   Ans: B   Section: 27-6

84. I thought black holes gobbled up matter! If the central engine of a double-lobed radio source is a black hole swallowing matter from an accretion disk, where do the jets of matter come from that we see traveling OUTWARD from the galaxy?
   A)   They are squirted out by high pressure at the inner edge of the accretion disk, before the matter reaches the black hole.
   B)   The jets arise in the weak galactic magnetic field, not in the region near the black hole.
   C)   They are accelerated in the ergoregion of the rotating black hole and ejected outward in the black hole's equatorial plane.
   D)   They are accelerated outward by intense magnetic fields around the black hole, much like the beams of particles ejected from the magnetic poles of a pulsar.
   Ans: A   Section: 27-6

85. Why are there no nearby (and thus "young") quasars?
   A)   Eventually, most of the accretion disk falls into the black hole and the "central engine" runs out of fuel.
   B)   The central black hole eventually consumes the entire galaxy, and with no more matter in the vicinity, it becomes dormant until another galaxy happens to pass nearby.
   C)   The continual infall of material causes the mass of the black hole to grow until it explodes, resulting in a supernova.
   D)   The immense radiation output from the quasar carries away energy. The mass of the black hole gets smaller until it evaporates.
   Ans: A   Section: 27-6

86. Which of the following is *not* one of the reasons we believe gamma-ray bursters are supernova explosions in distant galaxies rather than eruptions in the nuclei of active galaxies?
    A)   Afterglow spectra are very similar to known supernova spectra.
    B)   The expanding shell of gas that follows the explosion is similar to that following a supernova.
    C)   Gamma-ray bursters do not appear at the centers of their host galaxies.
    D)   The amount of energy released in a burster is similar to that released in a normal supernova.
    Ans: D   Section: 27-7

87. What is the observed distribution of gamma-ray bursters in the sky?
    A)   clumpy, but not coinciding with any known galaxy clusters, indicating an origin in a new kind of astronomical object
    B)   concentrated primarily along the plane of the Milky Way, indicating an origin within our galaxy
    C)   clumpy, approximately coinciding with large clusters of galaxies such as the Coma cluster
    D)   uniform over the entire sky, indicating an origin at "cosmological" distances
    Ans: D   Section: 27-7

88. What is the duration of a gamma-ray burst?
    A)   as short as a hundredth of a second, indicating a source smaller than the Earth
    B)   several days, indicating a size much smaller than the distance from the Earth to the nearest star beyond the Sun
    C)   up to about a day, indicating a source several times the size of our solar system
    D)   several hours, indicating a source size about equal to the diameter of Uranus's orbit
    Ans: A   Section: 27-7

89. What property of gamma-ray bursters indicates that they are located at large ("cosmological") distances from the Earth?
    A)   absorption lines in their spectra, due to intergalactic clouds
    B)   the small apparent sizes of the objects producing the bursts
    C)   highly redshifted emission lines from the burster's nucleus
    D)   the faintness of the bursts
    Ans: A   Section: 27-7

Chapter 28: Cosmology: The Origin and Evolution of the Universe

1. What do cosmologists study?
   A) the origin, structure, and evolution of the solar system
   B) the formation, structure, and evolution of galaxies
   C) the formation, structure, and evolution of stars
   D) the origin, structure, and evolution of the universe
   Ans: D   Section: 28-1

2. In which of the following areas of scientific study will we never be able to follow the scientific method in repeating the observations of several different "samples" in order to verify the generality of the conclusions?
   A) biology, the study of living things
   B) cosmology, the study of the structure of our universe
   C) archeology, the study of the past evolution of living creatures
   D) geology, the study of our Earth as a planet
   Ans: B   Section: 28-1

3. The question asked in Olber's paradox of cosmology is
   A) "Why is the sky dark at night?"
   B) "How old is the universe?"
   C) "What is beyond the edge of the universe?"
   D) "Where did the universe come from?"
   Ans: A   Section: 28-1

4. In stating his paradox, Olber expected the night sky to be bright and not dark as we see it because he thought that
   A) the space between the stars would be filled with gas (such as the Orion Nebula), which would emit light.
   B) airglow and auroral light excited by solar particles, by his calculations, would produce significant illumination in our atmosphere.
   C) the Earth's atmosphere should refract (bend) the sunlight around the Earth to illuminate the night sky.
   D) every line of sight should eventually intersect a star in an infinite universe randomly scattered with stars.
   Ans: D   Section: 28-1

5. Newton reached the conclusion that the universe must consist of an infinite expanse of stars because
   A)   he was unable to detect the movement of stars around a common center, which his theory required for stability against collapse in a finite universe.
   B)   he reasoned that a finite number of stars would eventually fall together under their mutual gravity.
   C)   of his religious conviction that the creator would create nothing less than an infinite universe.
   D)   he and his colleagues had observed the uniform distribution of stars all over the sky.
   Ans: B   Section: 28-1

6. Which scientist discovered that his theory predicted an expanding universe, and because he doubted the existence of expansion, modified his equations to eliminate this expansion from his theory?
   A)   Edwin Hubble   C)   Isaac Newton
   B)   Stephen Hawking   D)   Albert Einstein
   Ans: D   Section: 28-1

7. Einstein's general theory of relativity, as originally formulated without the cosmological constant, predicts
   A)   a static universe.
   B)   a universe that must expand.
   C)   a universe that must contract.
   D)   a universe that must either expand or contract.
   Ans: D   Section: 28-1

8. In Newton's model of an infinite universe with stars distributed smoothly throughout, an individual star would feel
   A)   a preponderance of force pulling it toward the center of the universe.
   B)   a preponderance of force pushing it away from the center of the universe.
   C)   equal forces pulling in every direction, resulting in no net force.
   D)   forces that would vary greatly from one part of the universe to another.
   Ans: C   Section: 28-1

9. Which two parameters representing observations of distant objects in the universe are related in the Hubble Law?
   A)   the luminosity of a star and its distance from the center of the galaxy
   B)   the distance to the object and the redshift of its light
   C)   the mass of a distant object and its velocity away from our galaxy
   D)   the mass of an object and its luminosity
   Ans: B   Section: 28-2

10. The Hubble distance-velocity relationship states that
    A) all galaxies are being pulled toward a central gravitational attractor in the universe, the closest ones to the center traveling fastest.
    B) the farther away a galaxy is from the Local Group of galaxies, the faster it is traveling toward this group.
    C) the farther a galaxy is from our galaxy, the faster it appears to be traveling away from it.
    D) all galaxies are being repelled by the pressure from the very hot central "engine" of the universe, the ones closest to the center traveling fastest.
    Ans: C   Section: 28-2

11. For which objects in the universe has the Hubble relation been shown to hold experimentally?
    A) only stars in the near neighborhood of the Sun, in our galaxy
    B) distant galaxies only
    C) galaxies in the Local Group, in the near vicinity of the Milky Way
    D) all objects in the universe, from planets and stars out to the farthest galaxies
    Ans: B   Section: 28-2

12. Because of the general expansion of space, all distant galaxies appear to be moving away from us, with speeds that increase with distance from our galaxy. An observer in one of these distant galaxies would apparently see
    A) all galaxies on one side of the observer moving toward her and all galaxies on the other side moving away from her; the more distant the galaxy, the faster its motion.
    B) all galaxies moving away from her, the more distant galaxies moving faster.
    C) all galaxies moving away from her, with closer galaxies moving faster.
    D) all galaxies moving toward her, with more distant galaxies moving faster.
    Ans: B   Section: 28-2

13. The farther away a galaxy is, the more its light is redshifted, as seen by us on the Earth. This redshift-distance law is caused by
    A) energy losses. The universe does not really expand, but photons lose energy as they travel and hence their wavelength lengthens. Photons from more distant galaxies have traveled farther, are more "tired," and so are more redshifted.
    B) the expansion of space itself, which stretches the wavelength of the photon. The longer the photon travels, the more space expands and the more the photon is redshifted during the time it is traveling.
    C) the gravitational redshift. Photons leaving a more distant galaxy have traveled farther through the galaxy's gravitational field, so they have lost more energy and are more redshifted.
    D) the Doppler shift of light leaving a moving object. More distant galaxies are moving faster through space, so their light is more strongly Doppler-shifted toward the red wavelengths.
    Ans: B   Section: 28-2

14. What causes cosmological redshift of photons that reach us from distant galaxies?
    A)   The photons have moved from high gravitational field regions toward lower fields, thereby becoming reddened.
    B)   The photons were emitted from the galaxies much earlier in time when the overall temperature of matter was much lower. Hence, the observed photons are redder, the farther away from Earth that they were produced.
    C)   The photons have traveled across space that has been expanding and their wavelengths have expanded with it, becoming redder.
    D)   The photons were emitted by objects that were moving rapidly away from us, and thereby have been reddened by the Doppler effect.
    Ans: C   Section: 28-2

15. What is the "cosmological redshift"?
    A)   the stretching of wavelengths of photons by the Doppler shift, because they are emitted by galaxies that are moving away from us
    B)   the loss of energy of photons as they interact with virtual particles in the vacuum, so that their wavelengths gradually increase as they travel toward us through space
    C)   the stretching of the wavelengths of photons as they travel through expanding space
    D)   the stretching of the wavelengths of photons as they pass through absorbing matter in galaxies between us and the emitting galaxy
    Ans: C   Section: 28-2

16. The cosmological redshift of the light from very distant galaxies is caused by
    A)   the expansion of space, stretching the photon's wavelength while the photon is traveling toward us.
    B)   absorption of blue light by interstellar dust between us and the galaxy, so that only the red wavelengths reach us.
    C)   the rotation of the universe around its center (faster at greater distances from us).
    D)   the Doppler shift, in which the photon's wavelength is stretched as the photon is being emitted by the galaxy's motion away from us through space.
    Ans: A   Section: 28-2

17. The cosmological redshift of light from distant galaxies is explained by which of the following effects?
    A)   The photon wavelength, being a distance, is lengthened by the general expansion of the universe, thereby reddening the light.
    B)   The light was emitted by a massive body (e.g., a star or galaxy) and has passed many bodies in its journey to us, and thus has become shifted toward the red end of the spectrum by these gravitational fields, as predicted by Einstein.
    C)   The photons lose energy as they pass through space, the so-called "tired photon" idea, thereby becoming lower in energy and hence redder.
    D)   The light that we see was emitted by an object moving rapidly away from us and was therefore Doppler-shifted to longer wavelength.
    Ans: A   Section: 28-2

18. Why is the universe expanding?
    A)   It is not expanding—it is our local space that is getting smaller as we fall into a supermassive black hole, making the universe seem bigger and bigger.
    B)   because space itself is expanding, carrying the galaxies (or superclusters of galaxies) with it
    C)   because an infinitely small but infinitely dense clump of matter exploded, sending the galaxies (or superclusters of galaxies) hurtling out through space
    D)   because the energy from all the stars is heating the universe, making it expand like a gas that is heated
    Ans: B   Section: 28-2

19. Which one of the following statements represents a correct description of the expansion of the universe?
    A)   Space is a vacuum, but the vacuum has real properties. As galaxies (or superclusters of galaxies) hurtle outward, the expansion is gradually slowing down by the resistance of space to the passage of the galaxies.
    B)   Space is static, but exerts an outward pressure on the galaxies in it. This pressure is accelerating the galaxies (or superclusters of galaxies) outward through space and away from each other.
    C)   Space has a separate existence, with the galaxies inside it. As space expands, the galaxies (or superclusters of galaxies) are carried along by the expansion.
    D)   Space is a vacuum, which is really nothing at all. The galaxies (or superclusters of galaxies) are hurtling outward through this nothingness.
    Ans: C   Section: 28-2

20. In the expansion of the universe, the expansion takes place
    A)   only between objects separated by a vacuum; as a result, our bodies do not expand but the Earth-Moon system does.
    B)   primarily in the huge voids between clusters of galaxies: "small" objects like galaxies or the Earth do not expand.
    C)   only over distances about the size of a galaxy or larger; consequently, our galaxy expands but the solar system does not.
    D)   between all objects, even between the atoms in our bodies, although the expansion of a person is too small to be measured reliably.
    Ans: B   Section: 28-2

21. Where in the universe does the "general" expansion occur?
    A)   only within individual galaxies, while the space between them and between clusters of galaxies remains static
    B)   everywhere in the universe, including our local space upon Earth, the solar system, our galaxy and the space between galaxies
    C)   only in galaxy-sized and larger structures, such as clusters of galaxies and the voids between them
    D)   only in the space that separates clusters of galaxies
    Ans: D   Section: 28-2

22. In our universe, we can consider four different regimes of space in which distances between objects might be changing as a result of the general expansion of the universe. These are
    1. distances between different parts of the Earth.
    2. distances between planets in our solar system.
    3. distances between stars in our galaxy.
    4. distances between clusters of galaxies.
    In which of these regimes ARE the distances changing because of this expansion?
    A) 4, 3, and 2   B) 4, 3, 2, and 1   C) only 4   D) both 4 and 3
    Ans: C   Section: 28-2

23. What is it that keeps localized regions of space, such as things upon Earth, planetary systems, star clusters, and whole galaxies, from participating in the general expansion of the universe?
    A)   their locations in places where irregularities in the chaotic Big Bang explosion permitted matter to condense
    B)   the mutual gravity between objects in these systems
    C)   the powerful and all-pervading gravity from the central supermassive black holes of galaxies, which holds everything in place within the galaxies
    D)   the centrifugal force produced by their motion around a massive central object (e.g., the Sun, supermassive black holes, etc.)
    Ans: B   Section: 28-2

24. What is the look-back time (i.e., How long ago did the light leave its source?) for an object with a redshift $z = 0.05$, assuming that the Hubble constant is 21.5 kmsec^{-1} Mly^{-1}? (Assume non-relativistic speed for this object.)
    A) 322 billion years   C) 0.7 billion years
    B) 0.7 million years   D) 700 billion years
    Ans: C   Section: 28-2

25. In relation to the universe, what does the word "isotropic" mean?
    A) The expansion is the same in all directions.
    B) The speed of expansion is the same at all distances.
    C) The speed of expansion at any given distance is the same at all times.
    D) The universe is the same everywhere, neither expanding nor contracting.
    Ans: A   Section: 28-2

26. Where are we?
    A) near the edge of an expanding universe, as shown by the Great Wall of Galaxies
    B) somewhere in an expanding universe, but not in any special part of it
    C) at the exact center of an expanding universe, as shown by the universal expansion away from us in all directions
    D) off-center in an expanding universe, as shown by the fact that the microwave background radiation is at a different temperature in one direction than in the opposite direction
    Ans: B   Section: 28-2

27. What is the general meaning of the cosmological principle?
    A) There is no unique time in our universe; it has always looked the way it is now and will always do so.
    B) We do not occupy a special location in space, because the universe is the same everywhere, on average.
    C) The universe appears to be expanding outward, but this is because of our motion as we descend into a super-duper massive black hole which has distorted space to produce the illusion of general "expansion."
    D) We occupy a very special location near the original location of the Big Bang, because everything appears to be moving away from this location as the universe expands.
    Ans: B   Section: 28-2

28. What does $z = 0$ mean?
    A) Zero time—that is, the time at which the cosmic singularity occurred.
    B) Zero distance: only objects on the Earth have $z = 0$.
    C) Zero velocity: only objects at rest with respect to the Earth have $z = 0$.
    D) Zero expansion—that is, no cosmological redshift.
    Ans: D   Section: 28-2

29. Is there an advantage in using redshift z to describe the distances to far away galaxies?
    A) No. Because z is a known function of v (*which* function depends on whether the situation is relativistic or non-relativistic) and $v = H_0 d$, there is no real advantage to using z rather than d.
    B) No. Not all objects at the same d have the same z, so using z is actually a *disadvantage*.
    C) Yes, z can be determined rather easily from spectra, whereas H_0 is rather difficult to determine. So there is a real advantage in using z rather than d.
    D) No. Because one cannot always be sure whether to use relativistic or non-relativistic equations for z, z is somewhat ambiguous while d is unambiguous.
    Ans: C   Section: 28-2

30. The resolution of Olber's paradox (i.e., the reason why the sky is dark at night) is that
    A) we cannot see those stars that are farther away from us than the distance that light has traveled since the beginning of the universe.
    B) matter cannot have traveled farther than light has traveled during the age of the universe, so there ARE NO stars beyond a certain distance from us.
    C) the light from very distant stars is bent out of our line of sight by the gravitational fields of nearby galaxies.
    D) the light from stars beyond a certain, very large distance is completely absorbed by matter between us and the star.
    Ans: A   Section: 28-3

31. According to Hubble's law, how old is the universe? (H_0 = Hubble's constant, v is the recessional velocity of objects in the universe, and d = distance to objects in Mpc.)
    A) age $= v/H_0$.   B) age $= H_0$.   C) age $= d/H_0$.   D) age $= 1/H_0$.
    Ans: D   Section: 28-3

32. In cosmology, the constant that is intimately related to the present "age" of the universe is
    A) $1/G$, the inverse of the universal gravitational constant.
    B) $1/H_0$, the inverse of the constant in Hubble's universal expansion law.
    C) the constant in Wien's law of radiation, representing the redness of a spectrum for a certain temperature.
    D) the inverse of 10^{-43} s, the Planck time at which space and time came into existence.
    Ans: B   Section: 28-3

33. For any object moving uniformly, velocity = distance/time. If so, in the Hubble relationship for the expansion of the universe, $V = H_0 d$, what is the significance of the constant $1/H_0$?
    A)   It is the inverse of the velocity that the object would have at a standard distance of 10 parsecs.
    B)   It represents the average spacing between objects in the universe at the present time.
    C)   It is merely a constant of proportionality, to allow for the different units of V and d.
    D)   It represents the time since the expansion began, or the age of the universe.
    Ans: D   Section: 28-3

34. If the Hubble constant is found to be 25 km/s/Mly, what would then be an upper estimate for the age of the universe?
    A)   1.2 billion years or 1.2×10^9 years   C)   12 million years or 1.2×10^7 years
    B)   12 billion years or 1.2×10^{10} years   D)   380 billion years or 3.8×10^{11} years
    Ans: B   Section: 28-3

35. Calculate the age of the universe if Hubble's constant, H_0, is 71 km/s/Mpc.
    A)   2.27 million years   C)   13.8 billion years
    B)   1.43 billion years   D)   1,380 billion years
    Ans: C   Section: 28-3

36. If the uncertainty in the Hubble constant $H_0 = 71$ $kms^{-1}Mpc^{-1}$ is 10%, leading to values of between 63.9 kms^{-1}/Mpc and 78.1 kms^{-1}/Mpc, what is the corresponding range in the estimated age of the universe?
    A)   1 billion years, from 12.9 to 14.9 billion years
    B)   2.8 billion years, from 12.5 to 15.3 billion years
    C)   There is insufficient information to calculate this uncertainty from the given numbers.
    D)   1.4 billion years, from 12.7 to 13.9 billion years
    Ans: B   Section: 28-3

37. If Hubble's constant is 75 km/s/Mpc then the age of the universe is 13 billion years. Suppose it were discovered that Hubble's constant is actually larger than 75 km/s/Mpc. What effect would this have on the calculated age of the universe?
    A)   Without another factor, the average mass density of the universe, the age of the universe cannot be estimated from this information.
    B)   It would decrease the age of the universe.
    C)   Because the Hubble constant simply relates galaxy motion to its distance from our galaxy, it has no connection with the age of the universe.
    D)   It would increase the age of the universe.
    Ans: B   Section: 28-3

38. Astronomer A claims that the Hubble constant is 84 km/s/Mpc, whereas astronomer B claims that it is 63 km/s/Mpc. The age of the universe calculated by astronomer A would be
    A) 2/3 of that calculated by astronomer B.
    B) 3/4 of that calculated by astronomer B.
    C) 1.25 times that calculated by astronomer B.
    D) 1.33 times that calculated by astronomer B.
    Ans: B   Section: 28-3

39. What major problem would arise if the value of Hubble's constant turned out to be 100 km/s/Mpc?
    A) Some galaxies would be farther away than the edge of the universe.
    B) Galaxies would have had to have traveled faster than our observations indicate.
    C) Galaxies would be traveling too fast for the universe to be gravitationally bound.
    D) The age of the universe would be less than the ages of some of the stars in it.
    Ans: D   Section: 28-3

40. If the elliptical galaxy in Hydra, shown at the bottom of Fig. 26-14 (Freedman and Kaufmann, *Universe,* 7th ed.), were to be at a distance of 3 billion light years, what would be an upper limit to the age of the universe? (Be careful with units.)
    A) 0.47 billion years   C) 15 million years
    B) 4.5 billion years   D) 15 billion years
    Ans: D   Section: 28-3

41. What is the "cosmic particle horizon"?
    A) It is the maximum distance to which our own radio and television signals will have traveled through the universe since radio was invented.
    B) It is the distance from which light can travel to us over the finite age of the universe, representing a viewing distance limit for us upon Earth.
    C) It is the distance beyond which we cannot see because of absorbing matter in the universe.
    D) It is the distance at which (because we see back in time as we look out into space) galaxies are just being formed.
    Ans: B   Section: 28-3

42. Why does the observable universe have an "edge"?
    A) because there are so many galaxies in the universe that every line of sight eventually hits a galaxy, stopping us from seeing any farther
    B) because the density of neutrinos at the "edge" is so large that photons cannot pass through, preventing us from seeing beyond this point
    C) because absorbing matter prevents us from seeing out past a certain distance
    D) because we cannot see any farther than the distance that light has traveled over the lifetime of the universe
    Ans: D   Section: 28-3

43. Our view of the universe is a limited one because of what fundamental fact?
    A)   Light from objects farther away than a certain distance, defined by the travel time of light over the lifetime of the universe, has not yet reached us.
    B)   The expanding universe from the Big Bang only extends so far into space because matter can only travel at or below the speed of light.
    C)   The cosmological redshift has moved the light from very distant objects out of our detectable range, making these objects invisible to us.
    D)   Intergalactic space contains absorbing material which blocks our view of more distant objects.
    Ans: A   Section: 28-3

44. What was it that caused the apparent expansion of the universe?
    A)   our point of view, the expansion being a projection effect resulting from the Earth's motion in the galaxy
    B)   the centrifugal force upon all matter in the universe, caused by motion around its center
    C)   a universal repulsive force, stronger than the gravitational attraction between matter in the universe
    D)   no cause has yet been found, but expansion started suddenly and has continued to this time
    Ans: D   Section: 28-3

45. The Planck time refers to
    A)   the time of extremely rapid inflation, which started 10^{-35} second after the universe began.
    B)   the time at which the expanding universe became transparent to radiation.
    C)   the first 10^{-43} second of time, when the universe had such high density that all known science fails to explain its behavior.
    D)   the present age of the universe as given by Hubble's law.
    Ans: C   Section: 28-3

46. The first 10^{-43} second of the age of the universe, during which time matter was so compressed that all known science fails us, is called
    A)   the inflationary epoch.   C)   the Hubble time.
    B)   the event horizon.   D)   the Planck time.
    Ans: D   Section: 28-3

47. Within which time frame from the initial Big Bang is it felt that the present laws of physics completely fail us, because time and space as we know them did not exist?
    A) $t = 0$ to 1 second, during which time photons interchanged freely with electron-positron pairs
    B) $t = 0$ to 10^{-35} s, after which the strong nuclear force "froze out" of the universe
    C) $t = 0$ to 10^{-43} s, the Planck time, after which gravity "froze out" of the universe
    D) $t = 0$ to 10^6 years, over which radiation dominated the universe
    Ans: C   Section: 28-3

48. The formation of the solar system occurred at what point in the history of the universe?
    A) right at the beginning   C) about half-way through
    B) during the first third   D) about two-thirds of the way through
    Ans: D   Section: 28-3

49. We see distant objects as they were at the time that light left them. Assuming a Hubble Constant, H_0, of 71 km/sec/million parsecs, what would be the age of the universe? (See Table 27-1, Freedman and Kaufmann, *Universe,* 7th ed.)
    A) 13.8 million years   C) 13.8 billion years
    B) ∞ (infinity)   D) 4.13 billion years
    Ans: C   Section: 28-3

50. Good evidence for an original big bang, which "created" our universe, comes from
    A) the very high flux of 21-cm radio energy, coming from the atomic hydrogen atoms produced in the explosion.
    B) the rapid motions of some nearby stars, such as Barnard's Star.
    C) the amount of gas and dust in the solar neighborhood.
    D) a background "glow" of microwaves, with blackbody temperature of about 3 K.
    Ans: D   Section: 28-4

51. Who discovered the radiation left over from the Big Bang, the so-called cosmic microwave background?
    A) Anthony Hewish and Jocelyn Bell   C) Arno Penzias and Robert Wilson
    B) Robert Dicke and P.J.E. Peebles   D) Ralph Alpher and George Gamow
    Ans: C   Section: 28-4

52. The cosmic microwave background was discovered by
    A) rocket-borne telescopes, while they were searching for X-ray sources in space.
    B) the Voyager 2 spacecraft during one of its "coasting" periods between planetary encounters.
    C) the IRAS satellite, which produced an all-sky infrared survey.
    D) scientists testing a new antenna and receiver for satellite communications.
    Ans: D   Section: 28-4

53. The cosmic microwave background radiation was discovered by
    A) using the COsmic Background Explorer (COBE) satellite.
    B) using a microwave detector on the Hubble Space Telescope.
    C) using a satellite communications antenna on the Earth's surface.
    D) using the Ulysses spacecraft while it was observing above the Sun's north pole.
    Ans: C   Section: 28-4

54. What is the cosmic microwave background radiation?
    A) an almost-uniform background radiation from distant, unresolved, overlapping galaxies
    B) radiation left over from the Big Bang, after the universe expanded and cooled
    C) a uniform background of radiation from electrons spiraling in weak intergalactic magnetic fields
    D) radiation from a very tenuous, ionized gas that fills the universe equally in all directions
    Ans: B   Section: 28-4

55. The cosmic background radiation is
    A) the flux of visible radiation contributed to empty space by all visible stars in the universe.
    B) the beam of atomic nuclei, also known as cosmic rays, which rain down continuously upon the Earth from all directions in space.
    C) the radio noise generated by Earth-bound transmitters, spreading out into space since about 1920.
    D) low-intensity radio noise, with a 3 K blackbody temperature, almost uniform in intensity in all directions.
    Ans: D   Section: 28-4

56. The cosmic background radiation is
    A) the electromagnetic remnants of the explosion in which the universe was born.
    B) the radio noise caused by high energy atomic nuclei known as cosmic rays, moving through magnetic fields in space.
    C) the result of the radioactive decay of heavy, unstable elements produced in supernova explosions.
    D) the faint glow along the elliptic, caused by sunlight scattering from dust particles in the planetary system.
    Ans: A   Section: 28-4

57. What is the temperature of the blackbody radiation we detect that originated in the Big Bang (the cosmic microwave background radiation)?
    A) 3 K   B) 3,000 K   C) 30 billion K   D) 30 K
    Ans: A   Section: 28-4

58. The cosmic background radiation left over after the Big Bang of the universe and pervading all observable space has an effective blackbody temperature of approximately
    A) 273 K   B) 10 K   C) 3 K   D) 0 K
    Ans: C   Section: 28-4

59. I thought that the Big Bang was hot! If the cosmic microwave background radiation is the radiation left over from the Big Bang, why then is it only 3 K?
    A) The Big Bang itself was hot, but the temperature decreased as the universe expanded, and the temperature now is 3 K.
    B) It is not from the Big Bang itself—it is from cold, intergalactic hydrogen clouds that are left over from the Big Bang.
    C) The Big Bang itself was hot, but by the time the universe became transparent the temperature had already decreased to 3 K.
    D) The Big Bang was not hot—its temperature was the same as we observe it now from the cosmic background radiation.
    Ans: A   Section: 28-4

60. When did the universe cool to a temperature of about 3 K?
    A) very recently
    B) one second after the Big Bang, when electron-positron pair production ceased
    C) 300,000 years after the Big Bang, when the universe became transparent to radiation
    D) three minutes after the start of the Big Bang, when primordial nuclear reactions ended
    Ans: A   Section: 28-4

61. At what point in the age of the universe did the universe cool to a temperature of about 3 K?
    A) at the end of the Planck time   C) at the era of recombination
    B) very recently   D) at the end of the inflationary epoch
    Ans: B   Section: 28-4

62. What was the COBE satellite designed to measure?
    A) 21-cm radio radiation from intergalactic hydrogen
    B) redshifts of objects at cosmological distances, to obtain an accurate measurement of Hubble's constant
    C) X rays from quasars and other objects at cosmological distances
    D) the cosmic microwave background radiation
    Ans: D   Section: 28-4

63. When the intensity of the cosmic microwave background radiation is plotted against wavelength, what is the shape of the resulting curve?
    A) emission lines from hydrogen gas, strongest and most densely concentrated in the microwave region
    B) a blackbody curve modified by many deep, overlapping absorption lines and several emission lines
    C) a composite of many overlapping blackbody curves from gas clouds of different temperatures, peaking in the microwave region
    D) an almost perfect blackbody spectrum peaking in the microwave region
    Ans: D   Section: 28-4

64. The cosmic microwave background radiation is not uniform over the sky—it is slightly hotter toward the constellation Leo and slightly cooler in the opposite direction, toward Aquarius. Why?
    A)   The background radiation really is uniform; the observed difference is due to the Earth's motion through the universe.
    B)   That is the way the universe began—hotter in one direction and cooler in the other.
    C)   The difference is probably a statistical fluctuation, and therefore not real.
    D)   The Earth is slightly off-center in the universe, so one side of the universe is a bit closer and the other side is a bit farther away.
    Ans: A   Section: 28-4

65. Why does the cosmic microwave background appear to be slightly warmer in one direction in the sky and slightly cooler in the opposite direction?
    A)   because this is the direction in which the Big Bang occurred, hence we are seeing the remnant of the explosion in this direction.
    B)   because the center of the Local Group of galaxies is in this direction and this is a bright source of microwaves.
    C)   because the radiation in one direction is Doppler-shifted to shorter wavelengths by the Earth's motion in space and to longer wavelengths in the other direction.
    D)   because the amount of dark matter in that direction in space has focused the radiation slightly by gravitational lensing, making this direction appear hotter.
    Ans: C   Section: 28-4

66. The effect that makes the cosmic microwave background appear slightly warmer in one direction and cooler in the opposite direction is
    A)   the focusing effect of the gravitational field of the local galaxy upon the radiation.
    B)   the presence of many extra sources of the radiation in one direction.
    C)   a basic asymmetry in the background radiation, related to its origin.
    D)   the Doppler shift, caused by motion of our galaxy through space toward the constellation Leo.
    Ans: D   Section: 28-4

67. What is the *Great Attractor*?
    A)   the supermassive black hole at the center of the Milky Way Galaxy.
    B)   the immense black hole thought to be at the center of the universe and a remnant of the cosmic singularity
    C)   a large collection of mass about 50 Mpc from Earth in the direction of the Hydra-Centaurus supercluster toward which the Local Group of galaxies is being drawn
    D)   an immense black hole somewhere in the universe from the accretion disk of which the cosmic 3K background radiation is believed to be emitted
    Ans: C   Section: 28-4 and 26-6

68. Compared to the average density of matter in the present universe, the equivalent "mass density" of radiation, using Einstein's relation $E = mc^2$ for the photons, is
    A) much greater, leading to a radiation-dominated universe.
    B) almost nonexistent, because there is very little radiation left in the universe at the present time.
    C) equal, because these parameters remain balanced throughout the evolution of the universe as a consequence of the equipartition of energy.
    D) much less, leading to a matter-dominated universe.
    Ans: D   Section: 28-5

69. Which of the following sources contributes the greatest number of photons to the general radiation background in our universe?
    A) the cosmic microwave background, the remnant of the Big Bang
    B) the very large number of average solar-type cool stars, contributing vast numbers of visible and infrared photons
    C) atomic hydrogen, which is very abundant throughout the universe, contributing mainly 21-cm radio photons.
    D) extremely hot intergalactic gas in clusters of galaxies, producing copious numbers of X-ray photons
    Ans: A   Section: 28-5

70. What is the ratio of cosmic microwave background photons to hydrogen atoms, on average, in every cubic meter of our universe?
    A) about 500 million to 1
    B) about 500,000 to 1
    C) about 1 to 100, very few microwave photons
    D) about 1 to 1, equal numbers of photons and H atoms
    Ans: A   Section: 28-5

71. Even though the number of cosmic microwave background photons outnumbers hydrogen atoms by about 500,000,000 to 1 in our universe, this universe is still considered to be matter-dominated. This is because
    A) the photons, while collectively carrying a large amount of energy, do not carry an equivalent amount of momentum and hence play little role in collisions with matter.
    B) the photon energies are extremely small.
    C) the photons have no rest mass and hence can generate no gravity.
    D) the nature of these photons is such that they interact with nothing as they pass through the universe.
    Ans: B   Section: 28-5

72. In the present theory of the Big Bang in the universe, what significant event occurred at about 380,000 years after the start of the Big Bang?
    A) The universe became transparent to neutrinos.
    B) The temperature of the cosmic background radiation had cooled to its present level of about 3 K.
    C) The primordial helium in the universe was produced.
    D) The universe became transparent to photons of radiation.
    Ans: D   Section: 28-5

73. At about what time after the Big Bang did the universe pass through the transition from radiation-dominated to a matter-dominated universe?
    A) about 15 billion years, as stars began to form
    B) 2,500 years
    C) 380,000 years
    D) at the Planck time, 10^{-43} second.
    Ans: B   Section: 28-5

74. What significant event occurred about 380,000 years after the Big Bang started?
    A) The universe became transparent to radiation.
    B) All of the present galaxies in the universe were formed within a short time span.
    C) The temperature of the radiation decreased to 2.76 K.
    D) Quarks became confined.
    Ans: A   Section: 28-5

75. At an age of 380,000 years, the temperature of the universe had fallen to 3000 K, and electrons could then combine with protons to produce hydrogen gas instead of roaming freely through space. What major transition occurred as a consequence of this change in the universe at this time?
    A) The universe would have lost its electrical charge suddenly to become electrically neutral.
    B) The present laws of physics were applicable to the properties of the universe for the first time.
    C) The universe became transparent to light for the first time.
    D) Nuclear fusion no longer occurs below this temperature, and so, general fusion throughout the universe would have ceased.
    Ans: C   Section: 28-5

76. Which of the following statements correctly describes the universe for the entire first 380,000 years of its life?
    A) All of the fundamental forces were united into one force.
    B) It was filled with free quarks (not confined inside neutrons or protons).
    C) It was a sea of nuclear reactions occurring at a gradually decreasing rate.
    D) It was opaque.
    Ans: D   Section: 28-5

77. The conditions in the early universe, when the transition from radiation-dominated to matter-dominated conditions occurred, in terms of age t, peak background wavelength λ, and equivalent temperature T, were
    A)   t = 3 minutes, λ = 0.3 μm, near UV, T = 10^7 K
    B)   t = 380,000 years, λ = 1 μm, infrared, T = 3000 K
    C)   The universe was never radiation-dominated, because matter has always dominated by generating the gravitational field into which the universe has expanded
    D)   t = 3 × 10^{11} years, λ = 1 mm, microwaves, T = 3 K
    Ans: B   Section: 28-5

78. Which of the following statements does NOT correctly describe the universe at the era of recombination?
    A)   The universe was about 380,000 years old.
    B)   Electrons and protons combined to form neutral hydrogen atoms.
    C)   The temperature of the universe was about 3 K.
    D)   The universe became transparent to radiation.
    Ans: C   Section: 28-5

79. What was the approximate temperature of the universe at the time when the universe became transparent to radiation?
    A) 30 billion K   B) 3,000 K   C) 3 K   D) 300,000 K
    Ans: B   Section: 28-5

80. As we look at more distant regions of space, we see those regions as they existed at earlier times, but our farthest views are blocked by a "wall"—beyond which the universe is opaque. What event occurred at the time marked by this wall?
    A)   Electrons and protons combined to form neutral hydrogen atoms, making the universe transparent for the first time.
    B)   Quarks combined to form neutrons and protons, removing γ-ray absorbers for the first time.
    C)   Gravity froze out as a separate force.
    D)   Electrons and protons combined to form helium atoms, removing major absorbers of electromagnetic radiation from the universe for the first time.
    Ans: A   Section: 28-5

81. Because of the travel time of light, we see more distant parts of the universe as they were when the universe was younger; but we cannot see back "into" times when the universe was opaque and light could not travel freely. Using photons, then, what is the farthest back in time that we can see into the universe?
    A)   to a time 1/1,000,000 second (10^{-6} s) after the start of the Big Bang
    B)   to a time 3 minutes after the start of the Big Bang
    C)   to a time 380,000 years after the start of the Big Bang
    D)   to a time 3,000 years after the start of the Big Bang
    Ans: C   Section: 28-5

82. The very small detected irregularities in the uniformity of the cosmic microwave background are considered to be very important in the study of the evolution of our universe because
    A)   they were the seeds of supermassive black holes around which all galaxies then formed.
    B)   they are thought to have led to the development of the present concentrations of matter and energy in superclusters of galaxies.
    C)   they are thought to contain most of the elusive "missing matter" in the form of energy concentration in the universe.
    D)   they show us how non-uniform was the Big Bang explosion.
    Ans: B   Section: 28-5

83. When the universe was about 2,500 years old, the radiation density had decreased to the point where it was equal to the matter density. Yet it was only many years later that atoms formed. What happened to make possible the formation of atoms?
    A)   The average photon energy decreased until it could no longer ionize hydrogen.
    B)   Radiation pressure decreased until it was equal to the inward pressure due to gravity.
    C)   The temperature reached the point where the reaction $^1H \rightarrow {}^4He$ could proceed.
    D)   Neutrons decayed to produce protons and electrons, the building blocks of atoms.
    Ans: A   Section: 28-5

84. What condition is necessary for the universe to be unbounded (infinite in extent)?
    A)   The density of the universe must be equal to or less than some critical value.
    B)   The density of the universe must be equal to or greater than some critical value.
    C)   The universe must have no mass in it.
    D)   The density of the universe must be exactly equal to some critical value.
    Ans: A   Section: 28-6

85. What will happen if the universe is unbounded?
    A)   The universe will expand forever.
    B)   The universe will expand to some maximum size and then fragment into mini-universes.
    C)   The universe will reach a maximum size and stay there, like a balloon that has been inflated.
    D)   The universe will eventually fall back in on itself, heading toward a "Big Crunch."
    Ans: A   Section: 28-6

86. What will happen if the universe is bounded?
    A) The universe will expand to some maximum size and then fragment into mini-universes.
    B) The universe will eventually fall back in on itself, heading toward a "Big Crunch."
    C) The universe will reach a maximum size and stay there, like a balloon that has been inflated.
    D) The universe will expand forever.
    Ans: B   Section: 28-6

87. Which parameter of the present universe, more than any other, is considered to be critical in determining the ultimate fate of the universe?
    A) the average density of neutrinos
    B) the average density of matter
    C) the average density of black holes throughout the universe
    D) the average density of photons of radiation
    Ans: B   Section: 28-6

88. The future of the overall universe, in terms of its ultimate evolution and whether it will expand forever or eventually contract again, is determined by which of its parameters?
    A) the intensity of cosmic microwave background radiation
    B) the temperature of the gas within it
    C) the present volume of the universe
    D) the average density of matter within it
    Ans: D   Section: 28-6

89. In cosmology, the phrase "critical density" refers to
    A) the smallest density that will produce inflation of the universe.
    B) the density below which stars will never form.
    C) the density above which the universe is opaque to radiation.
    D) the density needed to produce precisely flat space on average throughout the universe.
    Ans: D   Section: 28-6

90. In cosmology, to what does the phrase "critical density" refer?
    A) the density of the universe above which matter is ionized and the universe is opaque
    B) the density of the universe above which the universe is bounded and below which it is unbounded
    C) the density of the universe below which the universe will stop expanding
    D) the density of the universe below which the universe is bounded and above which it is unbounded
    Ans: B   Section: 28-6

91. How does the measured mass density of matter in the universe, including the hypothesized dark matter, compare to the critical density required to just close the universe?
    A)   The measured density is about 5 times the critical density.
    B)   The measured density is equal to the critical density to within the measurement uncertainty.
    C)   The measured density is less than 0.1 of the critical density.
    D)   The measured density is between 0.2 and 0.4 of the critical density.
    Ans: D   Section: 28-6

92. What kind of curvature (geometry of space) does the universe have if the universe is just bounded (density = critical density)?
    A) flat   B) parabolic   C) spherical   D) hyperbolic
    Ans: A   Section: 28-6

93. What kind of curvature (geometry of space) does the universe have if the universe is unbounded (density < critical density)?
    A) flat   B) parabolic   C) hyperbolic   D) spherical
    Ans: C   Section: 28-6

94. What kind of curvature (geometry of space) does the universe have if the universe is bounded (density > critical density)?
    A) parabolic   B) flat   C) spherical   D) hyperbolic
    Ans: C   Section: 28-6

95. If space has a hyperbolic geometry (unbounded universe), what will happen to two initially parallel flashlight beams as they traverse billions of light years of space?
    A)   They will remain parallel.
    B)   They will gradually diverge (move apart) to a maximum separation, and then gradually converge and cross.
    C)   They will gradually converge (move together) and eventually cross.
    D)   They will gradually diverge (move apart).
    Ans: D   Section: 28-6

96. The degree of "flatness" of the universe, which determines whether we live in an open or a closed universe, has been determined recently by measuring
    A)   the average density of matter compared to the average density of radiation energy.
    B)   the typical size of the "hot spots" in the structure of the cosmic microwave background.
    C)   the hemispheric asymmetry in the temperature of the cosmic microwave background radiation.
    D)   the extent of the bending of light from distant galaxies, the so-called "lensing."
    Ans: B   Section: 28-6

97. Measurement of structure in the cosmic microwave background radiation has recently indicated that we live in a flat universe between a closed and an open universe and yet the measured density of detected matter and radiation is only 20–40% of the critical density required for a flat universe. In what form is the other 60–80% of the "matter" likely to be?
    A) antimatter, which generates a negative gravitational effect and emits radiation only if it meets matter and is annihilated
    B) neutrinos, which have very little rest mass and are very difficult to detect, but are very abundant
    C) miriads of small primordial black holes, whose gravitational effects are spread throughout the universe and which emit no radiation
    D) dark energy, emitting no radiation and generating no detectable gravitational effects
    Ans: D   Section: 28-6

98. What is "dark energy"?
    A) the energy associated with the matter that has fallen into a black hole
    B) the matter-energy needed to bridge the gap between the energy we see or infer and the energy needed to make the universe flat
    C) the energy associated with "dark matter"
    D) the unseen matter-energy needed to make the observed curvature of space spherical (as we believe it should be) while the observed matter-energy only makes it hyperbolic
    Ans: B   Section: 28-6

99. The present universe seems to require a "cosmological constant" equivalent to that introduced into general relativity by Einstein when his theory would not explain the expected static universe. What is the effect on the evolution of the present universe of the "new" cosmological constant?
    A) It produces a pressure to oppose the mutual gravitational pull of all the matter in the universe, accelerating its expansion.
    B) It is a term that accounts for the negative gravity generated by antimatter in the universe, the presence of which will produce an accelerated expansion.
    C) It just balances gravity to allow the universe to remain static, as Einstein predicted.
    D) It produces an extra attractive force in addition to gravity, slowing down the expansion of the universe.
    Ans: A   Section: 28-6

100. Einstein introduced a "cosmological constant" into his formulation of the structure of the universe on the basis of the general theory of relativity. How did he envision that this cosmological constant would manifest itself?
    A) as antimatter which, by annihilating with real matter, would translate matter into energy, thereby maintaining a constant mass density in an condensing universe
    B) as many "white holes" which would contribute matter to an expanding universe to maintain constant density, as required by the Cosmological Principle—a continuous creation universe
    C) as a form of energy which, on its own, would make the universe expand—a form of antigravity
    D) as an extra "gravity" which would hold the universe against continuous expansion
    Ans: C   Section: 28-7

101. The future of our universe, continuous expansion or eventual contraction, can be determined by observing the rate at which cosmological expansion is changing because of gravitational attraction between masses in the universe. How would this effect of deceleration be measured, in terms of the Hubble relationship between speed of recession and distance?
    A) The straight line will become slightly curved and steeper at the largest distances.
    B) The straight line will be found to be slightly curved and steeper at the shortest distances, but otherwise it will be straight.
    C) The straight line will become slightly curved and less steep at the largest distances.
    D) The "straight line" slope will become zero at some distance and will change to the opposite slope beyond this distance.
    Ans: A   Section: 28-7

102. What method is being used to discover whether we live in an unbounded universe, in which expansion will continue forever, or a bounded universe, in which expansion will eventually turn into contraction and lead us to the Big Crunch?
    A) careful monitoring of the Moon-Earth distance to detect slow-down of the expansion of the universe
    B) measurement of the deviation from uniformity of the cosmic background radiation
    C) measurement of the curvature of the Hubble relationship, $v = H_0 r$, at large distances
    D) measurement of the bending of light by distant galaxies as it follows the curvature of space
    Ans: C   Section: 28-7

103. It is not yet known whether we live in an unbounded universe that will expand forever or in a bounded universe that will eventually collapse into a Big Crunch. How are astronomers trying to settle this question?
    A)   by accurate measurement of the speed of a galaxy of known distance at two different times, to measure the deceleration directly
    B)   by measuring the curvature of space by tracing photon paths to the Earth from distant galaxies
    C)   by determining how much galaxy speeds depart from a straight-line Hubble relationship, $v = H_0 r$, at large distances
    D)   by careful observations of the size of the irregularities in the cosmic microwave background radiation
    Ans: C   Section: 28-7

104. On the basis of recent results from very bright and very distant type Ia supernovae, what seems to be the situation in our universe regarding the past and present motion of clusters of galaxies?
    A)   We live in a "flat" universe with an accelerating rate of expansion.
    B)   We live in a closed universe with a decelerating rate of expansion.
    C)   We live in an open universe with a constant rate of expansion given by the Hubble law.
    D)   We live in a "flat" universe with a decelerating rate of expansion.
    Ans: A   Section: 28-7

105. If space is flat, what is the future of the universe?
    A)   The future of the universe is not related to the geometry of space.
    B)   It will expand forever, not stopping even after infinite time.
    C)   It will expand to a maximum size and then collapse into a Big Crunch.
    D)   It will barely expand forever, reaching zero expansion speed after infinite time.
    Ans: D   Section: 28-7

106. If the shape of space is hyperbolic, what is the future of the universe?
    A)   It will barely expand forever, reaching zero expansion speed after infinite time.
    B)   It will expand forever and not stop, even after infinite time.
    C)   The future of the universe is not related to the geometry of space.
    D)   It will expand to a maximum size and then collapse into a Big Crunch.
    Ans: B   Section: 28-7

107. If space is spherical, what is the future of the universe?
    A)   It will expand forever, not stopping even after infinite time.
    B)   It will expand forever, but its rate of expansion slows so that it reaches zero expansion speed after infinite time.
    C)   The future of the universe is not related to the geometry of space.
    D)   It will expand to a maximum size and then collapse into a Big Crunch.
    Ans: D   Section: 28-7

108. In which of the following universe scenarios will the present universe evolve to a Big Crunch at some time in the future?
     A)   a Newtonian universe
     B)   a marginally bounded universe
     C)   an unbounded universe
     D)   a bounded universe
     Ans: D   Section: 28-7

109. Recent results from very bright supernovae in very distant galaxies seem to indicate that the expansion of the universe
     A)   is continuing at a constant rate and has done so since just after the Big Bang.
     B)   has now stopped and the universe will shortly begin to contract again toward a Big Crunch.
     C)   is accelerating (speeding up).
     D)   is decelerating (slowing down).
     Ans: C   Section: 28-7

110. Astrophysicists believe the dominant hot spots in the cosmic background radiation should be about 1° in angular size if the universe is flat. What do experimental measurements of this angular size tell us?
     A)   The measurements show angular sizes of less than 1°. This suggests that the universe is spherical.
     B)   The measurements show angular separations of about 1°. This suggests that the universe is flat.
     C)   The measurements show angular sizes larger than 1°. This suggests that the universe is hyperbolic.
     D)   The measurements thus far are inconclusive.
     Ans: B   Section: 28-7

111. As currently understood, what happens to the density of matter and the density of dark energy as the universe expands?
     A)   Both increase as the universe expands.
     B)   The matter density decreases but the density of dark energy increases.
     C)   The matter density decreases but the density of dark energy remains constant.
     D)   Both decrease as the universe expands.
     Ans: C   Section: 28-7

112. How is it that we can detect evidence of sound waves in the early universe?
    A) The energy-rich environment of the early universe gave these sound waves so much energy that, unlike ordinary sound waves, they have been able to travel through the vacuum of space.
    B) Space is not a complete vacuum. The tenuous material that fills all of space has been enough to sustain these sound waves.
    C) What we observe is not the sound waves themselves but rather the spectrum of light emitted from the compressions and rarefactions of the sound waves.
    D) What we observe is not the sound waves themselves but the gravitational lensing caused by the increased mass density in the compressions of the sound waves.
    Ans: C   Section: 28-8

113. How is the polarization of radiation used in studying the early universe?
    A) The polarization of the radiation reaching us from different directions of space is different. These differences tell us about the clumpiness of the early universe.
    B) The degree to which light is polarized is a measure of the energy of the environment in which the light is produced. The highly polarized cosmic microwave radiation suggests a highly energetic early universe.
    C) The cosmic microwave background radiation acquired a polarization when it scattered from a large hot spot associated with ancient sound waves. The polarization contains information about the hot spots.
    D) The decoupling of matter and radiation that occurred in the early universe resulted in an immense shock that distorted the polarization of the existing radiation. A comparison in the polarization of the radiation before and after the event contains much information about the event itself.
    Ans: C   Section: 28-8

114. If the universal expansion is decelerating, how does this affect the age of the universe derived from Hubble's law?
    A) Deceleration has no effect on the derived age.
    B) The derived age is lower than if the expansion is not decelerating.
    C) It can either increase of decrease the derived age, depending on the density of the universe and the resulting curvature of space.
    D) The derived age is higher than if the expansion is not decelerating.
    Ans: B   Section: 28-9

Chapter 29: Exploring the Early Universe

1. The flatness problem in cosmology asks the question:
   A) Why is the sky dark at night?
   B) Why was the density of the universe so close to the critical density just after the Big Bang?
   C) Why are the four forces (strong, weak, electromagnetic, and gravitational) not unified in the present-day universe?
   D) Why is temperature of the cosmic background radiation so smooth (isotropic) around the sky?
   Ans: D   Section: 29-1

2. Which of the following statements correctly describes the "flatness problem" in cosmology?
   A) Observations of the distant universe indicate that the universe is at least moderately flat, yet matter creates lumps in the geometry of spacetime. Therefore it is hard to account for the observed flatness.
   B) The density of the universe must have been equal to the critical density to a precision of 50 decimal places in order for us to see the universe we see today. This astounding flatness is hard to account for.
   C) The universe appears to have a hyperbolic geometry to within observational error, yet the universe is expanding, and expanding universes have to be flat.
   D) The universe appears to be flat to within observational error, yet the universe is expanding, and it is impossible for an expanding universe to be flat.
   Ans: B   Section: 29-1

3. Opposite sides of the universe have the same temperature, yet according to the standard Big Bang Theory these points are too far apart for light to have traveled from one side to the other in the age of the universe; i.e., they cannot have exchanged heat to even out their temperature. Why, then, do they have the same temperature?
   A) Light (and heat) could travel much faster in the early universe, allowing them to exchange heat while the universe was young.
   B) The expansion of the universe has always been the same everywhere; therefore all parts of the universe have the same temperature regardless of whether they have ever exchanged heat or not.
   C) pure coincidence
   D) They were originally close together and evened out their temperature, then a rapid inflation of the universe carried them far apart.
   Ans: D   Section: 29-1

4. The cosmic microwave background is found to be extremely uniform throughout space, with only very small fluctuations in intensity. The event that produced this remarkable smoothness in the early universe was
   A)   Heisenberg's uncertainty principle, which prevented the concentration of radiant energy in localized volumes of space.
   B)   a sudden but brief period of rapid expansion of the universe during the general expansion of the early universe.
   C)   the fact that the Big Bang occurred everywhere in space at the same time.
   D)   the start of the production of matter in the universe, which smoothed out the irregularities in space.
   Ans: B   Section: 29-1

5. The isotropy of the cosmic microwave background radiation (same temperature in all directions) indicates that
   A)   the universe has always been dominated by matter.
   B)   the universe had an early period of inflation in which regions initially in contact were carried out of contact with each other.
   C)   the universe did not begin to expand significantly until after the era of recombination.
   D)   regions that appear to us to be on opposite sides of the visible universe are in fact in close contact with each other.
   Ans: B   Section: 29-1

6. In cosmology, what is the "inflationary epoch"?
   A)   the period of universal expansion from the Big Bang to the present
   B)   a period when the cost of living rose faster than astronomers' salaries
   C)   the first 300,000 years of the life of the universe, when matter and radiation interacted vigorously
   D)   a short period of extremely rapid expansion when the universe was very young
   Ans: D   Section: 29-1

7. When did the inflationary epoch occur?
   A)   during the Planck time—that is, during the first 10^{-43} seconds after the cosmological singularity
   B)   immediately after the Planck time
   C)   throughout the first three minutes
   D)   throughout the first 380,000 years
   Ans: B   Section: 29-1

8. The inflationary epoch accomplished all of the following *except one*. Which is the exception?
   A)   took whatever curvature the early universe had and flattened it
   B)   allowed the early, pre-inflationary universe to be very small and thus capable of thermal equalization
   C)   permitted matter to move faster than the speed of light for a brief period
   D)   forced the observed density of the universe to be equal to the critical density to great precision.
   Ans: C   Section: 29-1

9. Immediately after the cosmological singularity the four forces were indistinguishable. Then they began to "branch off" and become separate. Which was the last of the four to branch off?
   A) gravitation   B) the weak force   C) the strong force   D) electromagnetism
   Ans: B   Section: 29-2

10. Physicists speculate that, early in its history, the universe shifted from a "false vacuum" state to a "true vacuum" state. What is the significance of this transition?
    A)   The "false vacuum" describes the state of the universe before the Planck time, 10^{-43} seconds. During this time the laws of physics, as we presently understand them, did not apply.
    B)   The transition was from a high-energy state to a low-energy state. The consequent release of energy fueled the inflationary epoch.
    C)   The transition was one from a low-energy state to a high-energy state. The consequent intake of energy caused the universe at the end of the inflationary epoch to be much cooler than it had been at the beginning of the inflationary epoch.
    D)   In its transition to the true vacuum the universe became trapped in a state of minimum energy, unable to expand or contract.
    Ans: B   Section: 29-2

11. Quantum electrodynamics describes forces in terms of the exchange of particles. The electromagnetic force, for example, involves the exchange of virtual photons. The weak force involves the exchange of
    A) gluons.   B) intermediate vector bosons.   C) gravitons.   D) virtual neutrinos.
    Ans: B   Section: 29-2

12. How many fundamental forces are known in science?
    A) five   B) three   C) four   D) six
    Ans: C   Section: 29-2

13. How many fundamental forces are there in nature?
    A)   three: strong, electromagnetic, and gravitational
    B)   six: color, strong, weak, magnetic, electric, and gravitational
    C)   five: strong, weak, magnetic, electric, and gravitational
    D)   four: strong, weak, electromagnetic, and gravitational
    Ans: D   Section: 29-2

14. What is the range of the electromagnetic force (the maximum distance over which it acts)?
    A)   a few thousand km, or roughly the size of the Earth
    B)   infinity
    C) 10^{-9} m (1 nanometer, or roughly the size of a hydrogen atom)
    D) 10^{-15} m (1 femtometer, or roughly the size of a proton)
    Ans: B   Section: 29-2

15. Which of the four fundamental forces holds the electrons in the atom?
    A)   the gravitational force   C)   the electromagnetic force
    B)   the weak nuclear force   D)   the strong nuclear force
    Ans: C   Section: 29-2

16. What is the range of the gravitational force (the maximum distance over which it acts)?
    A) 10^{26} m, or roughly the distance to the farthest quasars
    B)   infinity
    C) 10^{13} m, or roughly the size of the solar system
    D) 10^{21} m, or roughly the size of the Milky Way Galaxy
    Ans: B   Section: 29-2

17. The one physical force that extends farthest in our universe, and is not canceled out by other effects, is
    A)   the electromagnetic force.   C)   the gravitational force.
    B)   the strong nuclear force.   D)   the weak nuclear force.
    Ans: C   Section: 29-2

18. The forces of gravity and electromagnetism are long-range forces, extending in principle from their source (mass and electric charge respectively) to infinity. Why is it that in our universe, only gravity extends to infinity, whereas electromagnetic forces are much more limited in extent?
    A) Electromagnetic forces from charged particles will move other charged particles around to produce a uniform charge distribution and therefore zero electromagnetic forces, whereas gravity concentrates mass and enhances the overall gravity force.
    B) All atoms are electrically neutral so, in reality, the electromagnetic force never reaches beyond the size of an atomic nucleus.
    C) Gravity and electromagnetism are one and the same force, with electromagnetic effects extending over limited spatial ranges and transforming into gravitational forces at large distances from matter.
    D) Electromagnetic forces from positive charges are canceled by negative charges, whereas there are no negative "masses" to cancel the gravitational force.
    Ans: D   Section: 29-2

19. If gravity holds galaxies together and the electromagnetic force holds atoms together, what does the weak nuclear force hold together?
    A) nuclei
    B) nothing
    C) the quarks inside protons and neutrons
    D) leptons (particles including electrons and neutrinos)
    Ans: B   Section: 29-2

20. When is the weak nuclear force encountered?
    A) when a positively charged nucleus repels another positively charged nucleus in the core of a star like the Sun
    B) when two quarks interact inside a proton or neutron
    C) when a quark changes from one variety to another
    D) when an atom absorbs a photon, and one of the electrons in the atom is sent into a higher energy level
    Ans: C   Section: 29-2

21. The weak force
    A) acted only during the Big Bang, and has no known role in the universe at the present time.
    B) holds the quarks together inside a proton or neutron.
    C) acts during certain kinds of radioactive decay.
    D) attracts the electrons to the nucleus, holding the atom together.
    Ans: C   Section: 29-2

22. Tritium (H^3) is a heavy isotope of hydrogen, composed of one proton and two neutrons. Tritium decays into He^3, a light isotope of helium, composed of two protons and one neutron, through the reaction

    $H^3 \rightarrow He^3 + e^- + \bar{v}$

    The production of an electron and an antineutrino in this decay shows that the reaction was governed by

    A) the electromagnetic force.   C) the strong force.
    B) the gravitational force.   D) the weak force.
    Ans: D   Section: 29-2

23. The physical force that controls the structure of the nucleus and binds together protons and neutrons is the

    A) gravitational force.   C) strong nuclear force.
    B) electromagnetic force.   D) weak nuclear force.
    Ans: C   Section: 29-2

24. What is the range of the strong nuclear force (the maximum distance over which it acts)?

    A) 10^{-9} m (1 nanometer, or roughly the size of a hydrogen atom)
    B) infinity
    C) a few thousand meters, or roughly the size of the Earth)
    D) 10^{-15} m (1 femtometer, or roughly the size of a proton)
    Ans: D   Section: 29-2

25. What is the range of the strong nuclear force compared to the size of the nucleus, 10^{-14} m?

    A) ten times smaller than the size of an atomic nucleus
    B) infinite; it has no limit
    C) the same, because it is the strong force that holds the nucleus together
    D) ten times larger than the size of an atomic nucleus
    Ans: A   Section: 29-2

26. The four physical forces at work in the universe are gravitation, electromagnetic, strong nuclear and weak nuclear forces. Which two of these are very short-ranged, extending over distances of only about 10^{-15} m?

    A) strong nuclear and electromagnetic forces
    B) strong and weak nuclear forces
    C) gravitation and electromagnetic forces
    D) electromagnetic and weak nuclear forces
    Ans: B   Section: 29-2

27. What are quarks?
    A) the component particles making up protons and neutrons
    B) antielectrons (the antimatter form of electrons)
    C) particles of zero electric charge and zero mass that are emitted by nuclear reactions in the Sun's core
    D) the component particles making up electrons
    Ans: A   Section: 29-2

28. What are the particles that make up protons and neutrons?
    A) gravitons   B) neutrinos   C) quarks   D) muons
    Ans: C   Section: 29-2

29. In modern particle physics, the proton and the neutron are now thought to be composed of more fundamental particles called
    A) neutrinos.   B) quarks.   C) photons.   D) gluons.
    Ans: B   Section: 29-2

30. How many quarks are there in a proton (or a neutron)?
    A) six   B) one   C) three   D) four
    Ans: C   Section: 29-2

31. What is the difference between a proton and a neutron, in terms of their constituent quarks?
    A) A proton is made of two up quarks and a down quark, and a neutron is made of two down quarks and an up quark.
    B) A proton is made of two down quarks and an up quark, and a neutron is made of two up quarks and a down quark.
    C) A proton is made of three up quarks, and a neutron is made of three down quarks
    D) A proton is made of three down quarks and a neutron is made of three up quarks.
    Ans: A   Section: 29-2

32. The electromagnetic and weak nuclear forces are predicted to have been indistinguishable at some stage in the early universe. What conditions were required at this stage?
    A) very high density of matter such as the interior of the nucleus of an atom or a neutron star, where particles are so close that weak forces become equivalent to electromagnetic forces
    B) extremely high temperatures, producing very energetic collisions between components of matter
    C) extremely low temperatures, where collisions of particles were of low energy and extremely infrequent, such that electromagnetic and weak forces were equivalent
    D) very low density of matter, so that the weak force became as strong as the electromagnetic force in this region of space
    Ans: B   Section: 29-2

33. Over what time during the Big Bang were all four fundamental forces unified?
    A) until 10^{-24} second after the start of the Big Bang, when the inflationary epoch ended
    B) during the first 300,000 years from the start of the Big Bang, when the universe was dominated by radiation
    C) during the Planck time, up to 10^{-43} second after the start of the Big Bang
    D) until 10^{-6} second after the start of the Big Bang, when the era of quark confinement ended
    Ans: C   Section: 29-2

34. The Planck time refers to
    A) the time of extremely rapid inflation that started 10^{-35} second after the universe began.
    B) the time at which the expanding universe became transparent to radiation.
    C) the first 10^{-43} second of time, when all four fundamental forces were united.
    D) the present age of the universe as given by Hubble's law.
    Ans: C   Section: 29-2

35. The first 10^{-43} second of the age of the universe, during which all four fundamental forces were united, is called
    A) the Hubble time.   C) the event horizon.
    B) the inflationary epoch.   D) the Planck time.
    Ans: D   Section: 29-2

36. Within which time interval from the initial Big Bang do we believe all four fundamental forces of nature were united into a single force?
    A) $t = 0$ to 10^{-43} second, the Planck time, when gravity "froze out" of the universe
    B) $t = 0$ to 10^6 years, when radiation dominated the universe
    C) $t = 0$ to 10^{-35} second, when the strong nuclear force "froze out" of the universe
    D) $t = 0$ to 1 second, when photons interchanged freely with electron-positon pairs
    Ans: A   Section: 29-2

37. The predicted temperature of the early universe at which the four forces of nature would have been unified is
    A) 10^{15} K.   B) 10^{32} K.   C) 10^6 K.   D) 10^{27} K.
    Ans: B   Section: 29-2

38. At the start of the Big Bang, all of the fundamental forces were unified and behaved like a single force. As the universe expanded and cooled during the Big Bang, which was the first force to "freeze out" as a separate force?
    A) the electromagnetic force   C) gravity
    B) the weak nuclear force   D) the strong nuclear force
    Ans: C   Section: 29-2

39. When the Big Bang began, all of the fundamental forces were unified, and behaved like a single force. As the universe expanded and cooled during the Big Bang, when did the strong nuclear force "freeze out" and become a separate force?
    A)   at the Planck time, when the universe was about 10^{-43} second old
    B)   at the start of the inflationary epoch, when the universe was about 10^{-35} second old
    C)   when pair production ceased, when the universe was about one second old
    D)   at the start of quark confinement, when the universe was about 10^{-6} second old
    Ans: B   Section: 29-2

40. When did the inflationary epoch begin?
    A)   when the strong force "froze out" as a separate force
    B)   when pair production ceased
    C)   when gravity "froze out" as a separate force
    D)   when the electromagnetic force "froze out" as a separate force
    Ans: A   Section: 29-2

41. Grand unified theories, or GUTs, predict that for temperatures several orders of magnitude above 10^{27} K,
    A)   the weak and electromagnetic forces are indistinguishable from each other, but the other forces are different.
    B)   the strong, weak, electromagnetic, and gravitational forces are indistinguishable from each other.
    C)   the strong, weak, and electromagnetic forces are indistinguishable from each other, but gravity is different.
    D)   the strong and weak forces are indistinguishable from each other, but the other forces are different.
    Ans: C   Section: 29-2

42. In modern quantum physics, Heisenberg's uncertainty principle states that
    A)   the more precisely you know a particle's velocity, the more certain you are of its position in space.
    B)   the more precisely you know a particle's mass, the less certain you are of its size.
    C)   the more precisely you know a particle's position, the more certain you are of its speed and motion.
    D)   the more precisely you know a particle's position, the less certain you are of its speed and motion.
    Ans: D   Section: 29-3

43. Particle-antiparticle pairs are coming into existence all the time in the space around (and inside!) us. According to Heisenberg's uncertainty principle,
    A)   the more massive the particles, the shorter the time that they can exist.
    B)   the more massive the particles, the less precisely we know their position.
    C)   the more massive the particles, the longer the time that they can exist.
    D)   the more massive the particles, the more precisely we know their position.
    Ans: A   Section: 29-3

44. Can matter spontaneously come into existence, without having been created from energy?
    A)   No, never. Matter is a form of energy, and the spontaneous creation of matter would violate conservation of energy.
    B)   Yes, but only for extremely short times as required by the Heisenberg uncertainty principle.
    C)   Yes, but only if the particles created are electrically neutral.
    D)   Yes, but only if an equal amount of matter disappears from some other part of the universe.
    Ans: B   Section: 29-3

45. The mass of a proton is 1.67×10^{-27} kg. For what maximum length of time could a proton-antiproton pair spontaneously come into existence, without violating any laws of physics such as conservation of energy? (See Section: 29-3, Freedman and Kaufmann, *Universe*, 7th ed.)
    A) 3.5×10^{-25} s   B) 1.1×10^{-16} s   C) 2.2×10^{-16} s   D) 7.0×10^{-27} s
    Ans: A   Section: 29-3

46. What is a virtual particle?
    A)   a collection of particles that acts like a single particle
    B)   any particle that has no mass and is electrically neutral
    C)   a particle that can never have any detectable effect whatsoever on the real universe
    D)   a particle that exists for such a short time interval that we cannot detect it by direct measurement
    Ans: D   Section: 29-3

47. The constant creation and annihilation of virtual pairs of particles and antiparticles causes a slight change in the wavelengths of the hydrogen spectral lines. This effect is called
    A)   the Wolf effect.   C)   the Lamb shift.
    B)   the Rutherford shift.   D)   the Einstein effect.
    Ans: C   Section: 29-3

48. In high-energy physics, when two gamma-ray photons meet, they can
    A)   produce a huge number of low-energy photons.
    B)   disappear completely, leaving nothing behind.
    C)   disappear, creating two negative electrons.
    D)   disappear, creating a particle-antiparticle pair.
    Ans: D   Section: 29-3

49. Which of the following could result when two gamma-ray photons undergo pair production?
    A)   an electron and a positron (the antielectron)
    B)   an electron and an antineutrino
    C)   a proton, an electron, and an antineutrino
    D)   two X-ray photons, each with half the energy of the gamma rays
    Ans: A   Section: 29-3

50. Energy and mass are equivalent according to Einstein, and both can be measured in electron volts. (1 eV is the energy acquired by an electron when accelerated through 1 volt.) If the rest mass of an electron is 511 keV, what is the threshold energy of a gamma-ray photon in order that it can undergo electron pair production?
    A)   1.533 MeV
    B)   1.022 MeV
    C)   0 eV, because it produces a particle-antiparticle pair
    D)   511 keV
    Ans: B   Section: 29-3

51. What experimental evidence do we have for the direct transformation of energy into matter?
    A)   the blueshift of light because of the motion of its source
    B)   the relativistic increase in mass of an object when it is moving very rapidly
    C)   conversion of gamma-ray photons into electrons and antielectrons (i.e., positrons)
    D)   the increase in the force upon a body when it is accelerated upward (e.g., in an elevator)
    Ans: C   Section: 29-3

52. Suppose the inflationary epoch lasted 10^{-32} seconds. How much mass could have been created in virtual pairs during this time without violating the law of conservation of energy?
    A) 2×10^{-27} kg, about the mass of one hydrogen atom
    B) 10^{-19} kg
    C)   about one kilogram
    D) 2×10^{30} kg, about the mass of the Sun
    Ans: B   Section: 29-3

53. Why did the formation of particle-antiparticle pairs (such as protons and antiprotons) from gamma-rays come to an end within the first second after the start of the Big Bang?
    A) The universe became transparent to radiation, so gamma rays and particles no longer interacted.
    B) The gamma-ray energy decreased as the universe expanded.
    C) The formation of particle-antiparticle pairs exhausted the supply of gamma rays, preventing further formation of particle-antiparticle pairs.
    D) Expansion of the universe carried the gamma rays too far apart for them to collide and form particle-antiparticle pairs.
    Ans: B   Section: 29-4

54. During the first one-ten-thousandth second (10^{-4} s) of the life of the universe, antiprotons were very common. For every billion antiprotons, how many protons were there?
    A) an unknown number, because the early universe was opaque and we cannot see what conditions were like then
    B) one billion and one, thus producing the matter we see today
    C) ten billion, thus producing the dark matter we see today
    D) exactly one billion, because protons and antiprotons were created in equal numbers
    Ans: B   Section: 29-4

55. What is the period of quark confinement?
    A) Because of the very large pressure at these early times, all of the quarks were confined to a small volume. After the inflationary epoch the pressure dropped and the quarks were able to spread out to assume the distribution we find today.
    B) During this period the energy of the photons was sufficiently high that conglomerations of quarks, such as neutrons and protons, could not exist and quarks were free.
    C) During this period the energy of the photons was sufficiently low that conglomerations of quarks, such as neutrons and protons, could exist without being blasted apart as soon as they were formed.
    D) This refers to the very early period in the universe where all matter and energy were confined to a region the size of a single quark.
    Ans: C   Section: 29-4

56. The first 380,000 years of our universe, before matter and radiation decoupled, were dominated by the primordial fireball filled with an immense quantity of radiant energy. What was the source of these photons?
    A) They were created during the cosmic singularity and bounced around until the universe became transparent to radiation.
    B) They were given off when the free electrons were captured by protons to form the first hydrogen atoms.
    C) As the universe expanded and the radiation cooled, photons no longer had enough energy to create particles by pair production. But particles continued to annihilate and produce additional photons.
    D) The "fireball" that we see in the distant past is really a reflection of all the radiation produced before that time bouncing back from the universe in its early opaque state.
    Ans: C   Section: 29-4

57. What significant event occurred 380,000 years after the start of the Big Bang?
    A) The production of helium ceased.
    B) All of the galaxies we see today formed.
    C) Quarks became confined in nuclei.
    D) Electrons and nuclei combined to form neutral atoms.
    Ans: D   Section: 29-4

58. In the present theory of the Big Bang, what significant event occurred at about 380,000 years after the universe started expanding?
    A) The universe became transparent to neutrinos.
    B) The temperature of the cosmic background radiation had cooled to its present level of about 3 K.
    C) The universe became transparent to photons of radiation.
    D) The primordial helium in the universe was produced.
    Ans: C   Section: 29-4

59. Which of the following statements correctly describes the universe for the entire first 380,000 years of its life?
    A) All of the fundamental forces of nature were unified into one force.
    B) It was a sea of gradually decreasing nuclear reactions.
    C) It was filled with free quarks (not confined inside neutrons or protons).
    D) It was opaque to radiation.
    Ans: D   Section: 29-4

60. At an age of 380,000 years, the temperature of the universe had fallen to 3000 K, and electrons could then combine with protons to produce neutral hydrogen gas. What major transition took place in the universe at this time?
    A)   The universe suddenly lost its electrical charge and become neutral.
    B)   The present laws of physics began to apply for the first time.
    C)   It became transparent to light for the first time.
    D)   Nuclear fusion no longer occurred below this temperature.
    Ans: C   Section: 29-4

61. As we look at more distant regions of space, we see those regions as they existed at earlier times, but our farthest views are blocked by a "wall" beyond which the universe is opaque. What event occurred at the time marked by this wall?
    A)   Quarks combined to form neutrons and protons.
    B)   Protons combined with neutrons to form helium nuclei.
    C)   Gravity froze out as a separate force.
    D)   Electrons and protons combined to form neutral hydrogen atoms.
    Ans: D   Section: 29-4

62. Which one of the following statements does NOT correctly describe the universe at the era of recombination?
    A)   The temperature of the universe was about 3 K.
    B)   The universe was about 380,000 years old.
    C)   Electrons and protons combined to form neutral hydrogen atoms.
    D)   The universe became transparent to radiation.
    Ans: A   Section: 29-4

63. What was the temperature of the universe at the time the universe became transparent to radiation?
    A) 3 K   B) 30 billion K   C) 300,000 K   D) 3,000 K
    Ans: D   Section: 29-4

64. When did the universe cool to a temperature of 3 K?
    A)   very recently
    B)   3 minutes after the start of the Big Bang, when primordial nuclear reactions ceased
    C)   1 second after the start of the Big Bang, when pair production ceased
    D)   380,000 years after the Big Bang, when the universe became transparent to radiation
    Ans: A   Section: 29-4

65. At what point in the age of the universe did it cool to a temperature of about 3 K?
    A)   at the end of the inflationary epoch   C)   very recently
    B)   at the end of the Planck time   D)   at the era of recombination
    Ans: C   Section: 29-4

66. Because of the travel time of light, we see more distant parts of the universe as they were when the universe was younger; but we cannot see back "into" times when the universe was opaque and light could not travel freely. Using photons, then, what is the farthest back in time that we can see as we look out into the universe?
   A)   to a time 1/1,000,000 second after the start of the Big Bang
   B)   to a time 380,000 years after the start of the Big Bang
   C)   to a time 3 minutes after the start of the Big Bang
   D)   to a time 3,000 years after the start of the Big Bang
   Ans: B   Section: 29-4

67. In which one of the following four periods of time are we now living?
   A)   the inflationary period, in which the universe expands rapidly
   B)   the era of recombination, in which electrons and protons combine to form hydrogen atoms
   C)   the period of confinement, in which quarks are unable to travel freely
   D)   the Planck time, in which all four forces of nature are unified
   Ans: C   Section: 29-4

68. Why is it that we find no free (unbound) neutrons floating around in the universe today, whereas free protons and electrons exist in profusion?
   A)   Free neutrons decay radioactively in about 10 minutes to produce protons, electrons and neutrinos.
   B)   The free neutrons interact quickly with the free electrons to produce antiprotons, so there are few neutrons left.
   C)   The original Big Bang produced only charged particles, hence neutrons were not produced and those that now exist in nuclei of atoms have come from proton decay.
   D)   Free neutrons react readily with free protons to produce high-energy photons, or γ radiation.
   Ans: A   Section: 29-5

69. What is the deuterium bottleneck?
   A)   Deuterium had to form before helium could form, but deuterium is easily destroyed—thus preventing the formation of helium.
   B)   Deuterium absorbs neutrons efficiently, thus producing heavier and heavier isotopes of hydrogen instead of heavier elements such as helium.
   C)   Deuterium had to form before helium could form, but deuterium is almost impossible to create—thus preventing the formation of helium.
   D)   Helium is used up in the formation of deuterium. However, deuterium is difficult to create, thus leaving us with large amounts of helium.
   Ans: A   Section: 29-5

70. Where and how was most of the helium in the universe created?
    A)   by nuclear reactions in the cores of stars, and was then thrown out into space by
         supernovae
    B)   by the collision of cosmic rays with hydrogen nuclei in interstellar gas clouds
    C)   by high-energy processes during the collapse of pregalactic clouds during the
         formation of galaxies
    D)   by nuclear reactions during the Big Bang
    Ans: D   Section: 29-5

71. During what time was helium created in the Big Bang?
    A)   during the first 300,000 years   C)   during the first 10^{-6} second
    B)   during the first 10^{-43} second   D)   during the first 15 minutes
    Ans: D   Section: 29-5

72. Which elements were created during the Big Bang?
    A)   hydrogen, helium, and lithium
    B)   hydrogen, helium, lithium, and beryllium
    C)   hydrogen and helium
    D)   only hydrogen
    Ans: B   Section: 29-5

73. The cosmic photon background (i.e., the "cosmic background radiation") is observed to
    have a temperature of 3 K. What is believed to be the present temperature of the cosmic
    neutrino-antineutrino background?
    A)   2 K, because the universe has expanded more since it became transparent to
         neutrinos
    B)   3 K, because the expansion of the universe is the same for all particles in it
    C)   4 K, because the universe was hotter when it became transparent to neutrinos
    D)   1,000,000 K, because the neutrinos do not interact with matter and therefore have
         not been redshifted
    Ans: A   Section: 29-5

74. How was the "deuterium bottleneck" removed so that helium could form?
    A)   With the formation of the first stars, nucleosynthesis had a confined, uninterrupted
         space in which to produce both deuterium and hydrogen.
    B)   The formation of deuterium requires the strong force, and this did not separate out
         from the other forces until some time after the cosmic singularity. When it did,
         the deuterium bottleneck ended.
    C)   As the universe expanded, its photons cooled, lost energy, and eventually became
         unable to disrupting helium.
    D)   As the universe expanded, the protons and neutrons cooled, lost energy, and were
         eventually able to stick together without bouncing apart.
    Ans: C   Section: 29-5

75. The early universe had a large flux of neutrinos and antineutrinos. What happened to them?
    A) They annihilated to produce protons and antiprotons.
    B) They are still present as a cosmic background.
    C) They were absorbed by matter, giving it some of the additional energy required for inflationary expansion.
    D) They were absorbed by neutrons to form protons and electrons.
    Ans: B   Section: 29-5

76. At what speed will the neutrino travel if it is shown to have a small mass?
    A) Because it will be a particle with mass, its speed will be governed by the temperature of its surroundings because it will always be in thermal equilibrium.
    B) less than the speed of light, c
    C) faster than the speed of light, because this is the only way that it can have mass
    D) Because of its nature, it can only exist when it is traveling at the speed of light, just like photons of electromagnetic radiation.
    Ans: B   Section: 29-6

77. How do we know that matter in the early universe was extremely smooth (i.e., not really lumpy)?
    A) because the cosmic background radiation is almost completely isotropic
    B) because at the present time galaxies are spread almost completely uniformly through the universe
    C) because quasars are spread almost completely uniformly around the sky
    D) because the expansion of the universe is almost completely isotropic
    Ans: A   Section: 29-6

78. To what does the phrase "Jeans length" refer?
    A) the maximum distance over which a temperature fluctuation can occur in a "connected" universe
    B) the minimum diameter of a density fluctuation that can collapse gravitationally to form a galaxy or other astronomical object
    C) the minimum distance over which a temperature fluctuation can occur in a "connected" universe
    D) the maximum diameter of a density fluctuation that can collapse gravitationally to form a galaxy or other astronomical object
    Ans: B   Section: 29-6

79. Suppose that the Jeans length in a large interstellar cloud at a temperature of 20 K is 0.8 light year (ly). If the cloud gradually heats up to 40 K while its density remains constant, what would happen to the Jeans length? (See Section: 29-6, Freedman and Kaufmann, *Universe*, 7th ed.)
   A)   The Jeans length would decrease to 0.4 ly.
   B)   The Jeans length would increase to 1.6 ly.
   C)   The Jeans length would increase to 1.1 ly.
   D)   The Jeans length would decrease to 0.6 ly.
   Ans: C   Section: 29-6

80. Which one of the following statements correctly describes a major difference between galaxy formation with cold dark matter and galaxy formation with hot dark matter?
   A)   In both cases galaxies form by the breakup of larger objects, but the breakup occurs faster if the dark matter is hot than if it is cold.
   B)   With cold dark matter, galaxies form by the breakup of larger objects, whereas with hot dark matter galaxies form through the merger of smaller objects.
   C)   In both cases galaxies form through the merger of smaller objects, but the merger occurs faster if the dark matter is cold than if it is hot.
   D)   With cold dark matter, galaxies form through the merger of smaller objects, whereas with hot dark matter galaxies form by the breakup of larger objects.
   Ans: D   Section: 29-6

81. Consider a large cloud of hydrogen gas, all at a uniform temperature. How do density fluctuations within this cloud affect its tendency to collapse gravitationally?
   A)   In those regions where the density is larger the gas pressure will also be larger, and the gas will be less likely to collapse.
   B)   In those regions where the density is larger the Jeans length is smaller, meaning that smaller regions of the gas are likely to collapse.
   C)   The Jeans length must be calculated for the entire cloud. Density fluctuations *within* the cloud have no effect.
   D)   The likelihood of gravitational collapse cannot be calculated from the information given.
   Ans: B   Section: 29-6

82. When we apply the Jeans length criteria to the conditions of the early universe, it is found that the structures most likely to have formed first are
   A)   long filaments of galaxies.   C)   individual elliptical galaxies.
   B)   individual spiral galaxies.   D)   globular clusters.
   Ans: D   Section: 29-6

83. In what ways do the Kaluza-Klein multidimensional theories, including the cyclic model, simplify our picture of the universe? Three of the following statements are correct. Which one is *not* a simplification of Kaluza-Klein theory?
    A)   In three space dimensions the trajectory of an object influenced by gravity appears straight, but in the multidimensional space of Kaluza-Klein theory it appears straight.
    B)   Many of the additional dimensions cancel out leaving us with a simpler system than we had originally.
    C)   We may be able to account for the flatness of the universe without an inflationary epoch.
    D)   We may be able to account for the existence of dark matter and dark energy.
    Ans: B   Section: 29-7

84. Each of the following is an attribute of the Kaluza-Klein theories *except one*. Which one is the exception?
    A)   The theories have at least four space dimensions.
    B)   The dimensions we cannot see are curled tightly into loops.
    C)   Different loop vibrations correspond to particles with different masses.
    D)   In the new theories, gravitation no longer has an effect on space.
    Ans: D   Section: 29-7

Chapter 30: The Search for Extraterrestrial Life

1. Biological activity on Jupiter
    A)   might be possible suspended in the clouds, because lightning in methane, ammonia gases, and water vapor can generate organic compounds.
    B)   is impossible because it would be destroyed by the intense solar ultraviolet light.
    C)   is impossible because it would be destroyed by Jupiter's predominantly hydrogen atmosphere.
    D)   might be possible because the warm temperature below the clouds allows liquid-water oceans to exist on Jupiter's surface.
    Ans: A   Section: 30-1 and 14-4

2. Which of the following ideas has been borne out by astronomical observations over the past few centuries?
    A)   Our Sun is an unremarkable star in a commonplace galaxy and many such stars exist in the universe around which life could evolve on planets.
    B)   The probability of life existing elsewhere in the universe, even in our solar system, is infinitesimally small.
    C)   Our Sun is unique in its properties and position in a remarkable galaxy such that we appear to occupy a unique position in the universe, repeated nowhere else.
    D)   All the observational evidence so far suggests that conditions for the evolution of life exist only on our Earth, near to our Sun.
    Ans: A   Section: Chapter 30

3. One of the great lessons being learned from modern astronomy is that
    A)   we live at the center of a very massive black hole and all the observed cosmological effects, such as redshift and cosmic background radiation, are a consequence of the unique position that we occupy.
    B)   the chemistry, geology, and physics upon Earth are unique to our planet, and the behavior of matter anywhere else is significantly different from that upon Earth.
    C)   we occupy a unique position in the universe and nowhere else do we find conditions equivalent to those in our solar system.
    D)   our position and circumstances in the universe are quite ordinary and certainly not unique.
    Ans: D   Section: Chapter 30

4. Which of the following events of the past century do you think will have announced our presence upon Earth most effectively to extraterrestrial watchers?
   A) the appearance of artificial satellites orbiting Earth, after 1957
   B) the slow build-up of radio transmissions after the invention of radio, with modulated signals carrying sound and visual television images
   C) slow changes in vegetation patterns and the appearance of man-made structures such as road systems and cities upon Earth
   D) nuclear weapons explosions, producing extremely intense but brief flashes of light and electromagnetic radiation
   Ans: D   Section: Chapter 30

5. Why is the strategy of searches for extraterrestrial life usually based upon a carbon chemistry?
   A) Carbon dioxide is the main ingredient of planetary atmospheres, both terrestrial and Jovian.
   B) Carbon is abundant and is versatile in forming complex, long-chain molecules.
   C) Most meteorites that reach Earth are composed of carbon.
   D) No other atom can combine easily with the abundant hydrogen and helium to form long molecules in interstellar gas.
   Ans: B   Section: 30-1

6. In the search for intelligent life, scientists tend to assume that its biochemistry is more likely to be based upon the element carbon than upon any other element. Why is this?
   A) Carbon is the most versatile element, combining with the largest number of other elements in many different ways to produce long-chain molecules.
   B) Carbon is the only element that can combine into ring-shaped molecules, which is the shape of life-form molecular structure.
   C) Carbon releases far more energy than other similar atoms when it combines with other elements, a process that is essential for the support of life.
   D) They expect that life will mimic that on the surface of Earth, which is carbon-based.
   Ans: A   Section: 30-1

7. Why is it highly likely that life, should it exist elsewhere in the universe than upon the Earth's surface, will be based upon carbon chemistry?
   A) because carbon can bond with many more atomic species in a wider variety of complex forms than other equivalent elements such as silicon
   B) because carbon is expected to be far more abundant than silicon or other similar elements that can combine to produce complex molecules
   C) because carbon releases more energy than most other atoms when it combines with oxygen, thereby providing the energy for life processes in living organisms
   D) because carbon combines more readily than other atoms with nitrogen, the major component of atmospheres such as that of Earth, to produce complex molecules
   Ans: A   Section: 30-1

8. Which type of meteorite has been found to contain large organic molecules that make up the building blocks of life, thereby providing strong evidence for their extraterrestrial production?
   A) iron   B) stony   C) stony-iron   D) carbonaceous chondrite
   Ans: D   Section: 30-1

9. Which of the following was probably NOT a source of large organic molecules, the "building blocks" of life, on the early Earth?
   A)   comets
   B)   lightning flashes in the early terrestrial atmosphere
   C)   meteorites
   D)   volcanic eruptions
   Ans: D   Section: 30-1

10. Which wavelength range in the electromagnetic spectrum has been the most fruitful in the search for complex organic molecules in space?
   A)   visible radiation
   B)   infrared radiation
   C)   UV radiation
   D)   microwaves and short-wavelength radio waves
   Ans: D   Section: 30-1

11. Several lines of evidence now suggest that large and complex organic molecules, from which the building blocks of life could be formed, have evolved in outer space. Which of the following is NOT one of these observational findings?
   A)   the discovery of large organic molecules on and under the soils of Mars and the Moon
   B)   laboratory experiments in which electrical sparks passing through a combination of simple gases such as H_2O, H_2, N_2, and CO_2 produced large organic molecules
   C)   radio astronomical observations of large organic molecules in giant molecular clouds
   D)   the discovery of organic molecules inside certain meteorites which arrived upon Earth
   Ans: A   Section: 30-1

12. In which of the following environments have long-chain carbon-based molecules not been found?
   A)   in interstellar gas clouds
   B)   on the surface of Earth
   C)   inside meteorites
   D)   on the surfaces of nearby planets such as Venus and Mars
   Ans: D   Section: 30-1

13. The basic chemical molecules that are present in abundance in the planetary system, and that were used in the classical Urey-Miller laboratory experiments in which complex compounds essential to life were formed by electric discharges, were
    A) H_2 (hydrogen), O_2 (oxygen), CO_2 (carbon dioxide)
    B) CH_4 (methane), NH_3 (ammonia), H_2O (water), H_2 (hydrogen)
    C) CO_2 (carbon dioxide), H_2O (water), H_2 (hydrogen)
    D) H_2 (hydrogen), He (helium), Ar (argon), Ne (neon)
    Ans: B   Section: 30-1

14. The classical laboratory experiments performed by Urey and Miller in order to explore the necessary conditions for the production of organic molecules (the building blocks of living things) in the solar system involved the passing of electrical discharges through what mixture of gases?
    A)   hydrogen and helium
    B)   carbon dioxide, water vapor, and dust
    C)   nitrogen, oxygen, water vapor, and carbon dioxide
    D)   ammonia, methane, water vapor, and hydrogen
    Ans: D   Section: 30-1

15. Which of the following was found in the laboratory container after Urey and Miller had exposed a mixture of hydrogen, ammonia, methane, and water vapor (typical chemicals in the atmospheres of outer planets) to an electric arc (to simulate lightning) for a few days?
    A)   DNA and RNA molecules
    B)   amino acids
    C)   aqueous crystals of numerous salts of compounds of nitrogen, oxygen, and carbon
    D)   viruses
    Ans: B   Section: 30-1

16. What source of energy was used to trigger the manufacture of complex organic compounds in laboratory simulations of conditions in primordial planetary atmospheres?
    A)   thermal heating, to simulate volcanic conditions
    B)   electric discharges, to simulate lightning
    C)   heat from chemical reactions, simulating those expected in early reactive planetary atmospheres
    D)   UV and visible radiation, to simulate the intensity of sunlight at earlier times in planetary life
    Ans: B   Section: 30-1

17. The method used in the Urey-Miller experiment
    A) was to pass an electric arc through a mixture of hydrogen, ammonia, methane, and water and then look for organic compounds.
    B) was to send radio signals using a pulsed code toward nearby sun-like stars which may have planets.
    C) was to attach a metal plaque to the Voyager spacecraft to tell extraterrestrial beings about us, if they ever find the spacecraft.
    D) was to monitor tens of millions of frequencies at once in an effort to detect extraterrestrial radio communications.
    Ans: A   Section: 30-1

18. Modern laboratory experiments, which repeated those of Urey and Miller in exploring the possibility of producing organic molecules (the building blocks of life) from mixtures of gases expected to exist in the atmosphere of early Earth, passed electrical discharges through which mixture of gases?
    A) ammonia, methane, water vapor, and hydrogen
    B) hydrogen and helium
    C) carbon dioxide, water vapor, and dust
    D) nitrogen, hydrogen, water vapor, and carbon dioxide
    Ans: D   Section: 30-1

19. Which of the following observations regarding the likelihood of life existing elsewhere in the universe has NOT yet been made?
    A) discovery of long-chain amino-acid protein molecules in meteorites
    B) discovery of long-chain carbon-based molecules in interstellar clouds by radio astronomers
    C) the manufacture of organic compounds in laboratory simulations of primordial planetary atmospheres
    D) discovery of assemblies of organic molecules into cell-like, self-replicating structures in the soils of Mars and the atmosphere of Venus
    Ans: D   Section: 30-1

20. In what way was volcanism important to the development of life on Earth?
    A) Volcanoes provided the heat necessary for the chemical reactions to create complex organic molecules.
    B) Amino acids were probably present in the gases emitted.
    C) Carbon dioxide, water vapor, and nitrogen were outgassed from volcanoes.
    D) Molten lava dissolved various organic materials on the Earth's surface and allowed them to mix together so they could react.
    Ans: C   Section: 30-1

21. The primary constituents for the organic molecules needed for life do *not* include which one of the following?
    A) oxygen   B) sulfur   C) carbon   D) silicon
    Ans: D   Section: 30-1

22. On the surface of which planet or moon in our planetary system have experiments been carried out to search for life-forms or evidence of life?
    A) Venus   B) Jupiter   C) Mars   D) Jupiter's moon, Europa
    Ans: C   Section: 30-2

23. On which of the following objects in our planetary system is it UNLIKELY that life exists upon it or at least existed on it at an earlier time?
    A) Mars   B) Europa, a moon of Jupiter   C) Io, a moon of Jupiter   D) Earth
    Ans: C   Section: 30-2

24. Scientists are now targeting Europa, one of Jupiter's moons, as a likely site for searching for elementary life-forms because
    A)   radio signals that follow a recognizable pattern have been detected from this moon.
    B)   there is strong evidence for liquid water beneath the thick ice layer on its surface.
    C)   changes have been seen in the dark lines crossing the icy surface which have a spectral signature of vegetation.
    D)   there appears to be large amounts of dark organic material spread on its surface.
    Ans: B   Section: 30-2

25. The exploratory life-sciences experiments on board the Viking spacecraft landers found evidence
    A)   of very reactive chemistry in the Martian surface rocks but no evidence of life or remnants of life-forms.
    B)   of a very sterile environment in which life could not have existed, probably sterilized by intense solar UV radiation, and a very chemically inert soil, reacting with almost no reagents.
    C)   of primitive life-forms such as elementary bacteria, which should not be a hazard when Man explores Mars.
    D)   that primitive life-forms had existed upon Mars earlier in its history but that they had not survived.
    Ans: A   Section: 30-2

26. The Viking labeled-release experiment, which was used to look for life on Mars, was based on the idea that
    A)   in photosynthesis, gases are removed from the atmosphere and incorporated into the organism.
    B)   in running around a maze, an organism's heart rate goes up.
    C)   in respiration, organisms take in some gases and release others, thus altering the composition of the atmosphere around them.
    D)   in metabolism, organisms consume nutrients from the soil and produce gases as a byproduct.
    Ans: D   Section: 30-2

27. The Viking pyrolytic-release experiment, which was used to look for life on Mars, was based on the idea that
    A)   in respiration, organisms take in some gases and release others, thus altering the composition of the atmosphere around them.
    B)   in photosynthesis, gases are removed from the atmosphere and incorporated into the organism.
    C)   in running around a maze, an organism's heart rate goes up.
    D)   in metabolism, organisms consume nutrients from the soil and produce gases as a by-product.
    Ans: B   Section: 30-2

28. The Viking gas-exchange experiment, which was used to look for life on Mars, was based on the idea that
    A)   in metabolism, organisms consume nutrients from the soil and produce gases as a by-product.
    B)   in respiration, organisms take in some gases and release others, thus altering the composition of the atmosphere around them.
    C)   in photosynthesis, gases are removed from the atmosphere and incorporated into the organism.
    D)   in running around a maze, an organism's heart rate goes up.
    Ans: B   Section: 30-2

29. What were the results of the life-sciences experiments on board the Viking landers?
    A)   nothing at all; the Martian soil is completely chemically inert and biologically sterile
    B)   a slight fizzing due to released carbon dioxide, but very little else
    C)   strong reactions releasing oxygen, from apparent biological causes (e.g., bacteria)
    D)   strong reactions releasing oxygen, but from non-biological causes
    Ans: D   Section: 30-2

30. What process or observation misled scientists into believing initially that their life-seeking experiments on the Mars Viking lander had succeeded in detecting evidence of life on our neighboring planet?
    A)   the reaction of water with unstable chemicals that exist upon the surface of Mars
    B)   growth of substances when water was added, which later turned out to be crystal growth from inert chemicals
    C)   motions of microscopic components, looking like those of a life-form, but which were caused by the boiling of water under the artificial sunlight of the experiment
    D)   the extremely high absorptivity of Martian rocks to water, because these rocks mimicked life forms by absorbing water
    Ans: A   Section: 30-2

31. Several components of the atmosphere and the environment on Mars render it sterile and antiseptic and would destroy life on the planet. Which of the following is NOT one of these factors?
    A)   sulfuric acid in a mist in the atmosphere
    B)   solar UV radiation, which is only weakly absorbed by the thin atmosphere
    C)   unstable and highly reactive chemicals in the soil
    D)   a very thin atmosphere
    Ans: A   Section: 30-2

32. Why is the proposed British spacecraft Beagle 2, which will land and search for evidence of life on Mars in 2003, so named?
    A)   It comes from the initials of the British Experiment for Active Global Life Evaluation.
    B)   The mobile spacecraft will emulate a beagle dog in searching for life forms.
    C)   It is named for the dog of the experiment's chief scientist.
    D)   Beagle was Charles Darwin's exploration ship.
    Ans: D   Section: 30-2

33. Each one of the following was a mission of the Beagle2 Mars lander *except one*. Which is the exception?
    A)   Beagle2 was to look for traces of methane in the Martian atmosphere.
    B)   Beagle2 was to test for dead as well as living organic material.
    C)   Beagle2 was to test Martian CO_2 to determine if there is a preference for ^{12}C over ^{13}C.
    D)   Beagle2 was to probe one of the Martian polar ice caps to determine the amount of water it contains.
    Ans: D   Section: 30-2

34. Evidence for water on Mars during its ancient past includes all of the following *except one*. Which is the exception?
    A)   The polar caps appear to contain large amounts of frozen water.
    B)   Minerals observed by Opportunity on the Martian surface are those generally formed in a liquid environment.
    C)   Some of the landing areas resemble dry lake beds.
    D)   Shallow pools of liquid water have been discovered on a portion of the Martian surface where temperatures remain above freezing.
    Ans: D   Section: 30-2

35. How have we been able to obtain samples of Martian rocks?
    A)   Rocks have been collected and returned from the Moon to Earth by astronauts,
         now identified as Martian rocks blasted from this planet by a massive impact.
    B)   Rocks have been blasted off Mars by impacts, and have landed on Earth as
         meteorites.
    C)   We have not yet been able to obtain any Martian rock samples.
    D)   Sample return missions have been flown in which a robotic rover collected rocks
         and returned them to Earth.
    Ans: B   Section: 30-3

36. Which of the following has placed Martian rocks in the hands of scientists upon Earth?
    A)   materials recovered from a spacecraft that landed near to Roswell, New Mexico,
         USA, but that were never released to the general public
    B)   a sample-return mission by the former USSR space exploration program
    C)   rocks returned by astronauts from the Moon, whose Martian origin was
         established by their chemical make-up and red color
    D)   meteorites collected from Antarctica, the gases within them indicating that they
         have been blasted from Mars by an impact
    Ans: D   Section: 30-3

37. The SNC meteorites are
    A)   granitic rocks from Venus.
    B)   rocks discovered on Earth whose origin has been traced to Mars.
    C)   basaltic rocks from the center of a volcanic caldera on the Moon.
    D)   carbonaceous chondrites from the asteroid belt.
    Ans: B   Section: 30-3

38. Where have some scientists hypothesized that they have found direct evidence for life,
    either contemporary or ancient, beyond the Earth (although the hypothesis has been
    strongly disputed by many other scientists)?
    A)   in "orange soil" found on the Moon
    B)   in spectra of the dark deposits along fissures in the ice of Jupiter's satellite, Europa
    C)   in the "soil" (regolith) at the Viking 2 landing site on Mars
    D)   in a meteorite composed of ancient Martian rock
    Ans: D   Section: 30-3

39. What evidence have some scientists claimed for ancient life on Mars (although the
    hypothesis has been strongly disputed by many other scientists)?
    A)   calcium carbonate deposits similar to seashells in a sample of Martian limestone
    B)   an apparent thumbprint on a rock identified as cooled lava at the Mars Pathfinder
         landing site
    C)   peroxides in the "soil" (regolith), found by experiments on the Viking Martian
         landers
    D)   possible fossilized bacteria in a Martian meteorite
    Ans: D   Section: 30-3

40. In the "meteorite" AL 84001, recovered from Antarctica and traced to an origin on Mars, which of the following, indicating the possibility of life on that planet, has NOT been found?
    A)   rounded grains of carbonate minerals, which can be produced by life forms
    B)   magnetite and sulfide compounds, found together in carbonates, a sign of bacterial action
    C)   enclosed pockets of carbon dioxide, CO_2, and methane, CH_4, which were most likely produced by life forms
    D)   elongated tubelike structures, resembling fossilized microorganisms
    Ans: C   Section: 30-3

41. Why do we believe that the SNC meteorites, such as the Antarctic find ALH 84001, originated on Mars?
    A)   The color matches the red of the Martian soil.
    B)   Each of these meteorites landed in soft soil or snow in such a manner that the landing trajectory could be determined.
    C)   The ALH 84001 meteorite was actually tracked by radar on the final part of its inbound journey.
    D)   The air trapped in pockets in the meteorites matches the Martian atmosphere but is very different from the Earth's atmosphere.
    Ans: D   Section: 30-3

42. What do we estimate for the time delay between when ALH 84001 was blasted from the surface of Mars and when it landed in Antarctica?
    A)   only a few months   C)   millions of years
    B)   about a year   D)   almost 4.5 billion years
    Ans: C   Section: 30-3

43. In what way was the discovery of pulsars initially misinterpreted as evidence of intelligent life elsewhere in the universe?
    A)   It was not thought possible for a "natural" source to produce the rapid and extremely regular radio pulses detected from space.
    B)   The rate of pulses detected from space appeared to contain primitive coding similar to a crude Morse Code.
    C)   Radio telescopes occasionally detected the same sequence of 5 musical notes, which were then whistled or hummed regularly by all the people associated with these telescopes.
    D)   Pulses arriving from several nearby star systems showed Doppler shifts of frequency apparently caused by orbital motion of their source around the central stars, as if coming from planets.
    Ans: A   Section: 30-4 and 23-2

44. To what do the letters SETI refer?
    A) Sourcebook of Extrasensory Transient Incidents
    B) Search for Extra Terrestrial Invaders
    C) Search for Evidence of Terrestrial-planet Inhabitants
    D) Search for Extra Terrestrial Intelligence
    Ans: D   Section: 30-4

45. The first person to look for radio signals from extraterrestrial civilizations was
    A) Arno Penzias.   C) Martin Schwarzschild.
    B) Frank Drake.   D) Jocelyn Bell.
    Ans: B   Section: 30-4

46. The first search for radio signals from extraterrestrial civilizations was made in
    A) 1948.   B) 1995.   C) 1973.   D) 1960.
    Ans: D   Section: 30-4

47. The first successful detection of interpretable signals from extraterrestrial civilizations
    was accomplished in which year?
    A) 1960
    B) 1997
    C) Never—no such signals have been detected as yet.
    D) 2001
    Ans: C   Section: 30-4

48. The Drake equation attempts to predict
    A) the probability that primitive life exists elsewhere in our galaxy.
    B) the number of inhabitable planets around stars in our galaxy.
    C) the number of technologically advanced civilizations in our galaxy.
    D) the number of intelligent civilizations in the universe.
    Ans: C   Section: 30-4

49. In what way does the Drake equation combine the various factors (e.g., fraction of stars
    with planets, fraction of planets that can support life, etc.) in an attempt to determine the
    probability of life existing elsewhere in the galaxy?
    A) It takes the product of all the factors.
    B) It takes the sum of each of the factors.
    C) It divides the sum of three factors by the sum of the other four factors.
    D) It subtracts the sum of six factors from the initial factor, the rate of solar-type star
       formation.
    Ans: A   Section: 30-4

50. In the Drake equation for estimating the possible number of technically advanced civilizations in our galaxy, the factor for the rate at which solar-type stars form in a galaxy excludes massive stars with masses greater than about 1.5 times that of the Sun. Why?
    A) Such stars never develop a nuclear furnace in their interiors and hence can never heat any planet sufficiently to sustain life.
    B) These stars would never develop nuclear processes that could produce heavy elements (e.g., iron) for ejection outward to form planets such as Earth.
    C) Such stars are prone to repeated and violent supernova explosions which would destroy any developing life forms.
    D) Such stars have lifetimes shorter than it took for intelligent life to develop upon Earth, and hence should probably not be considered.
    Ans: D   Section: 30-4

51. Why do we only consider stars with masses less than about 1.5 solar masses in the Drake equation when estimating the number of possible stars in our galaxy around which planets could form that would support our kind of intelligent life?
    A) This type of star would produce so much damaging UV radiation that it would sterilize its planets.
    B) Such massive stars would never reach temperatures sufficient to maintain life-supporting conditions on the surfaces of its planets.
    C) Stars more massive than this would have evolved so rapidly that creatures with our intelligence (?) would not have had time to evolve and develop.
    D) Planets could not form sufficiently close to such stars for life to have survived and evolved.
    Ans: C   Section: 30-4

52. It is unlikely that planets near to stars much more massive than our Sun would develop life because
    A) planets would have to be too close to these cool stars in order to be sufficiently warm for life to evolve, and they would become tidally linked, resulting in no night and day.
    B) there would be no region around the star where UV, visible, and IR light intensities would be suitable for the evolution of life.
    C) no moon would form around a planet near to such a star, and a moon is considered essential for the evolution of life because of tidal variations.
    D) these stars would have evolved to red giant or even supernova stages before life could evolve.
    Ans: D   Section: 30-4

53. It is unlikely that intelligent life would develop on a planet circling a star of significantly less mass than the Sun because
    A)   such a planet would need to be very close to the star and would become tidally locked to the star, making one side of the planet too hot and the other side too cold.
    B)   the lifetime of such a star on the main sequence is too short; life forms on such a planet would not have time to evolve to a sufficient level of intelligence.
    C)   there would be no region around the star where UV, visible, and IR light intensities would be suitable for the evolution of life.
    D)   no Moon would form around a planet near to such a star and a Moon is considered to have been essential for the evolution of life because of tidal variations on the shorelines of Earth.
    Ans: A   Section: 30-4

54. Around which types of stars are we most likely to find planets supporting our kind of life forms?
    A)   red giant stars   C)   very low-mass stars
    B)   low-mass main-sequence stars   D)   high-mass main-sequence stars
    Ans: B   Section: 30-4

55. What is the current status of our search for inhabitable, Earth-like planets circling other stars?
    A)   Two stars have now been discovered with an Earth-mass planet orbiting at distances suitable for liquid water and life, but we cannot yet determine whether they have oxygen-rich atmospheres.
    B)   Planets have been detected orbiting other stars, but none of these appear to be suitable for life.
    C)   No extra-solar planets of any kind have yet been confirmed.
    D)   Several planets have been found with a mass similar to that of the Earth, but they are either too close to or too far away from their star to have liquid water or life on their surfaces.
    Ans: B   Section: 30-4

56. How often do Sun-like stars (of a type considered likely to be circled by an inhabitable planet) form in our galaxy, on average?
    A)   Hundreds of such stars form per year.
    B)   Less than one such star forms per thousand years.
    C)   We cannot yet answer this question.
    D)   About one such star forms per year.
    Ans: D   Section: 30-4

57. Probably the most difficult factor to estimate in the Drake Equation is
    A) R_*, the rate at which solar-type stars form in the galaxy
    B) f_p, the fraction of stars that have planets
    C) n_e, the number of planets per solar system that are Earthlike (suitable for life)
    D) L, the lifetime of a technologically advanced civilization
    Ans: D   Section: 30-4

58. For which of the following factors in the Drake Equation do we actually have observational knowledge rather than just a speculative estimate?
    A) R_*, the rate at which solar-type stars form in the galaxy
    B) f_l, the fraction of Earthlike planets on which life actually arises
    C) f_i, the fraction of life-forms that evolve into intelligent species
    D) f_c, the fraction of intelligent species that develop adequate technology and then choose to send messages out into space
    Ans: A   Section: 30-4

59. If we succeed in detecting signals from other civilizations in space, what method of communication will prove to be the fastest?
    A) neutrinos, because a beam of these particles, suitably modulated, can be made to travel almost infinitely fast because they can penetrate almost anything very easily
    B) nuclear powered rockets, because we can then use unlimited power to accelerate these systems to almost infinite speeds
    C) laser light, because this single-wavelength light can be directed into an extremely narrow and intense beam and can therefore be made to travel much faster than ordinary light
    D) It does not matter what is used because the speed of light can never be exceeded by anything in our universe, thereby setting the communication speed limit.
    Ans: D   Section: 30-5, 5-1, and 24-1

60. Most searches of space for evidence of intelligent life concentrated on radio wavelengths because
    A) it is likely that extraterrestrial beings will have developed radio transmitters before more complex lasers or IR light transmitters.
    B) radio energy is least affected by dust and gas in the interstellar medium.
    C) our atmosphere is most transparent at these wavelengths and such signals will be more easily detected from Earth.
    D) radio signals can carry the greatest amount of information per unit time, so information transfer will be most efficient at these wavelengths.
    Ans: B   Section: 30-5

61. What strategies and electromagnetic frequencies are thought to be the most logical for long-range communication across the universe with other intelligent beings?
    A) night-by-night photography of nearby stars at hydrogen Balmer wavelengths
    B) X-ray surveys of space at appropriate times (e.g., when Earth is closest to nearby stars in its orbit), in view of the penetrability of space at these wavelengths.
    C) explosion of nuclear devices at specific intervals and in specific patterns across the Earth when it is nearest to a nearby star
    D) continuous radio and microwave monitoring at specific frequencies at which the sky noise is low
    Ans: D   Section: 30-5

62. What are the parameters that limit the choice of wavelength for possible communication with extraterrestrial intelligence to the "water hole" in the high-frequency radio range of the electromagnetic spectrum (see Figure 30-8, Freedman and Kaufmann, *Universe*, 7th ed.)?
    A) cosmic background radio noise at low frequencies and radio noise from the Sun and Jupiter at high frequencies
    B) local radio noise from TV, radio, and aircraft across the band, except a narrow range in which transmission is prohibited by international agreement in order to permit such extraterrestrial communication
    C) atmospheric absorption by the ionosphere at low frequencies and by CO_2 at high frequencies in the long infrared range
    D) high galactic radio background noise at low frequencies and high atmospheric absorption by H_2O and O_2 at high frequencies
    Ans: D   Section: 30-5

63. The so-called "water hole," a region of the radio spectrum chosen for searches for signals from intelligent life because galactic and Earth-based noise and atmospheric absorption are at a minimum, is so-named because
    A) water vapor absorption in our atmosphere reaches a sharp minimum at this wavelength.
    B) water vapor, H_2O, has an intense laser-like emission line at this wavelength that extraterrestrials might use to communicate with us.
    C) water vapor emissions from planets at this wavelength will be a good indicator of life on other planets, because water is essential for life as we know it.
    D) two astronomically important wavelengths—the 21-cm line of H and a strong line from the hydroxyl radical OH—are in this region, and an astronomer invented this cute name using the letters H and OH, which together signify water.
    Ans: D   Section: 30-5

64. Why would intelligent alien beings who wanted to communicate with us probably choose the 21-cm radio wavelength associated with atomic hydrogen?
    A)   because this particular wavelength is very weak from natural sources in space, and messages would therefore be easily distinguished from other sources
    B)   because they would have detected this particular wavelength from our transmitters on Earth because it is used extensively for satellite communications, and they would therefore know that we could detect them easily
    C)   because this wavelength shows a very strong Doppler effect when its source is moving, and they would know that we would be able to detect the orbital motion of their home planet around their star by this method
    D)   because they would expect that many of our telescopes would already be tuned to this precise wavelength for scientific work
    Ans: D   Section: 30-5

65. What is the current state of the search for extraterrestrial radio communications?
    A)   Several extraterrestrial civilizations have been found, but they are not intelligent enough for us to bother with, and the search is continuing.
    B)   Several private or university-based searches using existing telescopes and links to millions of private home computers are searching at many frequencies.
    C)   Continuous transmissions are being sent out from the Earth at several frequencies in the "water hole," and tens of millions of other frequencies are being monitored.
    D)   Several dedicated telescopes are continuously monitoring the neighborhoods of nearby stars, which are known to have planets, for bright flashes or coded signals at common visible laser wavelengths.
    Ans: B   Section: 30-5

66. In what way is the SETI@home program helping to search for radio signals from intelligent life-forms elsewhere in our universe?
    A)   Thousands of people with satellite dish antennas for TV reception have donated time on their receivers to collect radio signals from selected regions of space.
    B)   More than a million personal computers analyze data from radio telescopes, sent to them from the University of California, when otherwise these computers would sit idle.
    C)   Thousands of dedicated amateur astronomers are each spending hundreds of hours searching the space around nearby stars suspected of having planets for very bright flashes from possible nuclear explosions on these planets.
    D)   Hundreds of thousands of people have responded to a request for money to continue a radio search for intelligent signals from space.
    Ans: B   Section: 30-5

67. The so-called "water hole" is a range in the electromagnetic spectrum in which searches for transmissions of extraterrestrial origin are being conducted. In what region of the electromagnetic spectrum does the "water hole" occur?
    A) ultraviolet   B) visible   C) infrared   D) microwave
    Ans: D   Section: 30-5

68. In searching for transmissions from intelligent civilizations, SETI is concentrating its efforts on a survey of
   A) about a dozen or so of the closest stars.
   B) just those stars around which we believe we have detected planets.
   C) thousands of stars within a hundred parsecs or so of the solar system.
   D) stars in giant elliptical galaxies because these, being oldest, are most likely to have advanced civilizations.
   Ans: C   Section: 30-5

69. The "Terrestrial Planet Finder" is
   A) a large 15-m diameter single-mirror orbiting telescope to be launched in 2012 or later to attempt to obtain direct observations of terrestrial planets around other stars at optical wavelengths, unhindered by atmospheric seeing effects.
   B) an orbiting telescope to be launched in 2012 or later, consisting of 4 collectors which will utilize interferometry at infrared wavelengths to try to obtain direct observations of terrestrial planets around other stars.
   C) an organization based in Dallas, Texas, dedicated to obtaining private funding for searches for extraterrestrial civilizations.
   D) a multidish set of 15-m diameter telescopes to be built on the summit of Mauna Kea and operated as an interferometer to search for terrestrial planets orbiting other stars.
   Ans: B   Section: 30-6

70. The "Terrestrial Planet Finder," a space telescope system to be launched sometime after the year 2011, will consist of
   A) two spacecraft launched in opposite directions to visit a succession of solar-type stars over the next 2,500 years and return images of all planets that they find.
   B) four 40-m-diameter radio telescopes equally spaced in orbit around the Sun, acting as a radio interferometer 1.25 AU in radius.
   C) a single 16-m-diameter telescope designed to image planets around other stars at optical and infrared wavelengths.
   D) four 8-m telescopes linked together as an infrared interferometer.
   Ans: D   Section: 30-6

71. Why will proposed future experiments to search for Earth-like planets use the infrared region of the spectrum?
   A) Life forms give off IR radiation preferentially when they are alive (and warm!).
   B) The ratio of IR to visible radiation from planets is much higher than for their parent stars.
   C) The Earth's atmosphere is more transparent over this wavelength range than at any other wavelength.
   D) Only at these wavelengths will spectra show spectral signatures which are identifiable as originating on Earth-like planets.
   Ans: B   Section: 30-6

72. Which molecules, whose absorption lines appear in the infrared, are considered most likely to indicate the presence of life if they were detected on any planet orbiting another star?
    A) hydrogen and helium
    B) methane and ammonia
    C) carbon dioxide
    D) carbon dioxide, ozone, and water vapor
    Ans: D   Section: 30-6

73. Kepler is an orbiting telescope scheduled for launch in 2007 and designed to search for Earth-sized planets. Which one of the following statements about Kepler is *not true*?
    A) Planets, to be detected, must be in orbits more or less edge-on as viewed from the Earth.
    B) Kepler will search for the wobble of a star caused by an orbiting planet.
    C) The dimming of distant stars as planets pass in front of them (which Kepler will do) has, in fact, been observed for relatively large planets.
    D) Kepler will be able to monitor thousands of planets at once.
    Ans: B   Section: 30-6

74. In a few decades, orbiting telescopes such as Kepler, Terrestrial Planet Finder, Darwin, and Planet Imager may be operational and sending us data. What might these results mean for our use of the Drake Equation?
    A) With these results in hand the Drake Equation will become irrelevant.
    B) The structure of the Drake Equation itself will undoubtedly have to be drastically revised.
    C) We will have much better values for the factors f_p (the fraction of stars that have planets), n_e (the number of planets per solar system that are Earthlike), and f_l (the fraction of Earthlike planets on which life actually arises).
    D) We will have much better values for the factors f_l (the fraction of Earthlike planets on which life actually arises), f_i (the fraction of life-forms that evolve into intelligent species), and f_c (the fraction of intelligent species that develop adequate technology and then choose to send messages out into space).
    Ans: C   Section: 30-4, 30-6